Fourth Edition

CHOICES IN *Sexuality*

David Knox

Caroline Schacht

Mark A. Whatley

BVT Publishing
Better textbooks, better prices
www.BVTPublishing.com

Publisher and Marketing Manager: Richard Schofield

Managing Editor: Joyce Bianchini

Permissions Coordinator, Project Research and Development: Jenefier Winchell

Production and Fulfillment Manager: Janai Bryand

Cover and Interior Design: Esther Scannell

Typesetting Manager: Rhonda Minnema

Proofreader: Annie Schofield

Pre-Production Manager: Shannon Waters

For information, address BVT Publishing, LLC, P.O. Box 492831, Redding, CA 96049-2831

Some ancillaries, including electronic and printed components, may not be available to customers outside of the United States.

Photo Credits: Cover and feature heading icon images from Shutterstock.

Softcover ISBN: 978-1-62751-313-5

Vital Source ISBN: 978-1-62751-311-1

Looseleaf ISBN: 978-1-62751-312-8

Textbook+ Bundle: 978-1-62751-317-3

BRIEF CONTENTS

CONTENTS

4 Male Sexual Anatomy, Physiology, and Response

5 Gender and Sexuality

6 Love and Sexuality

7   Communication and Sexuality

8 Individual and Interpersonal Sexuality

9 Lifespan View of Sexuality

10 Sexual Orientation and Sexuality

13 Sexual Dysfunctions and Sex Therapy

14   Variant Sexual Behavior

15 Sexually Transmitted Infections

16 Sexual Coercion

Preface

Preface to the Fourth Edition

A human sexuality course is not just an academic course in psychology, sociology, health, education, and family studies; it is also an opportunity to examine sexual choices and promote informed sexual decision making. We hope that this course results in increasing your fundamental understanding of human sexuality and enhances your life and relationships through wise sexual choices.

The title of the book, *Choices in Sexuality*, establishes the book's theme—to provide an understanding of how biological, social, and cultural influences affect your sexual choices and encourage you to take charge of your life by making deliberate, informed sexual choices. Students sometimes do not consider the alternatives to their choices. Nor do they always realize the potential consequences of their sexual choices on long-term psychological and physical health, their relationships, and the quality of their lives. In addition, some students have not considered that by not making a choice, they have already made a choice—by default. We hope that you will take this study seriously, and that you will have fun and enjoy it, too.

New to this Edition

This fourth edition of *Choices in Sexuality* builds on the features and strengths of the previous editions, continuing with the theme of "choices." Specific enhancements to this edition include the following:

- Updated research includes 524 new references, most of them from 2013.
- Contemporary issues—including legalization of same-sex marriage, sexting, and the new *DSM-5*—are included.
- New, original sexuality data has been collected and compiled (by the first author and Dr. Scott Hall), based on surveying 4,590 undergraduate students.
- A new author, Dr. Mark Whatley, joins Knox and Schacht from previous editions. Dr. Whatley, a psychologist, teaches Psychology of Sex at Valdosta State University.

This fourth edition continues to utilize the following features that students and faculty have emphasized as being helpful in understanding one's choices in relationships:

Personal Choices   These sections discuss specific sexual choices that students might face—considerations for having intercourse with a new partner, sharing your sexual fantasies with your partner, and deciding whether to disclose an affair.

Self-Assessments   A scale to measure a particular aspect of your sexuality and compare your score with others is provided in each chapter.   Examples include assessing body image (Chapter 1), identifying whether you are a romantic or realist about love (Chapter 6), and being alert to sexual signals conveyed by a partner (Chapter 7).

Social Choices   Society-wide social choices are addressed in each chapter. Examples include the legalization of same-sex marriage (Chapter 10), sex education content in the public schools (Chapter 1), and sexual harassment policies in the workforce (Chapter 16).

Personal Reflection   Embedded in each chapter are questions that encourage personal reflection on the sexual content being discussed. For example, a person's sexual values may not always be consistent with his/her sexual behavior. How often (if ever) have you made a sexual decision that was not consistent with your sexual values? If so, what influenced you to do so (alcohol, peer influence)? How did you feel about your decision then, and how do you feel about it now (guilt, regret, indifference)?

Think About It These situational questions call for critical thinking about sexuality content and are scattered throughout the text.

Up Close Offset in the text, these sections focus in on one aspect of sexuality. Examples include sexting (Chapter 1), a cross-dressing husband/dad (Chapter 5), and talking with a new partner about one's vibrator use (Chapter 8).

Acknowledgments

Choices in Sexuality is the result of the work of many people. We are indebted to the following professors who teach human sexuality and who have reviewed previous editions of the text:

Cynthia Akagi, University of Kansas

Richard B. Ellis, Washburn University

Robert W. Buckingham, New Mexico State University

Christopher Robinson, University of Alabama at Birmingham

Jan Campbell, California State University, Chico

G. Joseph Zieleniewski, University of Cincinnati

Marilyn Myerson, University of South Florida

Rhonda R. Martin, The University of Tulsa

Tami James Moore, University of Nebraska-Kearney

Wade C. Lueck, College of Eastern Utah

We appreciate the significant contributions of Susan McCammon, who was senior author for earlier editions of this text, and whose thinking and writing helped to shape the book. Dr. McCammon is Chair of the Psychology Department at East Carolina University.

We would also like to acknowledge Beth Credle Burt (health education specialist, Education Services Project Manager, Siemens Healthcare) for ensuring state-of-the-art information on contraception. Thank you, also, to Karen Vail-Smith for her contribution to the STI chapter and to Chelsea Curry and E. Fred Johnson for their stunning photographs. Appreciation is also expressed to Karen Sabbah for her comments on Chapter 1 and 2.

We are indebted to the following people at BVT Publishing: Jenefier Winchell (textbook development); Shannon Waters (preproduction); Joyce Bianchini (managing editor); Anne Schofield (proofreader); Esther Scannell (cover and interior design); and Rhonda Minnema (typesetting manager).

We are always interested in ways to improve the text and invite your feedback and/or suggestions for new ideas and material to include in subsequent editions. We welcome dialogue with professors and students about sexuality issues and encourage you to email us. We check our email frequently and will respond.

David Knox   knoxd@ecu.edu

Caroline Schacht cschacht@suddenlink.net

Mark Whatley   mwhatley@valdosta.edu

ABOUT THE AUTHORS

David Knox, PhD is Professor of Sociology at East Carolina University and teaches Human Sexuality, as well as marriage and family courses. His publications include five textbooks and over 100 research articles. In addition, Dr. Knox presents regularly at professional conferences and mentors graduate students in relationship/sexual therapy. He and his wife, Caroline Schacht, have three children.

Caroline Schacht received her master's degrees in sociology and family relations from East Carolina University where she has taught for 15 years. Her clinical work includes marriage, family, and sex therapy. In addition, she is a divorce mediator and co-author of several texts, including *Understanding Social Problems* (Cengage, 2014). She is also a trained Romana Pilates instructor.

Mark A. Whatley, PhD is a professor in the Department of Psychology and Counseling at Valdosta State University. He teaches Psychology of Sex as well as gender, social psychology, and experimental psychology. He received his doctorate in social psychology from the University of Kentucky and his bachelor's and master's degrees from California State University, Fullerton. His research interests include sexual assault, rape, sexual harassment, social behavior, social influence, and scale development.

SUPPLEMENTS & RESOURCES

Instructor Supplements

A complete teaching package is available for instructors who adopt this book. This package includes an online lab, instructor's manual, test bank, course management software, and PowerPoint™ slides.

BVT*Lab*	An online lab is available for this textbook at www.BVTLab.com, as described in the BVT*Lab* section below.
Test Bank	An extensive test bank is available to instructors in both hard copy and electronic form. Each chapter has a wide range of multiple-choice, true/false and short-answer questions. Each question is referenced to the appropriate section of the text to make test creation quick and easy.
Course Management Software	BVT's course management software, Respondus, allows for the creation of tests and quizzes that can be downloaded directly into a wide variety of course management environments such as Blackboard, WebCT, Desire2Learn, ANGEL, E-Learning, eCollege, Canvas, Moodle, and others.
PowerPoint Slides	A set of PowerPoint slides includes about 30 slides per chapter, comprising a chapter overview, learning objectives, slides covering all key topics, key figures and charts, as well as summary and conclusion slides.

Student Resources

Student resources are available for this textbook at www.BVTLab.com. These resources are geared toward students needing additional assistance as well as those seeking complete mastery of the content. The following resources are available:

Practice Questions	Students can work through hundreds of practice questions online. Questions are multiple choice or true/false in format and are graded instantly for immediate feedback.
Flashcards	BVT*Lab* includes sets of flashcards for each chapter that reinforce the key terms and concepts from the textbook.
Chapter Summaries	A convenient and concise chapter summary is available as a study aid for each chapter.
PowerPoint Slides	All instructor PowerPoints are available for convenient lecture preparation and for students to view online for a study recap.

BVT*Lab*

BVT*Lab* is an affordable online lab for instructors and their students. It includes an online classroom with grade book and chat room, a homework grading system, extensive test banks for quizzes and exams, and a host of student study resources.

Course Setup	BVT*Lab* has an easy-to-use, intuitive interface that allows instructors to quickly set up their courses and grade books, and to replicate them from section to section and semester to semester.
Grade Book	Using an assigned passcode, students register themselves in the grade book; all homework, quizzes, and tests are then automatically graded and recorded.
Chat Room	Instructors can post discussion threads to a class forum and then monitor and moderate student replies.
Student Resources	All student resources for this textbook are available in BVT*Lab* in digital form.
eBook	A web-based eBook is available within the lab for easy reference during online classes, homework, and study sessions.

Even if a class is not taught in the lab, students can still utilize the many student resources described above

Customization

BVT's Custom Publishing Division can help you modify this book's content to satisfy your specific instructional needs. The following are examples of customization:

- Rearrangement of chapters to follow the order of your syllabus
- Deletion of chapters not covered in your course
- Addition of paragraphs, sections, or chapters you or your colleagues have written for this course
- Editing of the existing content, down to the word level
- Customization of the accompanying student resources and online lab
- Addition of handouts, lecture notes, syllabus, etc.
- Incorporation of student worksheets into the textbook

All of these customizations will be professionally typeset to produce a seamless textbook of the highest quality, with an updated table of contents and index to reflect the customized content.

CHAPTER 1

Choices in Sexuality: An Introduction

Sex isn't good unless it means something. It doesn't necessarily need to mean "love" and it doesn't necessarily need to happen in a relationship, but it does need to mean intimacy and connection … There exists a very fine line between being sexually liberated and being sexually used …

Laura Sessions Stepp, *Unhooked*

Chapter Outline

Objectives

1. Identify the various elements which comprise the concept of human sexuality.

2. Know the importance of body image for one's sexuality.

3. Explicate the theme of "choices in sexuality" for the text.

4. Learn the skills needed to make sexual decisions.

5. Review the various influences on making one's sexual choices.

7. Know the legal dangers of sexting.

8. Understand the evolution of sex education programs in the United States.

TRUTH OR FICTION?

T/F In a study of 5,500 never married individuals, women were more likely than men to report that "bad sex would be a deal breaker."

T/F Heterosexual males and females differ in regard to what behaviors they regard as "having sex."

T/F College males who take the "virginity pledge" are more likely to have remained abstinent through all four years of college than college males who did not take the pledge.

T/F Partners in committed relationships report the highest sexual satisfaction.

T/F Sex education delivered online is not effective.

Answers: 1.T 2.F 3.T 4.T 5.F

This text is about making sexual choices. Consider the following situations:

You have just met someone at a party or bar. You have had a couple of drinks and are flirting. Your partner flirts back. How soon and how much sex is appropriate with this person?

Your partner watches a lot of porn. Do you join your partner? Confront your partner? Ignore the behavior?

You have an STI or have had an abortion or previously engaged in a sexual behavior your partner does not know about. Do you tell your partner?

The preceding scenarios reflect the need to make decisions about things like the timing of sex in a relationship, the role of pornography, and the appropriateness of keeping sexual secrets. A primary goal of this text is to emphasize the relentlessness of the sexual choices with which we are confronted and the importance of making deliberate and informed sexual choices throughout our lives. Our society also makes choices about sexuality: the availability of "Plan B" as an over the counter medication, the legalization of same-sex marriages, and sex education in the public school system.

Sexual choices remain at the core of who we are as individuals and as a nation. Making informed choices involves knowledge of the psychological, physical, and social consequences of those choices. A good sexual relationship is important to us. About half of never married individuals want to stay in a relationship only if the sex is good. In a study of 5,500 never married individuals, 50% of the women and 44% of the men said that "bad sex would be a deal-breaker" (Wright, Randall, & Arroyo, 2013).

We begin the text with identifying the factors used to define human sexuality.

1.1 **Defining Human Sexuality**

People define the term *sex* differently. Horowitz and Spicer (2013) asked 124 emerging adults (40 male heterosexuals, 42 female heterosexuals, and 42 lesbians) to identify various sexual behaviors on a six-point scale (from "definitely" to "definitely not")

Magazines at the checkout counter in the grocery store are a constant reminder of the cultural ideal body type for women.
Sources: People *and* Fitness *magazines*

as "having sex." There was agreement that vaginal and anal sex were "definitely" sex, whereas kissing was "definitely not" sex. Ratings given by heterosexual male and heterosexual females did not differ significantly, but the lesbians were more likely than the heterosexuals to rate various forms of genital stimulation as "having sex." Human sexuality is a multifaceted concept. No one definition can capture its complexity. Rather, human sexuality can best be understood in terms of various factors.

1.1a Thoughts

The thoughts we have about sexual phenomena are a major component of human sexuality. Indeed, the major "sex organ" of our body is our brain. The thoughts a person has about sexual behavior—through previous experience, pornography, movies, and the media—will impact the behavior that person is motivated to engage in.

Sexual fantasies are thoughts about what an individual is remembering or hoping that he or she will experience. A study of sexuality in the workplace of 774 undergraduates revealed that 41% of the respondents reported that they had fantasized about having a sexual relationship with someone in the office (Merrill & Knox, 2010).

Cultural Diversity

Comfort with visible body parts varies by culture. In the United States, the naked breasts of an adult female are viewed as erotic and not to be displayed in public. However, among the Chavantez Indian tribe in Brazil, women's breasts are openly displayed and have a neutral erotic stimulus value. In the U.S. we feel the penis should not be exposed in public, whereas in European cultures it is seen as neutral as well. Consider art sculptures. Michelangelo's *David* caused an uproar when displayed in the states.

1.1b Sexual Self-Concept

Your **sexual self-concept** is the way you think or feel about your body, your level of interest in sex (highly sexual to asexual), and your value as a sexual partner (from accomplished lover to lousy lover). Body image refers to the perception of your own physical appearance. Weight is such a major commercial focus that individuals are encouraged to think they are less valuable and attractive if their weight does not approximate the cultural ideal. Data provided by Morotti and colleagues (2013) reveal specific negative associations with weight. They noted that lean women reported more frequent intercourse and being more orgasmic than obese women.

Various industries also encourage Americans to feel bad about physical attributes, such as their breast size, loss of hair, wrinkles, and varicose veins. Notice the commercials on television designed to create shame for one's own body and to seek relief through the latest products for dieting or skin care. Jane Fonda, in her 70s, was asked how she could look so young. She replied, "A lot of money."

Although both men and women have thoughts about their bodies, Wiederman (2000) developed a scale for women to assess the degree to which they think self-conscious thoughts about their body image when with a partner (see Self-Assessment 1-1). Men might also take the scale to assess their own body image. (We predict that the number of male concerns will be lower.)

Most individuals are concerned about their body, how they look, since this is the stimulus others see and when deciding if they want to approach and interact. This female is "checking herself out" the way she hopes potential partners will.
Source: Chelsea Curry

1.1c Values

Sexual values are moral guidelines for making sexual choices in nonmarital, marital, heterosexual, and homosexual relationships. Among the various sexual values are absolutism, relativism, and hedonism.

> *Remember that sex is not out there, but in here, in the deepest layer of your own being.*
> Jacob Heusner, *Words of Wisdom*

Personal REFLECTION

Take a moment to express your thoughts about the following questions. Sexual values and sexual behavior may not always be consistent. How often (if ever) have you made a sexual decision that was not consistent with your sexual values? If so, what influenced you to do so (for example, alcohol, peer influence, etc.)? How did you feel about your decision then, and how do you feel about it now (guilt, regret, indifference)? Galperin and colleagues (2013) emphasized that there is a sex difference in regard to regret: women are more likely to regret casual sex since the chance of pregnancy with a partner who may not be present to provide economic support for her offspring is high. Men regret missed sexual opportunities which could have provided additional offspring (according to sociobiological/evolutionary theory).

Sexual self-concept
The way an individual thinks and feels about his or her body, self-evaluation of one's interest in sex, and evaluation of oneself as a sexual partner

Sexual values
Moral guidelines for making sexual choices

SELF-ASSESSMENT 1-1: BODY IMAGE

To assess your body image and self-consciousness about your body, read each statement and select a number to indicate how often you agree with each statement or how often you think it would be true for you. The term *partner* refers to someone with whom you are romantically or sexually intimate.

0	1	2	3	4	5
Never	Rarely	Sometimes	Often	Usually	Always

1. I would feel very nervous if a partner were to explore my body before or after having sex.
2. The idea of having sex without any covers over my body causes me anxiety.
3. While having sex, I am (would be) concerned that my hips and thighs would flatten out and appear larger than they actually are.
4. During sexual activity, I am (would be) concerned about how my body looks to my partner.
5. The worst part of having sex is being nude in front of another person.
6. If a partner were to put a hand on my buttocks, I would think, "My partner can feel my fat."
7. During sexual activity it is (would be) difficult not to think about how unattractive my body is.
8. During sex I (would) prefer to be on the bottom so that my stomach appears flat.
9. I would feel very uncomfortable walking, completely nude, around the bedroom in front of my partner.
10. The first time I have sex with a new partner, I (would) worry that seeing my body without clothes will turn off my partner.
11. If a partner were to put an arm around my waist, I would think, "My partner can tell how fat I am."
12. I (could) only feel comfortable enough to have sex if it were dark so that my partner could not clearly see my body.
13. I (would) prefer having sex with my partner on top so that my partner is less likely to see my body.
14. I (would) have a difficult time taking a shower or bath with a partner.
15. I (would) feel anxious receiving a full-body massage from a partner.

Scoring

Add the numbers you assigned for each of the statements. Possible scores could range from zero to 75. The higher your score, the more self-conscious/anxious you are about your body.

Norms

Two hundred and nine undergraduate women, ranging in age from 18 to 21 and mostly white (90.9%), completed the scale. Those who were currently in a dating relationship, had ever had vaginal intercourse, had ever received oral sex from a male, and who had ever performed oral sex for a male scored a mean of 20.28, 22.23, 22.18, and 22.34 respectively. In contrast, those who were not in a dating relationship, had never had vaginal intercourse, had never received oral sex from a male, and who had never performed oral sex for a male had mean scores of 32.29, 36.77, 41.08, and 37.66 respectively. Clearly, those who experienced or predicted the greatest degree of body image self-consciousness during physical intimacy with a partner had less heterosexual experience; conversely, increased heterosexual experience as a woman was associated with lower levels of being self-conscious about one's body.

Source: Used with the permission of *The Journal of Sex Research* from "Women's body image self-consciousness during physical intimacy with a partner" by M. W. Wiederman, (2000). *37*, 60–68. Scale from page 68.

Absolutism

Absolutism refers to a belief system that is based on the unconditional power and authority of religion, law, or tradition. Table 1-1 reveals that of 1,103 undergraduate males, 12% reported having absolutist sexual values. Of 3,464 undergraduate females, 15% reported having absolutist sexual values. Religion is a major source of absolutist sexual values in that many religions teach waiting until marriage to have sexual intercourse. An example is "True Love Waits," which is an international campaign designed to challenge teenagers and college students to remain sexually abstinent until marriage. Under this program (created and sponsored by the Baptist Sunday School Board), young people are asked to agree to the absolutist position and sign a commitment to the following: "Believing that true love waits, I make a commitment to God, myself, my family, my friends, my future mate, and my future children to a lifetime of purity including sexual abstinence from this day until the day I enter a biblical marriage relationship." Williams and Thompson (2013) followed the sexual behavior of 795 males through four years of college and found that males who made private virginity pledges were significantly more likely to remain abstinent all four years of college and to report having had fewer sexual partners at the end of their third and fourth years of college—even after controlling for age, race, high-risk drinking, impulsivity, and religiosity. Making a pledge was not related to condom use (LifeWay Student Ministry, 2013).

A sexual value held by this female is absolutism. She has had neither oral sex nor sexual intercourse and regards these as appropriate only when she is married. *Source: James Davis*

Relativism

Relativism is a value system emphasizing that sexual choices should be made in the context of a particular situation. Table 1-1 reveals that of 1,103 undergraduate males, 59% reported having relativist sexual values. Of 3,464 undergraduate females, 68% reported having relativist sexual values. Whereas an absolutist might feel that it is wrong for unmarried people to have intercourse, a relativist might feel that the moral correctness of sex outside marriage depends on the particular situation. For example, a relativist might feel that in some situations, sex between casual dating partners is wrong (such as when one individual pressures the other into having sex or lies in order to persuade the other to have sex). Yet in other cases—when there is no deception or coercion and the dating partners are practicing *"safer sex"*—intercourse between casual dating partners may be viewed as acceptable.

> *Give me chastity and continence, but not quite yet.*
>
> St. Augustine

Absolutism
A belief system that is based on the unconditional power and authority of religion, law, or tradition

Relativism
A sexual value that emphasizes that sexual decisions should be made in the context of a particular situation

TABLE **1-1**	Sexual Values of 4,567 Undergraduates		
Respondents	Absolutism	Relativism	Hedonism
Male students (N = 1,103)	12%	59%	29%
Female students (N = 3,464)	15%	68%	17%

Source: Hall, S. and Knox, D. (2013). Relationship and sexual behaviors of a sample of 4,567 university students. Unpublished data collected for this text. Department of Family and Consumer Sciences, Ball State University and Department of Sociology, East Carolina University.

Hedonism

Hedonism is the sexual value that reflects the philosophy that the pursuit of pleasure and the avoidance of pain provide the ultimate value and motivation for sexual behavior. Table 1-1 reveals that of 1,103 undergraduate males, 29% reported having hedonist sexual values. Of 3,464 undergraduate females, 17% reported having hedonist sexual values. The hedonist's sexual values are reflected in the creed "If it feels good, do it." Hedonists are sensation seekers; they tend to pursue novel, exciting, and optimal levels of stimulation and arousal. Their goal is pleasure.

I need more sex, OK? Before I die I wanna taste everyone in the world.

Angelina Jolie

The **sexual double standard**—the view that encourages and accepts sexual expression of men more than women—is reflected in Table 1-1. Indeed, men were almost twice as likely to be hedonists as women. Cultural labels for male hedonists include "real men," "stud," and "stallion" whereas the cultural labels for female hedonists include "whore," "slut," and "trollop." The double standard exists not only in the U.S. but also in Australia (Flood, 2013).

Personal REFLECTION

Take a moment to express your thoughts about the following question. An individual's sexual values may change over time. It is not uncommon for individuals that are absolutist prior to involvement in an emotional relationship to become relativistic after they are involved sexually. When a relationship ends, persons may even become hedonistic for a brief time before becoming relativistic in a new relationship. How have your sexual values changed?

1.1d Emotions

Love and intimacy are contexts that influence the expression of sexual behavior. As will be noted in the chapters on gender and love, women have traditionally been socialized to experience sex in the context of an emotional relationship. Indeed, the sexual value of relativism suggests that people decide to have sex on the basis of the context of a rela-

Remember, we're madly in love, so it's all right to kiss me anytime you feel like it.

Suzanne Collins, *The Hunger Games.*

tionship, such as one of emotional intimacy. The fact that men are more often hedonists and women are more often absolutists and relativists reflects the value of an emotional context for women.

1.1e Behaviors

The term *human sexuality* implies a variety of behaviors. Although people commonly associate the word *sex* with *intercourse*, vaginal intercourse is only one of many sexual behaviors. Masturbation, oral sex, breast stimulation, manual genital stimulation, and anal intercourse are also sexual behaviors.

One's virginity is a concept that is often muddled. Rather than it being dichotomous "one is or is not a virgin," a three part view of virginity might be adopted: oral sex, vaginal sex, and anal sex. No longer is the term *virgin* synonymous with absence

---

Hedonism
Sexual value that reflects a philosophy that the pursuit of pleasure and the avoidance of pain are the ultimate values and motivation for sexual behavior

Sexual double standard
One standard for women and another for men regarding sexual behavior (i.e., in U.S. society it is normative for men to have more sexual partners and women to have fewer partners)

of sexual behaviors in any one of these three areas. Rather, whether one has engaged in each of the three behaviors must be identified. Hence, an individual would not just say, "I am a virgin." Rather, the individual would state, "I am an oral virgin" or "intercourse virgin" or "anal virgin," as the case may be.

National DATA

Based on a survey of 5,865 adult respondents (ages 20–24) in the U.S., 83% of men and 64% of women reported having masturbated alone (rather than with a partner) in the past 12 months. In addition, 63% of the men and 70% of women reported having received oral sex from their heterosexual partner, and 70% of the men and 9% of the women received oral sex from their same sex partner. "Having experienced vaginal intercourse" was reported by 63% of men and 80% of women, and 23% of women reported engaging in penile-anal intercourse with their male partner (Reece, Herbenick, Fortenberry, & et al., 2012).

1.1f Anatomy and Physiology

The idea of sex often brings to mind the thought of naked bodies or anatomy. Hence, the term *human sexuality* implies sexual anatomy, referring to external genitalia, secondary sex characteristics (such as a deepened voice in males and breast development in females), and internal reproductive organs of women (e.g. ovaries) and men (e.g. testes). *Physiology* refers to how the parts work or the functioning of the genitals and reproductive system.

1.1g Reproduction

The term *human sexuality* includes reproduction of the species. Sociobiologists, who believe that social behavior has a biological basis, emphasize that much of the sexual interaction that occurs between men and women has its basis in the drive to procreate. Indeed, the perpetuation of the species depends on the sperm and egg uniting.

1.1h Interpersonal Relationships

Although masturbation and sexual fantasies can occur outside the context of a relationship, much of sexuality occurs in the context of interpersonal relationships. Such relationships vary—heterosexual or homosexual; nonmarital, marital or extramarital; casual or intimate; personal or business-related (e.g. web cam sex or prostitution); and brief or long term. The type of emotional and social relationship a couple has affects the definition and quality of their sexual relationship. Indeed, relationship satisfaction is associated with sexual satisfaction (Stephensen, Rellini, & Meston, 2013). The comment by a spouse, "I can't fight with you all day and want to have sex with you at night" illustrates the social context of the sexual experience. Partners in committed relationships report the highest sexual satisfaction (Galinsky & Sorenstein, 2013). Indeed, it is the nature of the interpersonal relationship that creates reported sexual satisfaction, which affects mental health (Hughes & Umberson, 2004). Whitton and colleagues (2013) also found that female college students who were involved in committed dating relationships reported fewer depressive symptoms. Both female and male college students who were in committed relationships reported less problematic alcohol use (e.g. less binge drinking).

> *If people invest a great deal in sexual relationships that provide little in the way of non-sexual rewards, these relationships may, in fact, be punishing.*
> Michael Hughes & Debra Umberson, sociologists

Diversity

Sexual behaviors, thoughts, emotions, and values vary within the same person, between people, and between cultures. For example, the same person may have multiple sex partners at one age, but may be monogamous or asexual at another age. The more diverse the population of a society, the greater the variation in the types of sexual behaviors, thoughts, feelings, values, and relationships. Given the ethnic, racial, and religious diversity of the population in the United States, it comes as no surprise that there are a range of sexual choices being made at both the micro and macro level.

1.2 **Nature of Sexual Choices**

Whenever we are confronted with a sexual choice, at least five factors are involved:

1. Not to decide is to decide.
2. Choices involve trade-offs.
3. Choices include selecting a positive or negative view.
4. Choices produce ambivalence and uncertainty.
5. Some choices are revocable; some are not.

1.2a Not to Decide Is to Decide

Not making a decision is a decision by default. For example, if you are having oral, vaginal, or anal intercourse and do not make a conscious decision to use a latex condom (or dental dam), you have inadvertently made a decision to increase your risk for contracting a sexually transmitted infection—including HIV. If you are having vaginal intercourse and do not decide to use birth control, you have decided to risk pregnancy. If you do not monitor and restrict your alcohol or drug use at parties or in a new relationship, you have made a decision to drift toward unprotected sex. If you are in a relationship with someone you love and have not made a decision to be emotionally and sexually faithful to that person, you are vulnerable to cheating. Indeed, if you do not make explicit sexual decisions about what you will and will not do, and you are still choosing a course of action and may have chosen by default to contract an STI, to get pregnant, or to be unfaithful.

1.2b Choices Involve Trade-Offs

All the choices you make will involve trade-offs or disadvantages, as well as advantages. The choice to cheat on your partner may provide excitement, but it may also produce feelings of guilt and may lead to the breakup of your relationship. The choice to tell your partner of an indiscretion may deepen your feelings of intimacy; but by doing so, you may also risk that your partner leaving you. The choice to have an abortion may enable you to avoid the hardship of continuing an unwanted pregnancy; however, it may also involve feelings of guilt, anxiety, or regret. Likewise, the choice to continue an unwanted pregnancy may enable you to experience the joy of having a child and allow you to avoid the guilt associated with having an abortion, but it may also involve the hardships of inopportune parenting or having to place the baby for adoption.

1.2c Choices Include Selecting a Positive or Negative View

Regardless of your circumstances, you can choose to focus on the positive aspects of a difficult situation and to approach a difficult situation as a problem to be solved.

The skill of developing a positive problem-solving approach can be used in every situation. The discovery of your partner having an affair can be viewed as an opportunity to open channels of communication with your partner and strengthen your relationship. One woman reported that her diagnosis of genital herpes not only "slowed her down from a path of sexual oblivion" but also focused her on selecting partners with whom she "could have a real relationship and communicate how to navigate her STI." Despite being rejected by one's family members because of sexual orientation, a person might pursue the opportunity to develop closer relationships with those family members who accept homosexuality. It is not the event, but rather how we respond to the event that affects the outcome. You always have a choice to view an event positively.

In addition to viewing personal events from a positive perspective, you can choose to view sexuality, in general, through a positive lens. Traditionally, sex has been viewed as restrictive, repressive, "nasty", etc. Williams and colleagues (2013) encourage a society wide "sex positive" view of sexuality:

> A sex-positive approach is about allowing for a wide range of sexual expression that takes into account sexual identities, orientations, and behaviors; gender presentation; accessible health care and education; and multiple important dimensions of human diversity.

1.2d Choices Produce Ambivalence and Uncertainty

Choosing among options often creates **ambivalence**—conflicting feelings that produce uncertainty or indecisiveness about the next course of action. Many sexual choices involve ambivalence. For example, consider the conflicting feelings and uncertainty that would accompany the following decisions:

- When and with whom should I become sexually active?
- Should I report a family member who has sexually abused me?
- Should I have an abortion, or continue an unwanted pregnancy?
- Should I keep an unplanned child that was conceived in a casual relationship, or place the baby for adoption?
- Should I come out of the closet and tell my family that I am gay?
- Should I accept my co-worker's invitation to spend the night together at a conference (which means cheating on my partner)?
- Should I forgive my partner for having an affair, or should I terminate the relationship?

Ambivalence occurs when one has many options to choose from. In the United States, for example, a young unmarried pregnant woman can choose to have an abortion, to rear the baby in a single-parent home, to place the baby for an adoption, or maybe to marry the biological father and keep the baby. A woman choosing any one of these options may forever reconsider if she made the right decision and blame herself for whatever decision she did make. She may think, "If only I had … "

Ambivalence may also occur when there are conflicting norms and values. For example, in the United States individuals may be ambivalent about abortion because there are conflicting values regarding abortion, as evidenced by the pro-choice and antiabortion movements. Similarly, the decision of whether to engage in nonmarital sex may produce ambivalence because of the conflicting norms and values regarding nonmarital sex. One's parents and religion (e.g. the Mormon faith is adamantly against oral sex and intercourse before marriage) may convey that nonmarital sex is wrong, whereas one's peers and the media may indicate that it is acceptable and desirable.

Ambivalence
Conflicting feelings that coexist, producing uncertainty or indecisiveness about a person, object, idea, or course of action

1.2e Some Choices Are Revocable; Some Are Not

Some sexual choices are revocable; that is, they can be changed. For example, a person who has chosen to have sex with multiple partners can subsequently decide to be faithful to one partner or to abstain from sexual relations. An individual who, in the past, has chosen to accept being sexually unsatisfied in an ongoing relationship ("I never told him how to get me off") can decide to address the issue or seek sex therapy with the partner.

Although many sexual choices can be modified or changed, some cannot. You cannot eliminate the effects of some sexually transmissible infections, undo an abortion, or be a virgin (by some definitions) after you have had intercourse. However, it is possible to learn from choices that, in retrospect, were not good ones. Reflecting on good and poor choices one has made could provide useful information for current and future decisions.

1.3 **Making Sexual Choices**

Having reviewed the nature of sexual choices, we look at what is involved in making wise sexual choices. Although few of us carefully think out each sexual choice we

Between two evils, I always pick the one I haven't tried before.

Mae West, actress

make, we might benefit from following basic decision-making steps. Willingness to learn from previous decisions is also important in making wise sexual choices.

1.3a Basic Decision-Making Steps

We will use the example of a couple facing the issue of the future of their relationship in presenting the following basic steps in decision making:

1. *Clarify values and goals.* Assess the degree to which the partners agree on whether they want to continue the relationship with the goal of a permanent relationship, including marriage. If only one wants a future, and in the meantime wants a "friends with benefits" relationship, is the other willing to continue the relationship under these conditions?

2. *Understand one's motives and identify feelings and emotions.* Each partner should make clear his or her feelings about the other and his or her reasons for wanting to continue, or discontinue, the relationship. The range of expressions can be from "I love you and want to marry you because I have never felt so right about a relationship before" to "I wish I loved you, but my feelings are more of friendship; and I think it would only damage a great friendship to lead you on."

3. *Identify and explore alternative courses of action.* Breaking up now, continuing the relationship now with no further discussion to see what happens, or continuing the relationship with both parties knowing that there are different definitions of the relationship and goals for the future—all three are the alternative courses of action. One option is to identify and discuss these alternatives with your partner. Doing so reflects your skill in being deliberate about your choices.

4. *Seek information that makes the short-term and long-term consequences clear for each choice.* Seeing a therapist who will help the partners assess their feelings about each other and the relationship, reading "relationship books," and/or exploring information via the Internet will provide additional databases for the partners. The goal is to predict the outcome of each choice for the individuals and their relationship.

5. *Weigh the positive and negative consequences for each alternative.*
   - Break up now
     - Positive consequence: The partners will get the hurt over with now.
     - Negative consequence: The partners would be ending a relationship that might eventually flourish.
   - Continue the relationship
     - Positive consequence: The partners can continue to enjoy each other.
     - Negative consequence: The partners are not making themselves available to new relationships that have a joint future.

6. *Select an alternative that has maximum positive consequences and minimal negative consequences.* The partners might decide that because their relationship will eventually end, they will continue to see each other but make themselves open to seeing other people. Ideally, each partner would meet someone new and launch a new life as he or she slowly disengages from the current relationship. In reality, the more likely scenario is that the more involved person will have difficulty disengaging from the current relationship and finding a new partner, and experience the attendant negative feelings. Hence, there is not always a solution that provides an immediate positive outcome for both parties. However, the long-term consequence of breaking up and moving on is that each partner can end up in a mutually valued relationship that has a future. Table 1-2 reviews some of the self-reported best and worst sexual decisions of our students.

7. *Implement one's decision.* This step involves identifying and putting into action the steps needed to carry out the decision.

TABLE 1-2 | Best and Worst Sexual Decisions: Student Experiences

Best Choice	Worst Choice
Ending my relationship with someone I loved who was unfaithful to me	Cheating on my partner: It wasn't worth it. The guilt has been almost unbearable.
Insisting on using a condom with a person I had just met and later finding out the person had an STI	Cheating on my partner
Forgiving my partner for cheating on me	Being unfaithful to my partner
Getting out of a relationship with someone who was married	Getting into a relationship with someone who was married
Waiting for more than a year to have sex in a relationship	Getting drunk and having sex with people I didn't know
Getting out of a sex-and-drugs-focused relationship	Having unprotected sex on a one-night stand
Getting out of a relationship with a partner who was jealous	Trying to make my partner jealous

1.3b Important Skills for Sexual Decision Making

Various skills are helpful when making decisions. Information-gathering skills, such as reading and library or computer research, may be helpful in identifying alternative courses of action and projecting negative and positive consequences of various alternatives. Implementing one's decision may require skills in assertiveness and the ability to resist social pressure from peers or parents. It may also involve assertiveness in seeking guidance and social support.

Sometimes couples or groups, rather than individuals, make sexual choices. For example, a couple may be faced with the choice of whether to have a vasectomy, whether to seek sex therapy, or whether to take fertility drugs to become pregnant. A group, such as a state legislature, may be faced with the decision of whether to mandate sex education in public schools—and if so, at what grade levels and with what curriculum. When couples or groups make decisions, they need additional decision-making skills, including communication and listening skills that enable individuals to effectively convey and listen to each other's ideas and concerns. Negotiation and collaboration skills are also important for couple and group decision making.

1.4 **Influences on Sexual Choices**

Whether sexual choices operate at the micro (individual) or macro (societal) level, there are various cultural, social, and psychological influences.

1.4a Culture

We have noted that there are cross-cultural variations in sexuality. For example, although homosexual behavior has struggled for acceptance in the United States, in the New Guinea Highlands, it is regarded as a pathway to heterosexuality. Among the Sambia in the (New Guinea Highlands), preadolescent boys are taught to perform fellatio (oral sex) on older unmarried males and ingest their sperm. They do so because they are taught that it enables them to produce their own sperm in adulthood, thereby ensuring their ability to impregnate their wives.

Think About It

Take a moment to answer the following questions. Did increased social acceptance of sex outside marriage lead to increased rates of cohabitation? Or, did increased rates of living together lead to increased social acceptance of sex outside marriage? Both changes have had their respective influences. Without the stigma and social disapproval previously associated with sex outside marriage and cohabitation, individuals are more likely to choose these options today than they were in previous generations.

The society in which you live affects the attitudes you develop about sexuality. The first author of this text has been involved in research comparing the sexual values of the United States and Iceland. When translating the U.S. questionnaire into the Icelandic language (which included asking questions about "hooking up"), the Icelandic researcher (Freysteinsdóttir, 2013) noted that there was no word in the Icelandic language for "hooking up." Indeed, meeting, flirting, and having protected sex soon in a relationship is normative in Iceland. Icelanders also have a different view of marriage: It is to follow a long (decade or more) period of living together and having children. In the U.S., the norm is meet, live together a relatively short time, marry, and then have children.

1.4b Media

In the United States a major source of sexual norms is television. *Glee* and *Modern Family* feature individuals and partners who are gay. Talk shows (e.g. *Jerry Springer*), regularly feature programs on infidelity, acquaintance rape, and transsexualism. MTV features specials in which college students are shown on spring break amid a frenzy of alcohol and sex. Music videos often convey sexual messages. Vandenbosch et al. (2013) conducted a content analysis of 9,369 scenes from 1,393 music videos and 180 programs, broadcast on Belgian music entertainment channels. Results revealed that 39.3% of the coded scenes of these music videos contained sexual messages.

Fifty Shades of Grey has sold over 70 million copies worldwide.
Source: Chelsea Curry

Contemporary films can be used to show how sexual norms are both reflected and created (Clarke, 2013). Print media, such as *The New York Times*, use sex to sell newspapers. From 2001 to 2007, there have been 61 articles in various publications on "sex addiction" (Reay, Attwood, & Gooder, 2013). Books also convey sexual content. The E. L. James book *Fifty Shades of Grey* created enormous visibility in regard to being open to seeking sexual variety (Hollomotz, 2013).

Media coverage of sexuality has both positive and negative influences on sexual choices. On the positive side, reports on sexual abuse, date rape, and the date rape drug Rohypnol have helped to bring these abuses into public awareness. Media attention to HIV infection and other sexually transmitted infections provides a valuable public educational service and help to increase condom use (Hennessy, et al., 2013). Colleges and universities, billboards, subways, buses, and other public places often display educational posters with such messages as "Use condom sense" and "Against her will is against the law."

On the negative side, the media have been criticized for portraying women as sexual objects, depicting sexuality in violent contexts, and contributing to women's negative body images and self-concepts by portraying desirable women as only those who are young, thin, and beautiful. The media also may be criticized for exposing youth to sexually explicit images (e.g. pornography) before they are old enough to make responsible sexual choices. Gottfried and colleagues (2013) found that adolescents who reported exposure to sexual content via dramatic programs on television had more negative attitudes about sex and were more likely to engage in sexual behavior within a year of exposure.

Clearly, social and cultural values, roles, norms, and laws also influence sexual choices. For example, the current emphasis on the social value of safer sex has influenced the percentage of individuals who are choosing to use condoms. Traditional gender roles taught women that they should not initiate sexual intimacy and taught men to be the initiator in relationships. The changing roles of women and men have led to more women choosing to initiate sex in their relationships. Finally, governmental laws and policies may affect sexual choices by restricting or allowing, for example, access to abortion, prostitution, and certain methods of birth control. Additionally, sexual harassment laws and policies influence individuals' choices about how to interact with their employees, co-workers, and students.

BVT *Lab*

Improve your test scores. Practice quizzes are available at **www.BVTLab.com**.

1.4c Peers and Family

Peers are a major source of sexual knowledge and sexual values. Your first source of information about sex was likely to have been your peers, and the sexual values of your closest friends are probably very similar to your sexual values.

Various family factors—including family composition and relationships, values, and economic resources—influence sexual choices. For example, your family's economic resources may influence your choices about what type of birth control to use, whether to seek sexual health care (such as Pap smears and mammograms), and whether to continue an unplanned pregnancy. If your parents are an interracial couple or have values that are accepting of interracial couples, you may be more open to date and/or marry individuals of various races. Conversely, if your parents disapprove of interracial couples, you may feel less freedom to date individuals of a different race. Ozay and colleagues (2012) analyzed data on 251 parents of undergraduates and found that over a third (35%) disapproved of their child's involvement in an interracial relationship. Parental disapproval (which did not vary by gender of parent) increased with the seriousness of relationship involvement (e.g. dating or marriage), and parents were more disapproving of their daughters' interracial involvement than that of their sons.

Our lives are shaped by the choices and actions of others around us.

Lorne Tepperman, Susannah Wilson, sociologists

Family influences may override media influences. Wright and colleagues (2013) studied the effect of adolescent exposure to MTV's *16 and Pregnant* and *Teen Mom* on 313 females and found that frequent viewing was associated with a decreased probability of having engaged in recent intercourse for females whose fathers often communicated about sex with them while growing up. Conversely, for females who viewed the programs and who did not report their fathers communicating about sex, there was an increased frequency of reporting recent intercourse behavior.

National & International **DATA**

Based on a survey of 4,700 respondents in the United States and seven other countries (China, United Kingdom, India, South Korea, South Africa, Indonesia and Brazil), 9 in 10 carry a phone. One in four check it every 30 minutes, whereas one in five check it every 10 minutes (Gibbs, 2012).

1.4d Technology

Cindy Gallop is a consultant who emphasizes that the major impact of technology today (through its distribution of pornography on the Internet) is to undermine the capacity of youth to understand how to connect emotionally and sexually with a partner. Her YouTube discussion, (http://www.youtube.com/watch?v=HJ3kP-0Mu3k), 2013 exposes the atrocious myths that youth are buying as reality (e.g., all girls love to have their partner ejaculate on their face) and the associated lies some women must tell to maintain their relationships (e.g. "I love cum on my face ... Give me more big boy").

You can change the world through sex and sexuality.

Cindy Gallop, *Make Love, Not Porn*

Technology has also changed the way individuals initiate, maintain, and end relationships, including sexual relationships (Bergdall, et al., 2012). Indeed personal, portable, wirelessly networked technologies in the form of iPhones, Droids, iPads, etc. have become commonplace in the lives of individuals (Gibbs, 2012; Looi, et al., 2010) as a way of staying connected with one's offline friends and partners (Reich, Subrahmanyam, & Espionoza, 2012). Some have difficulty not answering their smart phones as was reported by one in ten out of a sample of 2,000 in a Harris Interactive survey. DeHaan and colleagues (2013) examined the use of online technology by gay, lesbian, bisexual and transsexual (LGBT) individuals and found that the Internet sometimes provides an easier way of connecting with others who understand or share their lifestyle than trying to meet like-minded individuals in their more limited social world.

Bauerlein (2010) noted that today's youth are being socialized in a hyper-digital age where traditional modes of communication will be replaced by gadgets and texting will become the primary mode of communication, with an average of 2,272 messages a month. Text messages have become a primary means for flirting (73% of 18–25 year olds) according to Gibbs (2012). Sexting is a direct combination of technology and sexuality (see Up Close 1-1).

Sexting: Sexual Content and Images in Romantic Relationships

This study reported the analysis of data provided by 483 undergraduates who completed a 25-item Internet survey designed to assess the degree to which respondents used technology to send sexual messages, photos, and videos to a romantic partner (primarily via a cell phone). Findings included the following:

1. *Use of technology*   Almost two thirds (64%) of the respondents reported sending a sexual text message, 42.9% a sexual photo, and 12.7% a sex video to a romantic partner.
2. *Frequency of use*   The frequency of sending sexual content varied from daily (4%) to less than once a month (26%).
3. *Sex differences*   There were no gender differences in sexting. However, male respondents were more likely than female respondents to have been the first to initiate sending sexual content. In addition, males were more likely to perceive sexting as having a positive effect on the couple's relationship.
4. *Racial differences*   Nonwhites, compared to whites, were more likely to report ever having used technology to send sexual content to a romantic partner.
5. *Class in school*   When compared to first year students, sophomores, juniors, and seniors were more likely to report ever having used technology to send sexual content to a romantic partner. In effect, the older the student, the more likely the student had used technology to send sexual content.
6. *Type of technology*   Text messaging was the technology used most frequently to send sexual content to a current or frequent partner.

Sexting has the potential to be catastrophic for the individuals involved. Since one's private cell phone is the technology of choice for sending this erotic content, the behavior occurs out of view of one's parents and employers. However, should an individual use their email account at work, there could be trouble. In 2010 the Supreme Court ruled that employers can monitor emails of employees if there are reasonable grounds to assume that emails are personal and not work related. Hence, employees can get fired for sending sex messages.

While these undergraduates are not at risk as long as the parties are age 18 or older, sending erotic photos of individuals younger than age 18 can be problematic. Many countries consider sexting child pornography, and laws related to child pornography have been applied in cases of sexting. Six high school students in Greensburg, Pennsylvania, are facing child pornography charges after three teenage girls allegedly took nude or semi-nude photos of themselves and shared them with male classmates via their cell phones. While there is disagreement if sexting by teenagers in romantic relationships constitutes child pornography, caution is warranted (Zhang, 2010; Jaishankar, 2009).

Source: Parker, M., Knox, D., and Easterling, B. (2011). SEXTING: Sexual content/Images in romantic relationships. Poster, Eastern Sociological Society, Philadelphia, PA. Feb. 24–26.

1.4e Education

Education level is a demographic that helps to predict sexual behavior. Over 65 years ago, Alfred C. Kinsey and his colleagues observed that college educated individuals reported higher masturbation rates than those with high school educations. More recently, Lyons and colleagues (2013) confirmed that young adults enrolled in or who graduated from four-year educational institutions reported fewer casual sex partners on the variables of lifetime vaginal, lifetime oral, and recent vaginal sex.

The Social Choices feature that follows emphasizes the controversy over sex education in the public school system and the outcome of sex education for students.

Social Choices 1-1

Sex Education in Public Schools

Dauda (2013) noted that the U.S., Canada and the UK reflect a common norm of developing social policies that regulate children, who are seen as being in need of protection. Related to this perspective is that those children grow up to be adults, and society values their "proper expression of adult sexuality." Sex education is a major area of concern for control by society and was introduced in the American public school system in the late nineteenth century with the goal of combating STIs (sexually transmitted infections) and instilling sexual morality (typically understood as abstinence until marriage). Over time, the abstinence agenda became more evident. In the Bush administration, only sex education programs that emphasized or promoted abstinence were eligible for federal funding. Programs that also discussed contraception and other means of pregnancy protection, referred to as **comprehensive sex education programs**, were not eligible. The Obama administration has been in favor of the latter, however. While these philosophical differences have been pervasive, a trend has emerged whereby schools and communities provide both abstinence education and contraception information (more comprehensive sex education). Chen and colleagues (2011) evaluated the cost effectiveness of such health education intervention programs, which improve preadolescents' attitudes toward abstinence and pregnancy avoidance through contraceptive use. For each $1,000 spent in these programs, 13.67 unintended pregnancies among preadolescents were avoided.

Other researchers have provided evidence of the positive outcomes of sex education. Erkut and colleagues (2013) examined whether a nine-lesson sex education intervention, "Get Real: Comprehensive Sex Education That Works," implemented in the sixth grade, can reduce the number of adolescents who might otherwise become "early starters" of sexual activity (defined as heterosexual intercourse) by the seventh grade. Participants were 548 boys and 675 girls who completed surveys in both sixth grade (baseline) and seventh grade (follow-up). Students randomly assigned to the control condition were 30% more likely to initiate sex at follow-up. Hence, exposure to the sex education program was associated with a delay in early sexual debut. In another study, Vivancos and colleagues (2013) surveyed British university students about their sex education in school when they were age 14 and their subsequent sexual behavior. The researchers found that school-based sex education was effective at reducing the risk of unprotected intercourse and STIs in early adulthood. McKee and colleagues (2012) confirmed that students can also profit from online sex education.

Comprehensive sex education programs
Programs that discuss abstinence as well as the use of contraception

Your Opinion?

1. To what degree do you support abstinence education in public schools?
2. Should condoms be made available for students already having sex?
3. Should parents control the content of sex education in public schools?

1.4f Religion

Religion is a central element of culture and has an enormous influence on sexual beliefs and decisions (Woodford, Levy, & Walls, 2013). Persons high on religiosity (group affiliation, attendance at religious services, adherence to sanctions) tend to make more conservative sexual choices. Religion may also dictate one's sexual behavior in reference to a spouse. Ravanipour and colleagues (2013) interviewed 15 married Iranian women who reported that it was their sacred duty to be a frequent and willing sexual partner for their husbands. Indeed, their status with God depended on their being a good wife (pleasing their husband sexually).

TABLE **1-3**	How Five Major Religions View Sexuality
	Five Major Religions and Sexuality
Judaism	For Jews, sex is for procreation and for personal satisfaction. It is not a shameful thing. However, sex is only fitting between two married people. Within that context, it is required. Men owe sex to their wives, and women ought to engage in sex with their husbands. To withhold sex as punishment or out of spite is wrong. The Talmud also discusses the husband's responsibility in foreplay (length of time, activities performed, etc.) prior to engaging in coitus. Prior to marriage, all sexual relations are forbidden. Whilst married, people are not to engage in sexual relations with others. Homosexuality is strictly forbidden. Male masturbation is also a no-no, as it is a waste of seed that God has given. Female masturbation does not seem to be explicitly forbidden.
Christianity	There is a wide variety of views on sex from the Christian perspective. For example, there are conservative Christians who argue that masturbation is sinful and prohibited, that gay marriage is wrong, and that sex is solely for producing children. However, there are people who call themselves Christians who support same sex marriage, sex outside of marriage, and polyamory. What is the correct Christian view on sexual values? There are many views.
Islam	Sex is regarded as a very natural thing in Islam. God gave sex to men and women as a blessing, so that they could experience pleasure and procreate. It is to be enjoyed by lawful husbands and wives. Pre-marital sex is forbidden. The Qur'an permits a man to marry as many as four wives—if he has the wealth and the moral character to treat them equally. For Sunnis, having sex with women outside of marriage has always been forbidden. Shi'i have traditionally practiced temporary marriages, which are as fleeting as an hour or as enduring as decades. The parties sign a contract, which is witnessed by another person. The specifications of what will happen sexually and otherwise are spelled out, as are the monetary terms. Sunni critics regard this as barely more than prostitution. In most places, Shi'i no longer engage in the practice.
Hinduism	The issue of sexuality among Hindus is a puzzling contradiction. On the one hand, the Hindu religion is by far the most lascivious and sexually liberated of all. Hindu deities cavort and frolic in promiscuous liaisons, explore gymnastic sexual positions that boggle the mind, and savor sex, like true gastronomes. Yet at the same time, Indian people tend to be rather reserved sexually. They go to the Shiva temple and pour libations over the deity's phallus, simulating ejaculation, and then avoid pre-marital sex more assiduously than adherents to many other major religions. Ancient Indian sacred art is bawdy and raucous, while contemporary Indian cinema is modest and sexually restrained.
Buddhism	Buddhism does not provide a very nuanced discussion of human sexuality. The primary reason for this is that the tradition urges adherents to become celibate monks and nuns. Desire and the problematic patterns of life that emerge from it are among the key preoccupations of Buddhists. It is believed that sentient beings transmigrate through a series of births impelled by the accumulation of karma, unripened effects of previous actions. These karmas arise from the performance of all types of positive and negative behaviors, all driven by self-concerned mental outlook. Sexual desire is merely a notable subset of the broader category of desire, and so the tradition frowns upon desire and encourages all people to abandon it. The beliefs of Buddhists vary tremendously, nearly as much I would argue, as is the case with Christians. For Buddhists, the reason for this variety is that Buddhist missionaries who carried their tradition to the far corners of Asia mainly concerned themselves with advancing monasticism. Cultural practices relating to marriage customs, sexual norms, and the like were mainly provided by local traditions.

Source: Maher, D. Department of Religious Studies, East Carolina University. Developed exclusively for this text.

The researchers summarized the interviews with the Iranian wives as follows:

> Most women mentioned that satisfying their husband's sexual needs was a divine rule. They also believed that rejecting such desires was a sin. They claimed they met their husband's sexual needs to save themselves from hell and sinfulness ... pleasing God meant pleasing their husbands, especially their sexual needs. If their husbands desired to have sex, their wives could not refuse without any acceptable reason. They believed it was a sin not to follow God's rules. In some cases, the husbands misused such beliefs to force their wives to have sex. (p. 185)

1.4g Alcohol

Lu and colleagues (2013) surveyed 2,668 Chinese senior high school students in Shanghai. The percentages of females and males who reported ever having had sexual intercourse were 3% and 11%, respectively. Those reporting sexual intercourse were also more likely to report alcohol and cigarette use.

1.4h Psychological Factors

Many psychological constructs are believed to influence sexuality, including sexual self-concept, self-esteem, attachment style, personality characteristics and styles (impulsiveness, sensation-seeking, dependency, etc.), and locus of control. The term **locus of control** refers to an individual's beliefs about the source or cause of his or her successes and failures. A person with an **internal locus of control** believes that successes and failures in life are attributable to his or her own abilities and efforts. A person with an **external locus of control** believes that successes and failures are determined by fate, chance, or some powerful external source, such as other individuals. See the personal choices section to follow in regard to what factors control sexual choices.

Locus of control
An individual's beliefs about the source or cause (internal or external) of his or her successes and failures

Internal locus of control
The belief that successes and failures in life are attributable to one's own abilities and efforts

External locus of control
The perspective that successes and failures are determined by fate, chance, or some powerful external source

personal choices 1-1

Do You or Other Factors Control Your Sexual Decisions?

What do the following questions have in common?

- Is sex with an attractive stranger worth the risk of contracting HIV or other sexually transmitted infections?
- How and when do I bring up the issue of using a condom with a new partner?
- Can I find partners who will honor my value of being abstinent until marriage?
- How much do I tell my new partner about my previous sexual experiences (i.e., masturbation, number of sexual partners, homosexual encounters)?
- Do I disclose to my partner that I have fantasies about sex with other people?

- Can I make a thoughtful decision about having sexual contact with a partner if I've been drinking alcohol?
- What type of birth control should my partner and I use?

Each of these questions involves making a sexual decision. One of the main goals of this text is to emphasize the importance of making deliberate and informed choices about your sexuality. The alternative is to let circumstances and others decide for you. Informed choice making involves knowledge of the psychological, physiological, and social components of sexual functioning, personal values, and the interaction between cultural values and sexual behaviors.

Choices may be the result of **free will**. The belief in free will implies that although heredity and environment may influence our choices, as individuals we are ultimately in charge of our own destinies. Even when our lives are affected by circumstances or events that we do not choose, we can still choose how to view and respond to those circumstances and events.

An alternative and competing assumption of making deliberate choices is **determinism**—the idea that our choices are largely determined by heredity and environment. Being born with a particular sexual orientation reflects determinism in the sense that sexual orientation may have a biological or genetic base. Determinism may also have a social basis. Sociologists emphasize that social forces—such as the society in which one lives, one's family, and one's peers—all heavily influence choices. This is a social context view of choices. Hence, most people are not free to live a homosexual lifestyle because of social disapproval. Similarly, the fact that less than 5% of all marriages in the United States consist of a black and a white spouse (*The National Data Book*, 2012) suggests that social factors may be operative in mate selection with social approval for selecting same race individuals and disapproval for selecting other race individuals.

Rather than view sexual decisions as something we control or as something that is controlled by other factors, each view contributes to an understanding of sexual choices. Table 1-4 presents some of the advantages and disadvantages of these two views.

Free will
Belief that individuals are ultimately in charge of their own destinies

Determinism
Belief that one's choices are largely determined by heredity and environment

---

TABLE **1-4** | **Who Controls Our Choices? Advantages and Disadvantages of Different Views**

Are you wondering if taking a human sexuality course will influence your sexual attitudes and behaviors?

Views	Advantages	Disadvantages
View 1: We control our choices.	Gives individuals a sense of control over their lives and encourages individuals to take responsibility for their choices	Blames individuals for their unwise sexual choices and fails to acknowledge the influence of social and cultural factors on sexual choices
View 2: Other factors influence our choices.	Recognizes how emotions, peers, and cultural factors influence our lives and choices; implies that making changes in our social and cultural environment may be necessary to help us make better choices	Blames social and cultural factors for our own sexual choices and discourages individuals from taking responsibility for their behaviors and choices

Chapter **Summary**

This chapter defined human sexuality in terms of its various components, delineated the nature of sexuality, identified the steps in sexual decision making, and reviewed the influences on sexual choices.

Defining Human Sexuality

Human sexuality can best be defined in terms of its various components: thoughts, sexual self-concept, values, emotions, behaviors, anatomy/physiology, reproduction, and interpersonal relationships. The key to sexual satisfaction is a positive interpersonal relationship.

Nature of Sexual Choices

We are continually making choices, many of which are difficult because they involve trade-offs, or disadvantages, as well as advantages. Choices that result in irrevocable outcomes, such as becoming a parent or having an abortion, are among the most difficult ones individuals may face. However, we cannot avoid making choices because not to choose is, itself, a choice. For example, if we have oral, vaginal, or anal intercourse and have not decided to use a condom, we have made a decision to risk contracting and transmitting HIV and other sexually transmissible infections. Another factor involved in sexual decision making is that we can always choose a positive view (e.g., "my having contracted a sexually transmitted infection has taught me to use a condom in future sex"). Some ambivalence and uncertainty are inherent in making most choices.

Making Sexual Choices

Steps involved in making sexual decisions include (1) clarifying values and goals; (2) understanding one's motives and identifying feelings and emotions; (3) identifying and exploring alternative courses of action; (4) seeking information that makes the short-term and long-term consequences clear for each choice; (5) weighing the positive and negative consequences for each alternative; (6) selecting an alternative that has maximum positive consequences and minimal negative consequences; and (7) implementing one's decision. These steps in conjunction with learning from our previous decisions can help in making sexual decisions that have positive outcomes.

Influences on Sexual Choices

Although we like to think we make our own sexual choices and have free will to do so, we are actually strongly influenced by a number of factors when making sexual choices. These influences include culture, media, peers and family, technology, education, religion, and such psychological factors as locus of control.

Web Links

Go Ask Alice

http://www.goaskalice.columbia.edu/

Positive Sexuality

http://positivesexuality.org/

http://www.positive.org/

Make Love Not Porn

http://makelovenotporn.com/

SIECUS

http://www.siecus.org

Sexual Health Network

http://sexualhealth.com

Key Terms

Absolutism   7

Ambivalence   11

Comprehensive sex education
   programs   18

Determinism   21

External locus of control   20

Free will   21

Hedonism   8

Internal locus of control   20

Locus of control   20

Relativism   7

Sexual double standard   8

Sexual self-concept   5

Sexual values   5

Additional study resources are available at www.BVTLab.com

CHAPTER 2

Sex Research and Theory

We are recorders and reporters of the facts—not judges of the behavior we describe.

Alfred C. Kinsey

Chapter Outline

Objectives

1. Know how scientific knowledge is different from other sources of knowledge.

2. Identify and distinguish between deductive and inductive research.

3. Review the various biological, psychological, and sociological theories used to study sexuality.

4. Differentiate between classical and operant conditioning.

5. Describe the three basic principles protecting human subjects.

6. Identify and explain the six methods of data collection and the pros/cons of each.

7. Explain the three levels of data analysis.

Source: Shutterstock

TRUTH OR FICTION

T/F   A review of the content of four prestigious journals in sexuality over a 50-year period revealed a focus on love, sex and intimacy.

T/F   The links between female hormones and sexuality are now clearly understood.

T/F   In a study comparing a lecture and DVD on positive aspects of masturbation, only the lecture method was effective in increasing positive attitudes.

T/F   In a study of individuals born in India, "love at first sight" was seen as based on physical attraction and was a lesser kind of love.

T/F   The new frontier of sex research is genetic studies as related to environmental factors.

Answers:
1. F 2. F 3. F 4. T 5. T

Acceptance of the serious study of human sexuality has come slowly. Students taking courses in human sexuality are often kidded about being in such classes. Peers may tease and ask questions like, "Does the class have a lab?" Biologists, psychologists, sociologists, health care professionals, and others who study human sexuality in their occupational fields may also be subjected to ridicule or smirks. Nevertheless, the study of human sexuality is a serious endeavor. Professional organizations such as the Society for the Scientific Study of Sex, institutional structures (e.g., Institute for Sex Research), and journals (18) testify to the validity of the study of sexuality today.

Critical sexuality studies reflect the commitment of academia to the scientific study of sexuality. Critical sexuality studies identify core sexuality research content from researchers in 171 institutions and 88 study programs who reviewed

> **Critical sexuality studies**
> Generic term for current core content of sexuality, theory and research that is multifaceted and multidisciplinary (crossing several social science and humanities disciplines)

370 articles in 18 professional journals. These researchers captured the essential data, research and theory of sexuality (Fletcher, Dowsett, Duncan, Slavin, & Corboz, 2013) from the following journals:

AIDS Care; AIDS Education and Prevention; Annual Review of Sex Research; Archives of Sexual Behavior; Canadian Journal of Human Sexuality; Critical Public Health; Culture, Health & Sexuality; Gay and Lesbian Review Worldwide; Global Public Health; GLQ; International Journal of Sexual Health; Journal of Homosexuality; Journal of Sex Research; Journal of the History of Sexuality; Sex Education; Sexualities; Sexuality Research and Social Policy; and *Sexual Health.*

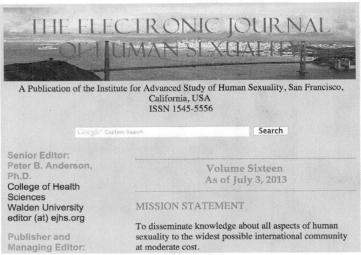

A Publication of the Institute for Advanced Study of Human Sexuality, San Francisco, California, USA
ISSN 1545-5556

Volume Sixteen
As of July 3, 2013

Senior Editor:
Peter B. Anderson, Ph.D.
College of Health Sciences
Walden University
editor (at) ejhs.org

Publisher and Managing Editor:

MISSION STATEMENT

To disseminate knowledge about all aspects of human sexuality to the widest possible international community at moderate cost.

Some sex research articles can be accessed online. EJHS is only available online (there is no print version in the library). *Source: E. Fred Johnson, Jr.*

The five core fields of research, education and training covered by the critical sexuality studies included the following: (1) HIV and AIDS, (2) gender, (3) sexology, (4) sexual and reproductive health (as distinct from HIV and AIDS), and (5) human rights.

Arakawa (2013) pointed out that due to the influence of conservative ideology and religious authority (focusing on the dangers of sexuality and the need for social control and chastity) in our society, the focus of sex research has been on the negative aspects of sexuality. In a content analysis of articles appearing in four prestigious journals: (*The Journal of Sex Research, Archives of Sexual Behavior, The New England Journal of Medicine,* and *Obstetrics and Gynecology*), from 1960 to the present, the researchers revealed that "only a slim minority of articles investigated the delights of love, sex, and intimacy." Indeed, "the vast majority focused on the problems associated with sexual behavior."

Google is not a synonym for 'research.'

Dan Brown, *The Lost Symbol*

2.1 The Nature of Sex Research

Scientific research involves collecting and analyzing **empirical evidence**, or data that can be observed. What makes scientific knowledge different from other sources of knowledge—such as common sense (e.g., "living together before marriage means people get to know each other better and results in happier marriages"), intuition ("it just feels like cohabitants would have happier marriages"), tradition ("Icelanders have always lived together before marriage"), and authority (religion disapproves of cohabitation)—is the fact that scientific knowledge is supported by observable or empirical evidence. In contrast to these assumptions about cohabitation and subsequent marital happiness/durability, research generally shows a *higher* divorce rate if couples lived together before marriage (the exception being if the partners had only lived with each other prior to their marriage and had not been in any previous cohabitation relationships with others).

Researchers are also expected to publish not only their findings but also the methods they used to arrive at their findings. In this way, other researchers and academicians can replicate, scrutinize, and critically examine previous research findings.

Finally, human sexuality research involves gathering empirical data and using theory to make sense out of the data, although not necessarily in that order.

Empirical evidence
Data that can be observed, measured, and quantified

FIGURE **2-1** ‖ **Links Between Theory and Research: Deductive and Inductive Reasoning**

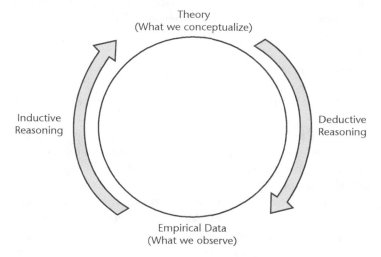

Theory
(What we conceptualize)

Inductive
Reasoning

Deductive
Reasoning

Empirical Data
(What we observe)

Thus, theory and research are both parts of the scientific process. Theory and empirical research are linked through two forms of reasoning: deductive and inductive.

Deductive research involves starting with a specific theory, generating a specific expectation or hypothesis based on that theory, and then gathering data that will either support or refute the theory. For example, researchers may hypothesize that men might move a new acquaintance faster toward sex than women would do in the same situation, and thus may ask university students to complete a questionnaire on hooking up scripts and pacing sexual behavior. Alternatively, researchers might engage in **inductive research** that begins with specific data that are then used to formulate (induce) an explanation (or theory). In this case, researchers might have a data set that shows that men are more aggressive sexually and might hypothesize that such aggressiveness is biologically and socially induced. In this chapter, after summarizing basic theories of sexuality, we describe how researchers conduct scientific studies of sexuality. First, however, we review the interdisciplinary nature of the study of sexology.

Personal ~~REFLECTION~~

Take a moment to express your thoughts about the following question. How much of your knowledge about human sexuality is based on each of the various sources of knowledge: common sense, intuition, tradition, authority, and scientific research?

2.2 **The Interdisciplinary Nature of Sexology**

Although nearly two dozen educational institutions in the United States have human sexuality programs, only Widener University offers a doctorate leading to specialization as a sex educator or as a sex therapist (http://www.widener.edu/academics/schools/shsp/hss/default.aspx).

Deductive research
Sequence of research starting with a specific theory, generating a specific expectation or hypothesis based on that theory, and then gathering data that will either support or refute the theory

Inductive research
Sequence of research that begins with specific empirical data, which are then used to formulate a theory to explain the data

Sex researchers represent a broad range of disciplines. The study of sexuality is an interdisciplinary field including psychology, health, sociology, family studies, medicine, public health, social work, counseling and therapy, history, and education. While courses in human sexuality are most often taught in departments of psychology, health, sociology, and family studies, the three major sources of content are biosexology, psychosexology, and sociosexology.

Biosexology is the study of the biological aspects of sexuality. Studies in this field focus on such topics as the physiological and endocrinological aspects of sexual development and sexual response, the biological processes involved in sexually transmitted infections, the role of evolution and genetics in sexual development, the physiology of reproduction, and the development of new contraceptives. Biosexology is also concerned with the effects of drugs, medications, disease, and exercise on sexuality.

Psychosexology involves the study of how psychological processes influence, and are influenced by, sexual development and behavior. For example, how do emotions and motivations affect sexual performance, the use of contraception, and safe sex practices? What psychological processes are involved in the development of sexual aggression and other forms of sexual deviance? How do various sexual and reproductive experiences (such as pregnancy, rape, infertility, sexual dysfunction, and acquisition of a sexually transmitted disease) affect the emotional state of the individual?

In theory there is no difference between theory and practice. In practice there is.

Yogi Berra, baseball legend

Sociosexology is concerned with the way social and cultural forces influence—and are influenced by—sexual attitudes, beliefs, and behaviors. For example, how are culture, age, race, ethnicity, socioeconomic status, and gender related to attitudes, beliefs, and behaviors regarding masturbation, homosexuality, abortion, nonmarital sexual relationships, and HIV infection? Sociosexology is also concerned with the way social policy and social institutions (marriage, religion, economics, law and politics, and the healthcare system) influence and are influenced by human sexuality. Finally, this approach examines how sexual processes affect intimate relationships and how sexual processes are, in turn, affected by intimate relationships. Hence, **sexology** may be thought of as a unique discipline that identifies important questions related to sexuality issues and finds and integrates answers from biology, psychology, and sociology based on scientific methods of investigation.

Biosexology
Study of the biological aspects of sexuality

Psychosexology
Area of sexology focused on how psychological processes influence and are influenced by sexual development and behavior

Sociosexology
Aspect of sexology that is concerned with the way social and cultural forces influence and are influenced by sexual attitudes, beliefs, and behaviors

Sexology
Unique discipline that identifies important questions related to sexuality issues and finds and integrates answers from biology, psychology, and sociology based on scientific methods of investigation

Theory
Set of ideas designed to answer a question or explain a particular phenomenon

Think About It

Take a moment to answer the following question. In the sexuality education that you received from parents, peers, and school programs, which category of sex information received the most emphasis: biosexology, psychosexology, or sociosexology?

2.3 Theories of Sexuality

A **theory** is a set of ideas designed to answer a question or to explain a particular phenomenon (e.g., Why does one person rape another? Why do some men like to dress up in women's clothes?). In the following sections we review various theoretical perspectives and their applications to human sexuality.

2.3a Biological Theories

Biological theories of sexuality include both physiological theories and evolutionary theories. **Physiological theories** of sexuality describe and explain how physiological processes affect, and are affected by, sexual behavior. Cardiovascular, respiratory, neurological, and endocrinological functioning, and genetic factors—all are involved in sexual processes and behaviors. For example, what physiological processes are involved in sexual desire, arousal, lubrication, erection, and orgasm? How do various drugs and medications affect sexual functioning? How do various hormones affect sexuality? To what degree are behavioral differences between women and men attributable to their different genetic and hormonal make-ups? What role do hormones and genetics play in sexual orientation?

Evolutionary theories or **sociobiological theories** of sexuality explain human sexual behavior on the basis of human evolution. According to evolutionary theories of sexuality, sexual behaviors and traits evolve through the process of natural selection. Through **natural selection**, individuals who have genetic traits that are adaptive for survival and reproduction are more likely to survive and pass on their genetic traits to their offspring. For women it is in their sociobiological interest to discriminate among potential partners and mate with a partner who provides resources for supporting the development of their offspring.

Evolutionary explanations are coming under closer scrutiny and coming up short. Harris and Vitzthum (2013) note that in regard to "the links between hormones and sexuality in premenopausal and perimenopausal women, the causes of premenstrual syndrome, and the existence (or not) of menstrual synchrony, in none of these cases is as much known as is often claimed."

Related to evolutionary, sociobiological theories is the **biosocial framework**, which emphasizes the interaction of one's biological/genetic inheritance with one's social environment to explain and predict human behavior. Borrowing from evolutionary psychology, sociobiology, and psychobiology, biosocial theory uses the concept of natural selection to explain such phenomena as mate selection. Natural selection emphasizes that it is natural for the individual to want to survive. That men tend to seek young women with whom to procreate is related to the biological fact that young women are more fertile and produce more healthy offspring than older women. Women, on the other hand, tend to seek men who are older and more economically stable because they can provide economic resources for their offspring. Hence, both biological (youth/fertility) and social (economic stability) factors combine to explain the mate selection process.

Evolutionary psychology theories and studies have particularly focused on sex differences. For example, parental investment (how much parents invest in their offspring), jealousy, spatial reasoning and memory task performance, interpretation of actions in the workplace as sexual harassment, content of sexual fantasies, and predicted response to sexual assault have all been examined in terms of hypothesized, intrinsic differences between the sexes. However, young men and women—with a more accurate knowledge of human nature—can choose to behave adaptively in interpersonal or social (instead of evolutionary) terms.

2.3b Psychological Theories

Biological theories do not account for the influence of personality, learning, thoughts, and emotions on human sexuality. These aspects of sexuality are explained by psychological theories, including psychoanalytic theories, learning theories, and cognitive/affective theories.

Physiological theories
Theories that describe and explain how physiological processes affect and are affected by sexual behavior

Evolutionary theories
Theories that explain human sexual behavior and sexual anatomy on the basis of human evolution (See also Sociobiological theories.)

Sociobiological theories
Framework that explains human sexual behavior and sexual anatomy as functional for human evolution (See also Evolutionary theories.)

Natural selection
Theory that individuals who have genetic traits that are adaptive for survival are more likely to survive and pass on their genetic traits to their offspring

Biosocial framework
Theoretical framework that emphasizes the interaction of one's biological/genetic inheritance with one's social environment to explain and predict human behavior

Psychoanalytic Theories

Psychoanalytic theory, originally developed by Sigmund Freud (1856–1939), emphasizes the role of unconscious processes in our lives. This theory dominated the early views on the nature of human sexuality. A basic knowledge of Freud's ideas about personality structure is important for understanding his theories of sexuality.

Freud believed that each person's personality consists of the id, ego, and superego. The **id** refers to instinctive biological drives, such as the need for sex, food, and water. Freud saw human sexuality as a biological force that drove individuals toward the satisfaction of sexual needs and desires. Indeed, one of Freud's most important contributions was his belief that infants and children are sexual beings who possess a positive sexual drive that is biologically wired into their systems.

Another part of the personality, the **ego**, deals with objective reality as the individual figures out how to obtain the desires of the id. The ego also must be realistic about social expectations. Whereas the id is self-centered and uninhibited, the ego is that part of the person's personality that inhibits the id in order to conform to social expectations. While the id operates on the "pleasure principle," the ego operates on the "reality principle." The ego ensures that individuals do not attempt to fulfill every need and desire whenever they occur. Freud would see rape as a failure of the ego to function properly.

The **superego** is the conscience, which functions by guiding the individual to do what is morally right and good. It is the superego that creates feelings of guilt when the ego fails to inhibit the id and the person engages in socially unacceptable behavior.

Freud emphasized that personality develops in stages. When we successfully complete one stage, we are able to develop to the next stage. If we fail to successfully complete any given stage, we become fixated or stuck in that stage. Psychoanalysis untangles the repressed feelings created by a fixation at an earlier stage so that mature sexuality may emerge. The four basic psychosexual stages Freud identified are the oral, anal, phallic, and genital stages (see Table 2-1). Latency is not a stage, but rather a period of time when psychosexual development is dormant or on hold.

Psychoanalytic theory
Freud's theory that emphasizes the role of unconscious processes in one's life

Id
Freud's term that refers to instinctive biological drives, such as the need for sex, food, and water

Ego
Freud's term for that part of an individual's psyche that deals with objective reality

Superego
Freud's term for the conscience, which functions by guiding the individual to do what is morally right and good

The idea that boys want to sleep with their mothers strikes most men as the silliest thing they have ever heard. Obviously, it did not seem so to Freud, who wrote that as a boy he once had an erotic reaction to watching his mother dressing. But Freud had a wet-nurse and may not have experienced the early intimacy that would have tipped off his perceptual system that Mrs. Freud was his mother.

Steven Pinker, *How the Mind Works*

TABLE **2-1**	Freud's Four Stages of Psychosexual Development	
Stage	Age	Characteristics
Oral	Womb to 18 months	Pleasures are derived primarily from meeting the oral needs of sucking, licking, and chewing. The pleasure principle dominates, and id focuses on meeting pleasure needs.
Anal	1 to 3 years	Pleasures shift to anal needs and are derived from retention and elimination of urine and feces. The pleasure principle and id are still dominant mechanisms.
Phallic	3 to 6 years	Pleasures shift to stimulation of genitals. Girls discover they have no penis. Masturbation may be practiced, and ego negotiates with id and superego for social control of sexual impulses. Oedipus and Electra complexes develop during this period.
(Latency)	6 years to puberty	Repression of sexual urges occurs.
Genital	Adolescence	A shift takes place from immature masturbation to appropriate peer-sex interaction.

Although Freud developed his theories during an era of sexual repression, he proposed that **libido** was the most important of human instincts. While his libido theory was an important contribution, Freud has been criticized as overemphasizing sexual motivation for behavior. His clinical observations were based on people who came to him with their problems, but he often generalized broadly from them. His work would not meet the standards of scientific objectivity required today.

Karen Horney (1885–1952) recognized the importance of childhood personality development, but she believed that social—rather than sexual—factors were dominant in personality formation. She felt that the need to emerge from the helpless, controlled state of an infant to that of an independent, autonomous individual was the driving force of the development of the individual. Sex played a minor role in the drive for independence.

Erikson (1902–1994) believed that individuals progress through a series of stages as they develop; unlike Freud, however, he felt that the states were psychosocial, not psychosexual. He believed that central developmental tasks did not involve seeking oral, anal, and genital pleasures; but rather they involved establishing basic trust with people. Also, Erikson felt that personality formation did not end in adolescence, but was a lifelong process (most contemporary psychologists agree).

In contrast to Freud's psychoanalytic view of sexuality, other psychological theories explain human sexual attitudes and behaviors as learned. Learning theories include classical conditioning theory, operant learning theory, and social learning theory.

Classical Conditioning Theory

Classical conditioning is a process whereby a stimulus and a response that are not originally linked become linked. Ivan Pavlov (1849–1936), a Russian physician, observed that the presence of food caused dogs to salivate. Because salivation is a natural reflex to the presence of food, we call food an *unconditioned stimulus.* However, if Pavlov rang a bell and then gave the dogs food, the dogs soon learned that the bell meant food was forthcoming; and they would salivate at the sound of the bell. Hence, the bell became a *conditioned stimulus* because it had become associated with the food and was now capable of producing the same response as the food (an unconditioned stimulus).

Sexual fetishes can be explained on the basis of classical conditioning. A fetish is a previously neutral stimulus that becomes a conditioned stimulus for erotic feelings. For example, some people have a feather, foot, or leather fetish—and they respond to these stimuli in erotic ways. However, there is nothing about a feather that would serve to elicit erotic feelings unless the feather was associated with erotic feelings in the past.

How might a person become conditioned to respond to a feather as an erotic stimulus? Perhaps the person may have masturbated and picked up a feather and rubbed it on his or her genitals. Or the person may have observed a stripper in person or on a video who used a feather as part of the erotic dance. In either case, the feather would become a conditioned stimulus and would elicit erotic feelings in the same way the masturbation and stripper did as an unconditioned stimuli. Pedophilia can be explained as an example of classical conditioning. A child sitting or playing on the lap of a male may create an erection or ejaculation. He might then associate sexual pleasure with a child.

Operant Learning Theory

Operant learning theory, largely developed by B. F. Skinner (1904–1990), is also referred to as operant conditioning or radical behaviorism, and emphasizes that the consequences of a behavior influence whether or not that behavior will occur in the future. Consequences that follow a behavior may maintain, increase, or decrease (including terminate) the frequency of the behavior. A consequence that maintains

Libido
The sex drive

Classical conditioning
Behavior modification technique whereby an unconditioned stimulus and a neutral stimulus are linked to elicit a desired response

Operant learning theory
Explanation of human behavior that emphasizes that the consequences of a behavior influence whether or not that behavior will occur in the future

or increases a behavior is known as **reinforcement**. A consequence that decreases or terminates a behavior is known as **punishment**. A partner who has been reinforced for initiating sexual behavior is likely to do so again. A partner who has been punished for initiating sexual behavior is less likely to do so in the future. Operant conditioning has not been applied in sexuality research as much as classical conditioning and has mainly been used in the treatment of sexual dysfunctions and in (unsuccessful) attempts to alter sexual preferences.

Social Learning Theory

Another learning-based approach to understanding human sexuality is **social learning theory** (also referred to as modeling, observational learning, or vicarious learning). It emphasizes that a behavior may be increased without direct reinforcement, but in anticipation of reinforcement. For example, sexual pleasure and the anticipation of it can be a potent reinforcer! Social psychologist Albert Bandura put less emphasis on anticipated reward; he emphasized social learning as providing motivation through enhanced self-efficacy (belief in one's ability to be successful in a task). Observational learning may occur through observing a model that demonstrates attitudes and behavior. For example, we may imitate the sexual attitudes and behaviors that we observe in our parents, peers, and in the media. Advertisers are aware of the power of modeling and hire known/accepted/approved models to sell products.

> It is a surprising fact that those who object most violently to the manipulation of behaviour nevertheless make the most vigorous effort to manipulate minds.
>
> B. F. Skinner, *Beyond Freedom and Dignity*

Cognitive/Affective Theories

Cognitive/affective theories of sexuality emphasize the role of thought processes and emotions in sexual behavior. The importance of cognitions in human life was recognized nearly 2,000 years ago by Epictetus, a philosopher, who said, "Man is disturbed not by things but by the view that he takes of them." Aaron Beck and Albert Ellis, both cognitive therapists, emphasize that maladaptive or irrational thoughts may result in sexual problems. Thoughts such as "I must always have an orgasm" or "I should always be interested in sex" may result in unnecessary frustration. Through cognitive therapy (which is based on cognitive theory), these cognitions may be examined and changed.

Emotions are related to cognitions. As the preceding example illustrates, changing the person's cognitions will affect the way a person feels about his or her sexuality. Affective theories of sexuality emphasize the fact that emotions (such as love, jealousy, fear, anxiety, embarrassment, and frustration) may precede sexual expression, may be a component of sexual expression, and/or may be a consequence of sexual activity. The Self-Assessment 2-1 to follow may be used to assess one's need for sexual intimacy.

2.3c Sociological Theories

Sociological theories of human sexuality explain how society and social groups affect and are affected by sexual attitudes and behaviors. The various sociological theoretical perspectives on human sexuality include symbolic interaction, structural-functional, conflict, feminist, and systems theories.

Symbolic Interaction Theory

Symbolic interaction theory, which was developed by Max Weber (1864–1920), Georg Simmel (1858–1918), and Charles Horton Cooley (1864–1929), focuses on how meanings, labels, and definitions learned through interactions affect our attitudes, self-concept, and behavior. Horowitz and Spicer (2013) emphasized that definitions of what constitutes sexual behavior are variable.

Reinforcement
Consequence that maintains or increases a behavior

Punishment
Consequence that decreases or terminates a behavior

Social learning theory
Framework that emphasizes the process of learning through observation and imitation

Cognitive/affective theories
As related to sexuality, theories that emphasize the role of thought processes and emotions in sexual behavior

Symbolic interaction theory
Sociological theory that focuses on how meanings, labels, and definitions learned through interaction affect one's attitudes, self-concept, and behavior

SELF-ASSESSMENT 2-1: NEED FOR SEXUAL INTIMACY SCALE (NSIS)

Directions:

The items below address things we may 'need' in life. Some say we 'need' many things in order to survive (e.g., food, shelter, etc.). Below we have presented a series of items and would like you to rate each item as to how much you agree or disagree with them as things you may need. The term *partner* below refers to a sexual partner (e.g., dating partner, boyfriend/girlfriend, long-term partner/spouse). For each item identify a number which reflects your level of agreement with the statement given and write that number in the space provided.

1 = disagree definitely
2 = disagree mostly
3 = neither disagree or agree
4 = agree mostly
5 = agree definitely

Three Areas of Sexual Intimacy

Need for Sex

1. ___ I need to have more sex.
2. ___ I need sex every day.
3. ___ I need to have an orgasm every day.
4. ___ I need to let myself go sexually with someone.
5. ___ I need to have sex every couple of days.
6. ___ I need someone who is "great in bed."
7. ___ I need sex with a lot of partners.
8. ___ I need to take control of my partner when we are intimate.

Scoring:

Add up the scores for all 8 (each should have a value between 1 and 5) and divide by 8. The lowest possible score is 1 suggesting a low need for sex; the highest possible score is 5 suggesting a high need for sex.

Need for Affiliation

1. ___ I need a partner who loves me.
2. ___ I need someone to love.
3. ___ I need companionship.
4. ___ I need a companion in life.
5. ___ I need to have complete trust in the people I am intimate with.
6. ___ I don't need anyone special in my life.
7. ___ I need somebody to hold my hand.
8. ___ I need a few really good friends.
9. ___ I need someone to sleep next to me.

Scoring:

Reverse score number 6. (If you selected a 5, replace the 5 with a 1. If you selected a 1, replace it with a 5, etc). Add each of the 9 items (from 1 to 5) and divide by 9. The lowest possible score is 1 suggesting a low need for affiliation; the highest possible score is 5 suggesting a high need for affiliation.

Need for Dominance

1. ___ I need my partner to tell me where they are at all times.
2. ___ I need control over my partner.
3. ___ I need my partner to give me what I want (such as financial support, clothes, a car).
4. ___ I need a partner I can manipulate.
5. ___ I need the ability to order my partner to have sex with me if I want to.

Scoring:

Add each of the 5 items (from 1 to 5) and divide by 5. The lowest possible score is 1 suggesting a low need for dominance; the highest possible score is 5 suggesting a high need for dominance.

Participants:

Initial study participants were 347 students with a mean age of 21, mostly female (61%) and single (92%). Seventy-nine percent reported at least one sexual experience (Marelich & Lundquist, 2008). A second set (Marelich, Shelton, & Grandfield, 2013) of 422 psychology undergraduates also took the scale. The respondents were at least 18 years of age and reported having had at least one sexual intercourse experience.

Results:

In regard to the Marelich (2008) study, those showing a higher need for sex reported more lifetime sexual partners, more one night stands, less condom use, less ability to discuss condoms with their partners, and greater use of intoxicants during sex. Those showing a higher need for affiliation had a preference for being in a relationship (women more than men), more likely to be consumed with thinking about their partners, and less likely to mislead their partners about a negative HIV test. Those showing a high need for dominance had a preference for dominating their partner sexually, were more likely to ask their partners about past sexual experiences, and more likely to report that sex is an important part of a relationship.

A second study (Marelich, Shelton, & Grandfield, 2013) of 422 psychology undergraduates revealed that individuals who had a higher need for sex also had higher levels of sexual desire, more unrestricted sexual attitudes, and higher sexual awareness. Those reporting a higher need for dominance engaged in more dominant behaviors, and those reporting a higher need for affiliation had more positive attitudes about emotional support and closeness in relationships. Males reported a higher need for sex and dominance than females.

Validity and Reliability:

Details are provided in the 2008 reference below.

Scale is used with the permission of William D. Marelich (2008), Department of Psychology, California State University, Fullerton, CA

In addition, our definitions of what are appropriate and inappropriate sexual behaviors are learned through our relationships with others. Sexual self-concepts, including body image and perception of one's self as an emotional and sexual partner, are also influenced by interactions with others.

According to the symbolic interaction view of sexuality, humans respond to their definitions of situations, rather than to objective situations themselves. For example, your response to seeing a woman breast-feeding her infant in public is influenced by your definition of the event: Do you see a mother engaging in a natural, nurturing behavior? Or do you define the event as an inappropriate or even offensive display of public nudity? When you encounter a male college student who has not experienced sexual intercourse, do you view him as a person with high moral standards or as a nerd? Family, religion, peers, school, media, and the larger societies in which we live largely influence our definitions of situations and behaviors. Some examples include the following:

- In many developing countries where religion prohibits or discourages birth control, contraceptives, and abortion, women learn through interaction with others that deliberate control of fertility is socially unacceptable. When some women learn new, positive definitions of fertility control, they become role models and influence other women's attitudes and behaviors regarding contraceptive use.

- In the United States, female breasts are defined as an erotic, sexual part of the female body; women may be arrested for exposing their naked breasts in public. Other societies attach no sexual significance to female breasts. In these societies, female breasts are exposed in public; and the sight or touch of a woman's breast (to a heterosexual man) will not produce an erection or physiological response because no sexual meaning is attached to them.

An important component of symbolic interaction theory is the concept of **social scripts**, developed by John Gagnon (Gagnon, 1977; Gagnon & Simon, 1973). Social scripts are shared interpretations that have three functions: to define situations, name actors, and plot behaviors. For example, the social script operative in prostitution is to define the situation (sex for money), name actors (prostitute, and "john" or client), and plot behaviors (prostitute will perform requested sexual behaviors for money). An example of a traditional, heterosexual, new partner script is that the male wants recreational sex and the female wants relational sex. The following words reflect this script, reported by a male who was interviewed by Masters and colleagues (2013):

> She really had, uh, deep feelings for me ... but I didn't have the same deep feelings for her. I think it was more of a sexual thing for me, but for her it was more of a relationship thing. So I feel kind of bad in that part. Most of my relationships have been like that, where, um, I've broken their hearts. ... I've had, I've made plenty, I've made, you know, a couple girls cry ... (p. 416)

Karlsen and Traeen (2013) identified the various social scripts operative in 'friends with benefits' relationships including being good friends, being good lovers and being "on the hook." This latter type of script involved one partner in the FWBs relationship viewing the relationship as romantic and the other viewing it as "just sex"—hence the romantic partner was "on the hook." Below is an example of being on the hook.

> He was quite clear about not wanting a relationship, but he liked my companionship. We were friends, and visited cafés and friends together. But at the same time, I was thinking, "Oh, I want him so bad; I'm so in love with him." He never knew that. (Yvonne, 24 years old)

Social scripts
Shared interpretations that have three functions: to define situations, name actors, and plot behaviors

Take a moment to answer the following question. In general, women and men learn different social scripts in regard to sexuality, with women more likely to define meeting someone at a party as having the potential for emotional involvement—the actors being those of potential romantic companions, and the behaviors, those of escalating romance. In contrast, men are more likely to define the situation at the party as one devoid of an emotional future, the actors as two strangers who will remain so, and the behaviors as whatever the woman will allow sexually. How do you account for these different interpretations or scripts?

Structural-Functional Theory

Structural-functional theory, developed by Talcott Parsons (1902–1979) and Robert Merton (1910–2003), views society as a system of interrelated parts that influence each other and work together to achieve social stability. The various parts of society include family, religion, government, economics, and education. Structural-functional theory suggests that social behavior may be either functional or dysfunctional. Functional behavior contributes to social stability; dysfunctional behavior disrupts social stability. The institution of marriage, which is based on the emotional and sexual bonding of individuals, may be viewed as functional for society because it provides a structure in which children are born and socialized to be productive members of society. Hence, in the United States there is greater social approval for sex within marriage; children born to a married couple are cared for by the parents and not by welfare (as is more common of children born to single parents). Extramarital sex is viewed as dysfunctional because it is associated with divorce, which can affect the emotional well-being of children and disrupt the care and socialization of children.

Structural-functional theory also focuses on how parts of society influence each other and how changes in one area of society produce or necessitate changes in another. For example, some religious leaders denounce education programs that offer condoms to students. Similarly, the educational system in a society affects the birth rate in that society: low educational attainment of women is associated with high birth rates. Hence, reducing population growth in developing countries requires increasing the educational attainment of women in these countries. The economic institution in the United States—which includes more women in the workforce today than in previous generations—has influenced the government to establish laws concerning sexual harassment and family leave.

Conflict Theory

Whereas structural-functional theory views society as composed of different parts working together, **conflict theory**, developed by Karl Marx (1818–1883) and Ralf Dahrendorf (1929–2009), views society as composed of different parts competing for power and resources. For example, antiabortionist groups are in conflict with pro-choice groups; gay rights advocates are in conflict with groups who oppose gay rights; insurance companies are in conflict with consumers about whether contraceptives (and medications such as Viagra) should be covered in health insurance plans.

Conflict theory explains social patterns by looking at which groups control and benefit from a particular social action or meaning. For example, cultural portrayals of healthy sexuality that emphasize physiological functioning of the genitals (rather than relationship factors such as intimacy) benefit the medical and pharmaceutical industries that profit from medical treatments and drugs designed to enhance genital performance. Political actions and decisions related to sexual issues may also be understood by looking at which groups benefit from such actions or decisions. Lobbyists exist to provide reinforcement (campaign contributions) to members of Congress for approving various projects.

Feminist Theories

Feminist theories, which overlap with conflict theory, explain social patterns by examining which groups have the power and resources to meet their needs. Feminist theory specifically focuses on the imbalance of power and resources between women and men, and how these imbalances affect sexuality, studies in sexuality, and sexual healthcare delivery.

Structural-functional theory
Framework that views society as a system of interrelated parts that influence each other and work together to achieve social stability

Conflict theory
Sociological theory that views society as consisting of different parts competing for power and resources

Feminist theories
Perspectives that analyze discrepancies in equality between men and women, and how these imbalances affect sexuality, research studies in sexuality, and sexual healthcare delivery

Men and women do not have equal political or sexual power. Women's legacy of political and economic subordination is reflected in incomplete healthcare (limited access to abortion and poor insurance coverage for contraception), greater stigma associated with remaining unmarried, and greater burdens in homecare, childcare, and eldercare that limit energy for sex and other pursuits of the self.

A feminist analysis suggests that these social patterns are due to the power imbalance between men and women, and the fact that primarily men make and enforce the laws. Feminist analysis also suggests that rape and sexual assault may be viewed as an abuse of power that some men engage in as an attempt to intimidate women. (Up until the mid-90s, husbands could legally rape their wives in some states.)

Feminist theories are typically critical of **patriarchy**—a system of social organization in which the father is the head of the family and family descent is traced through the male line (meaning that wives and children take the last name of the husband and father). Patriarchy involves the connotation that women and children are the property of their husbands and/or fathers. Cultural attitudes toward women and children as property may contribute to some cases of abuse (including sexual abuse) of women and children. Socialist feminism posits that women are oppressed by capitalism, and Marxist feminism attributes women's oppression to the class structure. If women's work is not valued, then women are not valued. Finally, multicultural feminists emphasize the diversity among women of different classes and races. For example, women with low incomes, African American women, and Latino women may experience different forms of oppression that must be addressed.

Systems Theory

Systems theory, developed by Murray Bowen (1913–1990), emphasizes the interpersonal and relationship aspects of sexuality. One application of systems theory is in the area of sexual dysfunctions. For example, whereas a biological view of low sexual desire emphasizes the role of hormones or medications, and a psychological view might emphasize negative cognitions and emotions regarding sexual arousal, a systems perspective views low sexual desire as a product of the interaction between two partners. Negative and conflictual interaction between partners can affect their interests in having sex with one another.

Table 2-2 presents different theoretical explanations for various sexuality observations.

Think About It

Take a moment to answer the following questions. To what degree do you think that the different theoretical explanations for human sexuality are necessarily incompatible? Can biological, psychological, and sociological theories each contribute unique insights to our understanding of various aspects of sexuality?

2.4 Eclectic View of Human Sexuality

Whereas some scholars who study human sexuality focus on one theoretical approach, others propose an **eclectic view** that recognizes the contributions that multiple perspectives make to our understanding of sexuality. For example, sexuality of the aging can be understood in terms of the various biological, psychological, and social

Patriarchy
System of social organization in which the father is the head of the family and family descent is traced through the male line

Systems theory
Theoretical framework that emphasizes the interpersonal and relationship aspects of sexuality

Eclectic view
View that recognizes the contribution of multiple perspectives to the understanding of sexuality

aspects of the aging process. Is decreased libido a function of decreased testosterone/ progesterone, one's altered self-concept ("I am no longer sexually attractive"), or cultural expectations that deny a strong libido among the elderly?

Other influences on sexuality in aging women include the following psychosocial and cultural variables:

1. *Availability of a sexual partner who is interested in and capable of engaging in sexual activity*   Older women are frequently widowed or divorced; and if they do have a partner, the partner may not be interested in sex or may have erection difficulties.

TABLE 2-2 | Sexuality Observations and Theoretical Explanations

Observation	Theory
1. Men are more sexually aggressive than women.	**Operant Learning** Men have been reinforced for being sexually aggressive. Women have been punished for being sexually aggressive. **Social Script** Our society scripts men to be more aggressive and women to be more passive sexually. Each sex learns through interactions with parents, peers, and partners that this is normative behavior. **Physiological** Men have large amounts of androgen and women have larger amounts of progesterone, which accounts for male aggressiveness and female passivity.
2. Pornography is consumed primarily by men.	**Operant Learning** Men derive erotic pleasure (reinforcement) from pornography. **Social Script** Men script each other to regard pornography as desired entertainment. Men tell each other about Internet porn sites; this reflects a norm regarding pornography among males. Women rarely discuss pornography with each other. **Evolutionary** Men are biologically wired to become erect in response to visual sexual stimuli.
3. Men in most societies are allowed to have a number of sexual partners.	**Structural-Functional** In many societies, women outnumber men. Polygyny potentially provides a mate for every woman. **Conflict** The social, political, and economic power of men provides the context for men to exploit women sexually by making rules in favor of polygyny. **Evolutionary** Men are biologically wired for variety; women, for monogamy. These respective wirings produce reproductive success for the respective sexes.
4. Women and men tend to report lower levels of sexual desire in their elderly years.	**Social Script** Aging women and men learn social scripts that teach them that elderly persons are not expected to be sexual. **Systems** Elderly persons are often not in a relationship that elicits sexual desire. **Biological** Hormonal changes in the elderly account for decreased or absent sexual desire (physiological). There is no reproductive advantage for elderly women to be sexually active; there is minimal reproductive advantage for elderly men to be sexually active (evolutionary).
5. Extradyadic relationships, including marital infidelity, are common.	**Operant Learning** Immediate interpersonal reinforcement for extradyadic sex is stronger than delayed punishment for infidelity. **Biological** Humans (especially men) are biologically wired to be sexually receptive to numerous partners. **Structural-Functional** Infidelity reflects the weakening of the family institution. **Systems** Emotional and sexual interactions between couples are failing to meet the needs of one or both partners.

2. *Socioeconomic status and level of education*   Education may lead to greater freedom from cultural inhibitions and sexual stereotypes.

3. *Cultural views and stereotypes of aging women*   In some societies (e.g., China), older women are accorded higher status, and postmenopausal sexuality is characterized by openness and playfulness. The United States, on the other hand, has traditionally devalued older women and stereotyped them as being asexual.

2.5 Conducting Sex Research: A Step-by-Step Process

Several early twentieth-century scientists were instrumental in shifting society's ideas about sex from a religious perspective toward consideration of scientific ideologies and discoveries. These pioneers included Richard von Krafft-Ebing, Havelock Ellis and Alfred C. Kinsey.

Richard von Krafft-Ebing (1840–1902) was a Viennese psychiatrist and sexologist who focused on the study of abnormal or pathological sexuality. Originally published in 1886, *Psychopathia Sexualis* (1965) contains Krafft-Ebing's case histories of more than 200 individuals—some of them bizarre. For example, he revealed that some parents applied a white-hot iron to the clitoris of young girls for "treatment" of masturbation.

Havelock Ellis (1859–1939) emphasized that sexual behavior was learned social behavior, that "deviant" sexual behavior was merely that which society labeled as abnormal, and that an enjoyable sex life (a desirable goal) was not something that just happened, but rather had to be achieved. These early theorists paved the way for the next quantum leap and have served as a foundation for further research.

Alfred C. Kinsey (1894–1956) is regarded as the pioneer of human sexuality research. His marriage course at Indiana University became too controversial because of its explicit nature, so he was given the choice to tone it down or collect sex research full time. Choosing the latter resulted in the Institute for Sex Research, which housed the sexual histories of more than 18,000 individuals. Kinsey personally interviewed 8,000 individuals (1.5 to 2 hours per interview). His major impact was in influencing society to open sex as a social topic of conversation. His landmark *Sexual Behavior in the Human Male* (1948) and *Sexual Behavior in the Human Female* (1953) replaced speculation with data and facts. The National Sex Study at Indiana University updated his research in 2012.

Alfred C. Kinsey and his colleagues conducted the first large survey study of human sexuality. His research questions were quite broad: "to discover what people do sexually, and what factors account for differences in sexual behavior among individuals, and among various segments of the population" (Kinsey, Pomeroy, & Martin, 1948, p. 1). The project began with various questions about the frequency of, and the motivations for, certain beliefs and behaviors. Issues studied included such things as nonmarital and marital intercourse, attitudes toward sexuality, and the way social factors such as education and income affect sexual behavior.

Conducting sex research, like all scientific research, involves following the basic steps of the scientific process. These steps are identifying a research question, reviewing the literature, formulating a hypothesis, operationalizing variables, collecting data, and analyzing and interpreting the results. Research is valuable since it helps to provide evidence for or against a hypothesis. For example, there is a stigma associated with persons who have tattoos, and it is often assumed that students who have tattoos make lower grades than those who do not have tattoos. Yet when Martin and Dula (2010) compared the GPA of persons who had tattoos and those who did not, they found no significant differences.

2.5a Identifying a Research Question

A researcher's interest in a particular research question may be based on a personal life experience, or it may involve concern about certain human or social problems. Some researchers are hired by the government, by industry, or by some other organization to conduct research and investigate questions that are of interest to the organization.

Not all questions that concern us can be answered through scientific research. Questions involving values, religion, morality, and philosophical issues often fall outside the domain of science. For example, scientific research cannot answer the question of whether abortion is right or wrong. Scientific research can, however, reveal information that may help us make or evaluate our own moral or value choices. For example, researchers can investigate the psychological, social, physical, and economic consequences of various sexual choices. Regarding abortion, researchers can identify the psychological consequences of aborting a child, rearing a child as a single parent, placing a child with an adoptive family, or rearing a child with the father.

The social and political context of the time may also affect the framing of research questions. Research topics and approaches that may be acceptable at one point in time may not meet current sensitivities and standards of a later time. With more states approving same sex marriage, gay relationships and LGBT issues have become a focal point for research. To gain approval and funding for research on sexuality-related topics, researchers sometimes need to be especially aware of—and contend with—public perceptions of topics and "political correctness."

2.5b Reviewing the Literature

Numerous journals (identified earlier in this chapter) publish research on human sexuality. Reviewing the articles in these and other journals enables researchers to discover what other researchers have already learned about a topic, provides researchers with ideas about new research questions, and suggests ways to conduct research.

Students and researchers often find it helpful to locate review articles, which summarize, organize, integrate, and evaluate previously published material. Review articles are useful in conveying the current state of research, identifying gaps and inconsistencies, and recommending next steps in solving problems. University libraries provide online journals so that individuals can search through enormous databases on whatever topic they are researching.

2.5c Formulating a Hypothesis and Operationalizing Variables

To answer their research questions, researchers must transform their questions into testable hypotheses. A **hypothesis** is a tentative or educated guess designed to test a theory. Hypotheses involve predictions about the relationship between two or more variables (e.g., alcohol and condom use). A **variable** is any measurable event or characteristic that varies or is subject to change. There are two types of variables. The **dependent variable** is the variable that is measured to assess what, if any, effect the independent variable has on it. The **independent variable** is the variable that is presumed to cause or influence the dependent variable. Following is an example of a sex research hypothesis and its variables:

1. *Hypothesis:* High alcohol consumption is associated with lower condom use.
2. *Independent Variable:* Alcohol consumption
3. *Dependent Variable:* Condom use

Because human sexual behavior and attitudes are complex and influenced by many factors, researchers often assess the effects of several independent variables on one or

BVT *Lab*

Improve your test scores. Practice quizzes are available at **www.BVTLab.com**.

Hypothesis
A tentative and testable proposal or an educated guess about the outcome of a research study

Variable
Any measurable event or characteristic that varies or is subject to change

Dependent variable
Variable that is measured to assess what, if any, effect the independent variable has on it

Independent variable
Variable that is presumed to cause or influence the dependent variable

more dependent variables. For example, condom use is also influenced by the status of the relationship and whether the couple is in love. Partners who are "hooking up" are more likely to use a condom than those who are cohabiting and who are in love.

Researchers must also specify how they will **operationalize** variables or develop an **operational definition** (working definition) of their terms. Researchers must operationally define such terms as *sexual satisfaction, sexual desire, pornography, sexual orientation, rape,* and *cohabitation.* An operational definition of cohabitation is "two unrelated adults of the opposite sex who live in the same residence overnight for four nights a week for three months." Such a definition eliminates lovers who stay over at each other's apartment on the weekend. Frith (2013) noted the social construction of the term orgasm and the different connotations of the term.

Think About It

Take a moment to answer the following questions. Considering your personal, academic, or professional interests, what research question about sexuality would you be interested in investigating? Based on your research question, what hypothesis could you formulate? How might you operationalize your independent and dependent variables?

2.5d Caveats in Sex Research

Researchers are not immune to bias. Alfred Kinsey, as a biologist and international expert on the gall wasp, was a taxonomist. As such, he classified and described variations within and across species. In trying to find all the variations in human sexual behaviors and validate sexual variety, he pursued unusual sexualities and may have spent more time revealing the extremes of sexuality (e.g., pedophilia) than reflecting the population as a whole.

Another source of potential bias occurs when researchers present an interpretation of what other researchers have done. Two layers of bias may be operative here: (a) when the original data are collected and interpreted and (b) when the second researcher reads the study of the original researcher and makes his or her own interpretation. Much of this text is based on the authors' representations of someone else's research. As a consumer, you should be alert to the potential bias in reading such secondary sources. To help control for this bias, we have provided references to the original sources for your own reading.

Research is the process of going up alleys to see if they are blind.

Marston Bates

Some researchers may be deliberately deceptive. Dr. Anil Potti (Duke University) changed data on research reports and provided fraudulent results (Darnton, 2012). Table 2-3 summarizes other caveats to keep in mind when you hear of or read various research reports.

2.5e Research Ethics: Protection of Human Subjects

The American Psychological Association charges psychologists to uphold "high standards of ethics, conduct, education and achievement" (APA, 2012). While these ethics often focus on issues relevant to clinical work (APA, 2010), equally important are ethics in reference to participants involved in research projects. A major principle of ethics in regard to conducting research is informed consent: the person participating in the

Operationalize
Define how a variable will be measured

Operational definition
Working definition, how a variable is defined in a particular study

---

TABLE **2-3** | Caveats in Sex Research

Caveat	Consequences	Example
The sample wasn't random	Cannot generalize the findings	The sexual attitudes and behaviors of college students are not the same as those of noncollege adults.
There was no control group	Inaccurate conclusions	A study on the effect of exposure to pornography on sexual satisfaction needs a control group of persons not exposed to pornography for purposes of comparison.
There were differences (e.g., age) between groups of respondents	Inaccurate conclusions	Effect may be due to passage of time or to cohort differences.
The terms were not operationally defined	Inability to measure what is not clearly defined	What are "hooking up," "sexual satisfaction," "open sexual communication," and "orgasm"?
A research bias was present	Slanted conclusions	A researcher studying the preference for sex toy use should not be funded by a maker of sex toys.
There has been a time lag since the original research was done	Outdated conclusions	Often-quoted Kinsey sex research is over 60 years old.
The data are Distorted	Invalid conclusions	Research subjects exaggerate, omit information, and/or recall facts or events inaccurately. Respondents may remember what they wish rather than what had really happened.

research project must be fully informed as to the risks and dangers, and voluntarily agree to participate. While Nazi Germany provides egregious examples of forcing patients to submit to various research projects against their will, the United States has also been guilty of exposing subjects to physical harm against their will and without their knowledge. Two examples where American researchers did not obtain informed consent follow.

In 1932, the Public Health Service launched a research study, known as the Tuskegee Syphilis Experiment, at Tuskegee Institute in Tuskegee, Alabama. Almost 400 black men who had syphilis were enrolled in the project to determine how the disease spreads, progresses, and kills. The men were not told that they had syphilis, and they were not treated for it (even though penicillin became a standard cure for syphilis in 1947). The participants were told that they had "bad blood," a euphemism to describe several illnesses including syphilis, anemia, and fatigue. For their willingness to be involved in the study, the men were given free meals and free burial insurance (Jones, 1993).

The experiment lasted four decades, until public health workers leaked the story to the media. By then, dozens of the men had died, and many wives and children had been infected. In 1973, the National Association for the Advancement of Colored People (NAACP) filed a class-action lawsuit. A $9 million settlement was divided among the study's participants. Free healthcare was given to the men who were still living, and to infected wives, widows and children (NPR, 2002). In 1997 President Clinton apologized to the survivors of the U.S. Public Health Service Syphilis Study (which became known as the Tuskegee experiment). The goal of his apology was to ensure that such deceptive research be eliminated. Central to these guidelines is individual informed consent (Mays, 2012).

Another example of deceptive research occurred in Guatemala from 1946 to 1948. Public Health Service physicians (American doctors) deliberately infected prisoners, soldiers, and patients in a mental hospital with syphilis and, in some cases, gonorrhea. A total of 696 men and women were exposed to syphilis without their knowledge. When the subjects contracted the disease, they were given antibiotics although it is unclear if all infected parties were cured. This example of research deception was hidden from public exposure for much longer since there were only a few articles published in Spanish—in contrast to 13 published reports on the Tuskegee example of "malfeasance and ethical failings" (Reverby, 2012, p. 493). In October 2010, the U.S. formally apologized to the citizens of Guatemala for conducting these experiments.

While not a government funded study, another example of violating the principle of informed consent (by an independent researcher) is the participant-observer study of "tearoom trade" (sexual behaviors conducted between same sex strangers in public bathrooms) by Humphreys. He served as a "watch queen" (lookout), allowing him to observe sexual encounters without revealing his research role. He copied down automobile license numbers of participants, through which he then traced the owners' identities and addresses. A year later, he included these men as participants in an unrelated social health survey that he helped to conduct. In this way, he obtained background and personal information on those who had frequented the "tearooms" (without their knowledge or approval). In a retrospective discussion of his research, Humphreys (1975) responded to ethical critiques and agreed with the criticism of the part of his research in which he traced the license numbers to interview men in their homes. He recognized that he put these men at risk (they could have been arrested if law enforcement officers had retrieved the records). He stated:

> Since then, although I remain convinced that it is ethical to observe inter-
> action in public places, and to interview willing and informed respondents,
> I direct my students to inform research subjects before interviewing them.
> Were I to repeat the tearoom study, I would spend another year or so in culti-
> vating and expanding the category of willing respondents ... (p. 231)

Lofstrom (2012) confirmed that students are often not aware of the ethical standards and behaviors to which researchers should adhere. Specific courses in ethics, and socialization by their membership in a professional organization are two of the mechanisms whereby they learn these standards.

Think About It

Take a moment to consider the following. While the caveats regarding involvement in research as a participant may involve risk, often omitted is that participation in research may have benefits. "While there is no certainty that every person will benefit from research participation, generally there are tangible moral, if not psychotherapeutic benefits, relating to the exercise of choosing to participate, and the sense that one is contributing to the well-being of others or the collective good. The intent to help others is thought to contribute to the effectiveness of participation in self-help groups, and it is likely that this is also true for activities, such as research participation. In research involving participants' telling their stories or exploring experience, the benefits might be greater still, including the psychologically-important processes of feeling heard and consolidating memories" (Lakeman, McAndrew, MacGabhann, & Warne, 2013, p. 83).

To ensure compliance with human research protocol, researchers are required to get approval from the IRB (Institutional Review Board) of their university or institutional affiliation. This panel reviews each research proposal to ensure that the expected research ethics are being followed—including informed consent. Research involving human subjects should meet the requirements published in "Ethical Principles and Guidelines for the Protection of Human Subjects of Research," also known as the Belmont Report (http://www.hhs.gov/ohrp/humansubjects/guidance/belmont.html), named after the Belmont Conference Center where the Commission met when drafting the report in 1976.

The three basic principles protecting human subjects are respect of persons, beneficence, and justice. Respect for persons includes protecting persons with diminished capacity. Beneficence means doing no harm, maximizing possible benefits and minimizing possible harms. Justice means to maintain equality of treatment of subjects.

2.6 Methods of Data Collection

After identifying a research question, reviewing the literature, formulating a hypothesis, and operationalizing variables, researchers collect data. Methods of data collection include experimental research, survey research, field research, direct laboratory observations, case studies, and historical research.

2.6a Experimental Research

Experimental research involves manipulating the independent variable to determine how it affects the dependent variable. In conducting an experiment, the researcher recruits participants and randomly assigns them to either an experimental group or a control group. After measuring the dependent variable in both groups, the researcher exposes participants in the experimental group to the independent variable (also known as the experimental treatment). Then the researcher measures the dependent variable in both groups again and compares the experimental group with the control group. Any differences between the groups may be due to the experimental treatment.

For example, Keels and colleagues (2013) used an experimental pre-test/post-test design to examine whether a presentation on the topic of masturbation would

Experimental research
Research methodology that involves manipulating the independent variable to determine how it affects the dependent variable

University faculty are required to have their research projects approved by the IRB (Institutional Review Board), which ensures that persons who participate in research follow the recommended guidelines, including informed consent. This faculty member is looking at the IRB website for her university. *Source: Chelsea Curry*

IRB (Institutional Review Board) website.
Source: E. Fred Johnson, Jr.

influence female attitudes toward masturbation. The authors hypothesized that exposure to information via lecture or DVD would be associated with a positive attitude change toward masturbation. At a large southeastern university, 498 female undergraduates were randomly assigned to one of two groups (where the method of information presentation, or independent variable, was manipulated). Prior to the presentation of information, both groups completed a pre-test, "Attitudes toward Masturbation Scale." After completing the attitude measure, one group listened to a lecture on masturbation and the other group watched a six-minute DVD of an undergraduate female discussing her own masturbatory history and experiences, including a discussion of the vibrators she used. Once the information had been presented the, "Attitudes toward Masturbation Scale" was given again as the post-test. Comparison of the data revealed positive increases in attitudes toward masturbation from pre-to post-test, independent of type of exposure (with greater change, though not significant, occurring in the lecture format). To be a true experiment, there would have to have been a control group where females took pre- and post-tests and had no exposure to either the lecture or DVD. Any change would then be attributable to the independent variables.

> We must conduct research and then accept the results. If they don't stand up to experimentation, Buddha's own words must be rejected.
>
> Dalai Lama XIV

The major strength of the experimental method is that it provides information on causal relationships; that is, it shows how one variable affects another. A primary weakness is that experiments are often conducted on small samples, usually in artificial laboratory settings. For this reason, the findings may not be generalizable to other people in natural settings.

2.6b Survey Research

Most research in sexuality is survey research (Fletcher, Dowsett, Duncan, Slavin, & Corboz, 2013). **Survey research** involves eliciting information from respondents using questions. An important part of survey research is selecting a **sample**, or a portion of the population in which the researcher is interested. Ideally, samples are representative of the population being studied. A **representative sample** allows the researcher to assume that responses obtained from the sample are similar to those that would be obtained from the larger population. For example, the American Council on Education and the University of California at Los Angeles annually collect a random sample of first semester undergraduates at colleges and universities throughout the United States. In 2012, their data came from 192,912 first-time, full-time students entering 283 four-year colleges and universities reflecting a sample of the approximately 1.5 million first-time, full-time first-year students entering 1,613 four-year colleges and universities throughout the country (Pryor, et al., 2012). Similarly, the National Sex Study at Indiana University (Reece, et al., 2012) provides data based on a representative sample of U.S. adults.

> My latest survey shows that people don't believe in surveys.
>
> Laurence J. Peter

Although Kinsey is credited with having conducted one of the largest sex surveys, his sampling method was seriously flawed. The large number of interview respondents coming from people from the Midwest, especially Indiana, and the inclusion of special groups (homosexuals and prisoners) are factors that challenge the generalizability of Kinsey's results to the larger population of U.S. adults.

Kinsey argued that, because of the enormity of his sample, randomization was not necessary. His goal was to conduct 100,000 interviews. Although this ambitious goal was not realized, by the time of his death, Kinsey had interviewed 8,000 persons himself, and his staff another 10,000. Kinsey believed that random sampling would not produce a satisfactory sample because too many people would refuse to participate and the extremes in the population would be missed. He sought to avoid this by

Survey research
Research that involves eliciting information from respondents using questions

Sample
Portion of the population that the researcher studies to attempt to make inferences about the whole population

Representative sample
Sample the researcher studies that is representative of the population from which it is taken

approaching groups and obtaining interviews from every member of the group. He was most persuasive in obtaining interviews with individuals representing various groups (the YMCAs in a number of cities, state penal farms and prisons, an orphanage, the Nicodemus rural black community, etc.); and they constituted a quarter of his sample.

Most sex research studies are self-report studies that are not based on representative samples. Most sex research is conducted on convenient samples, such as college students to whom researchers have easy access. An overuse of college students for sex research is not unique to the United States. Reis and colleagues (2013), for example, reported on the condom use of university students in Portugal.

Another problem with research is volunteers. Students who volunteer for sexuality research have been shown to be more likely to have had sexual intercourse, performed oral sex, score higher on sexual esteem and sexual sensation seeking, and report sexual attitudes that are less traditional than nonvolunteers (Weiderman, 1999). Wiederman cautioned that if such volunteers are not representative of college students, then the validity of sexuality research might be particularly suspect. Notwithstanding these sample issues, there are several kinds of survey research.

Interviews

After selecting their sample, survey researchers either interview people or ask them to complete written questionnaires. In **interview survey research**, trained interviewers ask respondents a series of questions and either take written notes or tape-record the respondents' answers. Interviews may be conducted over the telephone or face-to-face. Bernert and Ogletree (2013) interviewed 14 women with intellectual disabilities about how they experienced sexuality. Most were apprehensive about sexual intercourse and intimacy, which resulted in self-imposed abstinence.

Cultural Diversity

Twamley (2013) confirmed the effect of context by comparing the views of love and intimacy of heterosexual middle-class Indians of Gujarati origin in the UK with heterosexual middle-class Indians born in and living in India. Those reared in India viewed "love at first sight" as based on physical attraction and as "a lesser kind of love." In contrast, those reared in the UK viewed "love at first sight" as desirable in that it demonstrates how the relationship is based on love only, without any concern for material gain. Such a love-based relationship is associated with an early transition to sex, usually before marriage, which was seen as both desirable and inevitable (the antithesis of what those reared in India thought and did).

One advantage of interview survey research is that it enables the researcher to clarify questions for the respondent and follow up on answers to particular questions. Face-to-face interviews provide a method of surveying individuals who do not have a telephone or mailing address. For example, some AIDS-related research attempts to assess high-risk behaviors among street youth and intravenous drug users—both high-risk groups for HIV infection. These groups may not have a telephone or address due to their transient lifestyle. However, these groups may be accessible if the researcher locates their hangouts and conducts face-to-face interviews.

A major disadvantage of interview research is the lack of privacy and anonymity. Respondents may feel embarrassed or threatened when asked to answer questions about sexual attitudes and behaviors. As a result, some respondents may choose not

Interview survey research
Type of research in which trained interviewers ask respondents a series of questions, and either take written notes or tape-record the respondents' answers either over the telephone or face-to-face

to participate, and those who do may conceal or alter information to give socially desirable answers to interviewers' questions (such as "No, I have never had intercourse with someone other than my spouse during my marriage" or "Yes, I use condoms each time I have sex"). Other disadvantages of interview survey research are the time and expense. Interviews can easily last over an hour and the cost can be enormous when including interviewer training, transportation to the respondents' homes, and computer data entry. Telephone interviews are less time consuming and cost less money, but may yield less information since nonverbal behavior—which may prompt follow-up questions, cannot be observed.

Although face-to-face interviews are often conducted one-on-one, sometimes they are held in a small group called a **focus group**. Advantages of focus group research include the minimal expense of time and money and the fact that it allows participants to interact and raise new issues for the researcher to investigate. Respondents can clarify their responses and can respond in more depth than in a survey. A disadvantage is the limited sample size, which means that the data from focus groups may not be representative of the larger research population.

Questionnaires

Instead of conducting face-to-face or phone interviews, researchers may develop questionnaires that they either give to a sample of respondents or post on the Internet where respondents answer in private. Such Internet questionnaire surveys also provide large quantities of data that can be analyzed relatively inexpensively as compared to face-to-face or telephone surveys. Such surveys yield less data yet take a great deal of time to complete.

Because researchers do not ask respondents to write their names on questionnaires, questionnaire research provides privacy and anonymity to the research participants. This reduces the likelihood that respondents will provide answers that are intentionally inaccurate or distorted. However, inaccurate information is still sometimes provided. Udry (1998) reported on the results of an honesty question on a self-administered questionnaire. "When we interviewed you a year ago, we asked you whether you had ever had sexual intercourse. What did you tell us? Was that true?" (Udry, 1998, p. 58.) From 5% to 20% (varying by sex and race) admitted they had lied during previous interviews. Many were incorrect in remembering their previous answers. Inconsistencies were not always due to dishonesty. One student explained, "Last year I

Focus group
Interviews conducted in a small group and typically focused on one subject

East Carolina University.   Student Project

COLLEGE STUDENT ATTITUDES AND BEHAVIORS
You are asked to voluntarily participate in a study designed to assess the attitudes and behaviors of college students on a variety of issues. Completing the survey will take about 25 minutes. Participation is completely voluntary and no compensation is provided for your participation. Should you be willing to participate, you may elect to skip questions and select only those to which you feel comfortable responding. Your responses are confidential and anonymous. There is no "capturing of your email or IP address" when you submit this questionnaire. In addition, no identifying code will be attached to any response. No identifying code will be attached to any response.

Thank you.

>>

Survey Powered By Qualtrics

Students often participate in research by taking online surveys.
Source: E. Fred Johnson, Jr.

told you I had had intercourse, because I thought I had. But now I know that I hadn't at that time because since then I *have* had intercourse" (p. 58).

When sexual information is sensitive or potentially stigmatizing, obtaining accurate information may be especially hard. For example, given the social pressure to avoid behaviors that increase risk to HIV exposure, it may be difficult for people to say they perform such behaviors.

The major disadvantage of mail questionnaires is that obtaining an adequate response rate is difficult. Many people do not want to take the time or make the effort to complete a questionnaire, and others may not be able to read or understand the questions. Typically, only 20% to 40% of individuals in a sample complete and return a mail questionnaire. A low response rate is problematic because nonrespondents (those people who do not respond to the survey) are usually more conservative from those people who do respond. Also, because respondents do not constitute a representative sample, the researcher may not be able to generalize the research findings to the larger population.

Studies on sexuality and relationships are commonly found in popular magazines such as *Cosmopolitan* and on the Internet. Sometimes these magazines or websites conduct their own research by asking readers/visitors to complete questionnaires and mail them to magazine editors or to take a survey online. The survey results are published in subsequent issues of such magazines or on the website. The research weakness of these surveys is that they reveal information from only a very select group of respondents—those who read the magazine or had logged on to the website. Individuals who don't read the magazine or who don't take online surveys are not represented.

The results of magazine and Internet surveys should be viewed with caution because the data are not based on representative samples. Other problems with magazine and Internet surveys include the inadequacy of some questions, the methods of analysis, and the inherent bias of the publication or website, which wants to reflect a positive image of its readership and visitors, entertain them, and sell magazines. Results that respondents to a magazine's questionnaire are depressed and unhappy are not likely to be published.

New Technologies for Research

A new method for conducting survey research is asking respondents to provide answers to a computer that "talks." Respondents report the privacy of computers as a major advantage. As the Internet is more broadly used, there will be more opportunity for its use to conduct sex research.

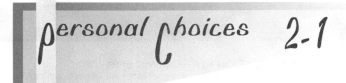

Participating in Sex Research as a Subject

As a student at a college or university, you may be asked to complete a questionnaire or participate in an interview as part of a sex research project being conducted by a professor or graduate student. Before deciding whether to participate in the study, you want to be sure that the research follows established ethical guidelines for research with human participants. These guidelines include being informed by the researcher(s) about the nature and purpose of the study, being protected from physical or psychological harm, being guaranteed anonymity and confidentiality if the material is sensitive, and having the option to choose not to participate (or to discontinue participation) without penalty.

Individuals who participate in sexuality research benefit the larger society. The sexual information they share with researchers, which is later disseminated in professional journals, may enable all of us to make more informed sexual and relationship choices. However, they must be careful not to jeopardize their own well-being. For example a person who has been the victim of sex abuse may still have nightmares about the experience and/or be unable to be sexually intimate. In this case completing a questionnaire on sex abuse may revive unpleasant memories of the abuse, and so declining to participate in the sex research may be indicated.

2.6c Field Research

Field research involves observing and studying social behaviors in settings in which they occur naturally. Two types of field research are participant observation and nonparticipant observation. In **participant observation** research, the researcher participates in the phenomenon being studied to obtain an insider's perspective of the people and/or behavior being observed. An example would be the researcher who goes as a nudist to a nudist resort to observe the behavior patterns of the nudists. Another would be a researcher who goes to a swinger's convention as a swinger with the real mission of finding out how swingers behave.

In **nonparticipant observation** research, the investigators observe the phenomenon being studied but do not actively participate in the group or the activity. For example, a researcher could study nude beaches and strip clubs as an observer without being a nudist or a stripper. The primary advantage of field research is that it yields detailed descriptive information about the behaviors, values, emotions, and norms of those being studied. A disadvantage of field research is that the individuals being studied may alter their behaviors if they know they are being observed. If researchers do not let the individuals know they are being studied, the researchers may be violating ethical codes of research conduct. Another potential problem with field research is that the researchers' observations are subjective and may be biased. In addition, because field research is usually based on small samples, the findings may not be generalizable.

2.6d Direct Laboratory Observation

One of the earliest U.S. investigators of the physiology of human sexual response was John B. Watson, who became famous for introducing the concept of "behaviorism" and serving as a president of the American Psychological Association. However, he became infamous for his study of human sexual response that he conducted "by connecting his own body and that of his female partner to various scientific instruments while they made love" (Magoun, 1981, p. 369). His wife discovered these records, confiscated the data, and sued him for divorce. This ended his research career and his professorship at Johns Hopkins University.

Dr. William Masters and Virginia Johnson worked together from 1957 to 1992 to research human sexual response. It was not until the work of Masters and Johnson that laboratory analysis of sexual response came to be regarded as legitimate scientific inquiry. William Masters (1915–2001) and Virginia Johnson (1925–2013), of the Masters and Johnson Institute in Saint Louis, conducted **direct laboratory observation** through a one-way mirror of 694 individuals who engaged in a variety of sexual behaviors. They published their research (conducted over a 12-year period) in the nationwide best seller, *Human Sexual Response* (Masters & Johnson, 1966). Their work

Field research
Method of data collection that involves observing and studying social behaviors in settings in which they occur naturally

Participant observation
Type of observation in which the researcher participates in the phenomenon being studied to obtain an insider's perspective of the people and/or behavior being observed

Nonparticipant observation
Type of research in which investigators observe the phenomenon being studied, but do not actively participate in the group or the activity

Direct laboratory observation
In human sexuality research, the actual observation of individuals engaging in sexual behavior, which Masters and Johnson and Alfred C. Kinsey utilized

provided basic information on the physiology of sexual response and ways to precisely measure genital response. Contemporary laboratory studies continue to analyze sexual arousal and response—but now from a psychophysiological perspective, assessing multiple dimensions (including the perceptions and affect of subjects).

In addition to focusing on basic understanding of sexual response, laboratory study has also contributed to the diagnosis and treatment of sexual dysfunction. Problems with laboratory-based research include the use of volunteers. Are those who volunteer to participate in such research similar to those who do not? Research volunteers are more likely to be sexually experienced, more interested in sexual variety, and less guilty about sex than non-volunteers. Thus, volunteer samples may not be representative of the group from which they are recruited, and caution should be used in making generalizations based on the findings.

2.6e Case Studies

A **case study** is a research approach that involves conducting an in-depth, detailed analysis of an individual, group, relationship, or event. Data obtained in a case study may come from interviews, observations, or analysis of records (medical, educational, and legal). Like field research, case studies yield detailed qualitative or descriptive information about the experiences of individuals. Lambert (2013) provided an example of a case study of a 22-year-old military man whose watching pornography on the Internet interfered with his job performance and his personal happiness. He sought help for his "Internet addiction" which he felt was out of control.

Case studies are valuable in providing detailed qualitative information about the experiences of individuals and groups. The main disadvantage of the case study method is that findings based on a small sample size (in some cases a sample size of one) are not generalizable.

2.6f Historical Research

Historical research involves investigating sexuality and sexual issues through the study of historical documents. Data sources used in conducting historical research include newspapers, magazines, letters, literature (such as novels and poetry), diaries, medical texts and popular health manuals, court records, hospital records, prison records, and official (government) statistics on such topics as birth rates, arrest and conviction rates, sexually transmittable infections (STIs), and nonmarital pregnancies. One example of historical research is an investigation of erotica in Song China (960–1279). Zhang (2013) reported of a Fei Shu who was on his way to the capital: …

> he stayed at a lodge at Yanzhi Slope near Chang'an [in Shaanxi]. By the time Fei put down his luggage, the sun was already setting behind the mountain. The daughter-in-law of the lodge owner, leaning against the doorframe and smiling, greeted the guest. In the middle of the night, she came alone to Fei's room and said, "I admire your elegant demeanor and would like to offer you pleasure for a night. Would you allow me?" (p. 253)

Other historical research involves examining data. Noted sexual historian Vern L. Bullough (1928–2006) was awarded the Distinguished Achievement Award by the Society for the Scientific Study of Sex for his studies over the past half-century. He observed that interpretations of historical data "vary with those doing the interpreting", and that "the same facts can be reinterpreted or ignored by others" these differences may be influenced by whether the writer is an "insider" or "outsider" to the focus of the study (Bullough, 1998, p. 13). For example, Bullough noted his disagreement with

Case study
Research method that involves conducting an in-depth, detailed analysis of an individual, group, relationship, or event

the historian John Boswell's conclusion of a friendly attitude toward homosexuality by the medieval Christian Church. However, Bullough allowed that this interpretation could be influenced by Boswell's background (a gay man and Catholic convert who hoped to impact existing Catholic policy regarding homosexuality) in contrast to his own (a humanist and a heterosexual). On the other hand, Bullough also mentioned a critique of his discussion of homosexuality in Hinduism, which one writer found too positive. In reflecting on his work, Bullough concluded, "In short, the history of sexuality can be fascinating, and I would urge others to study it, to challenge and correct me, or perhaps even to reaffirm what I have found" (p. 13).

Although the cost of a research study varies with the nature of the research question, the method of research used, and the number of participants, research is usually expensive. Who pays for sex research? Funding may come from private organizations and corporations, universities, or government agencies. Social Choices 2-1 discusses whether taxpayers should pay for sex research.

Public Funding for Sex Research

Conducting large-scale sex research is expensive. Staff are needed to draw samples, conduct interviews, analyze data, interpret findings, and write up the results. Congress is often not convinced of the validity of providing funding for sex research and fears the retribution of the voting public. Members of Congress also cite morality issues and suggest that funding should be used for finding the cure for cancer or autism, or for veterans. Sex researchers such as Heather Rupp of the Kinsey Institute noted that sexuality research has a greater chance of being funded when tied to health related issues (Merta, 2010). Below we look at the arguments for and against public funding sex research.

2.6g In Favor of Public Funding of Sex Research

Taxpayers fund projects all the time. Most of our tax money goes to things that we do not understand and to things that do not benefit the population as a whole. Sex research is something that can benefit people on every level of society. Sexual dysfunctions, STIs, AIDS, and other sexual concerns do not discriminate. These are problems that touch the old and the young, the rich and the poor. Sex research has given us answers and solutions to many problems about sex and things related to sex. New drugs have been discovered to treat sexual problems (e.g. erectile dysfunction) and AIDS. Without sex research, we would not have these medications to enhance sexual encounters. The more funding sex research gets, the more we learn about sexuality. The more we know sex and sexuality, the better.

2.6h Against Public Funding of Sex Research

People pay enough taxes already; sex research is the last thing people need to be throwing their money away on. Therefore, the public should not fund sex research. There are more important things to be putting tax money toward—like education and healthcare. Sex researchers seem to be doing just fine being funded by private organizations, so there's no reason for the public to help fund sex research. Why do we need to research sex anyway? We all know what sex is and what purpose it serves. What more is there to research?

Think About It

Take a moment to answer the following questions. In a previous "Think About It," you were asked to formulate a sex research question and hypothesis based on your personal, academic, or professional interests. Which method of research would you select to answer your research question? What are the advantages and disadvantages of using the method you selected?

2.7 Levels of Data Analysis

After collecting data on a research question, researchers analyze the data to test their hypotheses. There are three levels of data analysis: description, correlation, and causation.

2.7a Description

The goal of many sexuality research studies is to describe sexual processes, behaviors, and attitudes, as well as the people who experience them. **Descriptive research** may be qualitative or quantitative. Qualitative descriptions are verbal narratives that describe details and nuances of sexual phenomena. Quantitative descriptions of sexuality are numerical representations of sexual phenomena. Quantitative descriptive data analysis may involve computing the following: means (averages); frequencies; mode (the most frequently occurring observation in the data); median (the middle data point; half of the data points are above and half are below the median); and range (a measure of dispersion, comprising the highest and lowest values of a variable in a set of observations).

Descriptive research findings should be interpreted with caution. For example, research on sexting behavior of male and female undergraduates has revealed that men

Descriptive research
Qualitative or quantitative research that describes sexual processes, behaviors, and attitudes, as well as the people who experience them

Close 2-1

An Undergraduate's Decision Not to Participate in Sex Research

I was a broke college student and saw an advertisement which read "Money—be a research participant in sex research." I followed up and was told it was a study on a new antidote to cure a STI. I was offered $300 and told it would take only an hour of my time. They wanted to infect me with an STI but assured me that the new antidote worked and that I would be back to normal in three days.

Before I signed up, I talked to my folks who referred me to our family physician. She told me that it would not be a good idea for me to participate in this research. She noted that, in the future, I would need to check on subsequent health and insurance forms that I had had a sexually transmitted infection. Not to speak of the fact—suppose something went wrong and the antidote did not work? I declined.

are more likely to initiate sexting behavior (Parker, Knox, & Easterling, 2011). Does this mean that women never initiate sexting behavior? Hardly. What these findings mean is that men generally tend to be the first to send a sex text or photo to a romantic partner. As you read the research findings in this text, remember that they are generalizations, not absolute truths.

2.7b Correlation

Researchers are often interested in the relationships among variables. A variable is simply a measurable item or characteristic that is subject to change. **Correlation** refers to a relationship among two or more variables. Correlational research may answer such questions as "What factors (e.g., alcohol/drug use) are associated with contracting a sexually transmitted infection?"

If a correlation or relationship exists between two variables, then a change in one variable is associated with a change in the other variable. A **positive correlation** exists when both variables change in the same direction. For example, in general, the greater the number of sexual partners a person has, the greater the chance of contracting a sexually transmitted infection. As variable A (number of sexual partners) increases, variable B (chances of contracting a STI) also increases. Therefore, we may say that there is a positive correlation between the number of sexual partners and contracting STIs. Similarly, we might say that as the number of sexual partners decreases, the chance of contracting STIs decreases. Notice that in both cases, the variables change in the same direction.

A **negative correlation** exists when two variables change in opposite directions. For example, there is a negative correlation between condom use and the chance of contracting an STI. This means that as condom use increases, the chance of contracting STIs decreases.

Students often make the mistake of thinking that if two variables decrease, the correlation is negative. To avoid making this error, remember that in a positive correlation, it does not matter whether the variables increase or decrease, as long as they change in the same direction.

Sometimes the relationship between variables is curvilinear. A **curvilinear correlation** exists when two variables vary in both the same and opposite directions. For example, suppose that if you have one alcoholic beverage, your desire for sex increases. With two drinks, your sexual desire increases more, and three drinks raise your interest even higher. So far, there is a positive correlation between alcohol consumption (variable A) and sexual desire (variable B): As one variable increases, the other also increases. Now suppose that after four drinks, you start feeling sleepy, dizzy, or nauseous; and your interest in sex decreases. After five drinks, you are either

Correlation
Statistical index that represents the degree of relationship between two variables

Positive correlation
Relationship between two variables that exists when both variables change in the same direction

Negative correlation
Relationship between two variables that change in opposite directions

Curvilinear correlation
Relationship that exists when two variables vary in both the same and opposite directions

FIGURE **2-2** ‖ Graphs Depicting Positive, Negative, and Curvilinear Relationships

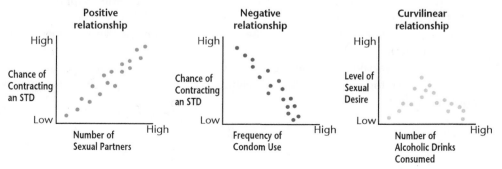

vomiting or semiconscious, and sex is of no interest to you. There is now a negative correlation between alcohol consumption and sexual desire: As alcohol consumption increases, sexual interest decreases.

A fourth type of correlation is called a spurious correlation. A **spurious correlation** exists when two variables appear to be related but only because they are both related to a third variable. When the third variable is controlled through a statistical method in which a variable is held constant, the apparent relationship between the dependent and independent variables disappear. For example, suppose a researcher finds that the more religiously devout you are, the more likely you are to contract a sexually transmitted infection. How can that be? Is there something about being religiously devout that, in and of itself, leads to STIs? The explanation is that religiously devout unmarried individuals are less likely to plan intercourse; and therefore, when they do have intercourse, they often are not prepared in terms of having a condom with them (or they would feel guilty about using one). Therefore, the correlation between religious devoutness and STIs is spurious. These variables appear to be related only because they are both related to a third variable (in this case, condom use).

2.7c Causation

If data analysis reveals that two variables are correlated, we know only that a change in one variable is associated with a change in the other variable. We cannot assume, however, that a change in one variable causes a change in the other variable unless our data collection and analysis are specifically designed to assess causation. The research method that best allows us to assess causal relationships is the experimental method.

To demonstrate causality, three conditions must be met. First, the research must demonstrate that variable A is correlated with variable B. In other words, a change in variable A must be associated with a change in variable B. Second, the researcher must demonstrate that the presumed cause (variable A) occurs or changes prior to the presumed effect (variable B). In other words, the cause must precede the effect. For example, suppose a researcher finds that a negative correlation exists between marital conflict and frequency of marital intercourse. For example, as marital conflict increases, frequency of marital intercourse decreases. To demonstrate that marital conflict causes the frequency of marital intercourse to decrease, the researcher must show that the marital conflict preceded the decrease in marital intercourse. Otherwise, the researcher cannot be sure whether marital conflict causes a decrease in marital intercourse or a decrease in marital intercourse causes marital conflict.

Third, the researcher must demonstrate that the observed correlation is nonspurious. A nonspurious correlation is a relationship between two variables that cannot be explained by a third variable. A nonspurious correlation suggests that an inherent causal link exists between the two variables. As we discussed earlier, the correlation between religious devoutness and sexually transmitted infections is spurious because a third variable—condom use—explains the correlation. Another example is the relationship between sexual assault history and current marital status. Suppose a study finds that persons with sexual assault history are less likely to be married. While it may seem reasonable to speculate that the previous assault caused with: anxiety about being intimate in a marriage relationship, an alternative possibility cannot be ruled out that a third variable—perhaps poor social skills, may increase both sexual assault risk and the risk for low social support. Figure 2-3 summarizes the steps involved in conducting a research project.

Spurious correlation
Pattern that exists when two variables appear to be related but only because they are both related to a third variable

2.8 Interpretation and Discussion

Following analysis of the data, the researcher is in a position to evaluate and interpret the results and their implications. The researcher may qualify the results, draw inferences from them, assess the theoretical implications, and discuss possible applications. Limitations of the data are also identified. Most often this implies a small, nonrandom sample or a sample that is specific to one group (e.g., college students) where analysis of the data would reveal very little about other groups (e.g., noncollege adults). Finally, the researcher often suggests new ideas, topics, or variables to be explored/examined in future research. Burri (2013) emphasized that the new frontier of sex research is genetic studies as related to environmental factors and gene-environment interactions in reference to sexual dysfunctions.

Source: Shutterstock

FIGURE **2-3** ‖ **Steps Involved in Conducting a Research Project**

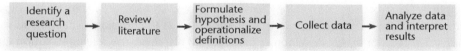

Identify a research question → Review literature → Formulate hypothesis and operationalize definitions → Collect data → Analyze data and interpret results

Chapter Summary

Research and theory provide ways of discovering and explaining new information about human sexuality. They are the bedrock of sexology as a discipline. Scientific research involves methods of collecting and analyzing empirical evidence, and is supported by observable evidence.

Nature of Sex Research

Scientific research involves methods of collecting and analyzing empirical evidence, or data that can be observed. Scientific knowledge is different from common sense, intuition, tradition, and authority in that it is supported by observable evidence.

Interdisciplinary Nature of Sex Research

Sexology, the scientific study of sexuality, is an interdisciplinary field that incorporates various fields including psychology, medicine, sociology, family studies, public health, social work, therapy, history, and education. Sexology can be divided into three broad disciplinary approaches: biosexology, psychosexology, and sociosexology. Biosexology is the study of the biological aspects of sexuality, such as the physiological and endocrinological aspects of sexual development and sexual response; the role of evolution and genetics in sexual development; the physiology of reproduction; the development of new contraceptives; and the effects of drugs, medications, disease, and exercise on sexuality.

Psychosexology involves the study of how psychological processes—such as emotions, cognitions, and personality—influence and are influenced by sexual development and behavior. Sociosexology is concerned with the way social and cultural forces influence and are influenced by sexual attitudes, beliefs, and behaviors. HIV and AIDS research is a continuing aspect of study for the three disciplines.

Theories of Sexuality

Biological, psychological, and sociological theories each contribute unique insights to our understanding of various aspects of sexuality. Biological theories include physiological and evolutionary theories. Psychological theories include psychoanalytic, classical conditioning, operant learning, social learning, and cognitive/affective theories. Sociological theories include symbolic interaction, structural-functional, conflict, feminist, and systems theories.

Eclectic View of Human Sexuality

Many aspects of human sexuality are best explained by using an eclectic theoretical approach that considers biological, psychological, and sociological explanations. For example, for a diabetic man with erection difficulties, physiological explanations would involve pelvic vascular changes attributable to diabetes; psychological explanations would focus on the anxiety that might trigger such difficulty; and sociological explanations would focus on the relationship with his partner and the fact that his family physician may disapprove of his interest in sex "at his age." Biological treatments might involve the diabetic man quitting smoking (to improve vascular circulation); psychological treatment may involve changing cognitions so that erection is not viewed as essential to sexual pleasure; and sociological treatment may involve changing cultural views regarding sexuality among aging persons and incorporating sex therapy into health insurance plans.

Conducting Sex Research: A Step-by-Step Process

Unlike casual observations of sexuality, scientific sex research is conducted according to a systematic process. After identifying a research question, a researcher reviews the literature on the subject, formulates a hypothesis, operationalizes the research variables, and collects data using one of several scientific methods of data collection. Researchers are obliged to follow research protocol. This includes informed consent.

Methods of Data Collection

Experimental research, survey research, field research, direct laboratory observation, case studies, and historical research each have advantages and disadvantages. The major strength of the experimental method is that it provides information on causal relationships; that is, it shows how one variable affects another. A primary weakness of this method is that experiments are often conducted on small samples in artificial laboratory settings, so the findings may not be generalized to other people in natural settings.

An advantage of interview survey research is that it enables the researcher to clarify questions for the respondent and pursue answers to particular questions. Face-to-face interviews can be conducted with individuals who do not have a telephone or mailing address. A major disadvantage of interview research is lack of privacy and anonymity, which often causes some respondents to choose not to participate, to conceal or alter information.

Questionnaire survey research provides privacy and anonymity to the research participants, which reduces the likelihood that they will provide answers that are intentionally inaccurate or distorted. Questionnaire surveys are also less expensive and time consuming than face-to-face or telephone surveys. The major disadvantage of mail questionnaires is that it is difficult to obtain adequate response rates.

An advantage of field research is that it yields detailed descriptive information about the behaviors, values, emotions, and norms of those being studied. A disadvantage of field research is that the individuals being studied may alter their behaviors if they know they are being observed. Also, the researcher's observations and interpretations may be biased, and the findings may not be generalized.

Masters and Johnson conducted direct laboratory observation through a one-way mirror of the sexual response patterns of women and men. One disadvantage of such research is that volunteers who participate in such research are not representative of the larger population. Like field research, case studies yield detailed descriptive information about the experiences of individuals. The case study method also allows rare cases of sexual phenomena to be investigated. The main disadvantage of the case study method is that findings based on a single case are not generalizable.

Historical research involves investigating sexuality and sexual issues through the study of historical documents. Historical research provides information on how sexual behavior, attitudes, and norms have changed with time.

Levels of Data Analysis

Levels of data analysis include description (qualitative or quantitative), correlation (positive, negative, curvilinear, or spurious), and causation. Determining causation is difficult because human experiences are influenced by so many factors that it is almost impossible to isolate one factor to assess its effects.

Interpretation and Discussion

Finally, following data analysis, the researcher evaluates and interprets the results and their implications. The researcher may qualify the results, draw inferences from them, assess the theoretical implications, and discuss possible applications.

Web Links

Electronic Journal of Human Sexuality

http://www.ejhs.org/

Institute for the Advanced Study of Human Sexology

http://www.iashs.edu/

Kinsey Institute

http://www.indiana.edu/~kinsey/

Psychological Research on the Net

http://psych.hanover.edu/research/exponnet.html

Society for the Scientific Study of Sex

http://www.sexscience.org

Key Terms

Biosexology   28

Biosocial framework   29

Case study   50

Classical conditioning   31

Cognitive/affective theories   32

Conflict theory   36

Correlation   53

Critical sexuality studies   25

Curvilinear correlation   53

Deductive research   27

Dependent variable   40

Descriptive research   52

Direct laboratory observation   49

Eclectic view   37

Ego   30

Empirical evidence   26

Evolutionary theories   29

Experimental research   44

Feminist theories   36

Field research   49

Focus group   47

Hypothesis   40

Id   30

Independent variable   40

Inductive research   27

Interview survey research   46

Natural selection   29

Negative correlation   53

Nonparticipant observation   49

Operant learning theory   31

Operational definition   41

Operationalize   41

Participant observation   49

Patriarchy   37

Physiological theories   29

Positive correlation   53

Psychoanalytic theory   30

Psychosexology   28

Punishment   32

Reinforcement   32

Representative sample   45

Sample   45

Sexology   28

Social learning theory   32

Social scripts   35

Sociobiological theories   29

Sociosexology   28

Spurious correlation   54

Structural-functional theory   36

Superego   30

Survey research   45

Symbolic interaction theory   32

Systems theory   37

Theory   28

Variable   40

Additional study resources are available at www.BVTLab.com

CHAPTER 3

Female Sexual Anatomy, Physiology, and Response

For women the best aphrodisiacs are words. The G-spot is in the ears.
He who looks for it below there is wasting his time.

Isabel Aliende

Chapter Outline

Objectives

1. Identify and label the internal and external female anatomy.

2. Understand female physiology.

3. Know the social issues surrounding breast-feeding in public, including various legislation.

4. Describe how a woman should perform a breast self-exam.

5. Review the guidelines about who should have mammograms and how often.

6. Describe the phases of the menstrual cycle.

7. List the potential problems of the menstrual cycle.

8. Discuss three models of sexual response.

9. Know how hormones influence sexual response.

Source: Shutterstock

TRUTH OR FICTION?

T/F   The makeup of the clitoris includes 8,000 nerve fibers.

T/F   Muslim communities approve of female genital cutting since it is sanctioned by the Qur'an.

T/F   A disadvantage of thermascan to detect breast cancer is exposure to radiation.

T/F   Research has consistently found that fluctuations in hormone levels in women are associated with predictable mood changes.

T/F   About a quarter of menstruating women report the prevalence of premenstrual dysphoric disorder in the past 12 months.

Answers:
1.T 2.F 3.F 4.F 5.F

The female form is branded into our individual and cultural consciousness. While standing in the checkout line at the grocery store, look at the covers of the various magazines for sale and notice the frequency with which the female body is featured. Think of the biblical Eve … She is without clothes and tempting Adam!

In this chapter we focus on female bodies (anatomy), physiology, and sexual response (Chapter 4 is devoted to male anatomy and functioning). Technically, anatomy is the study of body structure, and physiology is the study of bodily functions. **Sexual anatomy** refers to internal and external genitals, which are also called sex organs.

Sexual anatomy
Term referring to internal and external genitals, also called sex organs

Sexual physiology
Vascular, hormonal, and central nervous system processes involved in genital functioning

Vulva
External female genitalia

Sexual physiology refers to the vascular, hormonal, and central nervous system processes involved in genital functioning. Sexual sensations involve the whole body—not just the sex organs. Furthermore, what happens above the neck—in the brain—largely influences sexual functioning.

3.1 Female External Anatomy and Physiology

Despite living in a culture that seems sexually obsessed, some women do not know the correct scientific names for their genitalia. Little girls are often not taught names for their external genital parts, but vague reference may be made to "down there."

The external female genitalia are collectively known as the **vulva** which is a Latin term meaning "covering." External sex organs of the female include the mons venires, labia, clitoris, urethral opening, and vaginal opening (see Figure 3-1). Female genitalia differ in size, shape, and color, resulting in considerable variability in appearance (see Figure 3-2).

I didn't discover curves; I only uncovered them.

Mae West, actress in the '30s

FIGURE **3-1** ‖ External Female Genitalia

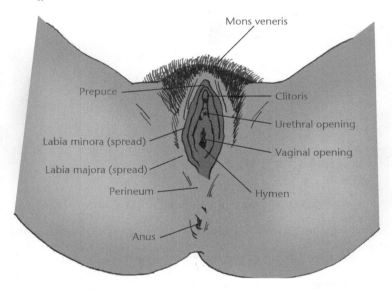

FIGURE **3-2** ‖ Variations in the Vulva

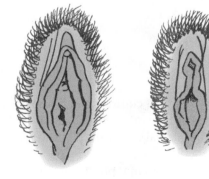

3.1a Mons Veneris

The soft cushion of fatty tissue that lies over the pubic symphysis (joint between the left and right pubic bones) is called the **mons veneris** (mahns vuhNAIR-ihs), which is Latin for "mound of Venus" (Venus being the goddess of love).

The mons acts as a cushion to protect the pubic region during intercourse. Because this area is filled with many nerve endings, women often find gentle stimulation of this area to be highly pleasurable. Also known as the mons pubis, this area becomes covered with hair during puberty. The evolutionary function of this hair may be to trap and concentrate pelvic odors (for attracting a mate). Increasingly, young women shave their pubic hair. Motivations include the perception that other women do, personal preference for the way it looks/feels, preference of partner, and partaking in a ritual of shaving with the partner.

3.1b Labia

The **labia majora** (LAY-be-uh mih-JOR-uh), or "major lips," are two elongated folds of fatty tissue that extend from the mons veneris to the **perineum** (PEHR-ih-NEE-um)—the area of skin between the opening of the vagina and the anus. The outer sides of these labia may be covered with hair, whereas the inner sides are smooth and supplied with oil and sweat glands. Located between the labia majora lie two hairless, flat folds of skin called the **labia minora** (mih-NOR-uh), or "little lips," (also called the *nymphae*) that enfold the urethral and vaginal openings. The labia minora join at the top to form the prepuce, or hood, of the clitoris. It is not uncommon for the labia minora to protrude beyond the labia majora; the nymphae vary considerably in size from woman to woman.

The labia minora have numerous nerve endings, making them very sensitive to tactile stimulation. They also have a rich supply of blood vessels; during sexual stimulation, the labia minora become engorged with blood, causing them to swell and change color. With prolonged stimulation, the inner surfaces of the labia minora receive a small amount of mucous secretion from the small **Bartholin's** (BAR-toe-linz) **glands**, which are located at the base of the minor lips. This does not significantly contribute to vaginal lubrication, however, and the main function of these glands remains unknown.

The labia (and entire vulval area) sweat. The vulval area also secretes a blend of oils, fats, waxes, cholesterol, and discarded cells called sebum, which gives the pelvis a slippery feel.

The most sensitive organ of the female genitalia is the **clitoris** (KLIH-ter-iss)—a sensory organ located at the top of the labia minora (see Figure 3-3) and equipped with 8,000 nerve fibers. The word *clitoris* is derived from the Greek. The clitoris is extremely sensitive to touch, pressure, and temperature and is unique in that it is an organ whose only known function is to provide sexual sensations and erotic pleasure. In a sexually unaroused woman, the only visible part of the clitoris is the glans—a small external knob of tissue located just below the clitoral hood. The size of the clitoral glans, about 1/4 inch in diameter and 1/4 to 1 inch in length, is not related to the subjective experience of pleasure. The shaft of the clitoris, which is hidden from view by the clitoral hood, divides into two much larger structures called *crura* (Kroo-ra), which are attached to the pubic bone.

Mons veneris
Soft cushion of fatty tissue that lies over the pubic symphysis (joint between the left and right pubic bones)

Labia majora
("major lips") Two elongated folds of fatty tissue that extend from the mons veneris to the perineum

Perineum
Area of skin between the opening of the vagina and anus

Labia minora
("little lips") Two smaller elongated folds of fatty tissue that enfold the urethral and vaginal openings

Bartholin's glands
Glands located at the base of the minor lips of the female genitalia that secrete a small amount of mucous to the inner surfaces of the labia minora

Clitoris
Sensory organ located at the top of the labia minora of the female genitalia

FIGURE **3-3** ‖ Anatomy of the Clitoris

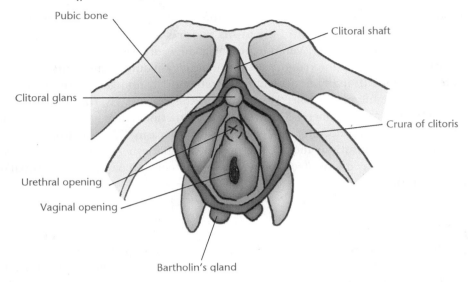

Pubic bone

Clitoral shaft

Clitoral glans

Crura of clitoris

Urethral opening

Vaginal opening

Bartholin's gland

3.1c Clitoris

The clitoris develops embryologically from the same tissue as the penis and has twice the number of nerve endings. The body of the clitoris consists of a spongy tissue that fills with blood during sexual arousal. This results in a doubling or tripling of its original size; it becomes swollen and springy, but not rigid. As with the penis, stimulation of any part of the female body may result in engorgement or swelling of the clitoris. However, describing the clitoris as a "miniature penis" is incorrect because the clitoris does not have a reproductive or urinary function. With sufficient sexual arousal, the glans of the clitoris disappears beneath the clitoral hood.

3.1d Vaginal Opening

Vestibule
Smooth tissue surrounding a woman's urethral opening

Introitus
Vaginal opening

Hymen
Thin mucous membrane that may partially cover the vaginal opening

Honor killing
The killing of an unmarried female who has had sex (which brings dishonor to her parents) done by the parents or another family member in order to restore the family's honor (they occur in middle eastern countries such as Jordan)

The area between the labia minora, called the **vestibule**, includes the urethral opening and the vaginal opening, or **introitus** (in-TRO-ih-tus). The vaginal opening, like the anus, is surrounded by a ring of sphincter muscles. The vaginal opening can expand to accommodate the passage of a baby at childbirth.

The vaginal opening is sometimes partially covered by a thin mucous membrane called the **hymen**. Throughout history, the hymen has been regarded as proof of virginity. A newlywed woman in the country of Jordan found to be without a hymen may be returned to her parents, disgraced by exile, or even tortured or killed (referred to as **honor killing** since she has brought dishonor/disgrace to her parents). It has also been a common practice in many societies to display a bloody bed sheet after the wedding night as proof of the bride's virginity. In Japan and other countries, sexually experienced women sometimes have plastic surgeons reconstruct their hymens before marriage.

The hymen is, however, a poor indicator of virginity. Some women are born without hymens or with incomplete hymens. For other women, hymens are accidentally ruptured by vigorous physical activity or by insertion of a tampon. In some women, the hymen stretches during sexual intercourse without tearing. Most doctors cannot determine whether a woman is a virgin by simply examining her vaginal opening.

3.1e Urethral Opening

Above the vaginal opening but below the clitoris is the urethral opening, which allows urine to pass from the body. A short tube called the **urethra** connects the bladder (where urine collects) with the urethral opening. Small glands called Skene's glands (also called the paraurethral glands) are just inside the urethral opening, and drain into the urethra and near the urethral opening. Usually, they are not seen or felt; however, when infected, they may become enlarged and tender. It has been speculated that they are the source of female ejaculate.

Because of the shorter length of the female urethra and its close proximity to the anus, women are more susceptible than men to **cystitis**, or bladder inflammation. The most common symptom is frequent urination accompanied by burning sensations. Women (and men) with these symptoms should see a health-care practitioner. A common cause of cystitis is the transmission of bacteria that live in the intestines to the urethral opening. Women can avoid cystitis by cleansing themselves from the vulva toward the anus after a bowel movement and by avoiding vaginal intercourse after anal intercourse (unless a new condom is used after anal intercourse).

3.1f Female Genital Alteration

Considerable attention has been given to the occurrence and severity of health problems resulting from cutting off parts (or total removal) of a female's external genitalia. **Female genital alteration** is more commonly known as FGC (**female genital cutting**), **female genital mutilation** or female circumcision, and involves cutting off the clitoris or excising (partially or totally) the labia minora. Worldwide about 140 million women in 40 countries have undergone FGC (Wilson, 2013). "In the USA, more than 168,000 females have had or are at risk for this procedure, and the number may be increasing as the admission ceiling for African refugees is raised. Federal law criminalizes the performance of FGC on females under age 18 in the USA; however, the procedure is not unknown in this country. More commonly, young women are sent back to their country of origin for the procedure. Over 90% of women from Egypt, Eritrea, Ethiopia, Mali, Sierra Leone, and Northern Sudan have had the procedure" (Nicoletti, 2007), as well as 98% of the women in Somalia (Simister, 2010) and Djibouti (Youssouf, 2013). The American Academy of Pediatrics condemns all types of female genital cutting (Policy Statement, 2010).

The practice of FGC is not confined to a particular religion. The reasons for the practice include the following:

A. *Sociological/cultural* Parents believe that female circumcision makes their daughters lose their desire for sex, which helps them maintain their virginity and helps to ensure their marriageability and fidelity to their husbands. Hence, the "circumcised" female is seen as one whom males will desire as a wife. FGC is seen as a "rite of passage" that initiates a girl into womanhood and increases her bonding and social cohesion with other females.

B. *Hygiene/aesthetics* Female genitalia are considered dirty and unsightly; thus their removal promotes hygiene and provides aesthetic appeal.

C. *Religion* Some Muslim communities practice FGC in the belief that the Islamic faith demands it, but it is not mentioned in the Qur'an.

D. *Myths* FGC is thought to enhance fertility and promote child survival (Nicoletti, 2007).

Elnashar and Abdelhady (2007) compared the sexuality of married women who had been circumcised with those who had not. The researchers found statistically

Urethra
Short tube that connects the bladder with the urethral opening

Cystitis
Bladder inflammation

Female genital alteration
Cutting or amputating some or all of the female external genitalia: the prepuce (or hood) of the clitoris and shaft of the clitoris, the labia minora, and the labia majora (also called Female genital mutilation)

Female genital cutting, female genital mutilation
See Female genital alteration

Secondary sex characteristics
Characteristics that differentiate males and females that are not linked to reproduction (e.g., beard in men, high voice in women)

significant differences—such that those who had been circumcised were more likely to report pain during intercourse, loss of libido, and failure to orgasm. The wives who had been circumcised also reported more physical complaints, anxiety, and phobias.

Changing a country's deeply held beliefs and values concerning this practice cannot be achieved by denigration. More effective approaches to discouraging the practice include the following:

1. Respect the beliefs and values of countries that practice female genital operations. Calling the practice "genital mutilation" and "a barbaric practice" and referring to it as a form of "child abuse" and "torture" convey disregard for the beliefs and values of the cultures where it is practiced. In essence, we might adopt a culturally relativistic point of view (without moral acceptance of the practice).

2. Remember that genital operations are arranged and paid for by loving parents who deeply believe that the surgeries are for their daughters' welfare.

3. It is important to be culturally sensitive to the meaning of being a woman. Indeed, genital cutting is mixed up with how a woman sees herself.

4. Simister (2010) studied national samples of genital alteration in Kenya and found that the higher the education level of the mother, the lower the incidence of genital alteration in daughters. Hence, increasing the educational level of women in a community is a structural way to reduce genital alteration in females.

Scientists now believe that the primary biological function of breasts is to make males stupid.

Dave Barry, author

Braun (2009) discussed the practice of female genital cosmetic surgery (FGCS) where Western women voluntarily have their genitals altered for aesthetic reasons. Such surgeries include those designed to reduce and make symmetrical the labia minora, those designed to 'augment' the labia majora, and those designed to tighten the vagina (so called 'vaginal rejuvenation' or vaginoplasty). These operations are sometimes called "designer vaginas" and have been critiqued by the American College of OBGYN. Researcher Braun finds it interesting that surgery on the genitals can be both a cause for public outcry and an issue of personal cosmetics.

3.1g The Female Breasts

The female breasts are designed to provide milk for infants and young children (see "Social Choices 3-1: Breastfeeding in Public?"). The breasts are not considered part of the reproductive system, and their development is considered to be a secondary sex characteristic, like pubic hair. **Secondary sex characteristics** are those that differentiate males and females that are not linked to reproduction. Female breasts begin to develop during puberty in response to increasing levels of estrogen. This hormone has a similar effect if injected in males.

Each adult female breast consists of 15 to 20 mammary, or milk-producing, glands that are connected to the nipple by separate ducts (see Figure 3-4). The soft consistency and size of the breasts are due to fatty tissues loosely packed between the glands. The amount of fat in the breasts is partly determined by heredity. Breasts vary in size and shape; it is common for a woman to have one breast that is slightly larger than the other. Breast size also varies as overall body size varies.

While breastfeeding is legally protected in many contexts, breastfeeding mothers are uncertain how they will be perceived or treated. *Source: Chelsea Curry*

Breastfeeding in Public?

Approximately 75% of mothers begin breastfeeding their infants, but less than 15% of those moms are breastfeeding, exclusively, 6 months later. There is national and federal support for babies getting breast milk. The Healthy People 2020 initiative identified the national goal to increase the proportion of mothers who breastfeed their babies in the early postpartum period to 81.9 % by the year 2020. Since one of the major reasons mothers stop breastfeeding is to return to work (Bonet, et al., 2013), President Obama signed legislation in 2010 to require an employer to provide reasonable break time for an employee, for 1 year after the child's birth, to express breast milk for her nursing child each time such employee has need to express milk. Mothers are also legally allowed to breastfeed their babies on government property.

Pollard (2011) noted that breastfeeding is an international issue citing that reactions varied in the 131 countries she studied. Canada and Norway are among the countries that have relatively high rates of breastfeeding and have favorable structural conditions, as well as strong cultural expectations, surrounding breastfeeding (Andrews & Knaak, 2013).

Leeming and colleagues (2013) noted, "breastfeeding remains a problematic social act, despite its agreed importance for child health" (p. 450). Reaction to breastfeeding in public varies from acceptance to toleration. Although it is not against the law to breastfeed in public in any state, nursing mothers may experience harassment, intimidation, and discrimination for breastfeeding in public. Many feel uncomfortable. Nursing mothers have been asked either to stop breastfeeding or to leave public places—including restaurants, malls, libraries, parks, bus stations, pools, movie theaters, hotel lobbies, department stores, and even doctors' offices.

Several states have enacted legislation dealing with other breastfeeding issues. For example, Idaho and Iowa have enacted legislation allowing breastfeeding mothers to be exempted from jury duty. Florida and Texas have created worksite breastfeeding support policies for all state employees. These policies address such issues as work schedule flexibility and accessible locations and privacy for pumping breast milk or nursing (see legislation above).

Studies show that breast milk has significant benefits for both mother and infant. Children fed breast milk have lower rates of death, meningitis, childhood leukemia and other cancers, diabetes, respiratory illness, bacterial and viral infections, ear infections, allergies, obesity, and developmental delays. Women who breastfeed have a lower risk for breast and ovarian cancers. They also have lower depression and are more likely to emotionally bond with their infant (Meese, 2013).

Furthermore, using deaths on four selected infant diseases—respiratory tract infections, gastroenteritis, necrotizing enterocolitis, and Sudden Infant Death Syndrome—and cost-analysis methods, Ping and colleagues (2013) calculated the effects of breastfeeding and low/very low birth weight rates in Louisiana. The researchers estimated that if 90% of newborns in Louisiana were exclusively breastfed for the first 6 months of life, with 80% compliance, there would be $186,371,125 in savings and 16 infant deaths prevented. As our society and legal system continue to recognize and encourage breastfeeding, a message is sent to the public at large that breastfeeding is an important issue—one that has an impact on our lives and the futures of our children.

There is no relation between the size and shape of breasts and their sensitivity or sexual responsiveness. Many women notice changes in their breast size during their menstrual cycle, with their breasts larger and fuller right before menstruation. Some

FIGURE **3-4** ‖ Internal and External Anatomy of the Female Breast

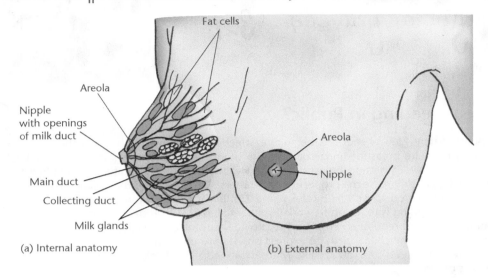

Fat cells

Areola

Nipple
with openings
of milk duct

Main duct

Collecting duct

Milk glands

Areola

Nipple

(a) Internal anatomy

(b) External anatomy

women experience subjective enjoyment in having their breasts stimulated; others may not experience the sensation as pleasurable.

The nipples are made up of smooth muscle fibers with numerous nerve endings, making them sensitive to touch. The nipples are kept lubricated during breastfeeding by secretions of oil from the **areola** (EHR-ree-OH-luh), the darkened area around the nipple. This area becomes permanently darker after pregnancy.

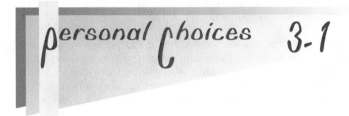

personal choices 3-1

Breast Self-Examination and Mammogram?

Breast cancer is the most common cancer in women. The American Cancer Society (2013a) estimates 232,340 new breast cancer cases, and almost 40,000 deaths, for 2013 (2013b). A woman with breast cancer is much more likely to survive if the cancer is detected and treated early, before it develops to an advanced stage and spreads to other parts of the body.

Women discover most breast lumps themselves. Although the majority of breast lumps are not cancerous, the American Cancer Society recommends that all women age 20 and older examine their breasts each month (preferably after menstruation) to feel for unusual lumps and look for any changes in the contour of each breast, such as swelling, dimpling of skin, or changes in the nipple. Any of these observations, as well as discharge that results from gently squeezing each nipple, should be reported to a doctor immediately. Figure 3-5 illustrates how to perform a breast self-exam.

Areola
Darkened ring around the nipple that keeps the nipples lubricated by secretions of oil during breastfeeding

Personal REFLECTION

Take a moment to express your thoughts about the following question. During your childhood and adolescence, what, when, and how did you learn about external female sexual anatomy? Does your experience differ from the way you want your children to learn?

Figure 3-6 shows the quadrants of the breast most likely to develop cancer: upper left, 50%; lower left, 11%; upper right, 15%; and lower right, 6%. Breast cancers in the center of the breast accounts for 18%.

Some breast tumors are too small to feel during a physical breast examination. A **mammogram** is a low-dose (similar to that for a dental exam) X-ray technique used by a radiologist to detect small tumors inside the breast. A breast biopsy, which involves removing breast tissue for examination under the microscope, is taken if a lump or nodule is found. The American Cancer Society and the Mayo Clinic recommend that all women should have a mammogram every year beginning at age 40. However, the

Mammogram
Low-dose X-ray technique used by radiologists to detect small tumors inside the breast

FIGURE **3-5** ‖ Breast Self-Exam

The best time to examine your breasts is after your menstrual period every month.
(Appreciation is expressed to Beth Credle Burt, MAEd, CHES, a health education specialist with the Wake Area Education Center at WakeMed Hospital, for providing this text.)

Observe:
Examine the breasts in the mirror, from both the front and side view. Place the arms in the three positions indicated in the diagram to observe different angles of the breasts. Take notice of any changes in the breast size, shape, or direction of growth, puckering or dimpling of the skin (including the nipple area), lumps, redness, or discharge.

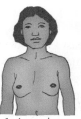 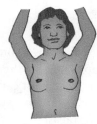 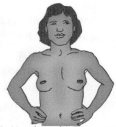

1. Arms down beside body.   2. Arms lifted overhead.   3. Hands on hips, pressing chest muscles forward.

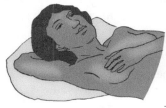 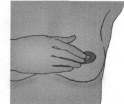 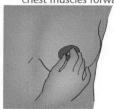

Self-Examination:
Lying on your back with a pillow beneath your shoulder, place your arm behind your head. Put the three middle fingers of your free hand together, and use the pads of the fingers to press into the breast tissue, feeling for lumps or changes in the breast area.

Think of each breast area as a grid that reaches from the top of the shoulder to the bra line vertically, and from the center of the chest to the center of the armpit horizantally. Check each breast area at least twice, using light to deep pressure to check the outer and inner tissue. Press into the breast tissue and move the fingers in small rotating motions covering the entire grid.

Check for any bleeding or discharge from the nipple by gently squeezing it. See a health-care provider immediately if you notice any changes in the breast.

FIGURE **3-6** ‖ Breast Cancer Quadrants

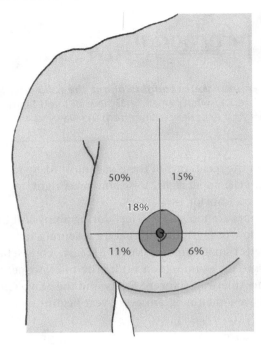

U.S. Preventive Services Task Force mammogram guidelines recommend women begin screening at age 50 and repeat the test every 2 years. While it has been documented that routine mammography screening does save lives, risks include radiation exposure and the stress, pain, and possible over treatment of having diagnostic tests to follow up abnormal mammogram results that are not breast cancer, or that detect cancers that would not be lethal.

Thermascan—also known as breast thermography, digital infrared imaging, or infrared mammography—is an alternative method for identifying breast disease that might ultimately lead to breast cancer. Use of this technology involves no direct contact, no pain, and no radiation exposure. Breast thermography provides a color-coded "fingerprint" of the breast. If the pattern appears to be normal, then future scans should show the same pattern. Any change in this pattern suggests the need to take measures to improve breast health and change conditions that could set the stage for breast cancer. Pittman (2013) recommends the following guidelines for thermascan:

1.   Start thermascan screening at age 25, and screen every 2 years.

2.   Beginning at age 35, have a thermascan screening every year until age 50.

3.   After age 50, return to the every other year thermascan screening, alternating with mammograms, so that one or the other procedure is performed annually. These recommendations are based on research that thermography alone had an average sensitivity of 83% for detecting breast cancer compared to 66% sensitivity for mammography; however, the combination of thermascan and mammography had a 95% sensitivity for all breast types, whether fatty or dense.

Thermascan
Digital infrared imaging or infrared mammography is an alternative method for identifying breast disease that might ultimately lead to breast cancer

3.2 **Female Internal Anatomy and Physiology**

The internal sex organs of the female include the vagina, uterus, and paired Fallopian tubes and ovaries (see Figure 3-7).

3.2a Vagina

The word *vagina* is derived from a Latin word meaning *sheath*. The **vagina** is a 3- to 5-inch long muscular tube that extends from the vulva to the cervix of the uterus. The vagina is located behind the bladder and in front of the rectum and points at a 45-degree angle toward the small of the back. The walls of the vagina are normally collapsed; thus, the vagina is really a potential space rather than an actual one. The walls of the vagina have a soft, pliable, mucosal surface similar to that of the mouth. During sexual arousal, the vaginal walls become engorged with blood, and the consequent pressure causes the mucous lining to secrete drops of fluid.

The vagina functions as a pathway for menstrual flow and as the birth canal, as well as an organ for sexual activity. The vagina can expand by as much as 2 inches in length and diameter during intercourse.

Some people erroneously believe that the vagina is a dirty part of the body. In fact, the vagina is a self-cleansing organ. The bacteria that are found naturally in the vagina help to destroy other potentially harmful bacteria. In addition, secretions from the vaginal walls help maintain the vagina's normally acidic environment. The use of feminine hygiene sprays, as well as douches, can cause irritation, allergic reactions, and vaginal infection by altering the natural, normal chemical balance of the vagina.

If a woman experiences a strong and unpleasant vaginal odor, she may have an infection and should seek medical evaluation. Some women seem more susceptible to imbalances in vaginal flora (e.g., those taking birth control pills) and are more susceptible to vaginosis (disease of the vagina) and yeast infection. In addition, intercourse with infected partners can increase a woman's susceptibility to various STI infections.

Vagina
Muscular tube 3- to 5-inches long that extends from the vulva to the cervix of the uterus

FIGURE 3-7 ‖ Female Reproductive Anatomy

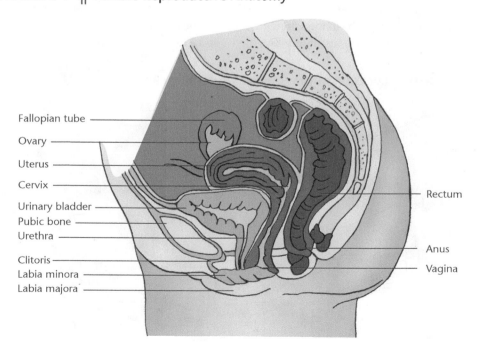

Fallopian tube
Ovary
Uterus
Cervix
Urinary bladder
Pubic bone
Urethra
Clitoris
Labia minora
Labia majora
Rectum
Anus
Vagina

The muscles of the pelvic floor, including the **pubococcygeus** (pyoo-boh-kahk-SIH-jee-us, or PC) and the levator ani, surround the lower third of the vagina. These muscles can influence sexual functioning—in that if they are too tense, vaginal entry may be difficult or impossible. On the other hand, some degree of muscle tone is probably desirable. Some sex therapists have advocated performing **Kegel exercises** (named after Dr. Arnold Kegel). They may also be used to improve bladder control and treat vulvar pain. Kegel exercises involve voluntarily contracting the PC muscle, as though stopping the flow of urine after beginning to urinate, several times at several sessions per day. Another way to find the pelvic floor muscles is to insert a finger halfway into the vagina and try to grip the finger with the vagina. Tense the PC muscle up and in, relaxing the muscles of the abdomen and buttocks. Squeeze up and in for 10 seconds, and then relax for 10 seconds. Some women practice Kegel exercises while waiting at a red light or during class!

3.2b The "G-Spot"

In 1950, German gynecologist Ernst Grafenberg reported that he found a highly sensitive area on the anterior wall of the vagina 1 to 2 inches into the vaginal canal. This area, named in 1981 as the "Grafenberg spot" or "**G-spot**," reportedly swells during stimulation, resulting in high arousal and orgasm (see Figure 3-8).

There is disagreement about the existence of the G-spot. Hines (2001) reviewed the literature on the G-spot and concluded the following:

> "The evidence is far too weak to support the reality of the G-spot. Specifically, anecdotal observations and case studies made on the basis of a tiny number of subjects are not supported by subsequent anatomic and biochemical studies. (p. 359)"

Hines characterized the G-spot as "a sort of gynecologic UFO: much searched for, much discussed, but unverified by objective mean" (p. 361).

Women differ in reporting their own experience with the G-spot. One woman reported:

> As for the G-spot, I definitely have one and my husband (an ideal lover, I might add) doesn't want me to miss "getting mine" so he reaches into our toy box. He helps me masturbate, using my favorite dildo to reach my G-spot, while I use

Pubococcygeus
Muscle surrounding the opening to the vagina that can influence sexual functioning, in that if it is too tense, vaginal entry may be difficult or impossible

Kegel exercises
Voluntary contractions of the PC muscle, as though stopping the flow of urine after beginning to urinate, performed several times at several sessions per day

G-spot
Alleged highly sensitive area on the front wall of the vagina 1 to 2 inches into the vaginal canal (also called the Grafenberg spot)

FIGURE **3-8** ‖ Location of the Alleged Grafenberg Spot

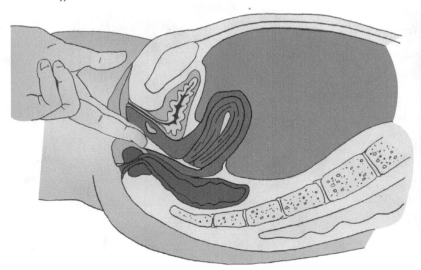

my fingers to stimulate my clitoris. To intensify the effect coming from inside me, I press down from the outside just above the hairline where I can feel the in and out motion of my favorite toy as it slides across my G-spot. Within a few minutes, my body is quivering from orgasmic pleasure. (authors' files)

Other women say, "I don't know what all the fuss is about—I need direct stimulation on my clitoris and if I don't get that, I don't get off" (authors' files).

Take a moment to answer the following questions. What is the advantage of having a "button" to push to excite female sexuality? Is sexism involved in the concept of "a spot" that is the location to launch a female orgasm? It should be noted that Grafenberg is a male; does this matter? Since there is little argument that the clitoris is the locus of female pleasure, how did the G-spot garner such interest?

3.2c Uterus

The **uterus** (YOO-ter-us), or womb, resembles a small, inverted pear. In women who have not given birth, it measures about 3 inches long and 3 inches wide at the top. It is here in the uterus that a fertilized ovum implants and develops into a fetus. No other organ is capable of expanding as much as the uterus does during pregnancy. Held in the pelvic cavity by ligaments, the uterus is generally perpendicular to the vagina. However, 1 in every 10 women has a uterus that tilts backward. Although this poses no serious problems, it may cause discomfort with some positions during intercourse.

The broad, rounded part of the uterus is the **fundus** and the narrower portion, which projects into the vagina, is the **cervix**. The cervix feels like a small, slippery bump (like the end of one's nose) at the top of the vagina. The **os**, or opening of the cervix (through which semen and menstrual flow both pass), is normally the diameter of a pencil; at childbirth, however, it dilates to about 4 inches to allow the passage of the baby. Secretory glands located in the cervical canal produce mucus that differs in consistency at different stages of the menstrual cycle.

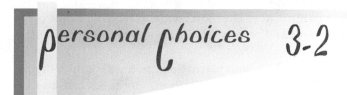

Personal Choices 3-2

Pap Test and Pelvic Exam

A **Pap test** is valuable in the detection of cervical cancer and is recommended annually for young women who are (or have been) sexually active. The test, named after Dr. Papanicolaou who originated the technique, involves swabbing a small sample of cells from the cervix,

Uterus
Womb; a hollow, muscular organ in which a fertilized egg may implant and develop

Fundus
Broad, rounded part of the uterus

Cervix
Narrower portion of the uterus, which projects into the vagina

Os
Opening of the cervix (opening to the uterus)

Pap test
Procedure in which surface cells are scraped from the vaginal walls and cervix, and examined under a microscope to detect the presence of cancer

transferring them to a slide, and examining them under a microscope for cancer cells. Women who smoke, have first intercourse at an early age, have specific strains of human papillomavirus (HPV; the virus that causes genital warts), have multiple sex partners, or have partners who have had multiple sex partners are at an increased risk for cervical cancer. Cervical cancer is almost 100% curable when detected and treated early.

In March 2012, updated screening guidelines were released by the United States Preventive Services Task Force and jointly by the American Cancer Society, the American Society for Colposcopy and Cervical Pathology, and the American Society for Clinical Pathology. These guidelines recommend that women have their first Pap test at age 21. Although previous guidelines recommended that women have their first Pap test three years after they start having sexual intercourse, waiting until age 21 is now recommended because adolescents have a very low risk of cervical cancer and a high likelihood that cervical cell abnormalities will go away on their own. According to the updated guidelines, women ages 21 through 29 should be screened with a Pap test every three years. Women ages 30 through 65 can then be screened every five years with Pap and HPV co-testing, or every three years with a Pap test alone.

The guidelines advise that routine Pap and HPV co-testing be limited to women age 30 and older because transient HPV infections are very common among women in their twenties. Including routine HPV testing in cervical screening of younger women would detect many infections that would be suppressed by the immune system and not lead to cancer. In older women, HPV infections are more likely to represent persistent infections—that is, infections that have the potential to progress to cervical cancer if not detected or treated. However, HPV testing can be used in women of any age to help clarify unclear Pap test findings and help doctors decide if further evaluation is needed. A thorough annual pelvic examination performed by a health-care practitioner is recommended for all women over age 21 (see Figure 3-9).

3.2d Fallopian Tubes

The **Fallopian** (fuh-LOE-pee-en) **tubes**, or oviducts, extend about 4 inches laterally from either side of the uterus to the ovaries. It is in the Fallopian tubes that fertilization normally occurs. The tubes transport the ovum, or egg, from an ovary to the uterus, but the tubes do not make direct contact with the ovaries. The funnel-shaped ovarian end of the tubes, or infundibulums (IN-fun-DIH-byoo-lumz), are close to the ovaries and have fingerlike projections called fimbriae (FIM-bree-ay), which are thought to aid in picking up eggs from the abdominal cavity.

Passage of an egg through one of the tubes each month, which takes about three days, is aided by the sweeping motion of hairlike structures, or cilia, on the inside of the tube. Occasionally, a fertilized egg becomes implanted in a site other than the uterus, resulting in an **ectopic pregnancy**. The most common type of ectopic pregnancy occurs within a Fallopian tube and poses a serious health threat to the woman unless surgically removed.

Tying off the Fallopian tubes so that egg and sperm (long cells with a thin, motile tail) cannot meet is a common type of female sterilization. The tubes can also be blocked by inflammation; serious infections can result in permanent scarring and even sterility.

3.2e Ovaries

The **ovaries** (OH-ver-reez), which are attached by ligaments on both sides of the uterus, are the female gonads—comparable to the testes in the male. These two almond-shaped structures have two functions: producing ova and producing the female hormones estrogen and progesterone. At birth, the ovaries combined have about 2 million immature ova, each contained within a thin capsule to form a follicle. Some

Fallopian tubes
Oviducts, or tubes, that extend about 4 inches laterally from either side of the uterus to the ovaries that transport the ovum from an ovary to the uterus

Ectopic pregnancy
Condition in which a fertilized egg becomes implanted in a site other than the uterus

Ovaries
Female gonads, attached by ligaments on both sides of the uterus, that have the following two functions: producing ova and producing the female hormones estrogen and progesterone

of the follicles begin to mature at puberty, but only about 400–500 mature ova will be released in a woman's lifetime.

An ovarian cyst is a fluid-filled sac in the ovary. Many cysts are normal and referred to as functional cysts in that they occur as a result of ovulation. Functional cysts usually shrink within 1 to 3 months; checkups are essential to ensure that cysts are shrinking. In some cases, birth control pills are recommended because cysts do not form unless the woman ovulates.

> *Women complain about premenstrual syndrome, but I think of it as the only time of the month that I can be myself.*
>
> Roseanne Barr, comedian

3.2f Menstruation

When girls reach about age 12, a part of the brain called the hypothalamus signals the pituitary gland at the base of the brain to begin releasing **follicle-stimulating hormone** (FSH) into the bloodstream. It is not known what causes the pituitary gland to release FSH at this time, but the hormone stimulates a follicle to develop and release a mature egg from the ovary. If the egg is fertilized, it will implant itself in the

Follicle-stimulating hormone
Hormone responsible for the release of an egg from the ovary

FIGURE **3-9** ‖ Pelvic Examination and Pap Smear Test

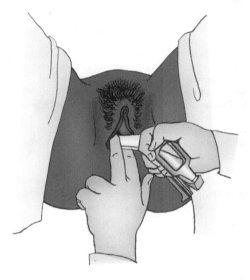

Preparing for the Exam

You will need to undress and cover yourself with a paper gown or sheet, lie down on the exam table, and rest your heels in the stirrups. The health-care provider will perform a manual breast exam (and possibly other routine checks, such as checking the thyroid glands in the neck area or listening to the heart/lungs) as well as a visual inspection of the outer genital area. He or she will use a bright light during the exam and will prepare you before touching the genital area by placing an arm or elbow on your thigh to prevent you from being startled when the exam is about to begin. If you are startled, anxious, frightened, or very nervous, the vaginal muscles can contract involuntarily around the instruments used, making the exam more difficult or possibly uncomfortable.

Speculum Examination

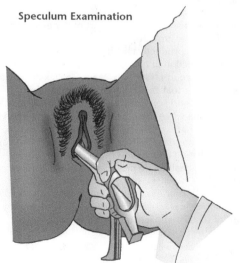

Inserting the Speculum

An instrument called a *speculum* will be used to separate and hold back the vaginal walls to give the health-care provider a clear view of the vagina. The speculum will be either plastic or metal, and a water-based lubricant will be applied to the instrument for easy insertion. The health-care provider will pull the labia (folds of skin covering the genital area) back with one hand and gently and slowly insert the speculum into the vagina at a comfortable angle. Insertion should not be painful. Different size speculums may be used for women who have never had sexual penetration, who have never had children, or who are postmenstrual. Be sure to relax, and talk to the health-care provider if adjustments need to be made to increase comfort.

(continues)

FIGURE **3-9** || **Pelvic Examination and Pap Smear Test** *(continued)*

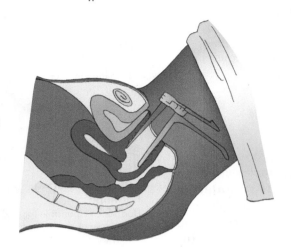

Inspecting the Cervix

To visually inspect the cervix (the bottom portion of the uterus that connects at the top of the vagina), the health-care provider will slowly rotate the speculum for the best view. There should be little or no discomfort as this occurs. The health-care provider will check the cervix for any visible signs or symptoms of infection, tearing, cysts or growths, and other health concerns.

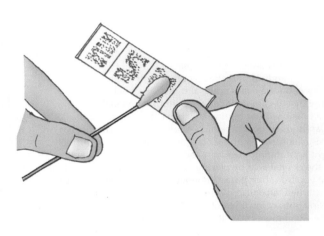

The Pap Smear Test

A researcher named Dr. George N. Papanicolau developed a medical procedure called the Pap smear test for the detection of abnormal changes in the tissue of the cervix. This procedure is capable of screening for precancerous/cancerous cells of the cervix. The Pap smear test is recommended annually for women who are 18 or older or after becoming sexually active. Women should not have sexual intercourse 24 hours prior to the exam, should avoid scheduling during the menstrual period, and should refrain from using products that change the environment of the cervix at least 48 hours prior to their screening, including douches, vaginal creams or lotions, yeast infection medications, etc., because they can distort the appearance of the cells when analyzed. While the speculum is in place, two samples of the cervical cells are collected by swabbing or rubbing the cervix with specially designed instruments. The samples are then placed on prepared slides or tubes for laboratory analysis. The health-care provider may also take samples of the natural vaginal mucus to test for certain types of infections.

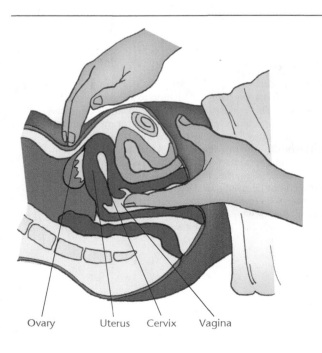

Ovary   Uterus   Cervix   Vagina

Pelvic/Bimanual Examination

After the speculum is removed, the health-care provider will perform the pelvic/bimanual exam. During this part of the exam, the health-care provider checks for growths, masses, tenderness or signs of infection, and other reproductive health concerns. Pelvic inflammatory disease, or PID, is infection in the upper reproductive system that may be diagnosed through the pelvic exam. This exam also allows the provider to ensure that the reproductive organs are of proper shape, size, position, and consistancy. The provider will insert one finger into the vagina while placing his or her other hand on the outer lower abdomen. He or she will palpate, or press firmly, around the abdomen area externally (where the uterus and ovaries are located), while elevating and feeling the cervix internally. After the bimanual exam, the health-care provider may further recommend a rectal exam, where he or she places one finger into the vagina while simultaneously inserting one finger into the rectum. This exam allows the provider to check the back of the vagina and to exclude signs of rectal complications, such as colon cancer.

(Appreciation is expressed to Beth Credle Burt, MAEd, CHES, a health education specialist, Education Services Project Manager, Siemens Healthcare, for providing this text.)

endometrium of the uterus, which has become thick and engorged with blood vessels in preparation for implantation. If the egg is not fertilized, the thickened tissue of the uterus is sloughed off. This flow of blood, mucus, and dead tissue (about 2–3 ounces worth) is called **menstruation**, or **menses**, from the Latin *mensis* (or month). The time of first menstruation is called **menarche**. Except during pregnancy, this process will repeat itself at monthly intervals until menopause. The average menstrual cycle is 28 days, but this varies from cycle to cycle and woman to woman. Some cycles range anywhere from 22 to 35 days.

More than 40 years ago, Martha McClintock (1971) found evidence for what she termed **menstrual synchrony** among the 135 undergraduates in her Wellesley College dorm. Roommates and close friends had an increased likelihood of their menstrual cycles occurring at relatively the same time.

3.2g Phases of the Menstrual Cycle

The menstrual cycle can be divided into four phases: preovulatory (follicular), ovulatory, postovulatory (luteal), and menstrual. In the preovulatory phase, a signal is sent from the hypothalamus for the release of FSH from the pituitary gland, stimulating the growth of about 20 follicles in one ovary. In about 10 days, one follicle continues to grow and secretes increasing amounts of estrogen. This causes growth of the endometrium in the uterus along with an increase in the cervical mucus, providing a hospitable environment for sperm. Estrogen also signals the pituitary gland to stop any further release of FSH and to begin secreting luteinizing hormone (LH). When the levels of estrogen reach a critical point, there is a surge in blood levels of LH, followed by ovulation within 36 hours. During ovulation, the follicle moves to the periphery of the ovary and expels the ovum into the abdominal cavity. Ovulation occurs about 14 days before the start of menstruation, regardless of cycle length.

In the postovulatory phase, the empty follicular sac (now called the corpus luteum, meaning yellow body) secretes hormones causing the endometrium to thicken further, building up nutrients. The breasts are also stimulated and may swell or become tender. If the egg is fertilized and implants in the uterine wall, the lining of the uterus is maintained during pregnancy by continuous secretions of hormones from the ovary. If fertilization does not occur, the corpus luteum disintegrates 10 days after ovulation, the levels of the hormones maintaining the endometrium decrease, and menstruation begins. The day menstruation begins is counted as Day 1 of the menstrual cycle. During menstruation, which lasts from 2 to 8 days, the endometrial matter is shed. In regard to the fertile window, it is about 6 days long, principally spanning the day of ovulation and the previous 5 days (Harris & Vitzthum, 2013).

Menstrual suppression, the use of hormones or drugs to suppress menstruation, is being investigated. New contraceptives such as Seasonale allow the woman to have a period once every 4 months. Women who experience menstrual symptoms as painful or bothersome may be pleased not to menstruate, but women who conceptualize their monthly cycle as a sign of health may not want to have fewer periods or intervene to stop them altogether. While health-care providers have used menstrual suppression to treat menstruation pain and problems, whether it is safe or desirable for healthy women to menstruate less is being debated.

3.2h Attitudes Toward Menstruation

Women can explore their own attitudes about menstruation by completing the Menstrual Attitude Questionnaire in Self-Assessment 3-1.

Menstruation or menses
Sloughing off of blood, mucus, and lining of the uterus

Menarche
First menstruation

Menstrual synchrony
Increased tendency for women living in close proximity to have their menstrual cycles occur at relatively the same time

Menstrual suppression
Use of hormones or drugs to inhibit menstruation

Cultural Diversity

In many societies throughout history, menstruating women were thought to have special powers or to be unclean. They have been blamed for such phenomena as crop failure and dogs going mad. They also have been feared as sources of contamination for their sexual partners. In China, men believe that having sex with a menstruating woman causes illness because it disrupts the balance of Yang (male) and Yin (female) energy (Tang, Siu, Lai, & Chung, 1996). In India, some believe that men who touch menstruating women must be decontaminated and purified by a priest (Ullrich, 1977). However, at times menstrual blood has been thought to contain therapeutic elements, and has been used by Moroccans in dressings for sores and wounds, and in the West to treat gout, goiter, worms, and menstrual disorders (Angier, 1999).

3.2i Problems of the Menstrual Cycle

Oligomenorrhea
Irregular monthly periods

Amenorrhea
Absence of menstruation for 3 or more months during which a woman is not pregnant, menopausal, or breastfeeding

Menorrhagia
Excessive or prolonged menstruation

Various problems have been associated with the menstrual cycle. Although most adolescent girls have regular monthly periods, irregularity or **oligomenorrhea**, is not unusual. The interval between periods may be highly variable. A missed period may or may not indicate pregnancy. Issues such as anxiety, overwork, relationship problems with a partner, or fear of being pregnant can cause a woman to miss her period, as can intense training for competitive athletics. Some women have periods only once a year. If the menstrual cycle has not stabilized by age 17, a gynecologist should be consulted. Spotting or bleeding between periods also indicates the need for a checkup.

Amenorrhea is the absence of menstruation for 3 or more months when a woman is not pregnant, menopausal, or breastfeeding. Pituitary or ovarian tumors or metabolic diseases are possible causes of amenorrhea; hence, a physician should be consulted. Excessive or prolonged menstruation, or **menorrhagia**, may suggest other problems. These include possible uterine infection and tumors.

SELF-ASSESSMENT 3-1: MENSTRUAL ATTITUDE QUESTIONNAIRE (MAQ)

The following scale measures attitudes and expectations toward menstruation. To complete the Menstrual Attitude Questionnaire, rate each statement on a 7-point scale (disagree strongly = 1, agree strongly = 7). Men can also complete the questionnaire by substituting the word *women* in items using the first person. For example, instead of "Menstruation is something I just have to put up with," revise the item to read, "Menstruation is something women just have to put up with."

Subscale 1

1. ____ A woman's performance in sports is not affected negatively by menstruation.*
2. ____ Women are more tired than usual when they are menstruating.
3. ____ I expect extra consideration from my friends when I am menstruating.
4. ____ The physiological effects of menstruation are normally no greater than other usual fluctuations in physical state.*

5. ___ Menstruation can adversely affect my performance in sports.
6. ___ I feel as fit during menstruation as I do any other time of the month.*
7. ___ I don't allow the fact that I'm menstruating to interfere with my usual activities.*
8. ___ Avoiding certain activities during menstruation is often very wise.
9. ___ I am more easily upset during my premenstrual or menstrual periods than at other times of the month.
10. ___ I don't believe my menstrual period affects how well I do on intellectual tasks.*
11. ___ I realize that I cannot expect as much of myself during menstruation, compared to the rest of the month.
12. ___ Women just have to accept the fact that they may not perform as well when they are menstruating.

Subscale 2

1. ___ Menstruation is something I just have to put up with.
2. ___ In some ways, I enjoy my menstrual periods.*
3. ___ Men have a real advantage in not having the monthly interruption of a menstrual period.
4. ___ I hope it will be possible someday to get a menstrual period over within a few minutes.
5. ___ The only thing menstruation is good for is to let me know I'm not pregnant.
6. ___ Menstruation provides a way for me to keep in touch with my body.*

Subscale 3

1. ___ Menstruation is a recurring affirmation of womanhood.
2. ___ Menstruation allows women to be more aware of their bodies.
3. ___ Menstruation provides a way for me to keep in touch with my body.
4. ___ Menstruation is an obvious example of the rhythmicity that pervades all of life.
5. ___ The recurrent monthly flow of menstruation is an external indication of a woman's general good health.

Subscale 4

1. ___ I can tell my period is approaching because of breast tenderness, backache, cramps, or other physical signs.
2. ___ I have learned to anticipate my menstrual period by the mood changes that precede it.
3. ___ My own moods are not influenced in any major way by the phase of my menstrual cycle.*
4. ___ I am more easily upset during my premenstrual or menstrual periods than at other times of the month.
5. ___ Most women show a weight gain just before or during menstruation.

Subscale 5

1. ___ Others should not be critical of a woman who is easily upset before or during her menstrual period.*
2. ___ Cramps are bothersome only if one pays attention to them.
3. ___ A woman who attributes her irritability to her approaching menstrual period is neurotic.
4. ___ I barely notice the minor physiological effects of my menstrual periods.
5. ___ Women who complain of menstrual distress are just using that as an excuse.
6. ___ Premenstrual tension/irritability is all in a woman's head.
7. ___ Most women make too much of the minor physiological effects of menstruation.

Scoring

A mean is computed for each subscale by dividing the sum of items by the number of items in each factor (reversing the scoring of items where necessary). An * indicates items for reverse scoring (a rating of 1 is changed to 7, 2 is changed to 6, 3 is changed to 5).

Interpretation

A higher score indicates stronger endorsement of the concept measured by each subscale. Following is a summary of data obtained from four different samples. You may want to compare your scores with these groups.

Summary Statistics for the Menstrual Attitude Questionnaire								
	Sample							
	College Women		College Women		College Men		Adolescent Girls	
Factor Scores	(N = 191)		(N = 154)		(N = 82)		(N = 72)	
	mean	SD	mean	SD	mean	SD	mean	SD
1. Menstruating as a debilitating event	3.39	1.09	3.61	0.98	4.45	0.73	3.75	1.28
2. Menstruation as a bothersome event.	4.18	1.26	4.65	1.09	4.13	0.93	3.99	1.54
3. Menstruation as a natural event	4.64	1.09	4.51	1.04	4.55	0.93	4.62	0.84
4. Anticipation and prediction of the onset of menstruation	3.79	1.16	4.98	1.11	5.04	0.74	3.85	1.34
5. Denial of any effect of menstruation	2.73	0.96	3.17	1.05	2.83	0.79	3.12	1.08

From Brooks-Gunn, J. & Ruble, D. N. (1980). Menstrual attitude questionnaire (MAQ). *Psychosomatic Medicine, 42*, 505–507. Reprinted with the permission of the authors and Lippincott, Williams & Wilkins.

Some women experience painful menstruation, or **dysmenorrhea**, symptoms of which can include spasmodic pelvic cramping and bloating, headaches, and backaches. In addition, they may feel tense, irritable, nauseated, and depressed. As the result of the hormone changes, some women retain excess body fluids and experience painful swelling of the breasts (mastalgia) during menstruation. Dysmenorrhea is caused by prostaglandins, chemicals in the menstrual flow that cause spasms of the uterus, and can be relieved by prostaglandin inhibitors. Masters and Johnson (1966) reported that orgasms provided relief from painful menstruation by speeding up the menstrual flow, thus eliminating the prostaglandins. Some women who experience dysmenorrhea report less intense symptoms after taking birth control pills, which contain estrogen and progesterone and disrupt the normal hormonal changes of the menstrual cycle. During ovulation, some women complain of lower abdominal pains, referred to as mittelschmerz (or middle pain).

Painful menstruation can also be caused by endometrial tissue growing outside the uterus (in the Fallopian tubes or abdominal cavity, for example). This condition is known as **endometriosis**. These tissues deteriorate during menstruation, just as the lining of the uterus normally does, and a painful infection can result when the tissue cannot be expelled. Treatment ranges from aspirin to surgery.

Dysmenorrhea
Painful menstruation

Endometriosis
Growth of endometrial tissue outside the uterus (in the Fallopian tubes or abdominal cavity) that may cause pain

Finally, some women experience **premenstrual syndrome** (PMS)—physical and psychological symptoms caused by hormonal changes from the time of ovulation to the beginning of, and sometimes during, menstruation. To assess the degree to which university females reported various symptoms before and during menstruation, Guler and colleagues (2013) asked a series of open-ended questions to 202 participants enrolled in the study (the mean age was 20.5 ± 2.1 years). Among the respondents, the five most common complaints reported were irritability (76.7 %), breast fullness (68.6 %), back pain (67.4 %), abdominal distension (60.5 %) and sentimentalism (56.4 %). Almost one in five (19.4 %) reported having impaired sexuality (predicted by headache and sentimentalism). Over three-fourths (77.3 %) reported that they have been using some medication (e.g. analgesics), but most (57.6 %) had never sought help. The authors concluded, "A majority of women experience mild to severe physical and psychological discomfort during the perimenstrual period, which may affect their life quality" (p. 93).

What is instructive is that there are no comparable studies of males to ask of their irritability, back pain, and headache. Indeed debate remains about PMS. Harris and Vitzthum (2013) reviewed the studies on PMS and behavior and concluded the following:

> In sum, of those studies in which investigators measured hormone concentrations throughout the course of the ovarian cycle in samples of women with and/or without cycle-attributed symptoms, all failed to find unequivocal evidence of any relationship between baseline and/or fluctuations in hormone levels and changes in mood or physical indicators. Given the substantial variability in hormonal, psychological, and physical measures reported in these and other studies, it could be that the sample sizes were too small to have sufficient statistical power to discern any phase- or hormone-associated variation in these indicators. Several analyses also neglected to account for autocorrelation among observations, repeated hypothesis testing, and potential confounders including age (p. 234).

It is also instructive to note that PMS primarily exists in heterosexual contexts where hetero-patriarchal constructions of both femininity and premenstrual issues occur—women are pathologised premenstrually (Ussher and Perz, 2013). In lesbian relationships, the context allows women to engage in coping strategies premenstrually, such as taking time out to be alone or to engage self-care with understanding. Hence, premenstrual change can be "contextualized within broader cultural representations of hetero-normativity, which provide the context for gendered roles and coping" (p. 132).

> *So I am perfectly happy if all the women in the world wish to say, "I have this thing called Premenstrual Syndrome" as long as they recognize that Harry has "testosterone swings" or "Excessive Testosterone Syndrome." Just give me equality.*
>
> Carol Tavris, psychologist

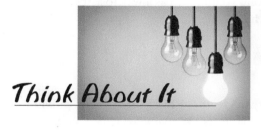

Think About It

Take a moment to answer the following questions. Males use the term PMS in a derogatory manner to identify the female who is being "crazy." She is defined as "being on the rag"—translation, she is to be left alone. Why is there no comparable term to denote depressive, irritable behavior in the male? In addition, specific to male sexuality, some males have a relentless drive to get a woman to have sex with them and an accompanying lack of concern for respecting the right of a female to not have sex with them. And what about the male preoccupation with pornography? Unlike female sexuality and PMS, none of these have been given labels and identified. Is this because of a predominance of males in the sexuality profession?

Premenstrual syndrome
(PMS) Physical and psychological symptoms caused by hormonal changes from the time of ovulation to the beginning of, and sometimes during, menstruation

Premenstrual dysphoric disorder (PMDD) is a diagnostic category, indicating a more severe form of PMS that interferes with the work, social activities, and relationships of the woman. The essential features of PMDD are symptoms such as markedly depressed mood (and mood swings), marked irritability/anger, marked anxiety, and decreased interest in activities. Other symptoms include difficulty concentrating, lethargy, and a sense of being out of control. The duration of the symptoms must have occurred most months for the previous 12 months (American Psychiatric Association, 2013, p. 172). The difference between premenstrual syndrome and premenstrual dysphoric disorder is that a minimum of five symptoms is not required for the former. Pilver and colleagues (2013) analyzed data of 3,965 American women ages 18–40 who were part of the Collaborative Psychiatric Epidemiology Survey to assess the relationship between PMDD (premenstrual dysphoric disorder) and suicide ideation. The researchers did find such an association.

National **DATA**

Between 2% and 6% of menstruating women report the prevalence of premenstrual dysphoric disorder in the past 12 months (American Psychiatric Association, 2013, p. 173).

Berman and colleagues (2013) conducted high-resolution magnetic resonance imaging (MRI) scans on 12 women diagnosed with PMDD and 13 healthy control subjects. Results showed that PMDD subjects had significantly greater GMV (grey matter volume) than controls in the posterior cerebellum, but not in any other brain area. "Although the mechanism underlying this finding is unclear, cumulative effects of symptom-related cerebellar activity may be involved" (p. 266).

3.3 Models of Sexual Response

Genital sexual response in women has been measured by assessing vascular changes (increased blood volume) in the blood vessels of the vagina and temperature changes in the labia. The device most frequently used to assess vascular changes is the photometer, made of clear plastic and shaped like a tampon. Temperature of the labia is monitored with surface temperature probes, which measure labial temperature and temperature of comparison sites (such as skin on the chest). An MRI (magnetic resonance imaging) has also been used to assess changes in clitoral volume and as a way to assess quantitatively the sexual arousal response in women.

3.3a Masters and Johnson's Four-Stage Model of Sexual Response

Premenstrual dysphoric disorder (PMDD) A proposed diagnostic category, indicating a more severe form of PMS, which interferes with the work, social activities, and the relationships of a woman

In the fall of 2013, the Showtime cable network featured *The Masters of Sex*, providing weekly episodes featuring the 1960s sex pioneers, William Masters and Virginia Johnson. They were the first sexologists to propose a four-stage model describing sexual response or the sequence of sexual events (Masters & Johnson, 1966). Their model focused on four stages of genital response: excitement, plateau, orgasm, and resolution. In this chapter we focus on the female sexual response, and in Chapter 4, the male sexual response.

Excitement Phase

During the **excitement phase**, individuals become sexually aroused in response to hormonal, tactile, auditory, visual, olfactory, cognitive, and relationship stimuli. For both women and men, the excitement phase of sexual response is characterized by peripheral arousal (increases in heart rate, blood pressure, respiration, and overall muscle tension) and genital arousal (**vasocongestion**, or increased blood flow to the genital region). In women, vasocongestion results in vaginal lubrication and engorgement of external genitals (labia majora, labia minora, and clitoris). During sexual excitement, the labia turn a darker color, and the upper two-thirds of the vagina expands in width and depth.

Physiological signs of sexual excitement are not always linked to feeling sexually aroused. Women can become lubricated without feeling aroused; they can become lubricated as a response to nervousness, excitement, or fear. Nevertheless, lubrication on the part of the woman is usually indicative of sexual arousal. The source of the vaginal lubrication in women is the moisture from the small blood vessels that lie in the vaginal walls. This moisture is forced through the walls as the vaginal tissues engorge and produce a "sweating" of the vaginal barrel. Individual droplets merge to form a glistening coating of the vagina.

Plateau Phase

After reaching a high level of sexual arousal, women enter the **plateau phase** of the sexual response cycle. The lower third of the vagina constricts and the upper two-thirds expands, presumably to form a pool to catch the semen. At the same time, the clitoris withdraws behind the clitoral hood, providing insulation for the extremely sensitive glans of the clitoris. Direct clitoral stimulation at this time may be painful or unpleasant because the glans has a tremendous number of nerve endings concentrated in a small area. Even though the clitoris is under the hood, it continues to respond to stimulation of the area surrounding it.

Other changes occur as well: **myotonia** (muscle contractions), **hyperventilation** (heavy breathing), **tachycardia** (heart rate increase), and blood pressure elevation. Also, some women experience a "sex flush" that looks like a measles rash on parts of the chest, neck, face, and forehead. This flush sometimes suggests a high level of sexual excitement or tension.

Cognitive factors are also important in the maintenance of the plateau phase. Individuals in this stage must continue to define what is happening to them in erotic terms. Without such labeling, there will be a return to prearousal levels of physiological indicators.

Orgasm Phase

Orgasm is the climax of sexual excitement and is experienced as a release of tension involving intense pleasure. Perhaps the easiest aspects of an orgasm to identify are the physiological changes that in both women and men involve an increase in respiration, heart rate, and blood pressure. Although everyone is different, as is each person's experience of orgasm, researchers have provided some information on the various experiences.

Physiologically, the orgasmic experience for women involves simultaneous rhythmic contractions of the uterus, the outer third of the vagina, and the rectal sphincter. These contractions begin at 0.8-second intervals and then diminish in intensity, duration, and regularity. A mild orgasm may have only 3 to 5 contractions, whereas an intense orgasm may have 10 to 15 contractions.

Excitement phase
Phase of sexual response cycle whereby increasing arousal is manifested by increases in heart rate, blood pressure, respiration, overall muscle tension, and vasocongestion, or increased blood flow to the genital region

Vasocongestion
Increased blood flow to the genital region

Plateau phase
Second phase of Masters and Johnson's model of the sexual response cycle, which involves the continuation of sexual arousal, including myotonia (muscle contractions), hyperventilation (heavy breathing), tachycardia (heart rate increase), and blood pressure elevation

Myotonia
Muscle contractions

Hyperventilation
Abnormally heavy breathing, resulting in loss of carbon dioxide from the blood, sometimes resulting in lowered blood pressure and fainting

Tachycardia
Increased heart rate

Orgasm
Climax of sexual excitement, experienced as a release of tension involving intense pleasure

Although there has been considerable debate on "clitoral versus vaginal" orgasm, Masters and Johnson (1966) stated that clitoral stimulation (either direct or indirect) is necessary for orgasm. They identified only one type of orgasm, refuting the categories of clitoral and vaginal orgasm.

Clitoral versus vaginal orgasm? I've never had a bad orgasm?

Woody Allen

Subsequently, Singer (1973) suggested that there are two basic variations in female orgasmic experiences: vulval orgasms and uterine orgasms. **Vulval orgasms** (also known as clitoral orgasms) result primarily from manual stimulation of the clitoris and are characterized by spastic contractions of the outer third of the vagina. In contrast, **uterine orgasms** are caused by deep intravaginal stimulation and involve contractions in the uterus as well as vagina. **Blended orgasms** are those in which women experience both vulval contractions and deep uterine enjoyment. Some women "ejaculate" at the time of orgasm; the ejaculate does not smell or stain like urine and is slightly milky; the amount is about half a teaspoon and rarely noticeable.

Resolution Phase

After orgasm, the **resolution phase** of the sexual response cycle begins, which involves the body's return to its pre-excitement condition. In women, the vagina begins to shorten in both width and length, and the clitoris returns to its normal anatomic position. In both women and men, breathing, heart rate, and blood pressure return to normal. A thin layer of perspiration may appear over the entire body.

In the resolution phase, individuals may prefer to avoid additional genital stimulation. "My clitoris feels very sensitive—almost burns—and I don't want it touched after I orgasm." This statement characterizes the feelings of some women. Other women say their clitoris tickles when touched after orgasm. When sexual arousal does not result in orgasm, resolution still takes place, but more gradually. Some women experience an unpleasant sensation of sexual tension or fullness in the genital area due to prolonged vasocongestion in the absence of orgasm.

Alternative Cycles in Women

Vulval orgasm
An orgasm that results primarily from manual stimulation of the clitoris and is characterized by contractions of the outer third of the vagina (also called Clitoral orgasms)

Uterine orgasm
In contrast to "clitoral" orgasm, an orgasm caused by deep intravaginal stimulation and involving contractions in the uterus as well as vagina

Blended orgasm
Orgasm whereby the woman experiences both vulval contractions and deep uterine enjoyment

Resolution phase
Final phase of Masters and Johnson's model of the sexual response cycle that describes the body's return to its pre-excitement condition

Masters and Johnson (1966) stated that a woman might experience the sexual response cycle in one of three ways. When there is sufficient and continuous stimulation, the most usual pattern is a progression from excitement through plateau to orgasm to resolution, passing through all phases and returning to none of these stages for a second time. Experientially, the woman gets excited, enjoys a climax, and cuddles in her partner's arms after one orgasm. If she is masturbating, she relaxes and savors the experience.

In another pattern (again, assuming sufficient and continuous stimulation), the woman goes from excitement to plateau to orgasm to another or several orgasms and then to resolution. The interval between orgasms varies; in some cases, it is only a few seconds. In effect, the woman gets excited, climbs through the plateau phase, and bounces from orgasm to orgasm while briefly reaching the plateau phase between orgasms.

Still another pattern of female sexual response is to move through the sequence of phases of the sexual response cycle but skip the orgasm phase. The woman gets excited and climbs to the plateau phase but does not have an orgasm. Insufficient stimulation, distraction, and/or lack of interest in the partner (if one is involved) are some of the reasons for not reaching orgasm. The woman moves from the plateau phase directly to the resolution phase.

Although the Masters and Johnson model is the most widely presented model of human sexual response, it has been criticized on several counts. First, the idea of a four-stage process is arbitrary and imprecise. Second, instead of being titled "The Sexual Response Cycle," perhaps "A Sexual Response Model" might be more accurate.

Whereas Masters and Johnson and Kaplan reported only one reflex pathway in sexual responding, Perry and Whipple described a second reflex pathway that might account for the ability of some women to experience the vulval, uterine, or blended orgasms as described by Singer (Whipple, 1999). Third, the Masters and Johnson model virtually ignores cognitive and emotional states, focusing almost exclusively on objective physiological measures (Basson, 2001a). The measurement of the physiological changes (primarily changes in the genitals) focuses on bodily response, which is just one aspect of sexuality. Their model of sexual response was not designed to assess the emotional, spiritual, and intimacy aspects of sexuality and sexual interaction.

3.3b Helen Kaplan's Three-Stage Model of Sexual Response

In an effort to emphasize the motivational and psychological aspects of human sexual response, Helen Kaplan (1979) proposed a three-stage model consisting of desire, excitement, and orgasm. The first stage, sexual desire, involves feeling "horny," sexy, or interested in sex; this stage may be accompanied by genital sensations. Kaplan's excitement and orgasm phases are very similar to those of Masters and Johnson—both models focus on vasocongestion and genital contractions in these two phases. However, Kaplan focused more attention on the motivational and psychological aspects of sexual response. The primary criticism of Kaplan's model is her suggestion that desire is a necessary prerequisite for excitement. However, desire is not necessary for arousal or orgasm to occur.

3.3c Basson's Model of Sexual Response

Rosemary Basson (2001a; 2001b) emphasized that psychological factors, as well as biological factors, affect the processing of sexual stimuli. She suggested that the beginning of sexual response in sex with a partner, for many women, is emotional intimacy, which may begin with sexual neutrality and openness to sexual involvement that leads to sexual stimulation, and then sexual arousal. So, for many women, it is not sexual desire that is the beginning point of sexual response (in a sexual interaction that is wanted, not coerced), but rather a willingness to be receptive to sexual stimuli. Their desire to share physical pleasure may be more for the sake of sharing than for satisfying sexual hunger. Men sometimes also experience intimacy-based desire; but more often than women, they experience "spontaneous" desire (probably largely biologically based).

Whipple (1999) emphasized that healthy sexuality begins with acceptance of self and a focus on the process, rather than just the goals, of sexual interaction. She said people should be encouraged to enjoy the variety of ways they can achieve sexual pleasure, instead of establishing specific goals (finding the G-spot, experiencing female ejaculation). Your textbook authors suggest that her advice, which follows, applies to men as well:

> Whatever the final outcome in terms of neural pathways and neurotransmitters involved in sexual response, it is important for you to be aware of the variety of sexual responses that women report and that have been documented in the laboratory. It is also important that women be aware of what is pleasurable to them, acknowledge this to themselves and then communicate what they find pleasurable to their partners. (Whipple, 1999, p. 15)

Table 3-1 summarizes frequently cited models of human sexual response. The most extensively studied aspects of sexual response have been genital responses and peripheral arousal—such as increases in heart rate, blood pressure, breath rate, skin

TABLE 3-1	Models of Human Sexual Response			
Researchers	**Stages**			
Masters & Johnson (1966)	Arousal (vasocongestion resulting in lubrication and swelling)	Plateau	Orgasm	Resolution
Kaplan (1979)	Desire	Arousal	Orgasm	
Bancroft (1989)	Sexual appetite	Central arousal and peripheral arousal	Genital response	
(Stayton, 1992)	Seduction	Sensations	Surrender reflex	Reflection
Everaerd and colleagues (2000)	Appraisal of sexual stimuli	Genital responding and subjective arousal	Orgasm and subjective experience	
Basson (2001b)	Sexual neutrality or spontaneous sexual desire	Sexual arousal	Sexual desire and arousal	Emotional and physical satisfaction

temperature, etc. However, investigators are increasingly attending to cognitive and emotional variables, and their impact on perception of sensory stimuli, arousal, and sexual satisfaction. (Note the attempts to integrate the physiological, cognitive, and emotional components of sexual response in the table.)

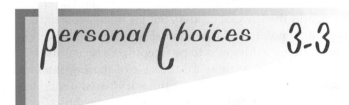

Having Sex with One's Partner when Desire Is Low

It is not unusual when one partner wants to engage in sex that the other does not. Should the partner who has low sex interest or desire agree to participate anyway?

Sex therapists confronted with a couple who have discrepant sexual desires may note that the less interested partner need not be interested in sex but rather receptive to sexual stimulation, which may then be labeled in positive sexual terms. Such labeling may result in enjoyment, which may lead to continuation of the stimulation and sexual involvement. Indeed, aside from pleasing the partner, a potential positive outcome from choosing to engage in sexual behavior independent of desire is that the individual may experience desire following involvement in sexual behavior. Cognitive behavior therapists conceptualize this phenomenon as "acting oneself into a new way of feeling, rather than feeling oneself into a new way of acting." Rather than wait for the feelings of sexual desire to occur before engaging in sexual behavior, the person acts as though there is feeling, only to discover that the feeling sometimes follows. An old French saying reflects this phenomenon: *"L'appetit vient avec mangent,"* which translates into "The appetite comes with eating."

We are not suggesting that an individual who lacks sexual desire routinely be open to sexual stimulation with her or his partner, or always comply with the partner's wishes. As we will emphasize in the chapter on sexual dysfunctions, sometimes it is the behavior of the partner that fails to entice one to participate in sex, through a lack of skill or context. Hence, the focus of the discrepancy in a couple's sexual relationship may not be the partner with the low sexual interest but the lover. The relationship of the couple becomes the focus of the therapist. More about this will follow in our sexual dysfunctions chapter.

3.4 Hormones and Sexual Response

Hormones are chemical messengers that typically travel from cell to cell via the bloodstream. The hypothalamus and pituitary gland near the center of the brain regulate the endocrine system's secretion of hormones into the bloodstream (see Figure 3-10). The reproductive hormones (estrogens, progesterone, and androgens) are mainly produced in the gonads. They influence reproductive development through organizing and activating effects. Organizing effects include anatomical differentiation (the development of male or female genitals) and some differentiation of brain structure. At puberty, they lead to the development of secondary sex characteristics. Activating effects include influences on behavior and affective states. For example, researchers have studied the role of reproductive hormones and their possible influence on adolescent aggression and behavior problems, adolescent sexuality, the menstrual cycle, and related mood changes.

Hormones
Chemical messengers that travel from cell to cell via the bloodstream

FIGURE **3-10** ‖ Endocrine System

Endocrine glands produce and release chemical regulators called hormones that affect sexual functioning.

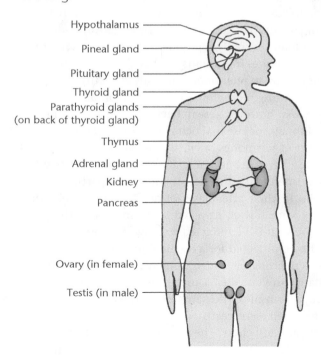

Hypothalamus
Pineal gland
Pituitary gland
Thyroid gland
Parathyroid glands
(on back of thyroid gland)
Thymus
Adrenal gland
Kidney
Pancreas
Ovary (in female)
Testis (in male)

Endocrine factors relevant to sexual response are androgens, estrogens, progesterone, prolactin, oxytocin, cortisol, and pheromones. Free testosterone (1%–2% of all testosterone in one's body may help account for our spirits, feeling lusty) and bound testosterone (bound to sex hormone binding proteins called globulins) may also be related to sex drive. Yet researchers do not agree on a direct link between hormones in the bloodstream and sex drive. Harris and Vitzthum (2013) reviewed the effect of hormones on sexual behavior and emphasized the lack of credible research (due to the challenges of controlling for variables, definitions, and time). Hence, while hormones may have an effect on sexual behavior, so might social factors—sexual activity increases on the weekend and on vacation. The state-of-the-art conclusion on the relationship between hormones and sexual desire is that social (one's partner/peers), psychological (sexual self-concept/previous positive sexual experiences), and cultural (Is it okay to be sexual?) factors may be far more important than hormone levels.

Think About It

Take a moment to answer the following questions. What are the implications of viewing sexual interest as a product of hormones versus social, psychological, and cultural influences? How would the respective views affect the way in which individuals and their partners conceptualize the absence of sex interest on the part of one or both partners?

3.5 Pheromones, Aphrodisiacs, and Sexual Response

The term *pheromone* comes from the Greek words *pherein* meaning, "to carry," and *hormone,* meaning to "excite." **Pheromones** are chemicals that activate the behavior of same species organisms. Niehuis and colleagues (2013) confirmed the existence of sex pheromones in many sexually reproducing organisms—their focus was on wasps! Research on sex pheromones in humans has been less convincing.

The functions of human pheromones include attracting the opposite-sex, repelling the same sex, and bonding mother and infant. Pheromones typically operate without the person's awareness; however, researchers disagree about whether pheromones do, in fact, influence human sociosexual behaviors. Two older studies are instructive. One examined the effect of hormones on sexual behavior; it involved 38 male volunteers who applied a male hormone to their aftershave lotion. They reported significant increases in sexual intercourse and sleeping next to a partner when compared to men who had a placebo in their aftershave lotion (Cutler, Friedmann, & McCoy, 1998). Hence, presumably women were attracted to the male with the pheromone.

Rako and Friebely (2004) conducted a study of 44 postmenopausal women (mean age = 57 years) who volunteered for a double-blind placebo-controlled study designed "to test an odorless pheromone, added to their preferred fragrance, to learn if it might increase the romance in your life." During the experimental 6-week period, a significantly greater proportion of participants using the pheromone formula (40.9%) than placebo (13.6%) recorded an increase over their own weekly average baseline frequency of petting, kissing, and affection. The authors concluded that the pheromone formulation worn with perfume for a period of 6 weeks had sex-attractant effects for postmenopausal women.

Pheromones
Chemicals that activate the behavior of same-species organisms

The term **aphrodisiac** refers to any food, drink, drug, scent, or device that arouses and increases sexual desire. One of the more prevalent myths of human sexuality is that specific foods have this effect. In reality, no food reliably increases a person's sexual desire. Where sexual interest does increase, it is often a result of a self-fulfilling prophecy. If a person thinks a substance will have a desire-inducing effect, it sometimes does. Nevertheless, folklore about aphrodisiacs has a long history, from the Chinese belief in the sex-enhancing power of a ground-up rhinoceros horn (the origin of the word *horny*) to beliefs regarding foods and other substances, such as oysters, crabs, tomatoes, eggs, carrots, celery, pepper, turtle soup, paprika, nutmeg, ginger, and saffron.

Coffee (with caffeine) has been confirmed as having a positive effect on maintaining sexual involvement. Diokno and colleagues (1990) observed that at least one cup of coffee per day is significantly associated with a higher prevalence of sexual activity in women (age 60 and over) and with a higher potency rate in men (age 60 and over).

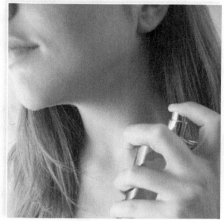

Women sometimes treat perfume as though it is a pheromone—a sex attractant.
Source: Chelsea Curry

Think About It

Take a moment to answer the following questions. Why is there such an obsession with pheromones and aphrodisiacs? Is it related to the ease with which these factors are mythologized to put one in touch with a sexual partner (e.g., just put on some aftershave or perfume)? The anxiety associated with engaging a person socially and being patient until the sexual aspect of the relationship emerges? Is it the instant, "I want it now," motif that keeps the idea of pheromones and aphrodisiacs alive?

Aphrodisiac
Any food, drink, drug, scent, or device that arouses and increases sexual desire

Chapter Summary

This chapter examined the basics of female internal and external sexual anatomy. We also reviewed some models for the human sexual response, the effect of hormones on sexual desire, and diseases women should be alert to and seek early detection for.

Female External Anatomy and Physiology

Female external sexual anatomy includes the mons veneris, labia, clitoris, vaginal opening, and urethral opening. The clitoris is the most sensitive part of a woman's sexual anatomy. Even though the female breasts provide the important function of nourishing offspring, they are secondary sex characteristics and are not considered part of the female reproductive anatomy.

Female Internal Anatomy and Physiology

The vagina, uterus, Fallopian tubes, and ovaries comprise the internal sexual anatomy of the female. Fertilization of the female egg, or ovum, usually occurs in the Fallopian tubes. Around age 12 or 13 years, the hypothalamus in a female signals the pituitary gland to begin releasing follicle-stimulating hormone (FSH) into the bloodstream. This hormone stimulates a follicle to develop and release a mature egg from the ovary. If the egg is fertilized, it will normally implant itself in the endometrium of the uterus, which will be thick and engorged with blood vessels in preparation for implantation. If the egg is not fertilized, the thickened tissue of the uterus is shed. This flow of blood, mucus, and tissue is called menstruation.

Models of Sexual Response

The Masters and Johnson's model of sexual response involves four phases: excitement, plateau, orgasm, and resolution. Their cycle has been criticized in that it is biologically and genitally focused. In contrast, Helen Kaplan proposed a three-stage model consisting of desire, excitement, and orgasm. Kaplan focused more attention on the motivational and psychological aspects of sexual response. The primary criticism of Kaplan's model is her suggestion that desire is a necessary prerequisite for excitement.

Rosemary Basson emphasized that the floor of sexual response for many women is emotional intimacy, whereby they are open to sexual involvement that leads to sexual stimuli and then sexual arousal. Basson noted that previous models did not address the fact that the beginning point for many women is not sexual desire but rather emotional involvement with the partner and an openness to sexual involvement.

Hormones and Sexual Response

Researchers disagree on the link between hormones in the bloodstream and sexual desire. The best evidence to date seems to suggest that social (one's partner/peers), psychological (sexual self-concept/previous positive sexual experiences), and cultural (Is it okay to be sexual?) factors may be far more important than hormone levels.

Pheromones, Aphrodisiacs, and Sexual Response

Although there is evidence of pheromone-induced sex attraction or behavior in other organisms, most of the research on pheromones and sexuality in humans has been centered on female menstrual synchrony of women living in close proximity. The term aphrodisiac refers to any substance that increases sexual desire. No food reliably increases a person's sexual desire. However, coffee (with caffeine) seems to have a positive effect on maintaining sexual involvement in persons over age 60.

Web Links

American Cancer Society

http://www.cancer.org

Breastfeeding

http://pregnant.thebump.com/new-mom-new-dad/breastfeeding.aspx

Female Genital Cutting Education and Networking Project

http://www.fgmnetwork.org

Menstruation Research

www.menstruationresearch.org

Our Bodies, Ourselves

www.ourbodiesourselves.org

Key Terms

Amenorrhea 78

Aphrodisiac 89

Areola 68

Bartholin's glands 63

Blended orgasm 84

Cervix 73

Clitoris 63

Cystitis 65

Dysmenorrhea 80

Ectopic pregnancy 74

Endometriosis 80

Excitement phase 83

Fallopian tubes 74

Female genital alteration 65

Female genital cutting, female
    genital mutilation 65

Follicle-stimulating hormone 75

Fundus 73

G-spot 72

Honor killing 64

Hormones 87

Hymen 64

Hyperventilation 83

Introitus 64

Kegel exercises 72

Labia majora 63

Labia minora 63

Mammogram 69

Menarche 77

Menorrhagia 78

Menstrual suppression 77

Menstrual synchrony 77

Menstruation or menses 77

Mons veneris 63

Myotonia 83

Oligomenorrhea 78

Orgasm 83

Os 73

Ovaries 74

Pap test 73

Perineum 63

Pheromones 88

Plateau phase 83

Premenstrual dysphoric
    disorder 82

Premenstrual syndrome 81

Pubococcygeus 72

Resolution phase 84

Secondary sex characteristics 66

Sexual anatomy 61

Sexual physiology 62

Tachycardia 83

Thermascan 70

Urethra 65

Uterine orgasm 84

Uterus 73

Vagina 71

Vasocongestion 83

Vestibule 64

Vulva 62

Vulval orgasm 84

Additional study resources are available at www.BVTLab.com

FIGURE **4-4** ‖ Cross-Section of Testicle

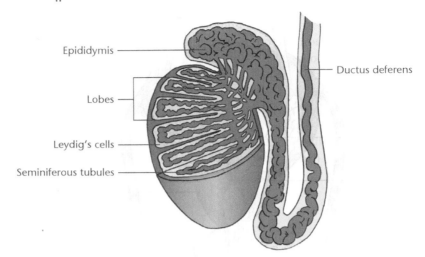

Epididymis

Lobes

Leydig's cells

Seminiferous tubules

Ductus deferens

Stimulated by LH, the male hormone testosterone is produced in the **interstitial** or Leydig's cells that are located between the seminiferous tubules (see Figure 4-4). The testes produce sperm; about 300 million are released with each ejaculation.

Testosterone and another androgen, dihydrotestosterone (DHT), are important for more than their sexual functions. Testosterone increases the size of muscle cells, thus increasing lean body mass and body weight. That is why some athletes use synthetic androgens (anabolic steroids) to build muscle mass and enhance performance. Androgens also regulate blood-clotting factors and liver enzymes, and regulate the high-density lipoprotein (HDL) to low-density lipoprotein (LDL) ratio, which effects risk for coronary heart disease.

National DATA

There are 7,920 new cases of testicular cancer annually. About 370 men will die annually from testicular cancer (American Cancer Society, 2013a).

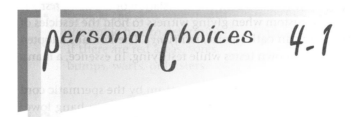

personal Choices *4-1*

Interstitial cells
Cells that are housed in the testes and produce testosterone (also known as Leydig's cells)

Conducting a Testicular Exam

The key to successful treatment of testicular cancer is early diagnosis and treatment. While men can have a testicular exam as part of their annual checkup, they may also conduct their own exam. The most frequently occurring symptoms are a lump or nodule on a testicle, or swelling of the testicles. Figure 4-5 illustrates the proper method for performing a testicular self-examination. A video is also available to help assess the presence of unusual bumps which may suggest something abnormal (e.g., testicular cancer) at http://www.webmd.com/sex/video/marks-testicular-self-exam (Web MD, 2013).

As recommended by the American Cancer Society, after showering or bathing check the scrotum visually for unusual swelling. Examine each testicle separately by rolling the testicle between the thumb and the first two fingers of both hands. Check for lumps, thickened tissue, or swelling. The American Cancer Society recommends that all men perform a monthly check for a change in size or consistency of the testicle. Feel the epididymis, a cord-like structure, on the top and back of each testicle. Don't interpret this as an abnormality. Make an appointment with a health-care provider if any lumps or other abnormalities are found.

Testicular cancer is not very common. A man's lifetime chance of developing testicular cancer is about 1 in 270. Because treatment is so successful, the risk of dying from this cancer is very low: about 1 in 5,000 (American Cancer Society, 2013a).

Risk factors for developing testicular cancer include having an undescended testicle or testicles (known as **cryptorchidism**), family history (e.g., father or brothers have testicular cancer), presence of HIV infection, and carcinoma in situ. The latter means that testicular germ cell cancers may begin as a non-invasive form of the disease called *carcinoma in situ* (CIS). Carcinoma in situ may or may not progress to become invasive cancer. If it does, it can take about 5 years. It is difficult to find CIS since there are no symptoms. In some cases, CIS is found by chance in men who have a testicular biopsy for some other reason, such as infertility. Experts don't agree about the best treatment for CIS. Since CIS doesn't always become an invasive cancer, many doctors in this country feel that observation (watching and waiting) is the best course of action. Other risk factors associated with testicular cancer are age (half of the cases are found in men between 20 and 34) and race—white males are 5 times more likely to get testicular cancer than African American men and 3 times more likely than Asian American men (American Cancer Society, 2013a).

Cryptorchidism
Undescended testes

Seminiferous tubules
Part of the spermatic duct system, located within the testicles

Epididymis
Part of the spermatic duct system connecting the testicles with the vas deferens

4.2b Duct System

The several hundred **seminiferous** (SEH-mih-NIH-fer-uhs) **tubules** come together to form a tube in each testicle called the **epididymis** (EH-pih-DID-ih-muss), the first

FIGURE **4-5** || Testicular Self-Exam

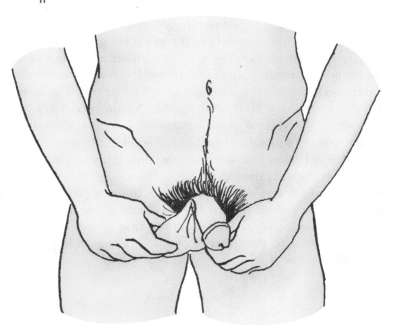

part of the duct system that transports sperm. The epididymis, which can be felt on the top of each testicle, is a C-shaped, highly convoluted tube, whose total length is more than 100 meters (Pinon, Jr., 2002). The sperm spend from 2 to six 6 traveling through the epididymis as they mature; the body reabsorbs them if ejaculation does not occur. Movement of the sperm through these tissues depends on the androgen supply.

The sperm leave the scrotum through the second part of the duct system, the **vas deferens** (VASS-DEH-fer-enz), or ductus deferens. These 14- to 16-inch-long paired ducts transport the sperm from the epididymis up and over the bladder to the prostate gland, where the sperm mix with seminal fluid to form semen. One form of male sterilization, vasectomy, involves cutting and tying off each vas deferens.

The final portion of the duct system is about 8 inches long and is divided into prostatic, membranous, and penile portions. In the prostatic portion, the previously paired duct system joins together to form the final common pathway. The male urethra transports urine from the bladder, as well as semen. The urethral sphincter muscles surround the membranous portion of the urethra, enabling voluntary control of urination. The penile portion of the urethra runs through the corpus spongiosum, and the urethral opening is at the top of the glans. As in women, transmission of bacteria to the urethral opening can result in inflammation of the urethra (urethritis) and bladder. The most common symptoms are frequent urination accompanied by a burning sensation and discharge. Men should consult a health-care practitioner if these symptoms appear.

Men are stereotyped as wanting to present the image of being self-sufficient, of not needing to ask others for help (e.g., directions). When it comes to healthcare, men may also be reluctant to ask for information or help. Self-Assessment 4-1 provides a way to assess the degree to which an individual seeks health information on the Internet.

4.2c Seminal Vesicles, Prostate Gland, and Bulbourethral Gland

Vas deferens
Tube from the ejaculatory ducts to the testes that transports sperm

Seminal vesicles
Two small glands about 2 inches in length, located behind the bladder in the male, which secrete fluids that mix with sperm to become semen

Prostate gland
Chestnut-sized structure in the male, located below the bladder and in front of the rectum, that produces much of the seminal fluid

Male G-spot
The prostate gland, which can be stimulated by a partner who inserts an index finger, up to the second knuckle, (facing the partner) into the anus and bends the finger in a "come hither" motion

The **seminal vesicles** resemble two small sacs about 2 inches in length located behind the bladder. They are mistakenly called vesicles because it was once believed that they were storage areas for semen. The seminal vesicles, however, secrete their own fluids that mix with sperm and fluids from the prostate gland. Substances secreted from the seminal vesicles include a sugar rich fluid (fructose) that provides sperm with a source of energy and helps with the sperms' motility (ability to move). Most of the seminal fluid involved in an ejaculation comes from the **prostate gland**, which mixes with the fluid from the seminal vesicles. The prostate gland is a chestnut-sized structure located below the bladder and in front of the rectum. It contains smooth muscle fibers and glandular tissue. Prostaglandins, the hormones secreted by the prostate and other tissues, stimulate contractility of smooth muscles. Sperm, which reach the ejaculatory duct as a result of both the muscular contractions of the epididymis and ductus deferens and the sweeping motion of hair-like cilia on their inner walls, are made active by fructose. Prostaglandins induce contractions of the uterus, possibly aiding movement of the sperm within the female.

The prostate gland has also been referred to as the *male pleasure gland*, and the **male G-spot**. A partner seeking to stimulate this gland would reach down between the man's legs, inserting the index finger into the anus to the second knuckle and pressing forward, in a firm "come hither" motion. Some men will have an explosive orgasm; others will feel very little.

SELF-ASSESSMENT 4-1: SEEKING HEALTH INFORMATION ON THE INTERNET

Directions

When searching for health information or advice on the Internet, how often do you engage in the following?

a = all the time
b = most of the time
c = sometimes
d = hardly ever
e = never

1. ___ Check the source of the information to make sure it is a reliable source.
2. ___ Check the date of the information to make sure it is current and up-to-date.
3. ___ Read the website's privacy policy to make sure your privacy on that site is protected.
4. ___ Spend at least 30 minutes searching the web.
5. ___ Visit at least four different websites.
6. ___ Consult a healthcare professional about information you find online.

Interpretation

If you answered "a" ("all the time") to each of the items, you are a vigilant Internet health consumer and are following the Medical Library Association's recommendations for using the Internet to find health information and advice. If you answered either "a" or "b" to each of the items, you are a concerned Internet health consumer, following most of the Medical Library Association's recommendations most of the time. However, if you answered "c," "d," or "e" for one or more of the items—especially items 1, 2, and 5—you are a risky Internet health consumer: you are not following important guidelines for finding health information on the Internet, and you may be at risk for finding information that, at best, can fail to help you—and at worse can hurt you.

Source: Information used to develop this self-assessment was obtained from *Vital decisions: How Internet users decide what information to trust when they or their loved ones are sick* by Fox, S., & Rainie, L. (2002). Pew Internet & American Life Project. Retrieved from www.pewinternet.org/.

The **bulbourethral glands** (also called the Cowper's glands) are two structures attached through their tiny ducts to the urethra in the penis. These pea-sized structures secrete a clear, sticky fluid during sexual arousal. While this fluid is not rich in sperm, they are nevertheless present. If a man is using a condom for contraception, he should put the condom on prior to beginning intercourse.

In the prostate, the ejaculatory ducts join the initial portion of the urethra from the bladder to form a single common passageway for urine and semen. The prostate enlarges at puberty as the result of increasing hormone levels. As the man ages in some cases, it becomes larger and constricts the urethra, interfering with urination. Treatments involve doing nothing, taking medication, receiving radiation, or surgically removing it. The prostate is also a common site of infection, resulting in an inflamed condition called prostatitis. Major symptoms are painful ejaculation or defecation, and it is a condition easily treated with antibiotics.

Bulbourethral glands
Pea-sized structures attached to the urethra in the penis that secrete droplets of clear, sticky fluid prior to ejaculation (also known as Cowper's glands)

Some men develop prostate cancer. Second to skin cancer, it is the most common type of cancer in men; the risk of the male getting prostate cancer increases with age. Radical surgery for prostate cancer typically results in the male not being able to get an erection. Radiation therapy is an alternative to radical surgery for prostate cancer. Sullivan and colleagues (2013) surveyed men who had radiation therapy and found that of 252 patients, 89% lost their ability to ejaculate at 5-year follow-up. All men should have their prostate checked annually, a procedure in which the physician inserts a finger into the rectum and palpates the prostate to check for any abnormalities.

Take a moment to answer the following questions. Do you think that most young adults know more about the internal reproductive systems of women or of men? Why?

Benign Prostatic Hyperplasia (BPH) refers to the normal enlargement of the man's prostate as he ages. More than half of men in their 60s, and as many as 90% in their 70s and 80s, have some symptoms of BPH. The most common symptoms of BPH are a hesitant, interrupted, weak stream; an urgency and leaking or dribbling; and/or more frequent urination, especially at night. Sometimes a man may not know there is a problem until he suddenly finds himself unable to urinate at all.

Men who have BPH with symptoms usually need some kind of treatment at some time. However, treatment may not be indicated when the gland is mildly enlarged since the symptoms may clear up without treatment. Instead of immediate treatment, physicians suggest regular checkups to watch for early problems. If the condition begins to pose a danger to the patient's health or causes a major inconvenience to him, treatment is usually recommended.

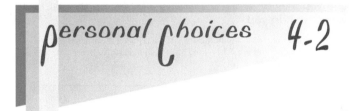

Assessing Prostate Cancer

It is estimated that there will be 238,590 new cases of prostate cancer and that 29,720 men will die from prostate cancer in 2013 (American Cancer Society, 2013b). Nearly two-thirds of all prostate cancers are diagnosed in men over the age of 65. The average age of diagnosis is 67.

One way for detecting prostate cancer is a digital rectal exam. The health-care professional inserts a gloved, lubricated finger into the rectal canal and then rotates the finger to see if the size of the prostate is normal and to check for any unusual lumps in the rectum. Another method of screening for cancer for men over 50 is to assess the amount of ___ tatic specific antigen (PSA) in the blood with a PSA test, which can provide ___

Benign Prostatic Hyperplasia (BPH)
Normal enlargement of the man's prostate, as he ages, which may eventually require treatment

information about the early presence of a cancerous growth. Because of the frequency of "false positives," however, the physician normally advises a prostate biopsy if the patient has a positive PSA result along with a family history of prostate cancer. The American Cancer Society (2013b) recommends, "If you are young and develop prostate cancer, it may shorten your life if it is not caught early. Screening men who are older or in poor health in order to find early prostate cancer is less likely to help them live longer. This is because most prostate cancers are slow-growing, and men who are older or sicker are likely to die from other causes before their prostate cancer grows enough to cause problems."

4.3 **Sexual Response Cycle of Men**

The physiology of sexual response in men may be measured by examining changes in the size of the penis (increases in length, circumference, or rigidity). The most common way of measuring an increase in penile size is the **penile strain gauge** composed of a flexible band that fits around the base of the penis and expands as the penis enlarges, measuring circumference. Useful outside the laboratory or in a lab connected to a computer, a Rigiscan monitor continuously monitors penile circumference and rigidity. Although expensive, it is likely the most broadly used instrument for measuring male genital response.

4.3a **Masters and Johnson's Four-Stage Model of Sexual Response**

Recall from Chapter 3, "Female Sexual Anatomy, Physiology, and Response," the four-stage model of sexual response described by Masters and Johnson (1966)—excitement, plateau, orgasm, and resolution. In this portion of the chapter, we focus on the male sexual response.

Excitement Phase

During the excitement phase, men become sexually aroused in response to hormonal, tactile, auditory, visual, olfactory, cognitive, and relationship stimuli. Peripheral arousal (increased heart rate, blood pressure, respiration, and overall muscle tension) occurs. Genital arousal (vasocongestion, or increased blood flow to the genital region) causes erection, or tumescence.

Physiological signs of sexual excitement are not always linked to feeling sexually aroused. Men can feel aroused without becoming erect and can have erections without feeling sexually aroused. For example, a man can have an erection as a response to fear, anger, exercise, or REM sleep. Nevertheless, erection on the part of the man is usually indicative of sexual arousal.

In Chapter 13 we discuss erectile dysfunction. For now we note that medications such as Viagra, Levitra, and Cialis are routinely used to increase blood flow to the penis (physical stimulation is necessary to produce an erection). These medications do not induce arousal but allow for arousal to occur when the context and stimulation are sexual.

Dawson and colleagues (2012) recruited 20 men and 20 women who agreed to have their genital responses measured while they were exposed to presentations of erotic film clips. Genital responses were measured continuously using penile strain gauges (assessing penile circumference) and vaginal probes (assessing vaginal pulse amplitude). Participants reported subjective sexual arousal, perceived genital arousal, and attention

Penile strain gauge
Flexible band that fits around the base of the penis and expands as the penis enlarges, measuring circumference—a way of measuring male arousal via penis size

Advertisers know that men are anxious about being able to "rise to the occasion" and promote their product on the basis of this fear.
Source: E. Fred Johnson, Jr.

after each film clip presentation. Results showed that men and women displayed very similar patterns of genital responses during the excitement/arousal phase.

Carvalho and colleagues (2013) studied the effect of thinking about one's partner on sexual arousal in 29 men and 28 women. Results revealed that fantasizing about one's partner resulted, overall, in higher subjective sexual arousal and higher levels of positive affect—and women reported higher subjective sexual arousal than men.

Plateau Phase

After reaching a high level of sexual arousal, men enter the plateau phase during which the penis increases slightly in diameter and the size of the testes increases considerably—from 50% to 100%. In some men, the head (glans) of the penis turns a deeper color. Other changes also include myotonia (muscle contractions), hyperventilation (heavy breathing), tachycardia (heart rate increase), and blood pressure elevation. Also, some men experience a "sex flush" that looks like a measles rash on parts of the chest, neck, face, and forehead. This flush sometimes suggests a high level of sexual excitement or tension.

Orgasm Phase

Male orgasm and ejaculation are not one and the same process, although in most men the two occur simultaneously. Orgasm refers specifically to the pleasurable, rhythmic muscular contractions in the pelvic region and the release of sexual tension. Ejaculation refers to the release of semen that usually accompanies orgasm. Orgasm without ejaculation is not uncommon in boys before puberty. It also can occur if the prostate is diseased or as a side effect of some medications.

Ejaculation in men occurs in two stages. In the first stage, **emission**, there is a buildup of fluid from the prostate, seminal vesicles, and vas deferens in the prostatic urethra (the area behind the base of the penis and above the testes). When this pool of semen collects, the man enters a stage of **ejaculatory inevitability**; he knows he is going to ejaculate and cannot control or stop the process. The external appearance of semen does not occur until several seconds after the man experiences ejaculatory inevitability due to the distance the semen must travel through the urethra.

Emission
First phase of a male orgasm in which semen pools in the urethral bulb and ejaculatory pressure builds

Ejaculatory inevitability
The feeling a male has when he becomes aware that he is going to ejaculate and cannot stop the process

In the second stage, **expulsion**, the penile muscles contract two to three times at 0.8-second intervals, propelling the semen from the penis. The contractions may then continue at longer intervals. The more time that has passed since the last ejaculation, the greater the number of contractions, and the greater the volume of ejaculate and sperm count. The anal sphincter contracts as well.

The subjective experience of orgasm in men begins with the sensation of deep warmth or pressure that accompanies ejaculatory inevitability, followed by intensely pleasurable contractions involving the genitals, perineum (the area between the anus and scrotum), rectum, and anal sphincter. The process of semen traveling through the urethra may be experienced as a warm rush of fluid or a shooting sensation.

Some men experience the orgasmic contractions but are able to inhibit the emission of semen and experience nonejaculatory orgasm. Such orgasms are not usually followed by a refractory period, so the man may have consecutive, or multiple, orgasms.

It is also possible for a man to experience the sensation of orgasm but not see any ejaculate come from the penis. In some illnesses, and as a side effect of some tranquilizers and blood pressure medications, the ejaculate empties into the urinary bladder instead of flowing out through the urethra. This is called **retrograde ejaculation**.

The probability of experiencing an orgasm for men (as well as for women) is related to being sexually touched. In a survey of 1,352 men and women ages 57–85, the odds of being unable to climax were greater by 2.4 times among men and 2.8 times among women who sometimes, rarely, or never engaged in sexual touching compared to those who always engaged in sexual touching (Galinsky, 2012).

While orgasm is typically associated with pleasure, Lee and colleagues (2013) documented the existence of **orgasmic headache**, or OH, which occurs as a sudden and severe headache at the time of, or shortly after, orgasm. The researchers discussed the case history of a 34-year-old man who complained of a severe headache that developed abruptly with orgasm and decreased over a period of 4 to 8 hours (30 mg of nimodipine alleviated the symptom).

Ejaculating before a man's partner wants him to wants is commonly referred to as premature ejaculation. In Chapter 13, Sexual Dysfunctions, we discuss premature ejaculation in detail. Here, we note that 25% of 3,016 men in five cities in China reported experiencing premature ejaculation. Older men, men who smoked, and those with higher body mass indexes were more likely to report the malady (Gao, et al., 2013).

Resolution Phase

After orgasm, the resolution phase—which involves the body's return to its pre-excitement condition of the sexual response cycle—begins. There is usually, although not always, a loss of erection; and the testes decrease in size and descend into the scrotum. Breathing, heart rate, and blood pressure return to normal. A thin layer of perspiration may appear over the entire body.

In the resolution phase, individuals may prefer to avoid additional genital stimulation. A man often wants to lie still and avoid stimulation of the head of the penis. When sexual arousal does not result in orgasm, resolution still takes place, but more gradually. Some men experience an unpleasant sensation of sexual tension or fullness in the genital area due to prolonged vasocongestion in the absence of orgasm.

4.3b Summary of Masters and Johnson's Different Sexual Response Cycles of Men

Men typically progress through the sexual response cycle in a less varied pattern than women. When sexual excitement begins for men, there is usually only one pattern—excitement through plateau to orgasm. (It is recognized that, for a variety

Expulsion
Second phase of a male orgasm in which semen is expelled by vigorous contractions of the muscles surrounding the root of the penis, pelvic region, and genital ducts

Retrograde ejaculation
Ejaculation during which a man experiences an orgasm where the ejaculate does not come out of the penis but is emptied, instead, into the bladder

Orgasmic headache
A sudden and severe headache that occurs at the time of, or shortly, after orgasm

of physiological and psychological reasons, the male may plateau but not have an orgasm.) Following orgasm, most men experience a longer refractory period than women, during which the person cannot be sexually aroused. During the refractory period, the penis usually becomes flaccid and further stimulation (particularly on the glans of the penis) is not immediately desired. However, some men remain erect after orgasm, desire continued stimulation, and are able to orgasm again.

The desire and ability to have another erection and begin stimulation depends on the man's age, fatigue, and the amount of alcohol or other drugs in his system. In general, the older, exhausted, alcohol-intoxicated individual will be less interested in renewed sexual stimulation than the younger, rested, sober man. The time of the refractory period varies. As noted previously, some men maintain an erection after orgasm and skip the refractory period to have another orgasm.

When the sexual response cycles of women and men are compared, three differences are noticeable:

1. Whereas men usually climax once (some men report multiple orgasms whereby they have an orgasm but do not ejaculate), women's responses are more variable. They may have an orgasm once, more than once, or not at all.

2. When the woman does experience more than one climax, she may be capable of doing so throughout her life span, although this may vary, depending on the type of orgasm. In contrast, the man usually needs a longer refractory period before he is capable of additional orgasms, especially as he ages.

3. Orgasm in men is never accompanied by urination, whereas this may occur in women.

As noted in the discussion in Chapter 3, the Masters and Johnson model focuses almost exclusively on objective physiological measures. The measurement of the physiological changes (primarily changes in the genitals) may be taken to represent one aspect of sexuality only. Their model of sexual response does not address the emotional, spiritual, and intimacy aspects of sexuality and sexual interaction. One man noted, "There are plenty of women I can have sex with. But I need to be able to look into the eyes of the woman I am having sex with and feel an emotional connection with her. If I don't, the experience leaves me feeling empty and unsatisfied. Being emotionally connected is critical to me; I'd rather masturbate without it" (authors' files).

BVT *Lab*

Visit **www.BVTLab.com** to explore the student resources available for this chapter.

Chapter **Summary**

This chapter examined the basics of male external and internal sexual anatomy. We also reviewed how men progress through the human sexual response cycle.

Male External Anatomy and Physiology

The penis and scrotum make up the external anatomy of the male. Penile erection is caused by dilation of the numerous blood vessels within the penis, which results in blood entering the penis faster than it can leave. The trapped blood within the penis creates pressure and results in penile erection.

Male Internal Anatomy and Physiology

The testes, duct system, seminal vesicles, and prostate gland make up the internal sexual anatomy of the male. Sperm are produced in the testes. Semen is the mixture of sperm and seminal fluid. Most seminal fluid comes from the prostate gland, but a small amount is also secreted by two Cowper's glands, or bulbourethral glands, that are located below the prostate gland.

Sexual Response Cycle of Men

Masters and Johnson's model of sexual response involves four phases: excitement, plateau, orgasm, and resolution. Their study of the cycle is biologically and genitally focused and does not address the emotional/spiritual component of sexuality. There are three major differences between men and women with men climaxing once (and women sometimes several times), men needing a longer refractory period as they age, and men never urinating at ejaculation.

Web **Links**

American Cancer Society

http://www.cancer.org

Circumcision Resource Center

http://www.circumcision.org

National Organization of Circumcision Information Resource Centers

http://www.nocirc.org

Human Anatomy and Physiology Society

http://www.hapsweb.org/

Key Terms

Additional study resources are available at www.BVTLab.com

CHAPTER 5

Gender and Sexuality

He said to me … Shall we try swapping positions tonight? I said to him … That's a good idea—you cook us dinner in the kitchen and I'll drink beer on the sofa.

Anonymous

Chapter Outline

Objectives

1. Explain the difference between sex and gender.
2. Define the terms gender identity, transgendered, gender role, sexual identity, and gender role ideology.
3. Identify the sex chromosomes of both males and females.
4. Describe preconceptual sex selection, and the reasons for and against the process.
5. List the most common chromosomal abnormalities.
6. Discuss the role of fetal hormones.
7. Describe the four theories of gender role development.
8. Know the five agents of gender role socialization.
9. Review the various effects of gender role socialization on relationships and sexuality.
10. Define androgyny, gender role transcendence, and gender postmodernism.

Source: David Knox

TRUTH *OR* FICTION?

T/F   Androgynous individuals have lower self-esteem than "masculine" individuals.

T/F   Transgender girls are more likely to be gay than transgender boys.

T/F   Sex selection for girls has a higher percentage of success than for boys.

T/F   Female body image dissatisfaction ends by the late 30s.

T/F   Men are more likely to say "I love you" to a romantic partner first.

Answers: 1.F 2.T 3.T 4.F 5.F

One of the defining moments in one's life is when one's sex is announced—male or female" (not just at birth, could be fetus too. The phrase "It's a boy" or "It's a girl" immediately summons an onslaught of cultural programming affecting the color of the nursery (e.g., blue for a boy and pink for a girl), the name of the baby (there are few gender-free names, such as Chris), and occupational choices (there are relatively few women in politics). In this chapter, we examine variations in gender roles and how these roles impact sexuality. We begin by looking at the terms used to discuss gender issues.

5.1 Terminology

In common usage, the terms *sex* and *gender* are often used interchangeably. To health educators, psychologists, sociologists, sexologists, and sex therapists, however, these terms are not synonymous. After clarifying the distinction between sex and gender, we discuss other relevant terminology—including *gender identity*, *gender role*, *sexual identity*, and *gender role ideology*.

5.1a Sex

Sex refers to the biological distinction between being female and being male. The **primary sex characteristics** that differentiate women and men include sex chromosomes (XX and XY); hormones (estrogen, progesterone, and testosterone); external genitalia (vulva and penis); internal sex organs (Fallopian tubes, uterus, and vagina for females and epididymis, vas deferens, and seminal vesicles for males); and gonads (ovaries and testes). Secondary sex characteristics include the larger breasts of women and the deeper voice and presence of a beard in men.

We have a secret in our culture, and it's not that birth is painful. It's that women are strong.

Laura Stavoe Harm, freelance writer

Even though we commonly think of biological sex as consisting of two dichotomous categories (female and male), current views suggest that biological sex exists on a continuum. This view is supported by the existence of individuals with mixed or ambiguous genitals (hermaphrodites and pseudo-hermaphrodites, or intersexed individuals). Indeed, some males produce fewer male hormones (androgens) than some females, just as some females produce fewer female hormones (estrogens) than some males.

5.1b Gender

Gender refers to the social and psychological characteristics associated with being female or male. Characteristics typically associated with the female gender include being gentle, emotional, and cooperative; characteristics typically associated with the male gender include being aggressive, rational, and competitive. In popular usage, gender is dichotomized as an either/or concept (feminine or masculine); however, gender may also be viewed as existing along a continuum of femininity and masculinity.

Whereas some researchers emphasize the role of social influences, others emphasize a biological imperative as the basis of gender role behavior. While some studies emphasize the role of social influences, the research of John Money inadvertently made clear the powerful impact of biological wiring. Dr. Money (1921-2006), a psychologist and former director of the now defunct Gender Identity Clinic at Johns Hopkins Medical School, encouraged the parents of a boy (David) to rear him as a girl (Brenda) because of a botched circumcision that rendered the infant without a penis. Money argued that social mirrors dictate one's gender identity; thus, if the parents treated the child as a girl (name, dress, toys, etc.), the child would adopt the role of a girl and later that of a woman. The child was castrated, and sex reassignment began.

The experiment failed miserably. At the age of 14, the child was finally informed of his medical history and made the decision (after much distress and struggle) to reclaim his life as a male. Indeed, David reported that he had never felt like a girl (Colapinto, 2000). Although he did marry and was the adoptive father of two children, he later committed suicide (reportedly due to financial issues).

David's situation is at the heart of the scientific debate on the "nature vs. nurture" question. In early publications by Dr. Money, David's situation was used as a textbook example of how "nurture" is the more important influence in gender identity, if a reassignment is done early enough. Dr. Milton Diamond followed up on David's case. After meeting David, Dr. Milton wrote a paper in 1994 with Keith Sigmundson (who had been one of David's psychiatrists), revealing the discrepant outcome. Their paper (Diamond & Sigmundson, 1997), which was published 3 years later, questions Money's articles and asserts that, while nurture may influence a person's degree of masculinity or femininity, nature is the stronger force in forming one's gender identity and sexual orientation. Genetic influences on the brain and nervous system emphasize the neurobiological basis of one's sex and caution against early surgical intervention for infants with ambiguous genitals.

BVT *Lab*

Flashcards are available for this chapter at **www.BVTLab.com**.

Sex
Term that refers to the biological distinction between being female and being male, usually categorized on the basis of the reproductive organs and genetic makeup

Primary sex characteristics
Characteristics that differentiate women and men, such as external genitalia (vulva and penis), gonads (ovaries and testes), sex chromosomes (XX and XY), and hormones (estrogen, progesterone, and testosterone)

Gender
Social and psychological characteristics associated with being female or male

5.1c Gender Identity

Gender identity is the psychological state of viewing one's self as a girl or a boy, and later as a woman or a man. Such identity is largely learned and is a reflection of society's conceptions of femininity and masculinity. Some individuals experience **gender dysphoria**, a term which applies to people who are emotionally distressed about their gender identity—their gender identity does not match their biological sex (transsexualism discussed below). (American Psychiatric Association, 2013).

Man has his will, but woman has her way.
Oliver Wendell Holmes

Think About It

Take a moment to answer the following question. For many years, gender dysphoria and transsexualism were viewed as "conditions" that were "cured" by sex reassignment surgery. However, a new paradigm has emerged that recognizes a category of individuals who transcend the gender dichotomy. These individuals, referred to as transgendered, live in a gender role that does not match their biological sex. How do you account for the increased societal acceptance of gender variance?

Gender identity
Psychological state of viewing one's self as a girl or a boy, and later as a woman or man

Gender dysphoria
Condition in which one's gender identity does not match one's biological sex

Transgendered
Term that refers to individuals of one biological sex (female or male) who express behavior not typically assigned to their gender

Transsexuals
Persons with the biological/anatomical sex of one gender (e.g., male) but the self-concept of the other sex (e.g., female)

5.1d Transgendered

The term **transgendered** refers to individuals of one biological sex (female or male) who express behavior not typically assigned to their gender. **Transsexuals** are persons with the biological/anatomical sex of one gender (e.g., male) but the self-concept of the other sex (e.g., female). A female-to-male transsexual (also referred to as FTM or transman) is one who is a biological/anatomical female but may feel "I am a man trapped in a female's body." This person may take male hormones to grow facial hair and deepen her voice and may have surgery to create an artificial penis. This person lives full-time as a man. FTMs may have been thought to be rare because they typically make less contact with the medical establishment. As women, they may have had fewer financial resources to pursue surgical transition.

Transsexuals may be distinguished between primary and secondary transsexuals. Primary transsexuals have had a lifetime history of gender dysphoria (and maybe cross-dressing). In contrast, the secondary transsexual does not report gender dysphoria dating back to early childhood but reports, instead, discovering in mid/late adolescence a self-concept of the other sex.

Whether primary or secondary, transsexuals experience extreme gender dysphoria, or unhappiness with their biological sex. Bandini and colleagues (2013) found that gender dysphoric female-to-males that had not had sexual reassignment surgery had the highest scores on body dislike/uneasiness. Bockting and colleagues (2013) reported data on 1,093 male-to-female and female-to-male transsexual persons and found clinical depression (44.1%), anxiety (33.2%), and body complaints, (27.5%) that were identified as being caused by social stigma—which was moderated by peer support. The source of these maladies was identified as social stigma, which was moderated by peer support. Prevention models

Loren is a female to male transsexual who regularly speaks on transgender issues to human sexuality classes.
Source: Chelsea Curry

emphasize changing social structures, norms, and attitudes that produce minority stress for gender-variant people.

What is it like to be partnered with a transsexual? Aramburu (2013) interviewed 16 females who were partnered with male-to-female transsexuals and found that they reconceptualized their relationships. While maintaining a heterosexual identity, some became "situational lesbians" and others dropped sexual activity as an expectation. Others continued regular sex with their partners.

Wood and colleagues (2013) reported data on 577 children (ages 3–12 years) and 253 adolescents (13–20 years) who had been referred to a gender identity service in Canada. An increase in the number of referrals to the service over a 30-year period suggests that being transgendered has come out of the closet (due to Internet exposure, blogs, and TV). In addition, the authors noted a comment made by some of their respondents: "In some ways, it is easier to be trans than to be gay or lesbian." One adolescent girl, for example, remarked, "If I walk down the street with my girlfriend and I am perceived to be a girl, then people call us all kinds of names, like lezzies or faggots; but if I am perceived to be a guy, then they leave us alone." In regard to the sexual orientation of transgendered individuals in the Woods and colleagues (2013) study, the percentage of girls and boys classified as homosexual was 76% and 57%, respectively.

Healthcare providers serve as gatekeepers for reconstructive surgery and prescribed hormone therapy. The protocol is a psychological evaluation, prescribe psychotherapy, and **real-life experience**, or living in the social role of the other sex for a year, prior to beginning hormonal or surgical therapy. Individuals need not take hormones or have surgery to be regarded as transsexuals. The distinguishing variable is living full-time in the role of the gender opposite one's biological sex. A man or woman who presents full-time as a woman or man is a transsexual by definition.

Some gender variant people prefer the term **transgenderist**, which means an individual who lives in a gender role that does not match his or her biological sex but who has no desire to surgically alter his or her genitalia (as do some transsexuals). The options are a genetic a genetic male who prefers to live as a female but does not want surgery, or a genetic female who wants to live as a male but does not want surgery. Another variation is the **she-male** who looks like a woman and has the breasts of a woman (from hormonal or surgical enlargement), yet has the genitalia and reproductive system of a man.

Transvestites are individuals who dress in a manner other than their biological sex—biological men dress as women (see Up Close 5-1) and biological women dress as men. While the clinical literature often uses the term *transvestites* (TVs), most of those who dress in the clothing of the other gender prefer the term cross-dresser (CDs). They may experience erotic stimulation from wearing clothing of the other sex or may cross-dress for social fun, camp ("drag queens"), or comfort. However, they retain their identity as a male or female, consistent with their respective genitals, and are not typically interested in sex reassignment surgery. Hence, a male cross-dresser enjoys dressing up as a woman but wants to keep his penis. "I like my plumbing," said one heterosexual cross-dresser who spoke in the authors' classes. Female impersonators are men who dress as women as part of their job in the entertainment industry; their counterparts are male impersonators (women who dress as men). They may or may not be transgendered or cross-dressers.

Real-life experience
Living in the social role of the other sex for a year, prior to beginning hormonal or surgical therapy

Transgenderist
Individual who lives in a gender role that does not match his or her biological sex but who does not surgically alter his or her genitalia (as does a transsexual)

She-male
Person who looks like a woman and has the breasts of a woman (from hormonal or surgical enlargement), yet has the genitalia and reproductive system of a man

Transvestites
Broad term for individuals who may dress or present themselves in the gender of the other sex; a more pejorative term than cross-dresser

My Life as a Cross-Dressing Husband and Dad*

*Being a cross-dresser can be very confusing and very frustrating. I told my "ex," about a month before we married, that I liked wearing women's clothing. I told her that I could quit and burned all of my clothing (called **purging**). How wrong I was! After about three months of being married, I told her that I needed to get some hosiery and panties to wear. She said that this would be OK, as long they were not lace. This progressed to the point that I needed to wear shoes, and later boots. Over time, I escalated to 5-inch stiletto heels, and I began to wear women's pajamas at night because I liked the silky feel.*

All of this progressed into my wearing various forms of lingerie, which I only wore with my wife's consent and presence. While I always tried to be very respectful of my wife's wishes, I soon realized that I needed to cross-dress more often and with more intensity than she was comfortable with. When my two daughters were born, I had to be very discreet as to when I would dress as a woman. I remember many a night of getting up with my oldest daughter and rocking her to sleep while wearing hose, high heels, and lingerie, in our moonlit living room.

On several occasions, my "ex" told me that she wanted me to get rid of my things. She "wanted my things out of her house." So, I put my clothes in a box that I kept in a utility building. But I missed my cross-dressing, continued to do it, and became very sneaky about it. When my workweek would end on Friday, I would rush home quickly, and dress for several hours before I picked up my daughters from kindergarten. Of course, I felt very guilty about my sneaking around.

When the girls were about 8 and 5, respectively, we bought a house. Again, my "ex" told me that she wanted me to get rid of my "things"; she wanted them out of her house. I only became sneakier and sneakier. For example, I started hiding my shoes and hosiery under a dresser in the bedroom, so that when the family was gone, to let's say, the grocery store, I could quickly and easily slip into some of my things for a few moments of ecstatic relaxing bliss (which often included masturbating while I was dressed.) I knew that I would pay for this later when my wife would want to have sex and I couldn't perform. Also, several times, I would underestimate when they would return from the store and they would almost catch me while dressed. ...

The older my girls got, the less time I had to dress. It finally got to the point that the only time that I could dress would be when the family would go out of town (to grandmother's house). I loved for them to be gone and was irritated by their return. Indeed, my daughters asked their mom if I was having an affair with another woman while they were gone. In essence, there was another woman, but this woman is the one who resided within me.

It is hard to explain the frustration of not being able to dress; it would lead to anger and anxiety. This anger reached its greatest point about two years before my wife and I ended our marriage. What caused this was that my "ex" demanded that I get rid of my feminine clothing. She actually insisted on one occasion that she accompany me to get rid of them. I finally did as she asked; I gave them to Goodwill so that I could get a tax break. I also went to see a psychiatrist who helped me realize that this was an important need, that cross-dressing was something that I was probably going to continue. My "ex" totally rejected this advice and we divorced.

*This heterosexual, formerly married father of two prefers to remain anonymous.

> *Few women admit their age. Fewer men act it.*
>
> (bumper sticker)

Purging
Cross-dresser's act of destroying the clothes of the other sex as an expression of trying to become free of the drive to cross-dress (rarely has any long-term effect, and the person returns to cross-dressing)

Women rarely say to their girlfriends, "let's go fishing." This woman loves to fish.
Source: David Knox

Women always worry about the things men forget. Men always worry about the things women remember.

Unknown

Gender roles
Social norms that dictate appropriate female and male behavior

Sex roles
Roles filled by women or men that are defined by biological constraints and can be enacted only by members of one biological sex only such as (wet nurse, sperm donor, child bearer)

Sexual identity
Composite term that refers to factors including one's biological sex, gender identity, gender role, and sexual orientation

Gender role ideology
Socially prescribed role relationships between women and men in any given society

5.1e Gender Role

Gender roles are the social norms that dictate what is socially regarded as appropriate female and male behavior. All societies have expectations of how boys and girls, men and women, "should" behave. Gender roles influence women and men in virtually every sphere of life, including family and occupation. Traditional gender roles have influenced women to be more concerned with family and child care, and men to be more concerned with career and income. Women have also been socialized to enter "female" occupations—such as elementary school teacher, day-care worker, and nurse. (See Personal Choices 5-1 on pursuing a nontraditional occupational role.)

The term *sex roles* is often confused with and used interchangeably with the term *gender roles*. However, whereas gender roles are socially defined and can be enacted by either women or men, **sex roles** are defined by biological constraints and can be enacted by members of one biological sex only—wet nurse, sperm donor, child bearer.

5.1f Sexual Identity

Sexual identity refers to a number of factors, including one's biological sex, gender identity, gender role, and sexual orientation. One's biological sex (also referred to as *natal sex*) refers to being male or female; gender identity, to seeing one's self as a woman or man; gender role, as the occupation of social/cultural roles defined as those appropriate for women or men; and sexual orientation, as heterosexual, homosexual, or bisexual. Individuals may have a clear sexual identity of being a heterosexual male who functions in "male" roles. Alternatively, one's sexual identity may be seen as a cluster of several variables, such as a biological male with the gender identity of a woman but the gender role of a man with a bisexual sexual orientation.

Disapproval toward gay individuals with various gender identities may have negative effects. Collier and colleagues (2013) reviewed 39 studies, published between 1995 and 2012 in 12 countries, on sexual orientation, gender identity and psychosocial and health outcomes. The researchers concluded that there is fairly strong evidence that peer victimization related to sexual orientation and gender identity or expression is associated with a diminished sense of school belonging and higher levels of depressive symptoms, disruptions in educational trajectories, and alcohol/substance abuse.

5.1g Gender Role Ideology

Gender role ideology refers to the socially prescribed role relationships between women and men in any given society. These role relationship norms become important since they script behavior for couples. Egalitarian scripts are presumed to be more prevalent in contemporary society, but examples continue that suggest traditional roles. Women are less aggressive in initiating relationships but still take the lead in moving the relationship toward commitment—having "the talk" (Easterling, Nelms, & Knox, 2012).

personal Choices 5-1

Pursuing a Nontraditional Occupational Role

Danica Patrick is the poster woman for pursing a nontraditional role. She is the most successful woman in the history of American open-wheel racing (NASCAR). In 2008 she won the Indy Japan 300; in 2009, she won third place in the Indianapolis 500, the highest finish ever by a woman.

Sheryl Sandberg is the CEO of Facebook. An MBA graduate of Harvard, she encourages women to "lean in" and seize business and corporate opportunities (Sandberg, 2013). The mother of two, she is also aware of the cultural programming for women to take responsibility for childcare and emphasizes that selecting one's mate "is the most important career decision a woman makes." Her husband is an equal partner in childcare and rearing, without which she says her level of career involvement would not be possible.

Patrick and Sandberg have pushed through traditional gender role socialization to seek roles in racing and corporate America. DiDonato and Strough (2013) reported that the college students in their study preferred gender-stereotypical occupations for themselves. However, both men and women reported that men should only hold masculine occupations (e.g., plumber), but that women should hold both masculine and feminine occupations (airline pilot).

For the person who chooses a nontraditional occupational role, there are personal and social advantages. On the individual level, women and men can make career choices on the basis of their personal talents and interests, rather than on the basis of arbitrary social restrictions regarding who can and cannot have a particular job or career. Because traditional male occupations are generally higher paying than traditional female occupations, women who make nontraditional career choices can gain access to higher paying and higher status jobs. In contrast, men who enter traditional female occupations—such as nursing and elementary school teaching—can develop their capacity for nurturing. Men are also likely to be promoted to supervisors and administrators in traditional female professions.

Lack of acceptance may be a disadvantage of entering a nontraditional role. Women in traditional all-male military careers or schools (such as Citadel cadets) have reported undue harassment. We will discuss sexual harassment in detail in the chapter on sexual coercion. For now we note that over 26,000 military women alleged sexual assault in 2012.

On the societal level, an increase in nontraditional career choices reduces **occupational sex segregation**, thereby contributing to social equality between women and men. In addition, women and men who enter nontraditional occupations may contribute greatly to the field they enter. For example, traditional male-dominated occupations—such as politics, science and technology—may benefit greatly from increased involvement of women in these fields. Similarly, the field of public school teaching, which is a female-dominated occupation, has not provided enough male role models for children. Additionally, when men enter a profession, broad-based salary increases tend to occur.

Choosing nontraditional occupations may also help to eliminate gender stereotypes. Women are stereotyped as being nurturing, in part, because of their service-oriented jobs, whereas men are believed to be more technically proficient and more competent decision makers because of the kinds of jobs they hold. Women as airline pilots and men as day-care workers help to crack the stereotypes.

Occupational sex segregation
Tendency for women and men to pursue different occupations

Think About It

Take a moment to answer the following question. Whereas traditional hetero-sexual relationships have reflected male dominance, homosexual relationships tend to be more equal, with greater gender role flexibility. When gender role ideology in homosexual relationships is assessed, lesbian relationships are more egalitarian and flexible than male relationships How do you explain these differences?

5.2 **Biological Beginnings**

The distinction between the female and the male sexes begins at the moment of fertilization when the man's sperm and the woman's egg unite to form a zygote. Both chromosomal and hormonal factors contribute to the development of the zygote.

5.2a Chromosomes

Chromosomes are threadlike structures located within the nucleus of every cell in a person's body. Each cell contains 23 pairs of chromosomes, a total of 46 chromosomes per cell. Chromosomes contain genes, the basic units of heredity, which determine not only such physical characteristics as eye color, hair color, and body type but also predispositions for such characteristics as baldness, color blindness, and hemophilia. One of these 23 pairs of chromosomes is referred to as *sex chromosomes* because they determine whether an individual will be female or male. There are two types of sex chromosomes, called X and Y. Normally, females have two X chromosomes, whereas males have one X and one Y chromosome. The human X chromosome contains about 3,000 to 4,000 genes and is two to three times longer than the Y chromosome.

When the egg and sperm meet in the Fallopian tube, each contains only half the normal number of chromosomes (one from each of the 23 pairs). The union of sperm and egg results in a single cell called a zygote, which has the normal 46 chromosomes. The egg will always have an X chromosome, but the sperm will have either an X or Y chromosome. Because the sex chromosome in the egg is always X (the female chromosome), the sex chromosome in the sperm will determine the sex of a child. If the sperm contains an X chromosome, the match with the female chromosome will be XX, and the child will be genetically female. If the sperm contains a Y chromosome, the match with the female chromosome will be XY, and the child will be genetically male.

The fact that chromosomes control the biological sex of a child has enabled some parents to select the sex of their offspring. Whether or not this choice should be an option is discussed in Social Choices 5-1.

Chromosomes
Threadlike structures of DNA within the cell nucleus that carry genes and transmit hereditary information

ocial Choices 5-1

Selecting the Sex of One's Unborn Child

Preconceptual sex selection, also called **family balancing**, is a way to select the sex of one's child. MicroSort technology involves a sperm sorting technique that identifies sperm cells which correspond to the desired gender. The pregnancy probability with the desired sex of child will vary according to the amount of motile cells and the gender selected, but it approximates 93% effectiveness for girls and 82% effectiveness for boys in 2013. Genetics and IVF Institute of Fairfax, Virginia, and Bethesda, Maryland, offer this MicroSort technology (http://www.microsort.net/). FDA approval is pending.

Kalfoglou and colleagues (2013) reviewed the arguments for and against nonmedical sex selection via sperm sorting. Arguments "for" include an individual's right to choose the sex of one's child since doing so harms neither the individual making the choice nor the child. Preconception sperm sorting avoids abortion of fetuses or destruction of embryos—positive outcomes for the child since the child will be of the desired sex. In addition, women in oppressive societies (e.g. China) may benefit since female infanticide could be avoided. Arguments against sperm sorting include that an imbalanced sex ratio will occur (fewer females) with the result that there will be men without wives (the loss of opportunity to have children), less church attendance, and more violence/wars. The researchers point out, In the larger society "there is little evidence to suggest that there is a sex preference in industrialized countries. Instead, families that have a preference want to have children of both sexes."

If preconceptual sex selection is not used and a couple wants a child of a particular sex, amniocentesis may be used. Best performed in the 16th or 17th week of pregnancy, **amniocentesis** involves inserting a needle into the pregnant woman's uterus to withdraw fluid, which is then analyzed to see if the cells carry XX (female) or XY (male) chromosomes. Alternatively, chorionic villi sampling (CVS) can be used to detect fetal sex as early as 8-weeks' gestation. Depending on the position of the fetus, ultrasound may reveal the fetus' genital area; however, it is not considered a reliable test to determine the sex of the fetus. After use of one or more of these various tests, the parents may allow the fetus to develop if it is the biological sex that the parents desire. Otherwise, the fetus may be aborted. Such a decision is not widely practiced (in the United States) by either physicians or parents but does occur. Selecting the sex of one's child through **prenatal sex selection** is highly controversial.

The strongest argument for prenatal sex selection is that it can prevent the birth of an infant with a serious and/or fatal sex-linked genetic disease. Another argument is that aborting a fetus of the "undesired sex" is less objectionable than killing the infant after it is born. The practice of female infanticide—the killing of female infants by drowning, strangling, or exposure—has been well documented in Eastern countries, including China and India. This practice occurs because of the cultural value that is placed on having male children. In China, India, and many other Eastern countries, boys are seen as an asset because they provide labor in the fields and take care of elderly parents. Girls are considered economic liabilities because they require a dowry and then leave the family to care for their own husbands and children. Almond and colleagues (2013) confirmed that sex selection in the form of abortion of females fetuses continues to occur among South and East Asian immigrants (who are not Christian).

Opposition to prenatal sex selection is strongest when abortion is the method used. Not only does abortion for sex selection outrage individuals who are against abortion for any reason, but it also offends many individuals who support women's right to choose abortion for other reasons. Many pro-choice individuals view abortion for the purpose of sex selection as morally unjustifiable and are concerned that using abortion for sex selection may generate so much public opposition that the freedom to choose abortion when there are strong moral reasons to do so may be jeopardized.

Preconceptual sex selection
Selection of the sex of a child before it is conceived (See also Family balancing.)

Family balancing
Act of selecting the sex of a child before it is conceived for a "balanced" one boy, one girl family and involves separating sperm carrying the X and Y chromosomes

Amniocentesis
Prenatal test in which a needle is inserted (usually in the 16th or 17th week of pregnancy) into the pregnant woman's uterus to withdraw fluid that is analyzed to see if the cells carry XX (female) or XY (male) chromosomes, and to identify chromosomal defects

Prenatal sex selection
Selection of whether to continue the pregnancy based on the sex of the fetus.

5.2b Chromosomal Abnormalities

As we have seen, normal development in males and females requires that the correct number of chromosomes be present in the developing fetus. Chromosomal abnormalities may result in atypical sexual development of the fetus. For every sex chromosome from the mother (X), there must be a corresponding sex chromosome from the father (X or Y) for normal sexual development to occur. Abnormalities result when there are too many or too few sex chromosomes. Either the father or the mother may contribute an abnormal sex chromosome.

Two of the most common of these abnormalities are Klinefelter's syndrome and Turner's syndrome. **Klinefelter's syndrome** occurs in males and results from the presence of an extra X sex chromosome (XXY). The result is abnormal testicular development, infertility, low interest in sex (low libido), and mental retardation, in some cases. Males with an extra X chromosome often experience language deficits, neuro-maturational lag, academic difficulties, and psychological distress. Common characteristics also include abnormally long legs and lack of a deep voice and beard. The main therapy involves androgen replacement, which may help with muscle strength, but does not restore fertility. It occurs in about 1 in 800 male births.

Turner's syndrome occurs in females and results from the absence of an X chromosome (XO). It is characterized by abnormal ovarian development, failure to menstruate, infertility, and the lack of secondary sexual characteristics such as armpit and pubic hair. Turner's syndrome is also associated with short stature, a short webbed neck, and a predisposition to heart and kidney defects. It occurs with a frequency of about 1 in 25,000 girls. Treatment for Turner's syndrome includes hormone replacement therapy to develop secondary sexual characteristics and the use of a biosynthetic human growth hormone to promote growth. Such treatment directs girls with Turner's syndrome toward normal female development.

5.2c Fetal Hormones

Hormones are also important in the development of the fetus. Male and female embryos are indistinguishable from one another during the first several weeks of intra-uterine life (described as the "indifferent gonadal stage"). In both males and females, two primitive gonads and two paired duct systems form about the 5th or 6th week of development. While the reproductive system of the male (epididymis, vas deferens, ejaculatory duct) develops from the Wolffian ducts and the female reproductive system (Fallopian tubes, uterus, vagina) from the Mullerian ducts, both ducts are present in the developing embryo at this stage (see Figure 5-1).

If the embryo is genetically a male (XY), a chemical substance controlled by the Y chromosome (H-Y antigen) stimulates the primitive gonads to develop into testes. The development of a female requires that no additional testosterone be present (referred to as the "constitutive" or "default" pathway). Without the controlling substance from the Y chromosome, the primitive gonads will develop into ovaries and the Mullerian duct system into Fallopian tubes, uterus, and vagina; and without testosterone, the Wolffian duct system will degenerate or become blind tubules. Differentiation of the female gonads begins at about the end of the 8th week and takes place over a longer period than in the male. In the female the genital tubercle does not enlarge; it forms the clitoris. The urogenital sinus and urogenital folds differentiate into the vagina and the labia.

Although the infant's gonads (testes and ovaries) produce the sex hormones (testosterone and estrogen), these hormones are regulated by the pituitary gland, which is located at the base of the brain about 2 inches behind the eyes. The release of

Klinefelter's syndrome
Condition that occurs in males and results from the presence of an extra X sex chromosome (XXY), resulting in abnormal testicular development, infertility, low interest in sex (low libido), and, in some cases, mental retardation

Turner's syndrome
Condition that occurs in females resulting from the absence of an X chromosome (XO)

FIGURE **5-1** ‖ Sexual Differentiation of External Genitalia

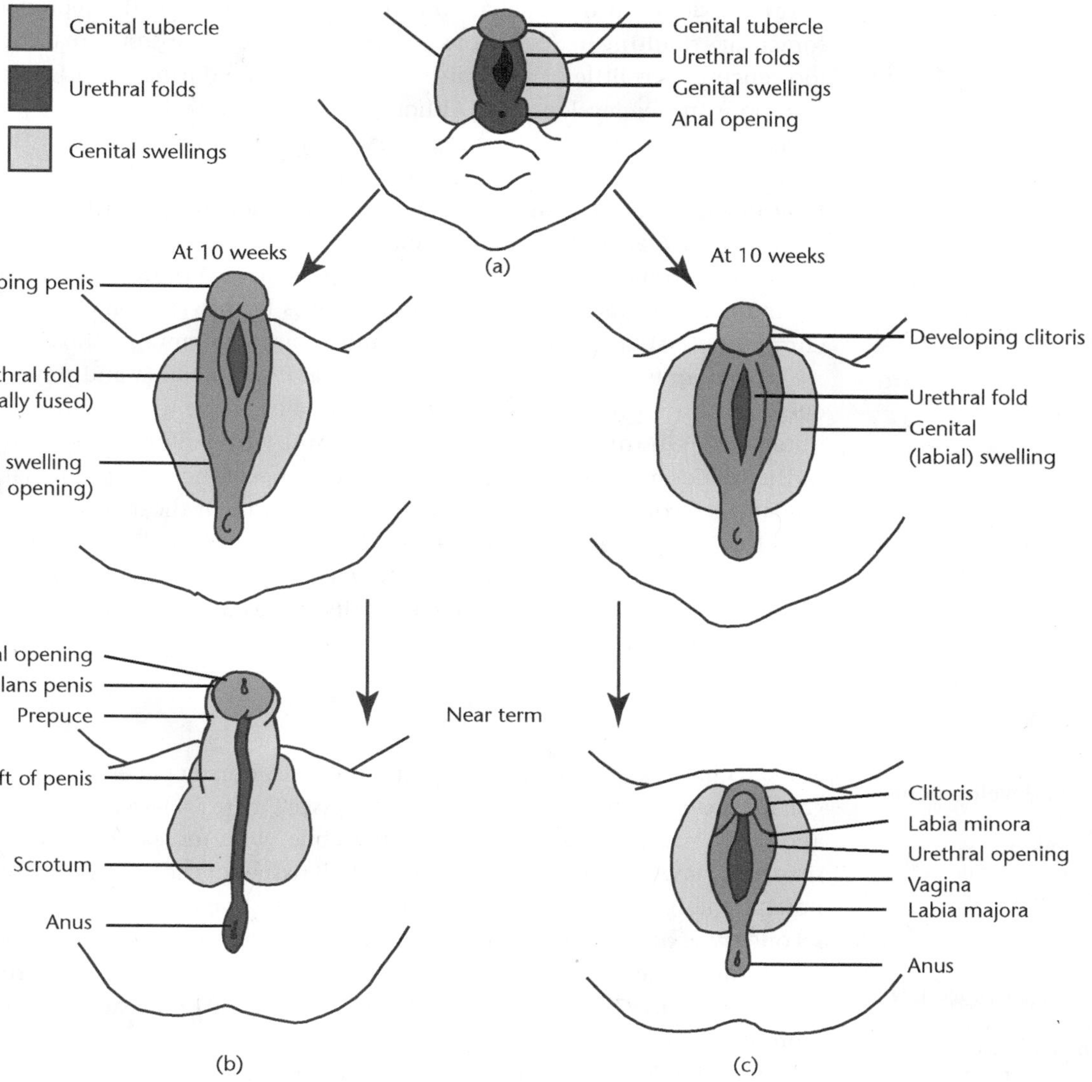

Sexual Differentiation of External Genitalia

(a) Undifferentiated stage (7 weeks) (b) Male development (c) Female development

pituitary hormones, as it turns out, is controlled by additional hormones (also called releasing factors) from the hypothalamus, a part of the brain just above the pituitary. It is the hypothalamus that differs in males and females in both the connections between cells and the size of various groups of cells. The presence of testosterone before birth stimulates not only the development of the male reproductive system, but also apparently, the development of a male hypothalamus. A female hypothalamus develops in the absence of testosterone.

There is no unisex brain. It follows that these two brain models can produce quite different behaviors.

Louann Brizendine, *The Female Brain*

5.2d Intersex Development

Intersex development refers to congenital variations in the reproductive system, sometimes resulting in ambiguous genitals. Even if chromosomal makeup is XX or XY, too much or too little of a certain kind of hormone during gestation can also cause variations in sex development. Although intersexed people currently prefer the term *intersexed*, in the medical literature intersex conditions that may result from hormonal abnormalities are referred to as *hermaphroditism* and *pseudohermaphroditism*. **True hermaphroditism** is an extremely rare condition in which individuals are born with both ovarian and testicular tissue.

More common than hermaphroditism is **pseudohermaphroditism**, which refers to a condition in which an individual is born with gonads matching the sex chromosomes, but with genitals either ambiguous or resembling those of the other sex.

When ambiguous genitals are detected at birth, parents and physicians face the decision of assigning either the male or female gender to the intersexed infant. As noted earlier in this section, in the past, infants with ambiguous genitals were reared in the gender most closely approximating the appearance of a particular sex. Current guidelines recommend that, unless there is a genuine medical need, surgical alteration of a child's genitalia should not be performed. When the child is of age to realistically understand the risks and benefits of surgery, and is capable of giving consent, then cosmetic surgeries may be performed. Finally, more education, and therapeutic support and follow-up, are recommended for these individuals and their families.

5.2e Pubertal Hormones

Marked changes in growth and maturation occur during puberty as a consequence of gonadal development and hormonal output (see Figure 5-2). In girls, increased estrogen and DHT are responsible for changes in physique, while increased androgens are responsible for changes in boys. Although almost all tissues of the body are affected, the most notable changes are the maturation of the reproductive system and the development of secondary sexual characteristics. The timing of pubertal onset varies across individuals but begins earlier for girls than for boys. Menarche (a girl's first menstruation) ranges in timing from 9.7 to 16.7 years (with a mean onset of 12.3 years). Puberty ends when reproductive capacity is established, with regular ovulatory and menstrual cycles for girls and high levels of sperm production and erectile function in boys.

5.3 **Theories of Gender Role Development**

A number of theories attempt to explain why women and men exhibit similar or different characteristics and behaviors.

Sex differences are real, biologically programmed, and important to how children are raised, disciplined, and educated.

Leonard Sax, *Why Gender Matters*

5.3a Sociobiology

Sociobiology emphasizes that social behavior has a biological basis in terms of being functional in human evolution. The differences between women and men were functional for survival. Women stayed in the nest, nurtured children, and gathered food nearby, whereas men could go afar to find food. Such a conceptualization focuses on the division of labor between women and men as functional for the survival of the species.

Although there is little agreement (even among sociologists) on the merits of sociobiology, the theory emphasizes that biological differences (such as hormonal and chromosomal differences) between women and men account for the social and

---

Intersex development
Congenital variations in the reproductive system, sometimes resulting in ambiguous genitals

True hermaphroditism
Rare condition in which individuals are born with both ovarian and testicular tissue (These individuals, called hermaphrodites, may have one ovary and one testicle, feminine breasts, and a vaginal opening beneath the penis.)

Pseudo-hermaphroditism
Condition in which an individual is born with gonads matching the sex chromosomes, but genitals resembling those of the other sex

Sociobiology
Framework in which social behavior is viewed as having a biological basis in terms of being functional in human evolution

FIGURE **5-2** ‖ **Effects of Hormones on Sexual Development During Puberty**

The body's endocrine system produces hormones that trigger body changes in male and female youth.

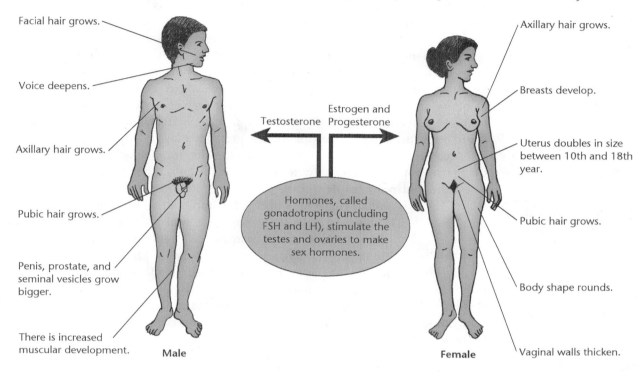

Facial hair grows.

Voice deepens.

Axillary hair grows.

Pubic hair grows.

Penis, prostate, and seminal vesicles grow bigger.

There is increased muscular development.

Male

Testosterone Estrogen and Progesterone

Hormones, called gonadotropins (uncluding FSH and LH), stimulate the testes and ovaries to make sex hormones.

Axillary hair grows.

Breasts develop.

Uterus doubles in size between 10th and 18th year.

Pubic hair grows.

Body shape rounds.

Vaginal walls thicken.

Female

psychological differences in female and male characteristics, behaviors, and roles. For example, testosterone is a male hormone associated with aggression; progesterone is a female hormone associated with nurturance. Such hormonal differences are used to help explain that men have more sexual partners than women, that men are more likely to engage in casual sex, and that men are the perpetrators of most acts of sexual coercion as well as sexual harassment.

In mate selection, heterosexual men tend to seek and mate with women who are youthful and attractive. These characteristics are associated with fertility, health, and reproductive potential for women. Similarly, women tend to select and mate with men whom they deem will provide the maximum parental investment in their offspring. The term **parental investment** refers to any investment by a parent that increases the offspring's chance of surviving and thus increases reproductive success. Parental investments require time and energy. Women have a great deal of parental investment in their offspring (9 months' gestation, taking care of dependent offspring) and tend to mate with men who have economic resources and are willing to share those resources. David Buss (1989) found that the pattern of men seeking physically attractive young women and women seeking economically ambitious men was true in 37 groups of women and men in 33 different societies.

The sociobiological explanation for mate selection is controversial. Critics argue that women may show concern for the earning capacity of a potential mate because women have been systematically denied access to similar economic resources, and selecting a mate with these resources is one of their remaining options. In addition, it is argued that both women and men, when selecting a mate, think more about their partners as companions than as future parents of their offspring. Finally, the sociobiological perspective fails to acknowledge the degree to which social and psychological factors influence our behavior.

I hope the 21st century sees an end to the nature-nurture argument … We need to move forward and investigate how nature and culture interact.

Helen Fisher, anthropologist

Parental investment
Any investment by a parent that increases the offspring's chance of surviving and thus increases reproductive success

5.3b Identification Theory

Although researchers do not agree on the merits of Freud's theories (and students question their relevance), Freud was one of the first theorists to study gender role acquisition. He suggested that children acquire the characteristics and behaviors of their same-sex parent through a process of identification. Boys identify with their fathers, and girls identify with their mothers. Freud believed that children identify with the same-gender parent out of fear. Freud felt this fear could be one of two kinds: fear of loss of love or fear of retaliation. Fear of loss of love, which results in both girls and boys identifying with their mother, is caused by their deep dependence on her for love and nurturance. Fearful that she may withdraw her love, young children try to become like her to please her and to ensure the continuance of her love.

According to Freud, at about age 4 the child's identification with the mother begins to change, but in different ways for boys than for girls. Boys experience what Freud called the **Oedipal complex**. Based on the legend of the Greek youth Oedipus, who unknowingly killed his father and married his mother, the Oedipal complex involves the young boy's awakening sexual feelings for his mother as he becomes aware he has a penis and his mother does not. He unconsciously feels that if his father knew of the intense love feelings he has for his mother, the father would castrate him (which may be what happened to his mother because she has no penis). The boy resolves the Oedipal struggle—feeling love for his father but wanting to kill him because he is a competitor for his mother's love—by becoming like his father by identifying with him. In this way, the boy can keep his penis and take pride in being like his father. According to Freud, the successful resolution of this Oedipal situation marks the beginning of a boy's appropriate gender role acquisition.

All women become like their mothers. That is their tragedy. No man does. That's his. ...

Oscar Wilde, novelist

The **Electra complex** is based on the Greek myth in which Electra assists her brother in killing their mother and her lover to avenge their father's death. In Freudian terms, the Electra complex refers to unconscious sexual feelings a daughter develops for her father. These feelings develop when 3- to 6-year-old girls become aware that they do not have a penis. Freud believed that girls blame their mothers for cutting off their penis or causing it to be severed and that they develop "penis envy" and wish that they had a penis. To retaliate, girls take their love away from their mothers and begin to focus on their fathers as love objects. Girls feel that they can be fulfilled by being impregnated by their fathers who will give them a baby to substitute for the penis they do not have. To become impregnated by their fathers, girls recognize that they must be more like their mother. So they identify again with the mother.

5.3c Social Learning Theory

Derived from the school of behavioral psychology, social learning theory emphasizes the role of reward and punishment in explaining how a child learns gender role behavior. For example, two young brothers enjoyed playing "lady." Each of them would put on a dress, wear high-heeled shoes, and carry a pocketbook. Their father came home early one day and angrily demanded they "Take those clothes off and never put them on again! Those things are for women," he said. The boys were punished for playing "lady" but rewarded with their father's approval for playing "cowboys," with plastic guns and "Bang! You're dead!" dialogue.

Reward and punishment alone are not sufficient to account for the way in which children learn gender roles. Direct instruction ("Girls wear dresses" and "Men walk on the outside when walking with a woman") is another way children learn through social interaction with others. In addition, many of society's gender rules are learned through modeling. In modeling, the child observes another's behavior and imitates

Oedipal complex
Freud's term based on the legend of the Greek youth Oedipus, who unknowingly killed his father and married his mother; involves the young boy's awakening sexual feelings for his mother as he becomes aware he has a penis and his mother does not.

Electra complex
In psychoanalysis, term that refers to a daughter's (unconscious) sexual desire for her father; refers to the Greek myth in which Electra assists her brother in killing their mother and her lover to avenge their father's death.

that behavior. Gender role models include parents, peers, siblings, and characters portrayed in the media.

The impact of modeling on the development of gender role behavior is controversial. For example, a modeling perspective implies that children will tend to imitate the parent of the same sex—but mainly women, rear children in all cultures. Yet this persistent female model does not seem to interfere with the male's development of the behavior that is considered appropriate for his gender. One explanation suggests that boys learn early that our society generally grants boys and men more status and privileges than girls and women; therefore, they devalue the feminine and emphasize the learning of masculine behavior.

Find out what a child will work for and will work to avoid, systematically manipulate these contingencies and you can change behavior.

Jack Turner, psychologist

5.3d Cognitive-Developmental Theory

The cognitive-developmental theory of gender role acquisition reflects a blend of biological and social learning views. According to this theory, biological readiness (in terms of the cognitive development of the child) influences how the child responds to gender cues in the environment (Kohlberg, 1966; 1976). For example, gender discrimination (the ability to identify social and psychological characteristics associated with being female and male) begins at about age 30 months. At that age, toddlers are able to assign a "boy's toy" to a boy and a "girl's toy" to a girl. However at this age, children do not view gender as a permanent characteristic. Thus, while young children may define people who wear long hair as girls and those who never wear dresses as boys, they also believe they can change their gender by altering their hair or changing clothes.

Not until age 6 or 7 does the child view gender as permanent (Kohlberg, 1966; 1969). In Kohlberg's view, this cognitive understanding is not a result of social learning. Rather, it involves the development of a specific mental ability to grasp the idea that certain basic characteristics of people do not change. When children learn the concept of gender permanence, they seek to become competent and proper members of their gender group. For example, a child standing on the edge of a school playground may observe one group of children jumping rope while another group is playing football. That child's gender identity as either a girl or a boy connects with the observed "gender appropriate" behavior, and she or he joins one of the two groups. Once in the group, the child seeks to develop the behaviors that are socially defined as appropriate for her or his gender.

5.4 Agents of Gender Role Socialization

Although biology may provide a basis for some roles (being 7 feet tall is helpful for becoming a basketball player), cultural influences in the form of various socialization agents (parents, peers, teachers, religion, and the media) shape the individual toward various gender roles. These powerful influences in large part dictate what a person thinks, feels, and does in her or his role as a woman or a man.

5.4a Parents

The family is a gendered institution with female and male roles highly structured by gender. The gendered world begins with the color of the nursery, names for children, and the toys put in the crib. While adolescent males are more likely to cut the grass and adolescent females are more likely to clean the kitchen, mothers and fathers are transitioning from modeling traditional gender roles towards co-parenting practices (Kwon, Han, Jeon, & Bingham, 2013). Hence, children of today are more likely to have exposure to egalitarian role models.

BVT *Lab*

Improve your test scores. Practice quizzes are available at **www.BVTLab.com**.

5.4b Peers

Although parents are usually the first socializing agents that influence a child's gender role development, peers become increasingly important during the school years. Martin and colleagues (2013) confirmed that children influence one another's engagement in gender-typed activities.

Whereas boys are encouraged to restrict their emotional expression, female adolescents are under tremendous pressure to be trim, pretty and popular. Female adolescents are sometimes in great conflict as high academic success may be viewed as being less than feminine.

Peer disapproval for failure to conform to traditional gender stereotypes is reflected in the terms *sissy* and *tomboy*. These terms are used pejoratively to refer to children who exhibit behaviors stereotypically associated with the other gender.

5.4c Teachers

Teachers are important influences on gender role development. They not only serve as models in the classroom, they also select textbooks that provide images of gender roles. Foulds (2013) noted that school textbooks present a continuum of gender identities, which include transformative gendered roles for women that are incongruent with student realities. They may be aware that women are CEOs of major corporations, and have careers and egalitarian husbands—they just don't know any of them.

5.4d Religion

Religion exists to provide answers to questions about meaning—of birth, of life, of death. Traditional Western religions are patriarchal; male dominance is indisputable in the hierarchy of the organizational structure, where power and status have been accorded mostly to men. Until recently, only men could be priests, ministers, and rabbis. The Catholic Church does not have female clergy, and men dominate the top positions in the U.S. dioceses.

Male bias is also reflected in the terminology used to refer to God in Jewish, Christian, and Islamic religions. For example, God is traditionally referred to as *He, Father, Lord,* and *King.* The Bible emphasizes the traditional ordering of the roles between husband and wife:

> Wives be subject to your husband, as to the Lord ... Husbands, love your wives, even as Christ also loved the church. (Ephesians 5:22–25; see also Colossians 3:18–19)

Religion also telegraphs to women the importance of being married as a social role. Brown and Porter (2013) analyzed national data of divorced women and found that those who were affiliated with organized religion or who self-identified as being religious were significantly more likely to get remarried.

Think About It

Take a moment to answer the following questions. In response to an interest in removing sexist language from religious works, hymns are being rewritten. The hymn "Rejoice, You Pure in Heart" no longer speaks of "strong men and maidens meek" but speaks, rather, of "strong souls and spirits meek." In addition, "The Father, Son, and Holy Ghost" has been changed to "Praise God the Spirit, Holy Fire." How aware do you feel persons who sing hymns are of the sex bias of the words? Why?

5.4e Media

Media—such as movies, television, magazines, newspapers, books, and music—both reflect and shape gender roles. Media images of women and men typically conform to traditional gender stereotypes; media portrayals depicting the exploitation, victimization, and sexual objectification of women are common. As for music, ter Bogt and colleagues (2010) studied 410 students, ages 13–16, and found that a preference for hip-hop music was associated with gender stereotypes (e.g., men are sex driven and tough, women are sex objects). In regard to music television videos, Wallis (2011) conducted a content analysis of 34 music videos and found that significant gender displays reinforced stereotypical notions of women as sexual objects, females as subordinate and males as aggressive.

Simon and Hoyt (2013) found that women exposed to media images of counter-stereotypical roles (e.g., a woman who is not in the kitchen but in the role of an attorney) subsequently reported stronger nontraditional gender role beliefs (e.g., women can excel in business) than women exposed to images depicting stereotypical roles. They also reported less negative self-perceptions and greater leadership aspirations than women exposed to images of women in stereotypical roles. Hence, women tend to adopt beliefs consistent with the media images with which they are presented.

More recently, strong female personalities have been featured in award-winning films and television series. The powerful role of Maya, the CIA operative who relentlessly pursued Osama Bin Ladin as depicted in *Zero Dark Thirty*, *Homeland's* unrelenting Claire Danes, and the aggressive get-the-job-done Kalina Sharma in *The Good Wife*—all are in sharp contrast to the sweet and passive Grace Kelly and Dorothy McGuire of the 1950s.

Finally, Vokey and colleagues (2013) examined the concept of hyper-masculinity (gender-based ideology containing exaggerated beliefs about what it is to be a man) and specified four interrelated beliefs: toughness as emotional self-control, violence as manly, danger as exciting, and callous attitudes toward women and sex. Since advertising is thought to play a role in constructing hyper-masculinity, eight U.S. men's magazines published in 2007–2008—differentiated by readership age, education, and household income—were analyzed for hyper-masculine depictions in their advertisements. Using a behavioral checklist with good inter-rater reliability, it was found that 56% (n = 295) of 527 advertisements depicted one or more hyper-masculine beliefs. Some magazines depicted at least one hyper-masculine belief in 90% or more of advertisements.

5.5 Effects of Gender Role Socialization on Relationships and Sexuality

Gender role socialization influences virtually every sphere of life, including self-concept, educational achievement, occupation, income, and health. Women and men learn their gender roles from the society and culture in which they are socialized. In the following sections we look at gender roles in other societies as well as the effects of traditional gender role socialization on women and men in U.S. society.

5.5a Gender Roles in Other Societies

Because gender roles are largely influenced by culture, it is clear that individuals reared in different societies typically display the gender role patterns of those societies. This section discusses how gender roles differ in the Caribbean, Latino countries and Cuba.

Gender Roles in the Caribbean

For spring break, college students sometimes go to the Bahamas, Jamaica, or other English-speaking islands in the Caribbean (e.g., Barbados, Trinidad, Guyana) and may wonder about the family patterns and role relationships of the people they encounter. The natives of the Caribbean number more than 30 million, with a majority being of African ancestry. Their family patterns are diverse but are often characterized by women and their children as the primary family unit. Women view motherhood, not marriage, as the symbol of their womanhood. Hence, men often live somewhere else, have children with different women, and can be psychologically and physically absent from their children's lives. When they do live with a woman, traditional division of labor prevails, with women taking care of domestic and childcare tasks.

Gender Roles in Mexican, and Latino/Hispanic Families

While all trace their roots to the Spanish and Mexican settlers in the Southwest of the United States, before the arrival of the Pilgrims in New England, Hispanic families are both those that are native born and those who immigrated from elsewhere. Hispanics today represent about 50 million or 15% of the U.S. population. Mexican Americans are the fastest growing and largest ethnic group in the U.S. (Becerra, 2012).

Although the traditional family model in Spain calls for men as providers and women as homemakers and mothers, Hispanic families have been influenced by social, economic, and political change. Mobility and urbanization have also had their impact. Not only have the marital roles moved away from domination by the male, but there has also been a loss of extended family in terms of number and influence. Today, much of the culture survives, yet change continues. Intermarriage of Hispanics to non-Hispanics (the highest of all intermarriage combinations) is another influence eroding traditional Hispanic patterns and values.

Gender Roles in the Cuban American Family

As diplomatic dialogue between the U.S. and Cuba continues, there is interest in the Cuban American family. About 2 million Cuban Americans live in the U.S. Traditional family patterns have undergone change from the original immigrant families strongly rooted in Cuban culture to the second generation, with half of their influence coming from American norms, to the third generation with most of their influence American (Suarez & Perez, 2012).

Some Cuban families have insulated themselves inside an "enclave" that reinforces their Cuban identity and is a rich source of social capital (which may translate into job opportunities). But as assimilation into American culture has continued, cultural traditions have also been challenged. Female labor force participation has increased the power of the wife and challenged male authority in the home. Divorce rates have increased, and singlehood has become more acceptable. A gradual transition from familism to individualism has occurred. "Although Cuban Americans can still be said to have strong family bonds, family patterns and values sustaining them seem to have weakened" (p. 120).

5.5b Female Sexuality

Women differ from men in regard to relationships and sexuality in a number of ways.

1. *Importance of Relationship Commitment*   Females are socialized to be involved in a committed romantic relationship as the context for their happiness and fulfillment. When they are not, they are more likely to report depressive symptoms and to drink more alcohol, including binge drinking. Researchers Whitton and colleagues (2013) revealed this finding in a study of 889

BVT *Lab*

Visit **www.BVTLab.com** to explore the student resources available for this chapter.

undergraduates. They compared females with males and those who were in committed relationships with those who were not. They explained their findings as being due to the gain in self-worth and valued social identity that the females derived from their committed relationships.

> *Men marry to make an end; women to make a beginning.*
>
> Alexis Dupuy, actress

2. *Body Image*   Beauty pageants for children bring into cultural focus the degree to which very young girls are socialized to emphasize beauty and appearance. A look at the cover of women's magazines (e.g., *Women's Health*, *Cosmopolitan*) begs the question, "Are these body images healthy or realistic?" The effect for many women who do not match the cultural ideal is to have a negative body image. Heron and Smyth (2013) studied 63 undergraduate females and found that they held conflicting beliefs about the body they would like to have and the body they actually had. The result was being both depressed and anxious. Runfola and colleagues (2013) confirmed that body dissatisfaction is not just during the college years but exists throughout the adult life span. The effects include sexuality. Erbil (2013) found that women who had a positive body image reported positive sexual functioning in terms of sexual desire, arousal, lubrication, orgasm and satisfaction.

> *We come in different sizes, so get over it.*
>
> Rosie O'Donnell, celebrity

3. *Masturbation*   In a national sample of 5,865 adults living in the U.S. between the ages of 20–29, 68% of the women compared to 84% of the men reported having masturbated in the past year (Reece, Herbenick, Fortenberry, et al., 2012). While traditional female socialization has taught women that it is "dirty" to touch themselves "down there," new cultural messages include that women are responsible for their sexual pleasure and that masturbation is normative among their female peers. For many women, having a vibrator in the bedroom drawer is common.

Cultural Diversity

Cross-cultural research on female masturbation has included Portuguese women. Carvalheira and Leal (2013) reported on the masturbatory behavior of 3,687 Portuguese women via completion of an Internet questionnaire. Twenty-nine percent reported having masturbated in the past month (91% reported ever having masturbated). Masturbation was related to having more sexual fantasies and greater ease in becoming sexually aroused and achieving an orgasm. A minority of the women reported feeling shame and guilt associated with their masturbation.

---

4. *Expressing Love*   Williams and Russell (2013) found that women in romantic relationships are significantly more likely to tell their partners that they love them.

5. *Sexual Thoughts*   Based on a national sample, women are much less preoccupied with sex than men: 19% of women, in contrast to 54% of men, report thinking about sex "every day" or "several times a day" (Michael, Gagnon, Laumann, & Kolata, 1994).

> *I don't think boys, in general, watch the emotional world of relationships as closely as girls do. Girls track that world all day long, like watching the weather.*
>
> Carol Gilligan, gender researcher

6. *Orgasm*   Women are less likely than men to experience orgasm. This is particularly true at first intercourse. Seven percent of women, in contrast to 79% of men, reported orgasm during their first intercourse experience (Sprecher, Barbee, & Schwartz, 1995). Lower orgasmic frequency is related not only to sexual technique (less contact with the clitoris) but also to traditional female role socialization that she be more attentive to her partner's than her own sexual enjoyment/pleasure.

7. *Number of Partners*   Women report having fewer sexual partners than men. In a national sample of interviews with 1,669 women, the mean total number of partners with whom they reported having had vaginal intercourse was 6.7; the mean total number of partners reported by 3,321 men was 13.6 (Cubbins & Tanfer, 2000). Traditional female role socialization teaches women to limit the number of sexual partners, so they will not be perceived as being "loose" or immoral. In India, women that adhere to Hinduism—especially among the upper castes—are expected to have only one husband, not to divorce and not to remarry when their husband dies.

Cultural Diversity

Lu and colleagues (2013), who surveyed 2,668 Chinese senior high school students in Shanghai, reported a lower incidence of female sexual behavior in China. The percentages of females and males who reported ever having had sexual intercourse were 3% and 11%, respectively.

8. *Other sexual differences*   Table 5-1 reveals several additional differences (although small) between women and men, including that women are less likely to report that they are hedonistic about sex, less likely to have hooked up, more likely to have been cheated on, more likely to have been stalked, and more likely to have been pressured to have sex by a person they were dating.

TABLE **5-1**	Differences in Reported Sexual Behavior Between Undergraduate Females and Males (n = 4,567)	
	Female (3,464)	Male (1,103)
"I am a hedonist."	17%	29%
"I have "hooked up" or had sex the first night I met someone."	22%	34%
"A romantic partner cheated on me."	51%	39%
"I have been stalked."	28%	18%
"I have been pressured to have sex by a person I was dating."	40%	19%

Source: Hall, S. and Knox, D. (2013). Relationship and sexual behaviors of a sample of 4,567 university students. Unpublished data collected for this text. Department of Family and Consumer Sciences, Ball State University and Department of Sociology, East Carolina University.

5.5c Male Sexuality

Male sexuality also differs from female sexuality in a number of ways including a reverse of the findings for women identified above. These differences include that men are less likely to value being in a committed relationship, show less concern about body issues, are more likely to masturbate, less likely to say "I love you," more likely to report thinking about sex, more likely to orgasm, and more likely to have a higher number of sexual partners than women. In addition, undergraduate males are more likely to report being hedonistic, having hooked up, having cheated, stalking a partner, and pressuring a dating partner to have sex. Simms and Byers (2013) emphasized that males are very clear in their intentions—they move the interaction and relationship toward a sexual outcome. Higher levels of sexual behavior among males is also true when race is considered. African American males reported higher incidence of sexual behavior than African American females. (Almendarez & Wilson, 2013). Not included in the discussion above is the fact that men are more likely to worry about sexual performance ("Will I be able to get or to keep my erection?"), pay for sex (e.g., hire prostitutes), and be interested in group sex.

> *We need a new definition of masculinity in this new century: a definition that is more about the character of men's hearts and the depths of their souls than about the size of their biceps, wallets, or penises …*
>
> Michael S. Kimmel, *Manhood in America*

Men and women are also held to different sexual standards. The double standard means that there is one standard for men and one for women. Men who have a high number of sexual partners are viewed with more approval than women who have a high number of sexual partners. Terms such as whore, slut, and trollop are specific to women.

The different gender roles sometimes means one or the other partner in a relationship is getting more or less out of the interaction. The Global Measure of Equity/Inequity is designed to measure this phenomenon.

SELF-ASSESSMENT 5-1: GLOBAL MEASURE OF EQUITY/INEQUITY

Consider what you put into your dating relationship or marriage, compared with what you get out of it, and what your partner puts in, compared with what she/he gets out of it. How does your dating relationship or marriage "stack up"? Record the number that best describes how you rate your relationship____

 +3 = I am getting a much better deal than my partner.
 +2 = I am getting a somewhat better deal.
 +1 = I am getting a slightly better deal.
  0 = We are both getting an equally good, or bad, deal.
 −1 = My partner is getting a slightly better deal.
 −2 = My partner is getting a somewhat better deal.
 −3 = My partner is getting a much better deal than I am

Scores range from +3.00 to −3.00. Scores between +3 and +1.5 reflect a partner who is over-benefiting in the relationship; scores between +1.49 to −1.49 suggest a degree of equity in the relationship; and scores from −1.50 to −3.0 indicate a partner who is under-benefitting in the relationship.

Source: Traupmann, J., Petersen, R., Utne, M., and Hatfield, E. (1981). Measuring equity in intimate relations. *Applied Psychological Measurement 5:* 467–480.

5.6 Gender Role Changes

Imagine a society in which women and men each develop characteristics, lifestyles, and values that are independent of gender role stereotypes. Characteristics such as strength, independence, logical thinking, and sexual aggressiveness are no longer associated with maleness, just as sexual passivity, dependence, emotions, intuitiveness, and nurturance are no longer associated with femaleness. Both sexes are considered equal: women and men may pursue the same occupational, political, and domestic roles. Some gender scholars have suggested that people in such a society would be neither feminine nor masculine but would be described as androgynous. The next sections discuss androgyny, gender role transcendence, and gender postmodernism.

5.6a Androgyny

Androgyny
Having traits stereotypically associated with both masculinity and femininity

Gender role transcendence
Abandonment of gender schema, or becoming "gender aschematic," so that personality traits, social and occupational roles, and other aspects of an individual's life become divorced from gender categories

Androgyny is a blend of traits that are stereotypically associated with masculinity and femininity. Lady Gaga is androgynous. Sometimes she appears publicly as a woman and other times as a man. Other androgynous celebrities include David Bowie, Boy George, Patti Smith, and Annie Lennox. The following explains the two forms of androgyny:

> *Well, there's a little bit of man in every woman and a little bit of woman in every man.*
>
> Betty Smith, American author
> *A Tree Grows in Brooklyn*

1. Physiological androgyny
    refers to intersexed individuals, discussed earlier in the chapter. The genitals are neither clearly male nor female, and there is a mixing of "female" and "male" chromosomes and hormones.

2. Behavioral androgyny refers to the blending or reversal of traditional male and female behavior, so that a biological male may be very passive, gentle, and nurturing and a biological female may be very assertive, rough, and selfish.

Androgyny may also imply flexibility of traits; for example, an androgynous individual may be emotional in one situation, logical in another, assertive in another, and so forth. Gender role identity (androgyny, masculinity, femininity) was assessed in a sample of Korean and American college students with androgyny emerging as the largest proportion in the American sample and the femininity group in the Korean sample (Shin, Shin, Yang, & Edwards, 2010). Xishan and colleagues (2012) assessed the gender role type (masculine, feminine, androgynous, undifferentiated) of 434 undergraduates and found that most were of two types: androgynous and undifferentiated. Of these, the androgynous group had the highest self-esteem and used positive coping strategies (e.g., exercise rather than drinking).

5.6b Gender Role Transcendence

Beyond the concept of androgyny is that of gender role transcendence. We associate many aspects of our world—including colors, foods, social or occupational roles, and personality traits—with either masculinity or femininity. The concept of **gender role transcendence** means abandoning gender frameworks and looking at phenomena independent of traditional gender categories.

This photo depicts the "feminine" Lady Gaga. But she also appears in public as a man.
Source: AP Wide World Photos

Transcendence is not equal for women and men. Although females are becoming more masculine—in part because our society values whatever is masculine—men are not becoming more feminine. Indeed, adolescent boys may be described as very gender-entrenched. Beyond gender role transcendence is gender postmodernism.

No longer is the female destined solely for the home and the rearing of the family nor the male for the marketplace.

William J. Brennen, Supreme Court Justice

5.6c Gender Postmodernism

Gender postmodernism abandons the notion of gender as natural and emphasizes that gender is socially constructed. Fifteen years ago, Monro (2000) noted that people in the postmodern society would no longer be categorized as male or female but be recognized as capable of many identities—"a third sex" (p. 37). A new conceptualization of "trans" people calls for new social structures, "based on the principles of equality, diversity and the right to self determination" (p. 42). No longer would our society telegraph transphobia but embrace pluralization "as an indication of social evolution, allowing greater choice and means of self-expression concerning gender" (p. 42).

Gender postmodernism
State in which there is a dissolution of male and female categories as currently conceptualized in Western capitalist society

Chapter Summary

Women and men have different biological makeups and socializations that influence differences in their sexuality.

Terminology

Sex refers to the biological distinction between females and males, whereas gender refers to the social and psychological characteristics often associated with being female or male. For example, characteristics typically associated with the female gender include being gentle, emotional, and cooperative; characteristics associated with the male gender include being aggressive, rational, and competitive. Other terms related to sex and gender include gender identity (psychological view of one's self as a man or a woman), transgendered (broad term describing persons of one biological sex displaying behavior typically associated with the other sex), gender role (behavior associated with being defined as male or female), sexual identity (broad term including one's being a man or woman and one's sexual orientation), and gender role ideology (the role relationship between women and men).

Biological Beginnings

The biological sex of an individual is determined by chromosomes (XX for female, XY for male); gonads (ovaries for female, testes for male); hormones (greater proportion of estrogen and progesterone than testosterone in the female, greater proportion of testosterone than estrogen and progesterone in the male); internal sex organs (Fallopian tubes, uterus, and vagina for female; epididymis, vas deferens, and seminal vesicles for male); and external genitals (vulva for female, penis and scrotum for male). MicroSort is technology that allows parents to select the sex of their unborn child with 93% accuracy for females and 82% accuracy for males.

Chromosomal abnormalities and fetal hormones have significant physical and psychological outcomes for the individual. Individuals may also be intersexed which suggests that males and females exist on a continuum with the possibility of having characteristics of both.

Theories of Gender Role Development

Sociobiology emphasizes biological sources of social behavior, such as sexual aggression on the part of males due to higher levels of testosterone. Identification theory focuses on the influence of the same-sex parent when children are learning gender roles. Social learning theory discusses how children are rewarded and punished for expressing various gender role behaviors. Cognitive-developmental theorists are concerned with the developmental ages at which children are capable of learning social roles. Social learning theory emphasizes the models that children are exposed to as they learn about gender roles

Agents of Gender Role Socialization

Parents, peers, teachers/educational materials, religion, and the media project and encourage traditional gender roles for women and men. The cumulative effect is the perpetuation of gender stereotypes. Each agent of socialization reinforces gender roles that are learned from other agents of socialization, thereby creating a gender role system that is deeply embedded in our culture.

Effects of Gender Role Socialization on Relationships and Sexuality

Female sexuality is characterized by the desire for relationship commitment, a negative body image, lower frequency of masturbation, greater comfort in expressing love, lower frequency of sexual thoughts, less frequent orgasms and fewer sexual partners than males. In contrast, are slower to engage in an emotional and committed relationship, have minimal body image issues, report higher frequency of masturbation, etc. They also worry about sexual performance ("Will I be able to get or to keep my erection?,"), pay for sex (e.g., hire prostitutes), and show a higher interest in group sex.

Gender Role Changes

Androgyny refers to a blend of traits that are stereotypically associated with masculinity and femininity. Androgyny may also imply flexibility of traits and is associated with high self-esteem. Gender postmodernism predicts a new era in which people are no longer characterized as male or female but will be recognized as capable of many identities.

Web Links

Genetics and IVF Institute
http://www.givf.com/contactus/index.shtml

Intersex Initiative
http://www.intersexinitiative.org

National Transgender Advocacy
http://www.genderadvocates.org/links/national.html

North American Task Force on Intersex
http://www.isna.org/node/153

The United Kingdom Intersex Association
http://www.ukia.co.uk/

Key Terms

Additional study resources are available at www.BVTLab.com

Love and Sexuality

The greatest fear in life is not that it will end, but that it will never begin.

J. H. Newman, Cardinal

Chapter Outline

Objectives

1. Describe historical and contemporary conceptions of love.

2. Explain the differences between romanticism and realism.

3. List the three central elements of love.

4. Review the various love styles.

5. Know the similarities and differences of love and sex.

6. Define "hooking up" and "friends with benefits."

7. Explain polyamory, the advantages and disadvantages.

8. List the various challenges to sexual intimacy.

9. Discuss love and sex in the workplace.

10. Identify the cultural, sociological, and psychological factors involved in mate selection.

Source: Chelsea Curry

TRUTH OR FICTION?

T/F   Most friends with benefits participants have a clear understanding of their relationship and the "rules" for their future.

T/F   Polyamory, like sexual orientation, is an innate predisposition for multiple sexual partners.

T/F   Women are more likely to report feelings of jealousy than men.

T/F   Over half of the workers in a national survey knew of a married person involved in an office romance.

T/F   A significant proportion of men in the United States seeking international wives have been married before.

Answers:
1.F   2.F   3.T   4.T   5.T

The opening quote for this chapter reflects that a core meaning of life is involvement in a romantic love relationship. The phrase "love of my life" reflects the value, yearning, and meaning we attribute to such a romantic involvement. Sex is also a core element of life. It is the basis of our existence (we resulted from a sexual act), where we came from in terms of our **family of origin** (the family in which we were born and reared), and where we are going in terms of our **family of procreation** (the family we begin when we have children with the partner with whom we pair bond). Since sex occurs in various contexts, this chapter is about the love context—the context most individuals report as the most fulfilling emotional and sexual context. We begin by reviewing the various ways love has been conceptualized.

Family of origin
Family into which an individual is born

Family of procreation
Family one begins by finding a mate, and having and rearing children

6.1 Love

Ask your friends or peers in your sexuality class to identify the characteristics of love. You will hear such words as *caring, commitment, trust, companionship, affection, happiness,* and *security*. The most notable characteristic of love is diversity—people have different conceptions of love, identify different elements associated with love, and categorize love as representing different styles.

6.1a Historical and Contemporary Conceptions of Love

Many of our present-day notions of love stem from early Buddhist, Greek, and Hebrew writings.

Buddhist Conception of Love

The Buddhists conceived of two types of love: an "unfortunate" kind of love (self-love) and a "good" kind of love (creative spiritual attainment). Love that represents creative spiritual attainment was described as "love of detachment," not in the sense of withdrawal from the emotional concerns of others, but in the sense of accepting people as they are and not requiring them to be different from their present selves as the price of friendly affection. To a Buddhist, the best love is one in which you accept others as they are without requiring them to be like you.

> *There's nothing half so sweet in life*
> *As love's young dream.*
>
> Thomas Moore, *Love's Young Dream*

Greek and Hebrew Conceptions of Love

Three concepts of love introduced by the Greeks and reflected in the New Testament are phileo, agape, and eros. *Phileo* refers to love based on friendship; it can exist between family members, friends, and lovers. The city of Philadelphia was named after this phileo type of love. Another variation of phileo love is *philanthropia*, the Greek word meaning "love of humankind."

Agape refers to a love based on a concern for the well-being of others. Agape is spiritual, not sexual, in nature. This type of love is altruistic and requires nothing in return. "Whatever I can do to make your life happy" is the motto of the agape lover, even if this means giving up the beloved to someone else. Such love is not always reciprocal.

Eros refers to sexual love. This type of love seeks self-gratification and sexual expression. In Greek mythology, Eros was the god of love and the son of Aphrodite. Plato described "true" eros as sexual love that existed between two men. According to Plato's conception of eros, homosexual love was the highest form of love because it existed independent of the procreative instinct and free from the bonds of matrimony. Also, women had low status and were uneducated, and therefore not considered ideal partners for the men. By implication, love and marriage were separate.

Love in Medieval Europe—From Economics to Romance

Love in the 1100s was a concept influenced by economic, political, and family structure. In medieval Europe, kings controlling geographical regions, or kingdoms, owned land and wealth. When so much wealth and power were at stake, love was not to be trusted as the mechanism for choosing spouses for royal offspring. Rather, marriages of the sons and daughters of the aristocracy were arranged with the heirs of other states with whom an alliance was sought. Love was not tied to marriage but was conceptualized— even between people not married or of the same sex—as adoration of physical beauty (often between a knight and his beloved), and as spiritual and romantic.

The presence of kingdoms and estates and the patrimonial households declined with the English revolutions of 1642 and 1688 and the French Revolution of 1789. No longer did aristocratic families hold power; instead, it was transferred to individuals through parliaments or other national bodies. Even today, English monarchs are figureheads, with the real business of international diplomacy being handled by Parliament. Because wealth and power were no longer in the hands of individual aristocrats, the need to control mate selection decreased and the role of love changed. Marriage became less of a political and business arrangement, and more of a mutually desired emotional union between spouses. Just as partners in medieval society were held together by bureaucratic structure, a new mechanism—love—would now provide the emotional and social bonding. Hence, love changed from it's medieval definition (in which it was irrelevant to marriage, since individuals from aristocratic families were to marry even though they were not in love) to a feeling that bonded a woman and man together for marriage.

This couple of 30 years represents conjugal (married) or realistic love.
Source: Bob Bradley

6.1b Love on a Continuum from Romanticism to Realism

Romantic love today may be conceptualized as existing on a continuum from romanticism to realism. Romantics believe in love at first sight, one true love, and that love conquers all. Realists disagree with all these beliefs. Realists believe that love takes time to develop, that there are numerous people with whom one may fall in love, and that love does not conquer all. The Self-Assessment: Love Attitudes Scale provides a way for you to assess where you fall on the continuum from romanticism to realism.

> We sometimes encounter people, even perfect strangers, who begin to interest us at first sight, somehow suddenly, all at once, before a word has been spoken.
>
> Fyodor Dostoevsky, Russian author

SELF-ASSESSMENT 6-1:
THE LOVE ATTITUDES SCALE

This scale is designed to assess the degree to which you are romantic or realistic in your attitudes toward love. There are no right or wrong answers.

Directions

After reading each sentence carefully, write the number to the left of each item that best represents the degree to which you agree or disagree with the sentence.

1 = Strongly agree
2 = Mildly agree
3 = Undecided
4 = Mildly disagree
5 = Strongly disagree

1. ___ Love doesn't make sense. It just is.
2. ___ When you fall "head over heels" in love, it's sure to be the real thing.
3. ___ To be in love with someone you would like to marry but can't is a tragedy.
4. ___ When love hits, you know it.
5. ___ Common interests are really unimportant; as long as each of you is truly in love, you will adjust.
6. ___ It doesn't matter if you marry after you have known your partner for only a short time as long as you know you are in love.
7. ___ If you are going to love a person, you will "know" after a short time.
8. ___ As long as two people love each other, the educational differences they have really do not matter.
9. ___ You can love someone even though you do not like any of that person's friends.
10. ___ When you are in love, you are usually in a daze.
11. ___ Love "at first sight" is often the deepest and most enduring type of love.
12. ___ When you are in love, it really does not matter what your partner does because you will love him or her anyway.
13. ___ As long as you really love a person, you will be able to solve the problems you have with the person.
14. ___ Usually you can really love and be happy with only one or two people in the world.
15. ___ Regardless of other factors, truly loving a person is a good enough reason to marry that person.
16. ___ It is necessary to be in love with the one you marry to be happy.
17. ___ Love is more of a feeling than a relationship.
18. ___ People should not get married unless they are in love.
19. ___ Most people truly love only once during their lives.
20. ___ Somewhere there is an ideal mate for most people.
21. ___ In most cases, you will "know it" when you meet the right partner.
22. ___ Jealousy usually varies directly with love; that is, the more you are in love, the greater your tendency to become jealous will be.
23. ___ When you are in love, you are motivated by what you feel rather than by what you think.
24. ___ Love is best described as an exciting rather than a calm thing.
25. ___ Most divorces probably result from falling out of love rather than failing to adjust.
26. ___ When you are in love, your judgment is usually not too clear.

27. ___ Love comes only once in a lifetime.

28. ___ Love is often a violent and uncontrollable emotion.

29. ___ When selecting a marriage partner, differences in social class and religion are of small importance compared with love.

30. ___ No matter what anyone says, love cannot be understood.

Scoring

Add the numbers you wrote down. 1 (strongly agree) is the most romantic response and 5 (strongly disagree) is the most realistic response. The lower your total score (30 is the lowest possible score), the more romantic your attitudes toward love. The higher your total score (150 is the highest possible score), the more realistic your attitudes toward love. A score of 90 places you at the midpoint between being an extreme romantic and an extreme realist. Both men and women undergraduates typically score above 90, with men scoring closer to 90 than women.

When you're in love, it's the most glorious two and a half days of your life.

Richard Lewis, comedian

Source: Knox, D. "Conceptions of Love at Three Developmental Levels" Dissertation, Florida State University. Permission to use the scale for research available from David Knox at davidknox2@yahoo.com or by contacting Dr. Knox, Department of Sociology, East Carolina University, Greenville, NC 27858.

Take a moment to answer the following questions. Do you and your partner tend to be romantics or realists? Is it important that you agree on your view of love? Can a romantic and a realist live happily ever after?

6.1c Three Elements of Love

Robert Sternberg (1986) identified several states of love on the basis of the presence or absence of three elements: intimacy, passion, and commitment. Sternberg defined the following three elements in his "triangular theory of love":

- *Intimacy:* Emotional connectedness or bondedness
- *Passion:* Romantic feelings and physical sexual desire
- *Commitment:* Desire to maintain the relationship

According to Sternberg (1986), various types of love can be described on the basis of the three elements he identified:

1. *Nonlove*   Absence of all three components

2. *Liking*   Intimacy without passion or commitment

3. *Infatuation*   Passion without intimacy or commitment

4. *Romantic love*   Intimacy and passion without commitment

5. *Companionate love*   Intimacy and commitment without passion

6. *Fatuous love*   Passion and commitment without intimacy

7. *Empty love*   Commitment without passion or intimacy

8. *Consummate love*   Combination of intimacy, passion, and commitment

Love is an ideal thing, marriage a real thing; a confusion of the real with the ideal never goes unpunished.

Goethe, German writer

Each of these types of love has some variation in reality. For example, some level of commitment is felt between romantic lovers (romantic love), and some level of passion is felt between companionate lovers (companionate love). However, the predominant focus of romantic love is passion, and the predominant quality of companionate love is commitment.

Individuals bring different love triangles to the table of love. One lover may bring a predominance of passion with some intimacy but no commitment (romantic love), whereas the other person brings commitment but no passion or intimacy (empty love). The triangular theory of love allows lovers to see the degree to which they are matched in terms of the three basic elements of passion, intimacy, and commitment.

Cultural Diversity

Love in the West and love in the East differ. Those in individualistic America tend to be more romantic, require that love be present before marriage, and believe that love continues as a prerequisite for staying together. Those in familistic Eastern countries (China, India, Indonesia) tend to be more realistic in their view of love, require that love follow rather than precede marriage, and do not require that love continue for the couple to stay together. The result is that Western societies (e.g., America) have a very high divorce rate (e.g., 40%–50%) compared to Eastern societies, which have very low divorce rates (e.g., under 10%).

6.2 Love Styles

Hendrick and Hendrick (1992) described and studied another schema for looking at types of love relationships or orientations toward love (based on the theory of Canadian sociologist John Alan Lee). Although people may show characteristics of more than one love style, they are often characterized as exhibiting one of six different love styles:

- *Eros*   Passionate love, not limited to physical passion
- *Ludus*   Game-playing love—for mutual enjoyment without serious intent
- *Storge*   Friendship; companionate love
- *Pragma*   Pragmatic and practical love
- *Mania*   Manic, jealous, obsessive love
- *Agape*   Selfless, idealistic love

Women tend to reflect eros and pragma styles, and men the ludus style. The love styles associated with the lowest relationship satisfaction are ludus and mania styles; eros and agape love styles are associated with the highest relationship satisfaction (Montgomery & Sorell, 1997).

6.2a Love and Sex: Similarities and Differences

In the following section, we review the similarities and differences between love and sex. In general, love and sex are more similar than they are different.

Similarities Between Love and Sex

1. Both love and sex represent intense, enjoyable feelings. To be involved in a love relationship is one of the most intense, enjoyable experiences individuals have. However, sex is also an intense and enjoyable experience. Being told that one is loved and experiencing an orgasm are both intense and enjoyable.

2. Both love and sex involve physiological changes. When a person is in an intense love relationship, his or her brain produces phenylethylamine, a chemical correlate of amphetamine, which may result in a giddy feeling similar to an amphetamine high. When a love relationship ends, the person goes through withdrawal because there is less phenylethylamine in his or her system. The emotional pain can be agonizing and similar to withdrawal from cocaine.

    The physiological changes the body experiences during sexual excitement have been well documented by Masters and Johnson (1966) in their observations of more than 10,000 orgasms. Such changes include increased heart rate, blood pressure, and breathing.

3. Both love and sex have a cognitive component. To experience the maximum pleasure from both, the person must label or interpret the experience in positive terms. For love to develop, each person in the relationship must define being together, looking at each other, sharing activities, and talking as enjoyable.

    Positive labeling is also important in sex. Each person's touch, kiss, caress, and body type are different; sexual pleasure depends on labeling sexual interaction with that person as enjoyable. "I can't stand the way he kisses me" and "I love the way he kisses me" are two interpretations of kissing the same person, but only one of these interpretations will make the event pleasurable.

4. Both love and sex may be expressed in various ways. Expressions of love may include words ("I love you"), gifts (flowers or candy), behaviors (being on time, a surprise text message, washing the partner's car), and touch (holding hands, tickling). Similarly, sex as well as love may be expressed through a glance, embrace, kiss, massage, and intercourse.

5. The need for love and sex increases with deprivation. The more we get, the less we feel we need; the less we get, the more we feel we need. The all-consuming passion of Romeo and Juliet, perhaps the most celebrated love story of all time, undoubtedly was fed by their enforced separation.

    Deprivation has the same effect on the need for sex. Statements of people who have been separated from their lover may be similar to "I'm horny as a mountain goat," "We're going to spend the weekend in bed," and "The second thing we're going to do when we get together is take a drive out in the country."

Differences Between Love and Sex

There are several differences between love and sex.

1. Love is crucial for human happiness; sex is important, but not crucial. Although sex is regarded as a life enhancing experience, no one has suggested that its value supersedes love.

2. Love is pervasive, whereas sex tends to be localized. Love is felt all over, but sexual feeling is most often associated with various body parts (lips, breasts, or genitals). People do not say of love as they do of sex, "It feels good here."

3. Love tends to be more selective than sex. The standards that people have for a love partner are generally higher than those they have for a sex partner. Expressions like "I'll take anything wearing pants," "Just show me a room full of skirts," and "I wouldn't kick him out of bed" reflect the desire to have sex with someone—anyone. Love wants *the* person rather than *a* person.

> The standards for a love partner may also be different from those for a sexual partner. For example, some people develop relationships to meet emotional/intimacy needs that are not met by their sexual partners. A sexual component need not be a part of the love relationship they have with those they love.

personal choices 6-1

Sex With or Without Love

Most sexual encounters occur on a continuum from no love involvement to love involvement. Opinions vary with regard to whether an emotional relationship is a worthy prerequisite for sexual involvement:

> Sex is good and beautiful when both parties want it; but when one person wants sex only, that's bad. I love sex, but I like to feel that the man cares about me. I can't handle the type of sexual relationship where one night I spend the night with him and the next night he spends the night with someone else. I feel like I am being used. There are still a few women around, like me, who need the commitment before sex. (authors' files)

The two most frequently identified regrets about their first intercourse experience made by the 292 undergraduate respondents in a study by Thomsen and Chang (2000) were that they wished they had waited and they wished they had been in a committed (love) relationship.

About half of undergraduates in one study reported that love is not necessary for a sexual encounter. In a sample of 1,102 undergraduate males, 52% reported that they had had sex without love compared with 49% of 3,468 undergraduate females (Hall & Knox, 2013). "Some of the best sex I've had," remarked one person, "was with people I was not in love with."

The ideal that sex with love is wholesome and sex without love is exploitative may be an untenable position. For example, two strangers can meet, share each other sexually, have a deep mutual admiration for each other's sensuous qualities, and then go their separate ways. Such an encounter is not necessarily an example of sexual exploitation. Rather, it may be an example of two individuals who have a preference for independence and singlehood rather than emotional involvement, commitment, and marriage.

Each person in a sexual encounter will undoubtedly experience different degrees of love feelings, and the experience of each may differ across time. One woman reported that the first time she had intercourse with her future husband was shortly after they had met in a bar. She described their first sexual encounter as "raw naked sex" with no emotional feelings. But as they continued to see each other over a period of months, an emotional relationship developed; and "sex took on a love meaning for us."

Sex with love can also drift into sex without love. One man said he had been deeply in love with his wife, but that they had gradually drifted apart. Sex between them was no longer sex with love. On the other hand, some people report being in relationships with partners who feign love but actually use them for sex. Both love and sex can be viewed on a continuum. Love feelings can range from nonexistent to intense, and relationships can range from limited sexual interaction to intense interaction. Hence, rarely are sexual encounters completely with or without love; rather, they include varying degrees of emotional involvement. Also, rarely are romantic love relationships completely with or without sex. Rather, they display varying degrees of sexual expression. Where on the continuum one chooses to be—at what degree of emotional and sexual involvement— will vary from person to person and from time to time.

6.3 Contexts for Sex: "Hooking Up" and "Friends with Benefits"

According to sociologists Barbara Risman and Pepper Schwartz (2004), the sexual revolution has changed the way American society thinks about sex as a an individual right, rather than being reserved for reproduction or marital intimacy. "Premarital, unmarried, and post-divorce sex are now seen as individual choices for both women and men. The revolutionary principle that separated the right to sexual pleasure from marriage (at least for adults) is no longer controversial" (pp. 276–277). However, if marital ties are no longer an assumed (or at least widely stated) requisite for sexual intimacy, what types or depths of relationship form the context for contemporary sexual expression? Hooking up and friends with benefits have emerged as two primary contexts.

6.3a Hooking Up

Hooking up is a sexual encounter that occurs between individuals who have no relationship commitment. There is generally no expectation of seeing one another again, and alcohol is often involved. Chang and colleagues (2012) identified the unspoken rules of hooking up: doing so is not dating, hooking up is not a romantic relationship, hooking up is physical, hooking up is secret, one who hooks up is to expect no subsequent phone calls from their hooking up partner, and condoms/protection should always be used (though only 57% of their sample reported condom use on hookups). Aubrey and Smith (2013) also noted that hooking up reflects a set of cultural beliefs.. These beliefs include that hooking up is shameless fun, will enhance one's status in one's peer group, and reflects one's sexual freedom/control over one's sexuality.

Data on the frequency of college students having experienced a hookup varies. Barriger and Velez-Blasini (2013), in their review of literature, found that between 77% and 85% of undergraduates reported having hooked up within the previous year. Sociologist Paula England—reporting on more than 17,000 students at 20 colleges and universities (from Stanford University's Social Life Survey)—revealed that 72% of both women and men reported having hooked up with some combination of the following: 40% intercourse, 35% kiss or touch, 12% hand/genital, and 12% oral sex. Men reported having 10 hookups, women 7 (Jayson, 2011). In another study of 832 undergraduates, 60% of Caucasians and 35% of African Americans reported having "hooked up."

Fieldera and Careya (2010) surveyed 118 first-semester female college students on their hook up experiences (60% had done so). Most hookups involved friends (47%) or acquaintances (23%) rather than strangers. Olmstead and colleagues (2012) surveyed

Hooking up
Meeting someone and becoming sexually involved that same evening with no commitment or expectation beyond the encounter

158 first-semester men to assess those factors predictive of hooking up their first semester on campus. Those who had hooked up before coming to college (77% had done so), those who had a pattern of binge drinking, and those who had casual sexual attitudes were more likely to hook up their first semester on campus.

Chang and colleagues (2012) surveyed 369 undergraduates (69% reported having hooked up) and found that those with pro-feminist attitudes were not more likely to hook up. However, women who hooked up were more likely than men to agree with the unspoken rules of hooking up: no commitment, no emotional intimacy, and no future obligation to each other. They were clear that hooking up was about sex with no future. These data reflect that hooking up is becoming the norm on college and university campuses. Female students outnumber male students (60 to 40), which means women are less able to bargain sex for commitment since men have a lot of options, and individuals want to remain free for summer internships to study abroad, and to marry later (Uecker & Regnerus, 2011). Kalish and Kimmel (2011) suggested that hooking up is a way of confirming one's heterosexuality.

Women and men may also experience the hooking up experience differently. Bradshaw and colleagues (2010) found that men benefited more since they were able to have casual sex with a willing partner and no commitment. Women were more at risk for feeling regret/guilt, becoming depressed, and defining the experience negatively. Women in hookup contexts were less likely to experience cunnilingus but often were expected to provide fellatio (Blackstrom, Armstrong, & Puentes, 2012).

Both women and men had experienced a hook up in the context of deception (neither being open about their relationship goals) and may have exposed themselves to an STI. Few long-term relationships begin with a "hook up." When 4,567 undergraduates were presented with the statement "People who 'hook up' and have sex the first night don't end up in a stable relationship," 45% of the males and 55% of the females agreed (Hall & Knox, 2013).

6.3b Friends with Benefits

While hooking up is not about love and commitment, friends with benefits involves a blurred understanding of the relationship between two friends who have sex: How close are they as friends, does their friendship include love feelings, are their feelings sometimes romantic feelings, and what is the future of the "friendship"? Karlsen and Traeen (2013) asserted that the majority of subjects did not explicitly define the relationship or have explicit rules to regulate it.

Mongeau and colleagues (2013) defined **friends with benefits** as involving platonic friends (i.e., those not involved in a romantic relationship) who engage in some degree of sexual intimacy on multiple occasions. This sexual activity could range from kissing to sexual intercourse and is a repeated part of a friendship, not just a one-night stand. In a sample of individuals who had had at least one FWB relationship in the last year, more men than women (54% versus 43%) reported having had such an experience (Owen & Fincham, 2011). Mongeau and colleagues (2013) identified seven types of friends with benefits relationships (FWBR) identified the percentages of each.

1. *True friends*   These are close friends who have sex on multiple occasions (similar to but not labeled as romantic partners). The largest percentage (26%) of the 258 respondents reported this type of FWBR.

2. *Just sex*   The focus is sex and a serial hookup with the same person, with no care about that person other than as a sexual partner (12%).

3. *Network opportunism*   Being part of the same social network "hanging out together, and sometimes" going home to have sex together when there is no better option—a sort of sexual fail safe (15%)

Friends with benefits
Nonromantic friends who also have a sexual relationship

4. *Successful transition*   The intentional use of a friends with benefits relationship to transition into a romantic relationship (8%)

5. *Unintentional transition*   A sexual relationship that morphs into a romantic relationship without that transition being the initial intent. The relationship results from regular sex, hanging out together, etc. (8%).

6. *Failed transition*   One partner became involved, while the other did not. As a result, the relationship stalled. The lowest percentage (7%) of the 258 respondents reported this type FWBR.

7. *Transition out*   The couple was romantic, but the relationship ended; however, the sexual relationship continued (11%). Advantages to ex-sex include having a "safe" sexual partner, having a predictably "good" sexual partner who knows one's likes/dislikes, not increasing the number of lifetime sexual partners, and "fanning sexual flames might facilitate rekindling partners' emotional connections" (Mongeau, Knight, Williams, Eden, & Shaw, C., 2013).

These individuals are in a polyamorous relationship. The female has an independent loving and sexual relationship with each male and they with her. Each of the three also have love and sexual relationships with others.
Source: David Knox

Advantages of being in a FWBs relationship involve having a regular sexual partner, not feeling vulnerable to having to "hook up" with a stranger just to have sex, minimizing one's exposure to STIs, not increasing the number of sexual partners, and feeling free to have other relationships (including sexual ones). Disadvantages include developing a bad reputation as someone who does not really care about emotional involvement, coping with the discrepancy of becoming more or less involved than the partner, and losing the capacity to give oneself emotionally.

6.4 Polyamory and Open Relationships

Polyamory means multiple loves (*poly* = many; *amorous* = love). Polyamory is a lifestyle in which two lovers embrace the idea of having multiple lovers. By agreement, each partner may have numerous emotional and sexual relationships. Antipolygamy legislation has framed polyamory as a sexual orientation, arguing that some people are immutably predisposed toward forming multiple relationships. Robinson (2013) interviewed 40 bisexual women and suggested that polyamory and monogamy are better viewed as strategies of sexual expression rather than as immutable orientations. Hence, one is not "born to seek polyamory" but may seek a context of multiple partners independent of sexual orientation. Aguilar (2013) was a participant observer at two communes who approved of polyamory. She noted how the social context in which a person lives influences him or her to behave consistent with the norms of the group.

About half of the 100 members of Twin Oaks Intentional Community in Louisa, Virginia, (www.twinoaks.org) are polyamorous in that each partner may have several emotional or physical relationships with others at the same time. Although most are not legally married, these adults view themselves as emotionally bonded to each other and may even rear children together. Polyamory is not swinging, as polyamorous lovers are concerned about enduring, intimate relationships that include sex. People in polyamorous relationships seek to rid themselves of jealous feelings and to increase their level of **compersion**—feeling happy for a partner who enjoys an emotional and sexual relationship with another.

> *To cheat one's self out of love is the most terrible deception. It is an eternal loss for which there is no reparation, neither in time or in eternity.*
>
> Søren Kierkegaard, Danish philosopher

Polyamory
Involvement of more than three individuals in a pair-bonded relationship (some of the individuals may be married to each other) who have an emotional, sexual, and sometimes parenting relationship

Compersion
The opposite of jealousy, whereby a person feels positive about a lover's emotional and sexual enjoyment with another person

Compersion Is My Challenge

My name is Kate, and one of the guys I'm in love with is Paxus. We live at Twin Oaks, and we are polyamorous (poly is Latin for many and amor is Latin for love), which means we're open to having intimate relationships with more than one person. We're not "swingers" and we aren't polygamists. Our relationships are not quick-sex-overnight-encounters, but instead deeply committed relationships that we nurture over time.

Compersion is when one feels good about one's lover getting romantically involved with someone else. It is one of the key aspects that can help "poly" relationships function well. It's important for me to celebrate and honor the happiness of my partners when they're getting involved with other people. It's taken me awhile to develop my capacity for compersion—it certainly isn't something we learn from popular culture! When Paxus (or another of my partners) is developing a relationship with someone else, I sometimes worry that she is more interesting than me, or better in bed, or that he is more attracted to her. When those feelings come up for me, I communicate openly and directly with my partner about my fears, and we work together to address the fears and strengthen our relationship. It's not easy, and it takes commitment to do the deep emotional processing. For me, the benefits of polyamory (e.g., having rich relationships with several wonderful people, and moving away from the idea of love as possession) are well worth the effort.

6.4a Advantages and Disadvantages of Polyamory

Embracing polyamory has both advantages and disadvantages. Advantages of polyamory include greater variety in one's emotional and sexual life; the avoidance of hidden affairs and the attendant feelings of deception, mistrust, or betrayal; and the opportunity to have different needs met by different people. The disadvantages of polyamory involve having to manage one's feelings of jealousy, greater exposure of one's self and partners to human immunodeficiency virus and other sexually transmitted infections, and limited time with each partner. Of the latter, one polyamorous partner said, "With three relationships and a full-time job, I just don't have much time to spend with each partner so I'm frustrated about who I'll be with next. And managing the feelings of the other partners who want to spend time with me is a challenge."

6.4b A Short Primer on Polyamory*

This very brief and incomplete discussion focuses on polyamory, a relationship style in which people openly conduct sexual relationships with multiple partners. Polyamory is more emotionally intimate than swinging and offers the possibility of greater gender equality than polygyny because both men and women can have more than one partner. These relationships have a number of different elements that include (but are not limited to) levels of sexual exclusivity, numbers of people involved, and various degrees of emotional intimacy between partners.

Sexual Exclusivity

Many community members use the term polyamory, or more commonly "poly," as an umbrella term to encompass both polyamory and polyfidelity. Those in *polyamorous* relationships generally have sexually and (ideally) emotionally intimate extra dyadic relationships, with no promise of sexual exclusivity. **Polyfidelity** differs from polyamory in that polyfideles (the term for someone who practices polyfidelity) expect their partners to remain sexually exclusive within a group that is larger than two people, though some polyfidelitous groups have members who do not have sex with each other. Almost all polyfideles see each other as family members, regardless of the degree of sexual contact within their relationships. Not all polys in a relationship have sex with each other, and I call those who are emotionally intimate but not sexually connected *polyaffective*.

Polygeometry

The number of people involved in poly relationships varies and can include open couples, vees, triads, quads, and moresomes (all described below). As the number of people involved in a relationship rises, the relationships become more rare and potentially less stable. The most common form is the *open couple*, which is usually composed of two people who often are in a long-term relationship, cohabitate (some married, others unmarried), and have extradyadic sexual relationships. **Vees** are three-person relationships in which one member is sexually connected to each of the two others. The relationship between the two nonlovers can range from strangers (who are aware of and cordial with each other), to casual friends, to enemies. A *triad*, commonly understood as *ménage à trois*, generally includes three sexually involved adults. Sometimes triads begin as threesomes, but more often they form when a single joins an open couple or a larger group loses member(s). *Quads*, as the name implies, are groups of four adults most commonly formed when two couples join, although sometimes they develop when a triad adds a fourth or a moresome loses member(s). Quads are notoriously unstable, frequently losing someone to poly-style divorce. *Moresomes*, groups with five or more adult members, are larger, more fragile, and more complicated than quads.

Emotional Intimacy

Polys frequently use the terms *primary*, *secondary*, and *tertiary* to describe their varied levels of intimacy. *Primary* partners—sometimes corresponding to the larger cultural conception of a spouse—usually have long-term relationships, have joint finances, cohabitate, and make major life decisions together, and sometimes they have children. *Secondary* partners tend to keep their lives more separate than primary partners, frequently maintain separate finances and residences, may have less intense emotional connections than primaries, and usually discuss major life decisions, though they generally do not make those decisions jointly. *Tertiary* relationships are often less emotionally intimate, sometimes with long distance or more casual partners. Some tertiary relationships closely resemble swinging. Some poly families have *spice*, the poly word for more than one spouse.

> * *This section was written by and used with the permission of Dr. Elizabeth Sheff, Department of Sociology, Georgia State University, Atlanta, Georgia. Dr. Sheff conducted more than 40 interviews with persons involved in polyamory.*

6.4c Rules of an Open Relationship

While polyamorous relationships involve emotional as well as sexual involvement with others, **open relationships** are more sexual and recreation focused. These relationships involve individuals agreeing that they may have sexual encounters with others.

There are various rules with open relationships—only 2.6% of 2,922 said they were comfortable (Hall & Knox, 2013). The following are rules of a couple in an open relationship (author's files):

Polyfidelity
Partners in the group remain faithful (sexually exclusive) to everyone else in the group

Vees
Three-person relationships in which one member is sexually connected to each of the two others

Open relationships
Each partner agrees that the other can have sexual (and sometimes emotional) relationships with someone outside the couple relationship

1. *Honesty*   We tell each other everything we do with someone outside the relationship. If we flirt, we even tell that. Openness about our feelings is a must; if we get uncomfortable or jealous, we must talk about it. One example is a husband who was told by a woman at his work that she wanted to have sex with him. He said, "You'll need to ask my wife." The woman asked his wife who said, "Go ahead and get it out of your system." The husband began a lifelong affair with the woman with his wife's knowledge and approval (and the wife also began an affair with the woman's husband, with her own husband's knowledge). Both couples remained married to their respective spouses 25 years later.

2. *Recreational sex*   Sex with the other person will be purely recreational—it is not love, and the relationship with the other person is going nowhere. The people with whom we select to have sex must know that we have a loving committed relationship with someone else.

3. *Condom use*   A requirement every time.

4. *Approval*   Every person we have sex with must be approved by the partner in advance. Each partner has the right to veto a selection. The person in question must not be into partner snatching, looking for romance, or jealous. Persons off the list are co-workers, family, old lovers and old friends.

5. *Online hunting*   This is prohibited. Each agrees not to go looking on the Internet for sex partners.

6.5 Challenges to Intimate Sexual Relationships

Love is sometimes associated with distressing emotions such as jealousy, guilt, obsession, and stalking.

6.5a Jealousy

Jealousy can be defined as an emotional response to a perceived or real threat to an important or valued relationship. People experiencing jealousy fear being abandoned and feel anger toward the partner or the perceived competition. People become jealous when they fear replacement. Jealousy is not uncommon among undergraduates. Of 424 university males, 46% agreed with the statement, "I am a jealous person"; Of 1,105 university males, 49% agreed with the statement, "I am a jealous person"; of 3,477 undergraduate females, 54% agreed (Hall & Knox, 2013).

> *Jealousy in romance is like salt in food. A little can enhance the savor, but too much can spoil the pleasure—and under certain circumstances, can be life-threatening.*
>
> Maya Angelou, poet

Jealously is also more likely to occur early in a couple's relationship (e.g., new couples are working out their trust/levels of commitment). When noncohabiting, cohabiting, and married couples are compared in regard to jealously, married couples are the least likely to report jealousy in their relationship (Gatzeva & Paik, 2011).

Causes of Jealousy

Jealousy can be triggered by external or internal factors. External factors can be behaviors a partner engages in that are interpreted as (1) an emotional and/or sexual interest in someone (or something) else or (2) a lack of emotional and/or sexual interest in the primary partner. Buunk and colleagues (2010) found that what makes a woman jealous is the physical attractiveness of a rival ("She's a beautiful woman; no wonder my partner is interested"). What makes a man jealous is the rival's physical dominance ("I'm a runt compared to that guy").

Jealousy
Emotional response to a perceived or real threat to an important or valued relationship

Internal causes of jealousy refer to characteristics of individuals that predispose them to jealous feelings, independent of their partner's behavior. Internal causes of jealousy include the following:

1. *Mistrust*   If an individual has been cheated on in a previous relationship, that individual may learn to be mistrustful in subsequent relationships. Such mistrust may manifest itself in jealousy. Mistrust and jealousy may be intertwined. Indeed, one must be careful if cheated on in a previous relationship not to transfer those feelings to a new partner. Disregarding the past is not easy, but constantly reminding oneself of reality ("My new partner has given me zero reason to be distrustful") is important.

2. *Low self-esteem*   Individuals who have low self-esteem tend to be jealous because they lack a sense of self-worth and hence find it difficult to believe anyone can value and love them. Feelings of worthlessness may contribute to suspicions that someone else is valued more. It is devastating to a person with low self-esteem to discover that a partner has, indeed, selected someone else.

3. *Lack of perceived alternatives*   Individuals who have no alternative person or who feel inadequate in attracting others may be particularly vulnerable to jealousy. They feel that, if they do not keep the person they have, they will be alone (e.g., no one will want them).

4. *Insecurity*   Individuals who feel insecure in a relationship with their partner may experience higher levels of jealousy. They feel at any moment their partner could find someone more attractive and end the relationship with them.

Desirable Consequences of Jealousy

Barelds-Dijkstra and Barelds (2007) studied 961 couples and found not only that jealousy may signify that the partner is cared for (the implied message is "I love you and don't want to lose you to someone else") but also that the partner may learn that the development of other romantic and sexual relationships is unacceptable.

One wife said:

> When I started spending extra time with this guy at the office, my husband got jealous and told me he thought I was getting in over my head and asked me to cut back on the relationship because it was "tearing him up." I felt he really loved me when he told me this, and I chose to stop having lunch with the guy at work. (authors' files)

The researchers noted that making the partner jealous might also have the positive function of assessing the partner's commitment and of alerting the partner that one could leave for greener mating pastures. Hence, one partner may deliberately evoke jealousy to solidify commitment and ward off being taken for granted. In addition, sexual passion may be reignited if one partner perceives that another would take the love object away. That people want what others want is an adage that may be a trigger for feelings of jealousy.

The jealous are troublesome to others, but a torment to themselves.
William Penn, *Some Fruits of Solitude*, 1693

Undesirable Consequences of Jealousy

Shakespeare referred to jealousy as the "green-eyed monster," suggesting that it sometimes leads to undesirable outcomes for relationships. Jealousy, with its obsessive ruminations about the partner's alleged infidelity, can make individuals miserable. They are constantly thinking about the partner being with the new person, which they interpret as confirmation of their own inadequacy. If the jealousy results in repeated unwarranted accusations, a partner can tire of such attacks and seek to end the relationship with the accusing partner.

BVT *Lab*

Improve your test scores. Practice quizzes are available at **www.BVTLab.com**.

In its extreme form, jealousy may have devastating consequences. Possessive jealousy involves an attack on a partner or an alleged person to whom the partner is showing attention. People have stalked or killed the beloved and then killed themselves in reaction to rejected love. One example is the 2010 murder of University of Virginia student Yeardley Love by George Huguely. Jealousy over Love having broken up with Huguely and her seeing someone else were contributing motives to the brutal murder; Huguely beat her to death.

Gender Differences in Coping with Jealousy

Defined as "one's emotional reaction to the perception that one's love relationship may end because of a third party," jealousy was the topic of a study of 291 undergraduates where 51.9% "agreed" or "strongly agreed" that "jealousy is normal" (Breed, Knox, & Zusman, 2004).

Analysis of the data in regard to the women's and the men's reactions to jealousy revealed four significant differences:

1. *Food*   Women were significantly more likely than men to report that they turned to food when they felt jealous. Women (30.3%), in contrast to men (22%), said that they "always, often, or sometimes" looked to food when they felt jealous. One coed said, "When I feel jealous, my favorite guys are 'Ben and Jerry.'"

2. *Alcohol*   Men were significantly more likely than women to report that they drank alcohol or used drugs when they felt jealous. Men (46.9%), in contrast to women (27.1%), said that they "always, often, or sometimes" drank or used drugs to make the pain of jealousy go away.

3. *Friends*   Women were significantly more likely than men to report that they turned to friends when they felt jealous, with 37.9% of women, in contrast to 13.5% of men, stating that they "always" turned to friends for support when feeling jealous.

4. *Nonbelief that "jealousy shows love"*   Women were significantly more likely than men to disagree or to strongly disagree that "jealousy shows how much your partner loves you," with 63.2% of women, in contrast to 42.6% of men, disagreeing with the statement. This difference may be related to the fact that jealous and abusive males more often victimize women.

Zengel and colleagues (2013) studied a national sample of women and men and found that women reported higher levels of jealousy than men. The researchers also noted that men were more jealous when their partners' engaged in sexual intercourse with another man than when their partners were emotionally involved with someone else. Evolutionary theorists point out that men are wired to care about the paternity of their offspring ("Am I the biological father of this child?"), which is the basis of their focus on physical fidelity.

6.5b Guilt

Guilt is another emotion that may affect the quality of relationships and may influence sexual behavior. **Sexual guilt** is the feeling that results from the violation of one's own sexual values. Guilt may result when one goes against what one thinks he or she should not do ("I should not have gotten drunk and had intercourse")—students often refer to returning home as the "walk of shame" the next morning—or when one does not behave consistently with the way one thinks one should ("I should have been faithful").

A team of researchers (Weinberg & Lottes, 1995) examined guilt feelings reported by women and men in reference to their first and most recent intercourse experience. In their study, 75% of U.S. women, compared to 44% of U.S. men, felt guilty after their first intercourse experience. However, when asked about their most recent intercourse experience, 31% of the women and 44% of the men reported feeling guilty afterward. The lower percentage of women reporting guilt in their most recent intercourse experience may reflect a more stable emotional relationship context, which is the condition needed for cultural approval for female sexual expression.

In some cases, sexual guilt may interfere with a person's sexual well-being. For example, some women feel guilty about experiencing sexual pleasure because they have been taught that "sex is bad" and "good women do not enjoy sex." In this situation, sexual guilt may interfere with a woman's ability to become sexually aroused and experience orgasm, even within a loving and committed relationship. One woman in the authors' classes said, "I never felt sex was OK, not even after I was married. I think my Catholic background and prudish parents did me in."

Sexual guilt
Personal emotional reaction to engaging in sexual behavior that violates personal sexual values

Obsessive relational intrusion
Behavior of a stranger or an acquaintance who repeatedly invades one's physical or symbolic privacy in his or her attempts to have an intimate relationship

Love is merely a madness; and, I tell you, deserves a dark house and a whip as madmen do: and the reason why they are not so punished and cured is that lunacy is so ordinary that the whippers are in love too.

William Shakespeare

6.5c Obsession

In the name of love, people have stalked the beloved, shot the beloved, and killed themselves in reaction to rejected love. Although most instances of unrequited love are resolved adequately, **obsessive relational intrusion** (ORI) has come to be recognized in various forms. A stranger or an acquaintance may employ ORI by repeatedly invading one's physical or symbolic privacy in his or her attempts to have an intimate relationship. Activities may include sending text messages, calls, gifts, and repeated requests for dates. Some of these relationships may begin in the office (see Social Choices 6-1 section).

The workplace is a common context for sexual and emotional relationships to begin.
Source: Chelsea Curry

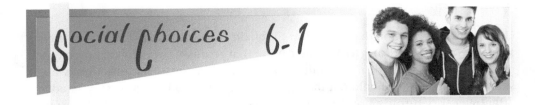

Love in the Workplace

With women being almost half of the American workforce, people delaying marriage until they are older, and workers being around each other for 8 or more hours a day, the workplace has become a common place for romantic relationships to develop. More future spouses may meet at work than in academic, social, or religious settings. Barack and Michelle Obama, Bill and Melinda Gates, and Brad Pitt and Angelina Jolie all met "on the job." A national survey of workers revealed that 44% of them had become involved in a romance with someone at work. In addition, 53% know a married co-worker who has had an office affair (Vault.com, 2013).

Although such relationships are most often between peers, sometimes a love relationship develops between individuals occupying different status positions. Such was the case of David Petraeus (CIA Director and retired four-star general) and Paula Broadwell, whom he met as his official biographer; that relationship resulted in Petraeus being fired. Other men who have become involved in office romances include David Letterman and John Edwards (former presidential candidate).

Advantages of an Office Romance

The energy that both fuels and results from intense love feelings can also fuel productivity on the job. If the coworkers eventually marry or enter a nonmarital but committed, long-term relationship, they may be more satisfied with and committed to their jobs than spouses whose partners work elsewhere. Working at the same location enables married couples to commute together, go to company-sponsored events together, and talk shop together. Workplaces, such as academia, often try to hire both spouses since they are likely to become more permanent workers.

In recognizing the potential benefits of increased job satisfaction, morale, productivity, creativity, and commitment, some companies encourage love relationships among employees. Aware that their single employees are interested in relationships, Hitachi Insurance Service provides a dating service, called "Tie the Knot," for its 400,000 employees (many of whom are unmarried) in Tokyo, Japan. Those interested in finding a partner complete an application and a meeting or lunch is arranged with a suitable candidate through the Wedding Commander. In America, some companies hire two employees who are married, reflecting a focus on the value of each employee to the firm rather than on their love relationship outside work.

Disadvantages of an Office Romance

However, workplace romances can also be problematic for the individuals involved, as well as for their employers. When a workplace romance involves a supervisor/subordinate relationship, other employees might make claims of favoritism or differential treatment. In a typical differential-treatment allegation, an employee (usually a woman) claims that the company denied her a job benefit because her supervisor favored another female coworker—who happens to be the supervisor's girlfriend.

If a workplace relationship breaks up, it may be difficult to continue to work in the same environment (and others at work may experience the fallout). A breakup that is less than amicable may result in efforts by partners to sabotage each other's work relationships and performance, incidents of workplace violence, harassment, and/or allegations of sexual harassment. In a survey of 774 respondents with experience in the workplace, over a third (36.3%) recommended avoiding involvement in an office romance (Merrill & Knox, 2010). Of the employees in the 2013 Vault.com, Romance Survey, 32% reported that they had deliberately avoided involvement in an office romance. Raso 2008 noted that such love relationships might also become a problem because coworkers do not want to be subjected to the open display of a roller coaster love affair at work.

Company Policies on Office Romances

Some companies such as Walt Disney, Universal, and Columbia have "anti-fraternization" clauses that impose a cap on workers talking about private issues or sending personal e-mails. Some British firms have "love contracts" that require workers to tell their managers if they are involved with anyone from the office.

Most companies (Wal-Mart is an example) do not prohibit romantic relationships among employees. However, the company may have a policy prohibiting open displays of affection between employees in the workplace and romantic relationships between supervisor and subordinate. These policies may be enforced by transferring or dismissing employees who are discovered in romantic relationships. Most companies have no policy regarding love relationships at work and generally regard romances between coworkers as "none of the company's business."

Your Opinion

1. To what degree do you believe corporations should develop policies in regard to workplace romances?
2. What are the advantages and disadvantages of a workplace romance for a business?
3. What are the advantages and disadvantages for individuals involved in a workplace romance?
4. How might an office romance of peers affect coworkers?

6.5d Stalking

Stalking is an extreme form of ORI defined as the repeated, willful, and malicious following or harassment of one person by another. It may involve watching a victim, property damage, home invasion, or threats of physical harm; it usually causes great emotional distress and impairs the recipient's social and work activities. Of 1,002 undergraduate males, 18% reported that someone had stalked them; 28% of 3,460 undergraduate females (Hall and Knox, 2013).

Various theories—patriarchal, social learning, and social conflict—provide explanations for men stalking women: As an expression of male authority, men learn to be dominant; and they use power to control women. Persons who stalk are obsessional and very controlling. They are typically mentally ill and have one or more personality disorders involving paranoid, antisocial, or obsessive-compulsive behaviors.

Here are some coping strategies for dealing with a stalker, abuser, or obsessional partner:

1. Make a direct statement to the person. ("I am not interested in dating you." "Stay away from me.")
2. Seek protection through formal channels. ("I am calling the cops if you bother me again.")
3. Avoid the perpetrator. (Do not respond to text messages, do not talk with the person on the phone, etc.).
4. Change phone numbers, address, etc.

Stalking
Extreme form of obsessive relational intrusion that may involve following a victim, property damage, home invasion, or threats of physical harm

6.6 Factors Operative in Selecting a Marriage Partner

Love relationships that endure usually end up in marriage. While young adults today are delaying marriage to complete their educations and to establish themselves in a career, they have not abandoned the idea of marriage and children. While it is not known what percentage of today's youth will eventually marry (estimates are around 85%–90%), of all adults in the U.S. today age 65 or older, 96% have married (*Statistical Abstract of the United States*, 2012–2013). How the respective spouses found each other has changed very little. In the section to follow, we review the cultural, sociological, and psychological factors that influence the attraction of two people to each other.

6.6a Cultural Factors in Mate Selection

Individuals are not free to marry whomever they please. Rather, their culture and society influence their choices. Two forms of cultural pressure operative in mate selection are endogamy and exogamy. **Endogamy** is the cultural expectation to select a marriage partner within one's own social group—such as race, religion, and social class. Endogamous pressures involve social approval and disapproval to encourage one to select a partner within one's own group. The pressure toward an endogamous mate choice is especially strong when race is concerned. When all racial combinations are considered, about 13% of American married couples are of different races or ethnicities. White-Hispanic and white-Native American pairings are the most common. African Americans are the least likely to marry whites (Burton, Bonilla-Silva, Bucklew, & Freeman, 2010).

National **DATA**

As for couples in which the wife is white and the husband is black, these marriages represent 0.5%; if the husband is white and the wife is black these marriages represent less than 0.2% (*Statistical Abstract of the United States*, 2012–2013, Table 60).

Endogamy
Cultural expectation that one will select a marriage partner within one's own social group, such as race, religion, and social class

Exogamy
Cultural expectation to marry outside one's own family group

Residential, religious, and educational segregation, coupled with parental disapproval for cross-racial pairings, help to explain the low frequency of these marriages. The result is that most people look within their own race to marry.

In contrast to endogamy, **exogamy** is the cultural expectation to marry outside one's own family group. Incest taboos are universal. In no society are children permitted to marry the parent of the other sex. In the United States, siblings and (in some states) first cousins are also prohibited from marrying each other. The reason for such restrictions is fear of genetic defects in children whose parents are too closely related.

When cultural factors have identified the general pool of eligibles for one's partner, individual mate choice becomes more operative. However, even when individuals feel that they are making their own choices, social influences are still operative.

6.6b Sociological Forces in Mate Selection: Homogamy

In addition to cultural factors, various sociological forces influence the choice of one's partner. Whereas endogamy is a concept that refers to cultural pressure, homogamy refers to individual initiative toward sameness. The **homogamy theory** of mate selection states that we tend to be attracted to and become involved with those who are similar to ourselves in such characteristics as age, race, religion, social class, grade point average, drinking behavior, IQ, sexual experience, and smoking. Levchenko and Solheim (2013) studied international marriages between women born in Eastern Europe and men born in the U.S. and found homogamy operative in race, education and marital status. A significant proportion of both the women and men had been married before. The explanation provided by the researchers was that previously divorced American men may have experienced "unfair treatment at the hands of self-centered American women" and sought a more traditional wife on the international market.

> *Love may be blind, but it knows what color a person's skin is.*
>
> Unknown

6.6c Psychological Factors in Mate Selection

Psychologists have focused on complementary needs, exchanges, parental characteristics, and personality types with regard to pair bonding.

Think About It

Take a moment to answer the following questions. To what degree is your current or past relationship characterized by homogamy or complementary needs? Do you think couples are happier if they have more in common or have less in common?

Complementary-Needs Theory

"In spite of the women's movement and a lot of assertive friends, I am a shy and dependent person," remarked a transfer student. "My need for dependency is met by Chris, who is the dominant, protective type." The tendency for a submissive person to become involved with a dominant person (one who likes to control the behavior of others) is an example of attraction based on complementary needs. "Opposites attract" is another way to think of complementary needs.

Complementary-needs theory states that we tend to select mates whose needs are opposite and complementary to our own needs. Partners can also be drawn to each other on the basis of nurturance versus receptivity. These complementary needs suggest that one person likes to give and take care of another, whereas the other likes to be the benefactor of such care. Other examples of complementary needs may involve responsibility versus irresponsibility, peacemaker versus troublemaker, and disorder versus order.

Exchange Theory

Exchange theory emphasizes that mate selection is based on assessing who offers the greatest rewards at the lowest cost. Five concepts help to explain the exchange process in mate selection:

Homogamy theory
Theory of mate selection that holds that individuals are attracted to and become involved with those who are similar in such characteristics as age, race, religion, and social class

Complimentary-needs theory
Theory of mate selection that states that one tends to select mates whose needs are opposite and complementary to one's own needs

Exchange theory
Theory of mate selection that holds that partners select each other on the basis of who offers the greatest rewards at the lowest cost

1. Rewards are the behaviors (your partner looking at you with the eyes of love), words (saying "I love you"), resources (being beautiful or handsome; having a car, condo, and money), (running errands for you) that you value and that influence you to continue the relationship.

2. Costs are the unpleasant aspects of a relationship. A woman identified the costs associated with being involved with her partner: "He abuses drugs, doesn't have a job, and lives nine hours away." The costs her partner associated with being involved with this woman included "she nags me," "she doesn't like sex," and "she wants her mother to live with us if we marry."

3. Profit occurs when the rewards exceed the costs. Unless the couple referred to in concept number two derives a profit from staying together, they are likely to end their relationship.

4. Loss occurs when the costs exceed the rewards.

5. It is also necessary that no other person who offers a higher profit is currently available.

Most people have definite ideas about what they are looking for in a mate. The currency used in the marriage market consists of the socially valued characteristics of the persons involved, such as age, physical characteristics, and economic status. In our free-choice system of mate selection, we typically get as much in return for our social attributes as we can.

Many men advertising in the personals section of a local newspaper want a young, slim, attractive woman. That means such a woman has her pick of partners; however, she also has ideas of what she wants in exchange—good looks, respect, security, status, etc.

When you identify a person who offers you a good exchange for what you have to offer, other bargains are made about the conditions of your continued relationship. Waller and Hill (1951) observed that the person who has the least interest in continuing the relationship can control the relationship. This **principle of least interest** is illustrated by the woman who said, "He wants to date me more than I want to date him, so we end up going where I want to go and doing what I want to do." In this case, the woman trades her company for the man's acquiescence to her choices.

Principle of least interest
Theory that holds that the person who has the least interest in a relationship controls the relationship

Think About It

Take a moment to answer the following questions. Who controls the relationship you are currently in? Are you or your partner more invested? Is it better to be the more or least invested partner?

The exchange theory of mate selection may be criticized on the basis that people do not consciously think of what they have and what they can trade. Rather, they have some vague notion of who they are attracted to and rely on past experience to know if the person would be interested in them. People also rarely think in terms of profit and loss—"I will stay in this relationship as long as there is profit and leave it when there is loss." Rather, they may think more in terms of love, commitment, and working out whatever issues may confront them.

Desired Personality Characteristics for a Potential Mate

In an impressive cross-cultural study, Buss and colleagues (1990) asked more than 10,000 men and women from 37 countries, located on six continents and five islands, to identify the personality characteristics they most desired in a potential mate. The preferences for the top four characteristics identified by both men and women were identical: mutual attraction (love), dependable character, emotional stability/maturity, and pleasing disposition. One of the differences between men and women was men's greater emphasis on good looks and women's greater importance placed on ambition and economic potential.

BVT *Lab*

Flashcards are available for this chapter at **www.BVTLab.com**.

Chapter Summary

Individuals are born into, live in, and work in social groups. Love is a profound emotion that bonds individuals to each other. It is also a context for sexual intimacy.

Love

Buddhists conceived of love as "unfortunate" love of self and as "good" love resulting in creative spiritual attainment. The Greeks saw love as friendly, selfless or as sexual in nature. Love may also be conceptualized on a continuum from romanticism to realism. Romantics believe in love at first sight, one true love, and that love conquers all. Sternberg's triangular theory of love identifies types of love based on the presence or absence of three elements: intimacy, passion, and commitment. Another typology of love was developed by Lee to describe various love styles: eros, ludus, storge, pragma, mania, and agape.

Sex and love have both similarities (both involve intense feelings and physiological changes; need increases with deprivation) and differences (love is crucial to human happiness, but sex is not; love requires the person, whereas sex wants a person).

Hooking Up and Friends with Benefits as Contexts for Sex

Sexuality occurs in relationship contexts, such as hooking up and friends with benefits. The former involves an understanding that the focus is fun with no future commitment. "Friends with benefits" is more vague and may involve both romance and a future (but it's unlikely).

Polyamory

Polyamory involves multiple loves on the part of both partners in a relationship. Advantages include absence of deception, sexual freedom, and multiple experiences. Disadvantages include coping with jealousy and fear of being left out. Compersion is the opposite of jealousy and seeks to embrace the partner's other loves and sexual interests. Open relationships (swinging) are more sex focused and involve rules such as alerting the partner of a new sexual encounter, not falling in love, and the partner getting the right to nix a specific selection.

Challenges to Intimate Relationships

Jealously results from feeling that one's love relationship with another is being threatened. Feelings of jealousy may ignite from both external and internal sources. Jealousy has both positive (establishes parameters) and negative (partner may feel unjustly accused and terminate relationship) consequences.

Sexual guilt is the feeling that results from the violation of one's own sexual values. Guilt may result when one goes against what one thinks one should do ("I should not have gotten drunk and had intercourse," which could be followed by what students refer to as the "walk of shame" home in the morning) or when one does not behave consistently with the way one thinks one should ("I should have been faithful").

Obsessive relational intrusion and stalking involve unwanted pursuit and invasion of the target person's privacy. The victim's social and work-related activities may be curtailed as a result. Direct communication of disinterest may be helpful in managing such unwanted attention.

Stalking is an extreme form of ORI defined as the repeated, willful, and malicious following or harassment of one person by another. It may involve watching a victim, property damage, home invasion, or threats of physical harm, and it usually causes great emotional distress and impairs the recipient's social and work activities.

Selecting a Marriage Partner

Individuals are attracted to each other in reference to cultural (endogamy, exogamy), sociological (homogamy), and psychological (complementary needs, exchange theory) factors.

Web Links

Polyamory

http://www.polyamorysociety.org/

Kenneth R. Haslam Collection on Polyamory

http://www.kinseyinstitute.org/library/haslam.html

Stalking Resource Center National Center for Victims of Crime

http://www.ncvc.org/src/

Twin Oaks Intentional Community

www.twinoaks.org

Key Terms

Compersion   154

Complimentary-needs theory   164

Endogamy   163

Exchange theory   164

Exogamy   163

Family of origin   144

Family of procreation   144

Friends with benefits   153

Homogamy theory   164

Hooking up   152

Jealousy   157

Obsessive relational intrusion   160

Open relationships   156

Polyamory   154

Polyfidelity   156

Principle of least interest   165

Sexual guilt   160

Stalking   162

Vees   156

Additional study resources are available at www.BVTLab.com

Communication and Sexuality

The single biggest problem with communication is the illusion that it has taken place.

George Bernard Shaw, playwright

Chapter Outline

Objectives

1. Review the various principles of communication.
2. Summarize the study on "the talk" including the context, strategies involved, and partner reactions.
3. Know the legal reasons why one should disclose an STI to his or her partner.
4. Differentiate between nonverbal and verbal communication.
5. Explain the difference between open-ended and closed-ended questions (give an example).
6. Discuss and explain the various communication theories: identity formation theory, social learning theory, and social exchange theory.
7. Understand the difference between privacy, secrecy, and deception.
8. Explain the extent of dishonesty among college students.
9. Describe how to resolve conflict in relationships.
10. Review various gender differences in communication.

Source: Chelsea Curry

TRUTH *OR* FICTION?

T/F   Both nonverbal and verbal communication are associated with sexual satisfaction.

T/F   Being dishonest in marriage is associated with divorce.

T/F   In a study of disclosure of cheating, most disclosures occurred in a text message.

T/F   Women are more likely than men to report when there is a communication problem.

T/F   Having a communication problem is associated with lower relationship quality.

Answers: 1.T 2.T 3.F 4.T 5.T

"You can't screw yourself into a good relationship with your partner" is a profound statement by psychologist Dr. Robert Birch, which emphasizes that sex alone is insufficient to nurture a satisfying relationship. Communication, not sex, is the one factor that distinguishes a mediocre from a great relationship. Notice that when people are proud of their relationship and want others to know how good it is, they will say, "We talked all night." When their relationship has turned sour, however, they say, "We have nothing to say to each other."

Just as communication, in general, facilitates a very satisfying relationship, sexual intimacy is enhanced by good sexual communication. The following examples illustrate the need for communicating about sexuality:

> Mary is involved in an emotional and sexual relationship with Tom. Cunnilingus is the only way she can experience an orgasm, but she is reluctant to talk to Tom about her need. She has a dilemma: If she tells Tom, she risks his disapproval and his rejection of doing what she asks. If she does not tell Tom about her need, she risks growing resentful and feeling dissatisfied in their sexual relationship.

***

José has drifted into a flirtatious relationship with a woman in his office. He is emotionally and sexually attracted to her. He knows she feels the same. Jose is also in love with his partner of three years and is committed to her emotionally and sexually. Should he tell Maria about his attraction to the woman at work? Should he disclose that he has dreamed about her? That he has sexual fantasies about her? How open should he be?

***

Sherry and her husband, Gary, get into frequent arguments. Their pattern is that after arguing they "cool off" by not talking to each other for a few hours. But Gary sometimes approaches Sherry for sex as a way to "make up." Sherry prefers to talk about their conflict and resolve it before having sex, but she is afraid that if she rejects Gary's sexual advances, he will become angry again. What should she do?

> *We tried to talk it over, but the words got in the way.*
>
> "This Masquerade", Leon Russell, musician and songwriter

Resolution of the above dilemmas involves talking about sexual expectations, attraction to others, and the timing of sex after an argument. In this chapter we focus on the details of communicating about sexuality in one's relationship. We begin by focusing on basic principles.

7.1 Principles of Relationship/ Sexual Communication

Communication involves both information and the process of exchanging information between individuals. The information, or the messages exchanged between individuals, is referred to as the content of the communication. The fact that the individuals are communicating, and the way in which they do so, is the process of communication. More broadly defined, communication is the exchange of accurate and timely information with each other. If information does not convey or is not received as the "talker" intended, the exchange has been inadequate/inaccurate. If the information comes too late ("You never told me you loved me"), it can be as worthless as no information at all.

As important as communication is for developing and sustaining fulfilling and enduring relationships, there are few contexts where we learn the skills of communication. In the following pages we review some of the basic principles of communication. These apply to relationships in general and to the sexual relationship specifically.

7.1a Initiate Discussion of Important Issues

Effective communication means addressing important issues. The three scenarios above require talking about sexual expectations, attraction to others, and the timing of sex after an argument. Failure to deal with these issues is to be frustrated sexually, to leave a relationship vulnerable to an affair, and to learn a destructive pattern in one's relationship (reinforcing arguing by having sex afterwards which will likely increase the frequency of arguments).

In regard to sexual expectations (the woman not receiving oral sex), a script with her partner might be: "Let's talk about making our sex life even better. I love/enjoy pleasuring you orally, and it looks like you enjoy it, too, ha! I also get pleasure from you going down on me. What can I do so this is something that you feel good about doing?"

In regard to the issue of José drifting into an affair, he needs to take responsibility for his behavior in reference to flirting with his office mate—and to stop it; there is

Communication
Exchange of messages between two or more people

no disclosure necessary to his wife. Each spouse needs to prioritize the other to ensure that others do not drain off their affections or time. (This strategy assumes that the spouses are not in an open relationship where other partners are normative.)

The solution to the third issue, of Gary wanting to have sex after an argument, is for the couple to decide not to do so. They should only have sex when they are feeling intimate, loving, and sexual toward each other, not as a consequence of an argument. Otherwise, they may learn that the condition of having satisfying sex with each other is to be mad at each other. Their talking about when they have sex and jointly deciding to avoid doing so just after an argument is a worthy goal.

Up Close 7-1 is an example of addressing the future of one's relationship—an important issue.

BVT *Lab*

Flashcards are available for this chapter at **www.BVTLab.com**.

Having "The Talk"

For dating couples "the talk" is culturally understood to mean a discussion whereby both parties reveal their feelings about each other and their commitment to a future together. Typically, one partner feels a greater need to clarify the future and instigates "the talk." The goal of "the talk" is to confirm that the partner is interested in and committed to a future. This study examined "the talk" in terms of how long partners are involved before they have "the talk," specific words/strategies used in having "the talk," and the context (e.g., during sex, after sex, while watching TV, dinner, etc.) of "the talk." Other research questions included how the partner responded and the effect of "the talk" on the couple's relationship.

Sample

The study was based on a sample of 211 undergraduate student volunteers at a large southeastern university who completed a 15-item in-class questionnaire. A majority of respondents were female (77.7% to 22.3% male) and white (78.0% to 11.4% African American).

Context of "The Talk"

Mealtime was the context in which "the talk" was most often initiated. Many respondents (30.5%) reported that they had "the talk" during a meal. Other contexts were "after sexual intimacy" (16.4%), "before sexual intimacy" (11.3%), and "while we were on a trip" (10.%). Alcohol was usually not involved. Of those initiating "the talk," 3% said that they had been drinking alcohol, and 0.6% reported that their partner was drinking when they initiated "the talk." In regard to being anxious about initiating "the talk," the mean level of anxiety was 4.6 on a 10-point scale, with 1 being minimal anxiety and 10 indicating extreme anxiety. Hence the respondents were moderately anxious when they initiated "the talk."

Strategies Involved in "The Talk"

Various strategies were used to initiate the talk and assess the level of commitment of the partner. The top ten are presented below:

1. Direct Question about Future (30%)   "What do you see as far as the future of this relationship? Where do you plan for this to go?"
2. Questioning of Motives (15%)   "What do you want out of this relationship?"
3. Direct Question about Marriage (8%)   "I asked if he ever saw a future in us and if he ever thought we would get married."
4. Assessment of Level of Interest in Relationship (7%)   "I just asked how serious he was about this relationship."
5. Assumption of Marriage (7%)   "We would just randomly be talking and say things like, 'when we get married.'"
6. Modeling (6%)   "I mentioned to my partner what my feelings were towards him and looked to see how he responded to what I said. He told me that he actually felt the same way."
7. Question and Evaluate (6%)   "I asked if there was a future for us, and we talked about the pros and cons."
8. Assessment of View of Partner (5%)   "Am I your soul mate?"

9. Soft Cotton Approach (4%)   "I mentioned something about the future without putting any pressure on the situation. Tried to avoid awkwardness and help him feel comfortable."
10. Ultimatum (4%)   "I just asked what he wanted out of this relationship; and if it wasn't the same thing I wanted, I would then end the relationship."

Reactions of the Partner to "The Talk"

Reactions of the partner who was asked about the future of the relationship fell into four categories:

1. *Commitment to the future*   The most frequent response to "the talk" was a clear statement that he or she wanted a future with the partner. Over half (50.5%) were quick to confirm that they wanted a future with the partner. While the word "marriage" was often not spoken, the assumption on the part of both partners was that the partners would eventually get married.
2. *Uncertain*   The second most frequent response (32.3%) to "the talk" was uncertainty. The partner simply said that he or she did not know about the future and kept the partner and the relationship in limbo.
3. *No future*   The third most frequent response (9%) was a "subtle revelation that there was no future." The partner was not brutal but implied that the relationship would not go anywhere.
4. *Other responses*   Aside from "yes," "not sure," and "no," other responses included "made a joke out of it" (4%) or was "brutal in making clear that there was no future" (1%).

Source: Abridged and adapted from Nelms, B. J., Knox, D., and Easterling, B. (2012). THE RELATIONSHIP TALK: Assessing Partner Commitment. *College Student Journal, 46:* 178–182.

7.1b Choose Good Timing

The phrase "timing is everything" can be applied to interpersonal communication. In general, it is best to discuss important or difficult issues when partners are alone together in private with no distractions, both partners have ample time to talk, and both partners are rested and sober. Avoid discussing important issues when you or your partner are tired or under unusual stress. If one partner (or both) is very upset, it may be best to wait awhile until things have "cooled off" before discussing an issue. If you are not sure whether the timing is right, you can always ask your partner by saying something like (assuming the topic is the future of the relationship) "Can we talk about where this relationship is going?" "Is this a good time for you to talk?" Likewise, if your partner brings up an issue and it is not a good time for you to discuss the matter, suggest a specific alternative time to have the discussion.

Good timing in communication also means that information should be communicated at a time that allows the receiver to make an informed response. For example, discussions about sexual issues—such as pregnancy prevention, STI protection, and monogamy—should occur *before* partners engage in sexual activity. The Social Choices feature to follow focuses on telling a partner about an STI.

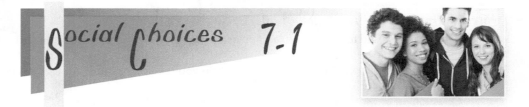

Social Choices 7-1

Disclosing One's STI

Sullivan and colleagues (2013) confirmed that individuals with STIs (including HIV) do not always disclose their infection to their sexual partners. Individuals often struggle over whether, or how, to tell a partner about their sexual health condition or history. If a person in a committed relationship becomes infected with an STI that individual—or his or her partner—may have been unfaithful and had sex with someone outside the relationship.

Thus, disclosure about an STI may also mean confessing one's own infidelity or confronting one's partner about his or her possible infidelity. (However, the infection may have occurred prior to the current relationship but was undetected.)

For partners in abusive relationships, telling their partner that they have an STI often involves fear that their partner will react violently. Individuals who are infected with an STI and who are beginning a new relationship face a different set of concerns. Will their new partner view them negatively? Will they want to continue the relationship or end the relationship abruptly?

An example of what an individual who had HPV disclosed, and the reaction, follows: The individual told …

In one case an individual told five partners in an upfront manner on the first date. Trying to make it a little funny, he said, "I guess I should tell you something … Before you fall madly in love with me and we run away and get married … I have herpes." In every case, five out of five, the first date was the last!

Although telling a partner about having an STI may be difficult and embarrassing, avoiding disclosure or lying about having an STI represents a serious ethical violation. Even if condoms are used (e.g., "I won't tell; I'll just use a condom"), they do not provide 100% protection; and the partner has a right to have the information of the presence of an STI so that he or she can make a decision about taking a risk.

The responsibility to inform a partner that one has an STI—before having sex with that partner—is a moral one. There are also legal reasons for disclosing one's sexual health condition to a partner. If you have an STI and you do not tell your partner, you may be liable for damages if you transmit the disease to your partner. In more than half the states, transmission of a communicable disease, including many STIs, is considered a crime. According to the North Dakota Century Code:

> [I]f the procedures of the previous section have been exhausted, and a person believed to be infected with HIV continues to engage in behavior that presents an imminent danger to the public health, a court may issue other orders, including an order to take the person into custody, for a period not to exceed 90 days and place the person in a facility designated or approved by the state health officer.

Some states and cities have **partner notification laws** that require healthcare providers to advise all persons with serious sexually transmitted infections about the importance of informing their sex or needle-sharing partner (or partners). Partner notification laws may also require healthcare providers to either notify any partners the infected person names or forward the information about partners to the Department of Health, where public health officers notify the partner (or partners) that he or she has been exposed to an STI and schedule an STI testing appointment. The privacy of the infected individual is protected by not revealing his or her name to the partner being notified of potential infection. In cases in which the infected person refuses to identify partners, standard partner notification laws require doctors to undertake notification without cooperation, if they know whom the partner or spouse is. Although there is some public support for partner notification laws, the American Civil Liberties Union is against such laws. The organization fears that such mandatory reporting laws will discourage people from being tested for HIV.

Partner notification laws
Set of laws that require healthcare providers to advise all persons with serious sexually transmitted infections about the importance of informing their sex or needle-sharing partner (or partners)

Before ending this section, let's examine how the partner being told of an STI might respond. One of the underlying causes for the spread of STIs among college-aged students is the fear that telling a potential partner will not only result in personal rejection but with "the whole university knowing." To express appreciation for the honesty of the disclosure, to show compassion, and to guarantee confidentiality would be a welcome response to the disclosing party. One coed disclosed to a partner that she had an STI. She said of his response, "He held me, told me he knew it was hard for me to tell him, and that we would get through this. He was wonderful and we are still together."

I didn't say that I didn't say it. I said that I didn't say that I said it. I want to make that very clear.

George Romney, former Michigan governor

Verbal messages
Words individuals say to each other

Nonverbal messages
Type of communication in which facial expressions, gestures, bodily contact, and tone of voice predominate

7.1c Give Congruent Messages

The process of communication involves both verbal and nonverbal messages. **Verbal messages** are the words individuals say to each other. **Nonverbal messages** include facial expressions, gestures, bodily contact, and tone of voice. What happens when verbal and nonverbal messages do not match? For example, suppose Lashanda and Brian are giving feedback about the last time they had sex. Lashanda says to Brian, "It was good." However, she has a sullen facial expression and tone of voice and does not make eye contact. Lashanda's verbal and nonverbal messages are not congruent—they do not match. When this happens, the other partner typically gives more weight to the nonverbal message. In this scenario, Brian would probably give more weight to the nonverbal message, thus believing that Lashanda did not enjoy their most recent sexual experience. He might also feel that she was not being honest with him. (See Up Close 7-2 on nonverbal/verbal behavior in two relationship contexts.)

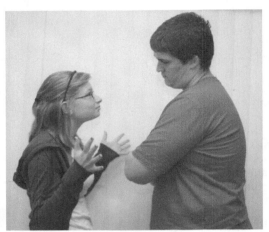

Regardless of what these lovers say, their nonverbal behavior communicates disapproval and disgust.
Source: Chelsea Curry

Up Close 7-2

Nonverbal and Verbal Communication in "Involved" and "Casual" Relationships

This study examined the nonverbal and verbal communication between partners in two categories of college students—the "involved" (emotionally involved in a reciprocal love relationship with one person) and "casual" daters (dating different people). At a large southeastern university, 233 undergraduates completed a 45-item questionnaire.

Findings and Discussion

Analysis of the data revealed several significant findings:

1. *Involved daters valued nonverbal communication more than casual daters.* When students were asked, "How important do you think nonverbal communication is in a relationship?"
    (1 = very important and 10 = not important at all—hence the lower the score, the greater the importance), the average scores of the involved and casual daters were 3.08 and 3.75, respectively. Being sensitive to and concerned about the nuances of nonverbal communication is an extension of being more serious about relationship issues.

2. *Involved daters worked on nonverbal behavior more than casual daters.* Not only did the involved respondents value nonverbal behavior in the abstract, they also were more likely than casual daters to "work hard" to ensure that their nonverbal behavior reinforced their verbal behavior. "I try to make sure that what I do backs up what I say," noted one respondent.

3. *Women valued nonverbal behavior more than men.* When women in our sample were compared with men, the former were significantly more likely than men to report that nonverbal behavior should be regarded as important.

4. *Women engaged in more nonverbal behavior.* When women were compared with men, the former were more likely to look their partner straight in the eye and to nod their heads when their partner spoke.

Source: Abridged and adapted from McGinty, K., Knox, D., and Zusman, M. E. (2003). Nonverbal and verbal communication in "involved" and "casual" relationships among college students. *College Student Journal, 37*, 68–71.

What sexual signals are these individuals sending to each other?
Source: Chelsea Curry

Self-Assessment 7-1 assesses the verbal and nonverbal ways in which an individual can communicate interest in engaging in sexual behavior with a partner.

SELF-ASSESSMENT 7-1: THE SEXUAL SIGNALING BEHAVIORS INVENTORY

The Sexual Signaling Behaviors Inventory

When you think your partner can be persuaded to have sex even though he or she has not yet become aware of your desire, what do you usually do? Check all items that apply.

A. ___ ask directly

B. ___ use some code words with which (s)he is familiar

C. ___ use more eye contact

D. ___ use touching (snuggling, kissing, etc.)

E. ___ change appearance or clothing

F. ___ remove clothing

G. ___ change tone of voice

H. ___ make indirect talk of sex

I. ___ do more favors for the other

J. ___ set mood atmosphere (music, lighting, etc.)

K. ___ share a drink

L. ___ tease

M. ___ look at sexual material

N. ___ play games such as chase or light "roughhousing"

O. ___ make compliments ("I love you." "You're nice.")

P. ___ use some force

Q. ___ use "suggestive" body movements or postures

R. ___ allow hands to wander

S. ___ lie down

T. ___ other (describe _____)

Dr. Clinton Jesser (1978), a sociology professor who was interested in determining how college students communicate to their heterosexual partners when they want coitus (sexual intercourse), developed this scale. He wondered whether women would use more indirect signals than men and whether men would evaluate women's indirect communication as more desirable. In the sample, he surveyed 153 students at a large midwestern university and examined the responses of the 50 men (90%) and 75 women (71%) who were coitally experienced. The most frequently reported signals were "use touching (snuggling, kissing, etc.)" and "allow hands to wander," which were both endorsed by more than 70% of the men and women. The next most frequent item was "ask directly," which was reported by 58% of the women and 56% of the men. Although there was essentially no difference in the reports of men and women who said they ask directly, women were more likely to report using eye contact, changing their appearance or clothing, and changing their tone of voice. The women who used the direct approach (42 of the 75) were no more likely to be rebuffed than those using an indirect approach. No formal checks of the reliability or validity of this measure have been made, although Dr. Jesser noted that more women report being direct than are perceived by men as being direct. Dr. Jesser (1998) suggested that the Sexual Signaling Behaviors Inventory could be used with gay and lesbian participants.

Source: Republished with permission of The Society for the Scientific Study of Sex, from "The Sexual Signaling Behaviors Inventory," by C. J. Jesser, (1978). *The Journal of Sex Research, 14(2),* 118–128; permission conveyed through Copyright Clearance Center, Inc.

7.1d Minimize Criticism; Maximize Compliments

Research on marital interaction has consistently shown that 1 brutal "zinger" can erase 20 acts of kindness (Notarius & Markman, 1994). Because intimate partners are capable of hurting each other so deeply, it is important not to criticize your partner. Calling a partner "fat," "stupid," or a "lousy lover" can devastate him or her. One couple exchanged negative barbs—he called her "little bump breasts" and she called him "short penis."

Conversely, complimenting your partner and making positive remarks can enhance the relationship. Sincere compliments and positive remarks are not only good to hear, they can also create a **self-fulfilling prophecy** effect. A partner who is often told that he or she is an attentive and affectionate lover is more likely to behave accordingly to make these expectations come true than a partner who receives no feedback or negative feedback.

Gottman and colleagues (1998) studied 130 newlywed couples to examine marital communication patterns that are predictive of marital satisfaction. They found that a high positive to negative statement ratio predicted satisfaction among stable couples. In longitudinal studies with more than 2,000 married couples, happy couples, on the average, have 5 times as many positive interactions and expressions as negative expressions. This 5-to-1 ratio of positives to negatives is "the magic ratio" according to Gottman (1994, p. 56). He compares this ratio to the pH of soil, the balance between acidity and alkalinity that is essential for fertility. Likewise, a relationship must be balanced by a great deal more positivity than negativity for love/sexual interest to be nourished.

In Gottman's research, he has also found four negative qualities that sabotage attempts for partner communication and that emerged as the strongest predictors of divorce: criticism, contempt, defensiveness, and stonewalling (Gottman, J., 1994). These qualities are so potentially destructive to a relationship that he calls them "the Four Horsemen of the Apocalypse." Criticism involves an attack on the partner's personality or character (rather than a specific behavior). Contempt involves an intention to insult a partner and may involve psychological abuse. Examples include hostile humor, name-calling, and insults. Defensiveness (denying responsibility, making excuses) tends to

Self-fulfilling prophecy
Behaving in such a way to make expectations come true, e.g., caustically accusing a partner of infidelity may lead that partner to be unfaithful

escalate conflicts. The most symptomatic of relationship disaster is stonewalling, or shutting a partner out. The stonewaller just removes himself by turning into a stone wall. (p. 94).

Making positive statements is particularly important during the beginning and end of a discussion. In psychology, the term **primacy/recency effect** refers to the tendency of individuals to remember best what occurs first and last in a sequence. After discussing a difficult issue, partners may be more likely to come away with a positive feeling about the interaction if it begins and ends with positive comments. For example, suppose your partner tries a new sexual position with you that you find unpleasant. You might tell your partner, "I didn't enjoy that; please don't do it again." You could also say, "I am glad that you want us to try new things, but that position was a bit uncomfortable/painful for me. I'd rather be on top. Being able to tell you what I like and don't like is one of the things I like most about our relationship." The latter statement will result in the partners continuing to explore/enjoy their sexual relationship (in contrast to the former statement which will shut the sex down).

Suppose you are so upset with your partner about an issue that you begin a discussion by blurting out a negative comment. You can still end the conversation on a positive note by saying something positive like "Thank you for listening to my anger and allowing me to vent." Or, if your partner begins a discussion with a negative remark, such as "Our sex life is so boring, you never want to try anything new," you can respond with a positive comment, such as "Thank you for telling me about your frustration with our sex life. I need to know when things aren't working. Let me know what you recommend to make things better."

> *Good communication is as stimulating as black coffee, and just as hard to sleep after.*
> Anne Morrow Lindbergh, author

7.1e Communicate Feelings

In intimate relationships, it is important to communicate feelings as well as thoughts. This advice sounds simple, but many people are not in touch with their feelings—or they confuse feelings with thoughts. If you listen to yourself and to others, you will hear people communicating thoughts, but these thoughts are often labeled as feelings. For example, the statement "I feel that we should be tested for STIs" is communicating an idea, not an emotion. Feelings include sadness, fear, anger, joy, excitement, guilt, boredom, anxiety, frustration, and depression. "We should be tested for STIs" is not an emotion. The statement "I am afraid to have sex with you because we have not been tested for STIs" is expressing a feeling—fear.

To communicate emotions, a person must first recognize and label, or describe, the emotions. Unfortunately, many people learn to hide and repress unpleasant feelings. Before you can communicate your emotions to a partner, you must access your feelings and give yourself permission to feel them and talk about them. Attempts to cover up or minimize unpleasant feelings may be made with the best intentions; however, repressing your emotions or interrupting the emotions of your partner often serves to prolong the emotional state rather than to resolve it. What are your feelings about your sexual relationship with your partner (e.g., joy, excitement, adventurousness, sadness, fear, hopelessness, guilt, apprehension)?

7.1f Tell Your Partner What You Want

In a relationship, it is important for partners to decide what behaviors they want from each other, to tell each other in clear behavioral terms what they want, and to do so in a positive way. Rather than complain about what you don't want, it is helpful to make requests for, or statements about, what you do want. Table 7-1 provides examples of how complaints can be reframed into requests.

Primacy/recency effect
Tendency of individuals to remember best what occurs first and last in a sequence

TABLE 7-1 | Rephrasing Complaints into Positive Requests

Complaints	Requests
I don't like to make love when you haven't showered.	Please take a shower before we make love. I'll guarantee better sex if you shower first.
Don't rub so hard.	Please rub more softly … like this.
I don't want you to stay up so late at night.	How about coming to bed at 10:00 and letting me know how I can make it worth your doing so?
Leave me alone; I'm trying to get ready for work!	We can have some long, slow sex after a glass of wine tonight.
Whenever I ask you to massage me, you end up wanting to have sex with me.	Give me an hour to finish this work and we can enjoy a glass of wine/slow sex together.

One common error people make when communicating is not being specific enough about what they want. When you tell your partner what you want, make sure you tell your partner is specific behavioral terms exactly what you want (see Table 7-2).

7.1g Make Statements Instead of Asking Questions

When partners are uncomfortable or unwilling to express their feelings and behavioral desires, they may put their statements in the form of questions. For example, partners who have difficulty expressing what they want may ask the question "Do you think we should see a sex therapist?" instead of making the statement "I think we might benefit from seeing a sex therapist."

Transforming statements into questions allows partners to mask or hide their true feelings, thoughts, and desires—and thus interferes with the development and main-tenance of relationship intimacy. Begin listening to your questions and those of your partner; try to discern which questions are really statements that are masking feelings, wants, or both. When you catch yourself or your partner doing this, rephrase the question into a statement.

Open-ended question
Broad question designed to elicit a great deal of information

Closed-ended question
Type of question that yields little information and can be answered in one word

7.1h Ask Open-Ended Questions

When you want information from your partner, asking open-ended questions will often yield more information than a closed ended question. An **open-ended question** is a broad question designed to elicit a lot of information. In contrast, a **closed-ended question** can be answered in one word. Open-ended questions are useful in finding out your partner's feelings, thoughts, and desires. Table 7-3 provides examples of open- and closed-ended questions. Both questions may be valuable.

TABLE 7-2 | Examples of Vague versus Specific Behavioral Statements

Vague	Specific
I want more foreplay.	I would like for us to kiss, hold, and gently rub each other for 20 minutes before we have oral sex or penetration.
I'd like us to try something new.	I'd like us to use a vibrator or try a new sexual position in a new place in the house.
Let's look at pornography together sometime.	Let's rent a porn DVD and watch it Saturday night.

TABLE 7-3 | Open-Ended and Closed-Ended Questions

Open-Ended Question	Closed-Ended Questions
What are your thoughts about condom use?	Do you have a condom?
What can I do to please you sexually?	Would you like oral sex?
Tell me your thoughts about having children.	Do you want to have children? How many? What interval?
How do you feel about trying something new?	Do you want to try anal sex? Do you want me to tie you up, blindfold you, and enjoy you orally?
What are your views on abortion?	Would you agree to have an abortion if we got pregnant?

One way to use open-ended questions in a sexual relationship is to follow the **touch-and-ask-rule**, whereby each touch and caress is accompanied by the question "How does that feel?" The partner then gives feedback. By using this rule, a couple can learn a lot about how to please each other. Guiding and moving the partner's hand or body are also ways of giving feedback. Babin (2013) confirmed that verbal and nonverbal communication during sex were positively related to sexual satisfaction.

My wife said I don't listen to her—at least I think that's what she said.

Laurence J. Peter, humorist

7.1i Use Reflective Listening

One of the most important communication skills is the art of **reflective listening**, or restating the meaning of what your partner has said to you in a conversation. When you use reflective listening, your partner is more likely to feel that you are listening and that you understand his or her feelings, thoughts, and desires. In practicing reflective listening, it is important to repeat the ideas or thoughts expressed by your partner, as well as the emotions that your partner has conveyed. For example, suppose that after you have made love, your partner says, "Next time, can we spend a little more time on foreplay?" You might respond by reflecting back your partner's message: "You are saying that you feel frustrated that we didn't take more time to be loving and affectionate before having intercourse and that more foreplay is something you definitely want us to include in our lovemaking."

Using the technique of reflective listening is particularly difficult when one partner blames or criticizes the other. When people are blamed or criticized, they typically respond by withdrawing from the interaction, attacking back (through blaming or criticizing the other person), or defending or explaining themselves. Each of these responses may produce further conflict and frustration. Alternatively, instead of withdrawing, attacking back, or defending and explaining, the listener can simply reflect back what the partner has said. At some point in the discussion, the criticized partner may, and should express, his or her thoughts, feelings, and views on the situation. However, it is best to first acknowledge the other person's feelings and thoughts through reflective listening. In Table 7-4 we present an example of a critical or accusatory remark, followed by four types of possible responses. Compare the reflective listening response with the other three responses.

7.1j Use "I" Statements

"I" statements focus on the feelings and thoughts of the communicator without making a judgment on others. Because "I" statements are a clear and nonthreatening way of expressing what you want and how you feel, they are likely to result in a positive change in the listener's behavior.

Touch-and-ask-rule
Sexual technique whereby each touch and caress is accompanied by the question "How does that feel?" and is followed by feedback from the partner

Reflective listening
Communication technique in which one person restates the meaning of what his or her partner has said in a conversation

"I" statements
Statements that focus on the feelings and thoughts of the communicator without making a judgment on what the other person says or does

TABLE **7-4**	Four Responses to a Critical or Accusatory Remark
"Critical or Accusatory Remark"	
"You told me you had only a couple of sexual partners before me. You lied."	
Four Possible Responses	
1. Withdraw from the interaction: "I can't handle this; I'm out of here."	
2. Attack back: "Well, you didn't tell me you had herpes. That's lying too."	
3. Defend or explain: "I was afraid you would break up with me if I told you the real reason ... I didn't want to hurt you or us."	
4. Reflective listening: "You are angry at me for giving you a bogus number of previous sexual partners. You wish that I had been honest with you. I'm sorry."	

In contrast, "**you**" **statements** blame or criticize the listener and often result in increasing negative feelings and behavior in the relationship. For example, suppose you are angry at your partner watching porno. Rather than say, "You are very deceitful watching porno ... I checked your history on the computer and you have been indulging yourself since we have been together" (which is a "you" statement), you might say, "It upsets me that you watch porno when I am not here. I much prefer that we watch porno together." The latter focuses on your feelings and what you would like to happen.

personal choices 7-1

What to Do When Your Partner Will Not Communicate

One of the most frustrating experiences in relationships occurs when one partner wants and tries to communicate, but the other partner will not. Of course, partners always communicate—not communicating is a way of communicating. What if your partner will not respond to something you say, however? You might try the following (Duncan & Rock, 1993):

1. Change your strategy. Rather than trying to coax your partner into talking, become less available for conversation and stop trying to initiate or maintain discussion. Keep it short if a discussion does start. This strategy removes the pressure on the partner to talk and shifts the power in the relationship.

2. Interpret silence in a positive way. For example, "we are so close that we don't always have to be talking" or "I feel good when you're quiet because I know that it means everything is all right between us." This negates any power your partner might be expressing through silence.

3. Focus less on the relationship and more on satisfying yourself. When you do things for yourself, you need less from others in the way of attention and assurance.

"You" statements
In communication theory, those statements that blame or criticize the listener and often result in increasing negative feelings and behavior in the relationship

7.1k Keep the Process Going

In the introduction to this chapter, we noted that communication involves both content (the words that are said) and process (the continued interaction/discussion). It is important to keep the process going and not allow the content to shut down the process. For example, Angela says to Andy, "I don't trust you." Instead of Andy blurting, "I don't care what you think," while he is leaving the room, a more helpful response might be, "I appreciate your telling me your feelings; tell me why you feel that way." In this way, the conversation continues, and the couple can move toward a resolution. Otherwise, the discussion stops and nothing is resolved.

Cultural Diversity

The culture in which one is reared will influence the meaning of various words. An American woman was dating a man from Iceland. When she asked him, "Would you like to go out to dinner?" he responded, "Yes, maybe." She felt confused by this response and was uncertain whether he wanted to eat out. It was not until she visited his home in Iceland and asked his mother, "Would you like me to set the table?"—to which his mother replied, "Yes, maybe"—that she discovered that "Yes, maybe" means "Yes, definitely."

7.1l Take Responsibility for Being Understood

Partners often blame each other for not understanding what is said. "Are you deaf? Didn't you hear what I said? Can't you understand anything?" are phrases that blame the partner. The result is that the partner feels bad, will become emotionally distant, and be less interested in subsequent communication. To avoid these negative feelings, which are likely to increase the distance between the partners, each partner should take full responsibility for making himself or herself heard. "I am sorry; I am not making myself clear. What I am trying to say is that I think we should stop talking about this issue and let it go." The partner may not like what is being said but doesn't feel belittled for not understanding.

7.1m Avoid Rehashing/Stay Focused

Partners sometimes get off the subject and turn a discussion into a "criticize the partner session." For example, if the topic is "where is our relationship going?" the conversation can easily degenerate into accusations of "you never loved me" and "let's break up." Alternatively, the partners can stay focused on what they do and do not want from their relationship.

Applying the communication principles presented in this chapter to everyday interactions can enhance both individual and relationship well-being and increase your sexual satisfaction with your partner. The principles and techniques are fairly simple, but not necessarily easy to apply. For effective application, you must first abandon old patterns of communication and deliberately replace them with the new. Most couples report that the effort is worthwhile.

7.2 Communication Theory

Because communication involves interaction in social contexts, we examine various theoretical frameworks for relationship communication. Models of communication come from the fields of mathematics, psychology, and sociology. Three that seem especially relevant to communication between partners include identity formation theory, social learning theory, and social exchange theory.

There are two theories to arguing with a woman ... Neither works.

Will Rogers, humorist

7.2a Identity Formation Theory

One reason that interpersonal communication is so important, according to such theorists as George Herbert Mead and Erik Erikson, is that our self-identity develops largely as a result of social interaction. We learn about ourselves from the responses others make to us; their communications give us cues about how important, capable, or inadequate we are. Cooley (1964) coined the term **looking glass self** to describe the idea that the image people have of themselves is a reflection of what other people tell them about themselves. Reflections from others that are inconsistent or contradictory with one's self-image may cause tension or anxiety. Individuals may see themselves differently from the way others do. For example when a male hooks up nightly with a new partner, he may see himself as a "stud that women love"—but others may see him as a lonely guy who is incapable of intimacy.

7.2b Social Learning Theory

Verbal behavior, positive or negative, is decreased or increased depending on whether the behavior is reinforced or punished. For example, if a person expresses an opinion ("I think that same sex marriage should be legalized throughout the U.S.") and the partner reinforces this view with "I agree," the person is likely to continue talking about the rights of gays. On the other hand, the partner might say, "How can you say that? Marriage is for women and men who can reproduce/have children." That response is likely to punish expressing one's opinion on same-sex marriage so that the person is more likely to change the subject.

Verbal statements may be discriminative or serve as cues for other types of responses. For example, a partner may say, "I am going upstairs to take a shower and will be ready for a glass of wine" (translation—"I am getting cleaned up for sexual intimacy"). A discriminative stimulus may also be used to cue that a behavior will not lead to reinforcement, as when the partner replies, "I am going to go to bed ... see you tomorrow."

7.2c Social Exchange Theory

Social exchange theorists combine behavioral psychology and economic theory. Exchange theorists suggest that the interaction between partners can be described as a ratio of rewards to costs. For example, two strangers who meet with the possibility of hooking up will continue to interact only if each has a high ratio of rewards to cost. *Rewards* are positive outcomes of the interaction—each smiles at the other, says nice things, touches the other gently and non-demandingly, etc. *Costs* refer to negative outcomes of the interaction, such as receiving criticism or feeling regret, which make the interaction painful. As long as the rewards outweigh the costs (and there is a profit for the interaction), the relationship will continue. When the costs are higher than the rewards (and there is a loss for the interaction), the relationship will stop. In long-term

Looking glass self
Idea that the image people have of themselves is a reflection of what other people tell them about themselves

relationships, a person may forgo immediate rewards in anticipation of long-term gain, especially if there is reciprocity in the exchanges between the partners. Although this idea doesn't sound romantic, sociological theorists observe that even love relationships are established and continued on the basis of reciprocity—exchanged benefits and costs. Social exchange theories have been applied to the study of relationships and sexuality in that persons who hook up can be understood as exchanging reinforcers throughout the evening as the partners move toward one apartment or the other: the partners smile at each other, they drink, they flirt, they touch each other, etc. If either partner stops reinforcing, the interaction will stop—and no hooking up will occur.

7.3 Honesty and Dishonesty in Interpersonal Communication

Deception, dishonesty, cheating, lying and infidelity—whatever the label—have become major sources of emotional distress and sexual dissatisfaction in relationships. Being cheated on is not uncommon among undergraduates. Of 3,462 undergraduate females, over half (52%) reported that they have been involved with a partner who cheated on them. Of 1,099 males, over a third (39%) reported that they had been cheated on (Hall & Knox, 2013).

There are no degrees of honesty.

Amish proverb

7.3a Forms of Dishonesty and Deception

Dishonesty and deception take various forms. In addition to telling an outright lie, people may exaggerate the truth, pretend, or conceal the truth. They may put up a good front, be two-faced, or tell a partial truth. People also engage in self-deception when they deny or fail to acknowledge their own thoughts, feelings, values, beliefs, priorities, goals, and desires.

7.3b Privacy Versus Secrecy and Deception

In virtually every relationship, partners have not shared with each other details about themselves or their past. Sometimes partners do not share their feelings and concerns with each other. However, when is withholding information about ourselves an act of privacy, and when is it an act of secrecy or deception? When we withhold private information, we are creating or responding to boundaries between ourselves and other people. There may be no harm done in maintaining aspects of ourselves as private, not to be disclosed to others. Indeed, it is healthy to have and maintain boundaries between the self and others. However, the more intimate the relationship, the greater one's desire is to share their most personal and private selves with the partner—and the greater the emotional consequences of not sharing.

College students also keep secrets from their partners. In a study of 431 undergraduates, Easterling and colleagues (2012) found the following:

1. **Most kept secrets.** Over 60% of respondents reported ever having kept a secret from a romantic partner, and over one quarter of respondents reported currently doing so.

2. **Females kept more secrets.** Sensitivity to the partner's reaction, desire to avoid hurting the partner, and desire to avoid damaging the relationship may be the primary reasons why females were more likely than males to keep a secret from a romantic partner.

3. **Spouses kept more secrets.** Spouses have a great deal to lose if there is an indiscretion or if one partner does something the other will disapprove of

(e.g., spending money on a purchase). Partners who are dating or "seeing each other" have less to lose and are less likely to keep secrets.

4. ***Blacks kept more secrets.*** Blacks are a minority who are still victimized by the white majority. One way to avoid such victimization is to keep one's thoughts to oneself—to keep a secret. This skill in deception may generalize to one's romantic relationships.

5. ***Homosexuals kept more secrets.*** Indeed, the phrase "in the closet" means keeping a secret. Transgendered individuals in Europe are required to reveal their secret before marriage (Sharpe, 2012).

Respondents were asked why they kept a personal secret from a romantic partner. "To avoid hurting the partner" was the top reason reported by 38.9% of the respondents. "It would alter our relationship," and "I feel so ashamed for what I did," were reported by 17.7% and 10.7% of the respondents, respectively.

7.3c Extent of Dishonesty Among College Students

Lying in relationships among college students is not uncommon. In one study, 77 college students kept diaries of their daily social interactions and reported telling two

Often the difference between a successful marriage and a mediocre one consists of leaving about three or four things a day unsaid.

Harlan Miller, author

lies a day (DePaulo, Kiekendol, Kashy, Wyer, & Epstein, 1996). Participants said they did not regard their lies as serious and did not plan them or worry about being caught. In another study, 137 students reported 21 lies they had told to a current or past partner. The most frequently told lie, reported by 31% of the respondents, was "the number of previous sex partners" (Knox, Schacht, & Turner, 1993).

College students and community members reported the most serious lies they ever told were to their closest relationship partners (DePaulo, Ansfield, Kirkendol, & Boden, 2004). Their motivations were to get something they wanted, do something to which they felt entitled, avoid punishment or confrontation, keep up appearances, protect others, or avoid hurting others. Theobald and Farrington (2013) noted that divorce is associated with being dishonest in a relationship.

personal choices **7-2**

Is Honesty Always the Best Policy?

Good communication often implies open communication, and there is a cultural script that total honesty with one's partner is always best. As evidence, there is an adage about marriage, "The secret of a good marriage is no secrets." In reality, how much honesty is good for a marriage/relationship? Is honesty always the best policy?

Some individuals believe that relationships can be functional only when a certain amount of illusion is maintained. Not to be told that you are overweight or that you aren't the best of lovers allows you to maintain the illusion that your partner never thinks of your weight (particularly when you eat a second bag of potato chips) or your sexual inadequacy. You are happier, and your relationship is not hampered by your partner's honesty.

If you are completely open with your partner, there may be negative consequences. Suppose you tell your partner about all of your previous partners or sexual relationships because you want an "open and honest relationship with nothing between us." Later, during times of anger, your partner brings this information up in the future. Was your honesty worth the consequences?

Disclosing an extramarital affair requires special consideration; spouses might carefully consider the consequences before disclosing. While there are exceptions, in general, if the affair was "one-time, drank too much and had casual sex," disclosure might result in a divorce and the lives of the affected children being changed forever. Such was the case for the woman as described in Up Close 7-3. Some couples, however, may find that the disclosure of an affair by one partner forces them to examine problems in their relationship, seek marriage therapy, or both. In such cases, disclosure may ultimately result in bringing the couple closer together in an emotional sense.

Most individuals are careful about what they say to each other and deliberately withhold information, in some cases for fear of negative outcomes. Some information, however, should not be withheld from the partner; that includes previous marriages and children, a sexual orientation different from what the partner expects, alcohol or other drug addiction, a sexually transmitted infection (such as HIV or genital herpes) or possible exposure, and any known physical disabilities (such as sterility). Disclosures of this nature include anything that would have a significant impact on the partner or the relationship.

Some individuals wait until after the marriage to disclose a "secret." One example is a cross-dresser who, fearing his wife's disapproval, did not disclose his proclivity until years after the marriage. Indeed, he never disclosed, but she found his bra and panties and confronted him. Although she was ultimately able to accept his desire to cross-dress (and they would shop together), his lack of disclosure was a definite risk. In another case a cross-dresser who had not told his wife during courtship was divorced by her. Although they had been married 16 years, had four children, and she viewed him as a good provider, good father, and faithful husband (he had never had sex outside their marriage), she regarded his deception across the years as unforgivable. (She found out because he had forgotten to remove his earrings one day after he had been cross-dressing.)

Close 7-3

Revealing My Affair Was a Disaster*

My husband and I had always talked about the importance of being open and honest with each other about whatever we did with other people. I took a five-hour flight to a conference and sat next to a guy. We had a couple of drinks and talked innocently throughout the flight. As the plane landed, I knew we were going to see each other, and we did. I came home from the conference guilty and told my husband. I did so in the belief that we had always talked of being open and honest. I was truly sorry and felt my disclosure would bring us closer together.

I was shocked at his reaction. I knew he would be hurt but expected him to view it as a chance for us to work on some of our problems. Instead, he called me a slut and said it was over between us. I reminded him that we had earlier talked of being open/honest with each other. He said that was academic, and the fact that I had actually had sex with a stranger threw him into disbelief and changed the way he viewed me. We had a bitter divorce; in retrospect, I should have kept my mouth shut.

*The author would like to remain anonymous.

Walters and Burger (2013) studied individuals who defined themselves as having cheated on a romantic partner and who made the partner aware of the cheating. While some felt guilty, others wanted to "come clean." Still others saw the infidelity as a sign that the relationship was not what it should be or saw it as a way to let the partner know that they wanted a polyamorous relationship (the right to see others). A significant portion of the respondents also felt that out of respect for the partner and their relationship, they needed to disclose. Most disclosures were done in person (38%) or over the phone (38%). Other means of disclosure included being informed by a third party (12%), via computer email (6%), and through text messaging (6%). The following is an example of an interview of an undergraduate talking about disclosing to her partner:

> I told him, you know, you weren't there for me. You haven't been a boyfriend to me the last few months. I don't know what you expect from me and everything. He was mad, and I expected him to be. But I mean [pause] he kinda understood. He didn't really say much, so there really wasn't much said after [the disclosure]. But the next day he was talking to me again and everything and he was like, it's going to be okay. We're going to get past it. But, we didn't. (p. 36)

The complexity of the reasons behind a partner's cheating and disclosing are revealed in the following words of a gay male:

> At first I started telling myself that I wasn't going to tell him too much of what happened—just let him know that I cheated and that I didn't want to again and that I now realized I, I, I wanted to explain to him why I did it: because I was unhappy with [pause] like I wanted him to know that because I felt it was important. I felt like it [the cheating] was almost an excuse to tell him. But it was never like ... like I never explained it to him the way I explained it to my friends. What I explained to my friends was like, very, like I just kept it real, ya know? Like one, two, three. Here's the reasons why I didn't want to be in this relationship. I want to stop. But obviously I didn't tell him that. So I guess it definitely made the relationship grey for me. Ummm, [pause] I like to tell myself that if I didn't cheat it [his perceptions of relationship satisfaction] would have been better, but I really don't think it would have. I think me cheating ... was the easiest way to get out of it. (p. 40)

I'm not upset that you lied to me; I'm upset that from now on I can't believe you.

Friedrich Nietzsche, German philosopher

Hence, the infidelity and the disclosure provided insight about the relationship as well as about the partner who cheated.

7.4 Resolving Conflict in Relationships

Being able to resolve conflict is an essential skill for relationship survival, maintenance, and satisfaction., More than half (56%) of the 343 university students surveyed reported having a very troublesome relationship within the past 5 years. Of those who had a troubled relationship, most (69%) reported talking to the partner in an attempt to resolve the problem, 19% avoided discussing the problem, and 18% avoided the partner (Levitt, Silver, & Franco, 1996). Knox and colleagues (1998) studied 203 undergraduates and identified the most to least difficult relationship problems to discuss: the future of the relationship, ex-partners, sex, and jealousy (in that order).

Howard Markman is head of the Center for Marital and Family Studies at the University of Denver. He and his colleagues have been studying 150 couples at yearly intervals (beginning before marriage) to determine those factors most responsible for marital success. They have found that communication skills that reflect the ability to handle conflict and disagreement are the single biggest predictor of marital success over time (Markman, Stanley, & Blumberg, 1994).

> Remember: It's not how much you love one another, how good your sex life is, or what problems you have with money that best predicts the future quality of your marriage … The key is for you to develop constructive tactics and ground rules for handling the conflicts and disagreements that are inevitable in any significant relationship. (p. 6)

There is also merit in developing and using conflict negotiation skills before problems develop. Not only are individuals more willing to work on issues when things are going well, but they also have not developed negative patterns of response that are difficult to change. In the following sections, we review principles and techniques that are helpful in resolving interpersonal conflict.

7.4a Approach Communication from a Place of Respect/Negotiation

Partners who care about each other and their relationship can best achieve their relationship goals by approaching communication on a particular issue or topic from a place of respect and negotiation. Each partner must regard the other as an equal

and acknowledge that each partner's perspectives and views deserve respect. Neither partner is to denigrate the other or dictate an outcome. Rather, the goal of a discussion is for each to have a positive feeling about the outcome rather than to have one's position accepted. As one spouse said, "It is better for us to be right with each other than to be right in getting our own way." This context of respect and negotiation implies that denigrating the partner or being emotionally abusive are both counter to productive discussion and conflict resolution.

7.4b Address Any Recurring Issues

Some couples are uncomfortable confronting their partner to talk about issues that plague them. They fear that such confrontation will further weaken their relationship. Pam is jealous that Mark spends more time with other people at

This couple is avoiding issues—he is focused on vacuuming; she is focused on talking on the phone.
Source: Chelsea Curry

parties than with her. "When we go someplace together," she blurts out, "he drops me to disappear with someone else for 2 hours." Her jealousy is spreading to other areas of their relationship. "When we are walking down the street and he turns his head to look at another woman, I get furious." If Pam and Mark don't discuss her feelings about Mark's behavior, their relationship may deteriorate as a result of a negative response cycle: He looks at another woman, and she gets angry. Then he gets angry at her getting angry and finds that he is even more attracted to other women. She gets angrier because he escalates his looking at other women, and so on.

To bring the matter up, Pam might say, "I feel jealous when you spend more time with other women at parties than with me. I need some help in dealing with these feelings." By expressing her concern in this way, she has identified the problem from her perspective and asked for her partner's cooperation in handling it (she did not attack but invited her partner's help in dealing with an issue).

7.4c Focus on What You Want (Rather than What You Don't Want)

Dealing with conflict is more likely to result in resolution if both partners focus on what they want rather than what they don't want. For example, rather than tell Mark she doesn't want him to spend so much time with other women at parties, Pam might tell him that she wants him to spend more time with her at parties. "I'd feel better if we go together and stay together," she said. "We don't need to be joined at the hip, and we will certainly want to talk with others; the bulk of our time there, however, should be spent with each other."

7.4d Find Out Your Partner's Point of View

We often assume that we know what our partner thinks and why our partner does things. Sometimes we are wrong. Rather than assume how our partner thinks and feels about a particular issue, we might ask our partner open-ended questions in an effort to get him or her to tell us thoughts and feelings about a particular situation. Pam's words to Mark might be, "What is it like for you when we go to parties? How do you feel about my jealousy?"

After your partner has shared his or her thoughts about an issue with you, it is important for you to summarize your partner's perspective in a nonjudgmental way. After Mark has told Pam how he feels about their being at parties together, she can summarize his perspective by saying, "You feel that I cling to you more than I should, and you would like me to let you wander around without feeling like you're making me angry." (She may not agree with his view, but she knows exactly what it is—and Mark knows that she knows.)

7.4e Generate Win-Win Solutions to the Conflict

A **win-win solution** is one in which both people involved in a conflict feel satisfied with the agreement or resolution to the conflict. It is imperative to look for win-win solutions to conflicts. Solutions in which one person wins and the other person loses involve one person not getting his or her needs met. As a result, the person who loses may develop feelings of resentment, anger, hurt, and hostility toward the winner and may even look for ways to get even. In this way, the winner is also a loser. In intimate relationships, one winner really means two losers.

Generating win-win solutions to interpersonal conflicts often requires brainstorming. The technique of **brainstorming** involves suggesting as many alternatives as possible without evaluating them. Brainstorming is crucial to conflict resolution because it shifts the partners' focus from criticizing each other's perspective to working together to develop alternative solutions. Any solution may be an acceptable one as long as the solution is one of mutual agreement.

When men cry, women are caring/nurturing and ask, "How can I help?" When women cry, men say, "I'm going to have a beer … let me know when you snap out of it."

Jay Leno, *Tonight Show*

7.4f Evaluate and Select a Solution

After a number of solutions are generated, each solution should be evaluated and the best one selected. In evaluating solutions to conflicts, it may be helpful to ask the following questions:

- Does the solution satisfy both individuals—is it a win-win solution?
- Is the solution specific? Does the solution specify exactly who is to do what, how, and when?

Win-win solution
Outcome of an interpersonal conflict whereby both people feel satisfied with the agreement or resolution

Brainstorming
Problem-solving strategy of suggesting as many alternatives as possible without evaluating them

FIGURE **7-1** ‖ **Steps in Resolving Conflict**

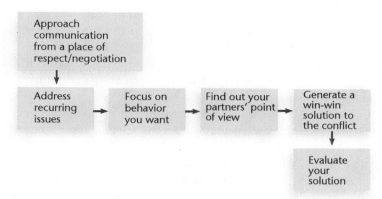

BVT *Lab*

Visit **www.BVTLab.com**
to explore the student
resources available for
this chapter.

- Is the solution realistic? Can both parties realistically follow through with what they have agreed to do?
- Does the solution prevent the problem from recurring?
- Does the solution specify what is to happen if the problem recurs?

Greeff and De Bruyne (2000) studied several styles of conflict and noted that the *collaborating style* was associated with the highest level of marital and spousal satisfaction. Each partner saying how he or she felt about a situation and cooperating to find a win-win solution characterized the collaborating style. Styles that were not helpful were the *competing style* (each partner tried to force his or her answer on the other—a win-lose approach) and the *avoiding style* (the partners would simply avoid addressing the issue and hope that it would go away). Depressed spouses who did not have the energy to engage their partners used this pattern of avoidance most frequently.

7.5 Gender Differences in Communication

Females begin to excel in communication skills early. Haapsamo and colleagues (2013) found that females at age 8 months to 36 months developed communication skills faster than males. Sociolinguistic scholar and author of 17 books, Deborah Tannen (1990) stated, "Male-female conversation is cross-cultural communication" (p. 42). By this she meant that men and women are socialized in different same-sex cultures; and when they talk to the other sex, they are talking to a member of another culture. Tannen also found that men and women differ in public and private speaking. She explained the differences using the terms *report talk* and *rapport-talk*. Men generally approach communication, even in private situations, like public speaking or giving a report. They see talk as a way to convey information. In contrast, women generally engage in rapport-talk, using talk for interaction and establishing connections. When there are problems in communicating with a partner, women are the first to notice. Pfeifer and colleagues (2013) studied 213 married couples in Taiwan and found that women were significantly more likely than men to report that communication was a problem. Such a communication problem means a drop in marital quality (Frye-Cox & Hesse, 2013).

To men, communication emphasizes what is rational; to women, communication is about emotion. To men, conversations are negotiations in which they try to "achieve and maintain the upper hand if they can, and to protect themselves from others' attempts to put them down and push them around" (p. 25). However, to women, conversations are negotiations for closeness in which they try "to seek and give confirmations and support, and to reach consensus" (p. 25). A woman's goal is to preserve intimacy and avoid isolation.

Greater use of social network sites by women emphasizes their goal to "connect" in regard to relationships. Based on a survey of 2,021 individuals ages 12 and over conducted by Arbitron and Edison Research Survey, 27% of the respondents reported using social networking sites/services "several times a day" (Carey & Trap, 2013). Kimbrough and colleagues (2013) confirmed that women use social networking sites more frequently than men.

A team of researchers reviewed the literature on intimacy in communication and observed that men approach a problem in the relationship cognitively, whereas women approach it emotionally (Derlega, Metts, Petronio, & Marulis, 1993). A husband might react to a seriously ill child by putting pressure on the wife to be mature (stop crying) about the situation and by encouraging stoicism (asking her not to feel sorry for herself). Wives, on the other hand, want their husbands to be more emotional (wanting him to cry to show that he really cares that their child is ill).

Chapter Summary

This chapter focused on the value of good communication to intimacy, and relationship and sexual satisfaction. Achieving these goals includes knowledge of the theories of communication, the issue of honesty in relationships, conflict resolution in relationships through generating win-win solutions, and the differences in the way men and women approach and execute communication.

Principles of Relationship/Sexual Communication

Effective communication in intimate relationships is based on understanding and using various communication principles. They include initiating discussions about important issues, giving congruent messages, minimizing negative remarks and maximizing positive remarks, expressing feelings, practicing reflective listening, and using "I" messages.

Communication Theory

Because communication involves interaction in social contexts, theories including identity formation (communication skills are learned through interaction with others), social learning (verbal statements are a consequence of reinforcers), and social exchange (people continue to interact or don't in reference to a rewards-to-costs ratio) may be used to help understand communication between partners.

Honesty and Dishonesty in Interpersonal Communication

Most individuals value honesty in their relationships. Honest communication is associated with trust and intimacy. Despite the importance of honesty in relationships, deception occurs frequently in interpersonal relationships.

Lying is not uncommon in college student relationships. Partners sometimes lie to each other about previous sexual relationships, how they feel about each other, and how they experience each other sexually. In one study, 77 college students kept diaries of their daily social interactions and reported telling two lies a day.

Resolving Conflict in Relationships

Having a plan to communicate about conflicts is essential. Such a plan includes approaching a discussion from the point of view of respect for the partner and a willingness to negotiate an outcome rather than dictate a solution, addressing recurring issues rather than suppressing them, focusing on what you want (rather than what you don't want), finding out your partner's point of view, generating win-win solutions to conflict, and evaluating and selecting the solution.

Gender Differences in Communication

Women excel in their development of language skills early in life, at ages 8 months to 36 months. Deborah Tannen observed that men and women are socialized in different same-sex cultures; and when they talk to the other sex, they are talking to a member of another culture. Men approach communication, even in private situations, like public speaking or giving a report. They see talk as a way to convey information. In contrast, women engage in rapport-talk, using talk to interact and establish connections.

Women engage in greater use of social network sites (e. g., Facebook) than men. They also approach an issue emotionally rather than cognitively. Women want men to "get in touch with their feelings" whereas men want women to "be sensible/rational/decisive."

Web Links

American Association for Marriage and Family Therapy

http://aamft.org

Gottman Institute

http://www.gottman.com/

Key Terms

Brainstorming   188

Closed-ended question   178

Communication   170

"I" statements   179

Looking glass self   182

Nonverbal messages   174

Open-ended question   178

Partner notification laws   173

Primacy/recency effect   177

Reflective listening   179

Self-fulfilling prophecy   176

Touch-and-ask-rule   179

Verbal messages   174

Win-win solution   188

"You" statements   180

Additional study resources are available at www.BVTLab.com

CHAPTER 8

Individual and Interpersonal Sexuality

Among men, sex sometimes results in intimacy; among women, intimacy sometimes results in sex.

Barbara Cartland, English romance novelist

Chapter Outline

Objectives

1. Differentiate between erotophilia and erotophobia.

2. Review the concepts of voluntary and involuntary abstinence.

3. Know how negative attitudes toward masturbation developed.

4. Learn the demographics of who masturbates and the advantages and disadvantages.

5. Explain sexual fantasies and dreams.

6. List and discuss the various sexual behaviors.

7. Know how to have a discussion with a partner about vibrator use.

Source: Chelsea Curry

TRUTH OR FICTION?

T/F   SIECUS takes the position that all individuals should choose to masturbate.

T/F   HPV can be transmitted via oral sex and cause throat cancers.

T/F   Binge drinkers have the lowest rate of condom use.

T/F   About half of 5,000 unmarried singles reported having had sex by the third date.

T/F   Greater alcohol use is associated with intercourse with a stranger

1.F 2.T 3.T 4.F 5.T

Answers:

"Masturbation—it's sex with someone I love" is a classic line from Woody Allen. It emphasizes that sex can be very individualistic. However, sex is more often a social behavior in that it occurs in the context of, and in reference to, someone else. In this chapter we focus on individual and interpersonal behaviors that are commonly recognized as sexual—including masturbation, touching, kissing, breast stimulation, manual and oral-genital stimulation, anal stimulation/anal intercourse, and vaginal intercourse. We begin by looking at the continuum of sexual interest from erotophilia to erotophobia.

8.1 Erotophilia and Erotophobia

For most individuals, sexual behavior—both individual and interpersonal—generally involves pleasure and enjoyment. Yet for a few individuals, how anyone could actually *enjoy* masturbation/oral sex/intercourse, etc., is a mystery because *they* certainly don't find these behaviors to be pleasurable. The range of feelings toward sexual behavior can be conceptualized on a continuum known as the *erotophilic-erotophobic* continuum.

SELF-ASSESSMENT 8-1: COMFORT WITH SEXUAL MATTERS FOR YOUNG ADOLESCENTS (CWSMYA)*

Directions:

The items below reflect an erotophobia-erotophilia disposition to respond to sexual stimuli with a negative-to-positive affect and evaluation. For each item identify a number which reflects your level of agreement and write the number in the space provided.

- 1 = strongly disagree
- 2 = moderately disagree
- 3 = slightly disagree
- 4 = in between
- 5 = slightly agree
- 6 = moderately agree
- 7 = strongly agree

1.* ___ It is not OK for a person to have more than one sex partner during their lifetime.

2. ___ It is OK for a person to masturbate if it makes him/her feel good.

3. ___ It is OK for two men to have sex with each other or two women to have sex with each other.

4.* ___ It is not OK for people to have sexual intercourse unless they are in a committed relationship.

5. ___ It is OK to enjoy being sexually aroused (turned on) by a sexy story, picture, or movie.

6.* ___ Oral sex is disgusting to me.

Scoring:

*Reverse score items 1, 4, and 6 (change a 1 to a 7 and vice versa). Add each of the items and divide by 7. The lowest possible score is 1 suggesting high erotophobia; the highest possible score is suggesting high erotophilia.

Participants and Results:

There were 1,752 female respondents with an average score of 5.02 (SD =1.45) where 1 would be the most erotophobic score and 7 would be the most erotophilic score. There were 883 men with an average score of 5.22 (SD =1.32). There was a significant difference between women and men in two ways: men were more erotophilic on the comfort scale while women had greater variability in responses on the comfort scale (i.e., unequal standard deviations).

Validity and Reliability:

Details are provided in the 2012 reference below.

* Scale is used with the permission of *Canadian Journal of Human Sexuality* (2012) and is the property of Sex Information & Education Council of Canada.

*Rye, B. J., Serafini, T. and Bramberger, T. (2013). Unpublished data. St. Jerome's University.

A very positive view of sexuality is referred to as **erotophilia** (*eroto* = sexual; *philia* = attracted to). Individuals who are erotophilic enjoy sex; find it pleasurable; and seek sexual partners, contexts, and experiences. A very negative view of sexuality is **erotophobia** (eroto = sexual; phobia = avoidance). Individuals who are erotophobic are uncomfortable about sex and try to avoid sexual partners, contexts, and experiences. Although erotophobic individuals are less likely than erotophilic individuals to be sexually active, those who do engage in sexual relations have a higher risk of pregnancy and HIV/STI transmission because they feel uncomfortable discussing or using contraception or condoms. The CWSMYA Self-Assessment assesses one's position on the continuum from being erotophobic to being erotophilic.

Various factors influence whether an individual is more erotophilic or erotophobic. Growing up in a family where parents were physically affectionate and conveyed the message that sex is an OK topic of conversation/to be enjoyed in the right context, having had positive masturbatory experiences, and having had positive interpersonal sexual experiences (and no traumatic ones), contribute to being erotophilic. In contrast, having parents who telegraphed that sex is "bad" or "dirty," having engaged in no masturbatory behavior, and having been forced to engage in sexual behavior (e. g., rape) are associated with erotophobia.

Individuals may move from one end of the continuum to the other. For example, an erotophilic person who delights in masturbation and who enjoys an intense reciprocal loving/sexual relationship can become erotophobic as a result of an intense negative sexual experience (e.g., gang rape). On the other hand, an erotophobic person can learn to enjoy sex by means of repeated exposure to sexual behavior with a loving partner who provides a context of intense positive/frequent sex.

Before discussing specific sexual behaviors, we explore concepts related to the absence of or limitations on sexual behavior: virginity, chastity, celibacy, and abstinence.

8.2 Virginity, Chastity, Celibacy, and Abstinence

Virginity refers to not having experienced sexual intercourse. Virgins may or may not have experienced other forms of sexual interaction, such as oral sex. Indeed, some individuals still define themselves as virgins even though they have engaged in oral sex. Of 1,088 university males, 75% agreed that, "If you have oral sex, you are still a virgin" (of 3,427 university females, 70% agreed). Hence, according to these undergraduates, having oral sex with someone is not really having sex (Hall & Knox, 2013). In addition to maintaining the self-concept that one is a virgin, engaging in oral sex rather than sexual intercourse may also be motivated by the desire to avoid getting pregnant, to avoid getting a STI, to keep a partner interested, to avoid a bad reputation, and to avoid feeling guilty over having sexual intercourse (Vazonyi & Jenkins, 2010).

Individuals conceptualize their virginity in one of three ways—as a process, gift or stigma. The process view regards first intercourse as a mechanism of learning about one's self, partner, and sexuality—it is a learning experience. The gift view regards being a virgin as a valuable positive status wherein it is important to find the "right" person since sharing the gift is special. The stigma view considers virginity as something to be ashamed of, to hide and to rid oneself of. When 215 undergraduates were asked their view, 54% classified themselves as process oriented, 38% as gift oriented, and 8.4% as stigma oriented at the time of first coitus (Humphreys, 2013).

> *I had begun to think my ripening body would wither untasted on the vine.*
>
> Jacqueline Carey, *Kushiel's Dart*

Erotophilia
Propensity to have very positive views of and emotional responses to sexuality

Erotophobia
Propensity to have very negative views of and emotional responses to sexuality

Virginity
State of not having experienced sexual intercourse

Most narratives about virginity refer to a heterosexual young women and an older experienced male. Caron and Hinman (2012) examined the experiences of undergraduate men who lost their virginity in an article, "I Took His V-card." The researchers identified 237 individuals (women and men) who provided 195 stories about the male losing his virginity. In most cases (58%) the woman knew ahead of time that the partner was a virgin with a similar percentage (59%) of them reporting that it was a good first experience; 12% said it was "really bad." Gender roles were operative with 71% reporting pressure to conform to traditional roles (but 49% said they enjoyed *the* role reversal).

Carpenter (2010) discussed the concept of secondary virginity—a sexually experienced person's deliberate decision to refrain from intimate encounters for a set period of time and to refer to that decision as a kind of virginity (rather than "mere" abstinence). Secondary virginity may be a result of physically painful, emotionally distressing, or romantically disappointing sexual encounters. Of 61 young adults interviewed (most of whom were white, conservative, religious women), more than half believed that a person could, under some circumstances, be a virgin more than once. Fifteen people contended that people could resume their virginity in an emotional, psychological, or spiritual sense. Terence Duluca, a 27-year-old, heterosexual, white, Roman Catholic, explained:

> There is a different feeling when you love somebody and when you just care about somebody. So I would have to say if you feel that way, then I guess you could be a virgin again. Christians get born all the time again, so ... When there's true love involved, yes, I believe that.

Those who follow **asceticism** believe that giving in to carnal lust is unnecessary and attempt to rise above the pursuit of sensual pleasure into a life of self-discipline and self-denial. Accordingly, spiritual life is viewed as the highest good, and self-denial helps one to achieve it. Catholic priests, monks, nuns, and some other celibate people have adopted the sexual value of asceticism.

I used to be Snow White, but I drifted.
Mae West

The term **chastity** also refers to not having had sexual intercourse, but chastity also implies moral purity or virtuousness in both thought and conduct. Mbotho and colleagues (2013) interviewed Christian youth in a university setting and found that Christian teachings of sexual chastity were the primary motivation for sexual abstinence. Spiritual, mental and physical health benefits of abstinence were secondary. The students noted that the pressures to have sex were extensive and came from biological urges, peer pressure and momentary loss of self-control.

Celibacy often refers to the condition of being unmarried, especially by reason of religious vows, and also implies refraining from having sexual intercourse, although a person who practices celibacy is not necessarily a virgin. Creek (2013) interviewed gay, celibate Christians and explored the management of desire. The source of such management is religious—Catholicism being a prime source. Indeed, the official position of the contemporary Catholic Church maintains that priests, nuns, and monks are expected to be celibate in order that they might have the maximum time, freedom, and energy for the work of the church. Keenan (2012) notes that while celibacy is not the cause of child sexual abuse, it is an "unnatural sate" for which the priest is poorly prepared.

Confirmed cases of child sexual abuse perpetrated by some Catholic priests have raised questions about the celibacy requirement for Catholic clergy: Is requiring celibacy realistic? Has the celibacy requirement contributed to the child sexual abuse perpetrated by the clergy? No, it is not celibacy that causes sexual abuse of children.

Asceticism
Belief that rising above carnal lust and the pursuit of sensual pleasure into a life of self-discipline and self-denial is desirable

Chastity
State of not having had sexual intercourse; also implies moral purity or virtuousness in both thought and conduct

Celibacy
Condition of refraining from sexual intercourse, especially by reason of religious vows; also used to refer to being unmarried

Rather, it is the role of priest and parishioner that allows the sex pedophile to hide as he molests his victims who are young, innocent, trusting and vulnerable.

Due to the exposure of young males to the atrocities of sexual molestation by some priests, the culture including (parents and professionals) is now on high alert. No longer is the priesthood a convenient place for the sex predator to hide. This fact coupled with the prohibition of marriage/requirement of celibacy has led to a shortage of priests. As such, church leaders may be increasingly open to dialogue regarding married priesthood—something already practiced by Episcopal priests.

The more commonly used term today that refers to refraining from having sexual intercourse is **abstinence**. Like celibacy, the practice of abstinence does not necessarily mean that the person is a virgin; a person who has experienced sexual intercourse can subsequently practice abstinence. For some individuals, abstinence means refraining from sexual intercourse, but not from other forms of sexual behavior (e.g., masturbation, oral sex). Abstinence can be voluntary or involuntary and can last for short or extended periods of time.

8.2a Voluntary Abstinence

Voluntary abstinence can be motivated by a number of reasons, including the desire to avoid sexually transmitted infections and the desire to avoid pregnancy. Other individuals practice abstinence in order to better focus their energy on personal, academic, or professional development without the distractions of sexual involvements. Still other individuals are voluntarily abstinent because they lack interest or sexual desire or may find sex aversive—for example, in cases in which sexual activity triggers negative emotions associated with prior sexual abuse. For some gay and lesbian individuals who do not accept their sexual orientation, abstinence may be a way to avoid dealing with the stigma of living a homosexual lifestyle. Some couples choose to abstain from sexual intercourse as a way to enhance their enjoyment of the nonsexual aspects of their relationship. The practice of abstinence can also be related to cultural or religious beliefs and customs. For example, during the Muslim observation of Ramadan, in addition to fasting, believers abstain from sexual intercourse during daylight hours.

There are also a variety of reproductive and medical reasons for practicing short periods of abstinence. For example, some women use the "natural family planning method" (also known as the "calendar method") to abstain from sexual intercourse during the time of month they are most likely to conceive. Some men are abstinent to increase the chance of impregnating their partners because the longer the time interval between ejaculations, the more volume and concentration of sperm are present in the semen. Medical conditions that can warrant short periods of abstinence include genital infections and pregnancy complications. In addition, a period of abstinence from sexual intercourse is recommended for women after having an abortion and after childbirth. For individuals dealing with "sexual addiction," abstinence is often a part of the treatment plan. Like the alcoholic who must abstain from using alcohol to maintain sobriety, the "sex addict" may be encouraged to "dry out and become sober" for a period of several months to kick start "recovery."

8.2b Involuntary Abstinence

One of the most common reasons for **involuntary abstinence** is the lack of a sexual partner. This situation is common to many of us at different times in our lives. We may be between relationships, separated, divorced, or widowed; or we may be in a marriage or relationship in which our partner is unwilling to have sexual relations. Involuntary abstinence may also be induced by separation of partners due to military deployment,

Abstinence
Condition of having refrained from having sexual intercourse

Voluntary abstinence
Forgoing sexual intercourse for a period of time by choice

Involuntary abstinence
Condition of not having sexual relations due to environmental factors, such as not having a partner or being confined to an institution that does not encourage sexual expression

work-related travel, being in a long-distance relationship, or prison. Hospital, nursing, and retirement homes are also contexts of involuntary **sexual celibacy** (see Social Choices 8-1 section).

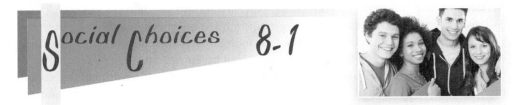

Social Choices 8-1

Institutional Restrictions on Sexual Expression

Hospitals are notorious for encouraging or enforcing abstinence. It is assumed that if you are in the hospital, you should have no sexual experience of any kind. There is no discussion of sexual activity, no privacy for masturbation (nurses, physicians, attendants can walk in at any time), and no accommodations for engaging in sexual relations with one's partner.

Nursing homes also institutionalize abstinence. Some nursing homes (believing that the elderly are sexless) do not even allow spouses to occupy the same room. Sexual expression among nursing home residents may also be infrequent due to chronic illness, the lack of willing partners, and a loss of interest. Some of these factors are related to the physiological effect of aging on sexual interest and behavior; other factors are under the control of physicians and staff. Barriers to sexual activity among nursing home residents may be removed by educating staff about sexuality in the elderly, providing privacy ("do not disturb" signs, closed doors, private rooms designated for intimacy), allowing conjugal visits or home visits, changing medications that may impair sexual function, and providing information and counseling about sexuality to interested residents.

Experiencing involuntary abstinence over a long period of time can be a very difficult emotional experience. The movie *The Surrogate* detailed the life of a man who was celibate because he was in an iron lung and had no available sexual partners. His anguish in being celibate and his joy in experiencing sex with the surrogate revealed the feelings associated with celibacy.

8.3 Masturbation

Masturbation may begin early (Cartaxo, Peixoto, Rolim, Neto, & deAbreu, 2013). Rodoo and Hellberg (2013) confirmed that masturbation might begin in infancy. They followed 19 healthy females from 3 months to an average of 8 years. The mean age for onset of masturbation was 10.4 months.

> *Philosophy is to the real world as masturbation is to sex.*
>
> Karl Marx

The position statement of SIECUS (Sex Information and Education Council of the United States) on **masturbation** (also called autoerotic behavior) is that it is "a natural, common, and nonharmful means of experiencing sexual pleasure. Masturbation can be a way of becoming comfortable with one's body and enjoying one's sexuality, whether or not in a sexual relationship. Masturbation is a safe alternative to shared sexual behavior. SIECUS believes that no one should be made to feel guilty for choosing or not choosing to masturbate" (SIECUS, 2013). Terms other than *autoerotic behavior* for masturbation include *self-pleasuring, solo sex,* and *sex without a partner.* Several older, more pejorative terms for masturbation are *self-pollution, self-abuse,*

Sexual celibacy
State of not having sexual intercourse or activity

Masturbation
Natural, common, and nonharmful means of sexual self-pleasuring that is engaged in by individuals of all ages, sexual orientations, and levels of functioning (also called Autoerotic behavior)

solitary vice, sin against nature, voluntary pollution, and *onanism.* The negative connotations associated with these terms are a result of various accounts and myths that originated in religion, medicine, and traditional psychotherapy. Traditionally, parents have also transmitted a negative view of masturbation to their children. Shame, guilt, and anxiety continue to be common feelings associated with masturbation in our society due to traditional negative attitudes toward masturbation.

Despite current knowledge suggesting that negative views of masturbation are based on myths (see Table 8-1), social disapproval of masturbation persists due to a long history of masturbation being viewed as being both the cause and result of sin and sickness.

> *The guilt, fear, anxiety, and repulsion that surround masturbation is astounding, especially when one realizes not only how pervasive it is among human beings, but how beneficial, pleasurable, and relaxing an experience it can be.*
>
> Lonnie Garfield Barbach

TABLE 8-1 | Myths and Truths about Masturbation

Myths	Truths
Masturbation causes insanity, headaches, epilepsy, acne, blindness, nosebleeds, "masturbator's heart," tenderness of the breasts, warts, nymphomania, undesirable odor, and hair on the palms.	There is no evidence that masturbation impairs physical or mental health.
Masturbation is an abnormal, unnatural behavior.	Many people masturbate throughout their lives.
Masturbation is immature.	Masturbation is a normal function.
Masturbation is practiced mostly by simple-minded people.	Masturbation is an effective way to experience sexual pleasure. Many sexually active people with available partners masturbate for additional gratification.
Masturbation is a substitute for intercourse. Masturbation is antisocial.	Intercourse and masturbation can be viewed as complementary sexual experiences, not necessarily as mutually exclusive. Masturbation can be an effective way to learn about your own sexual responses so you can communicate them to a partner. Masturbation can also occur during sexual interaction with one's partner.

8.3a Historical Origins of Negative Attitudes Toward Masturbation

While masturbation, which may begin in infancy (Cartaxo, Peixoto, Rolim, Neto, & deAbreu, 2013), is more often thought of today in terms of its benefits, religion, medicine, and traditional psychotherapy have messaged a very negative view of masturbation historically.

Religion and Masturbation

A number of religious traditions have associated masturbation with something evil or sinful. St. Augustine and other early Christians believed that sexual fantasies (which often accompany masturbation) were caused by demons who led their victims down a hellish path of sin. Medieval Jewish and Christian leaders believed that ejaculated semen would breed devils (Allen, 2000). Those guilty of masturbating could still be "saved" through prayer, abstinence, holy water, and absolution.

Negative religious views toward masturbation stemmed from the belief that any nonprocreative sexual act (i.e., any sex act that cannot lead to pregnancy and reproduction) is morally wrong. Traditional religious doctrines also disapprove of other forms of nonprocreative sex—such as oral sex, anal intercourse, homosexual sex, and coitus interruptus. However, as Allen (2000) explained, "[M]asturbation inspired a special fear in the ... Catholic Church, since it represented a purely physical act of sex, unredeemed by even the possibility of procreation—and also since it could be performed even by monks in the isolation of their cells" (p. 82).

Some religious groups have adopted more accepting views of masturbation. For example, a curriculum developed for Presbyterian youth asserts that masturbation can be bad if it is used as a way to avoid relationships with other people or is done out of fear of becoming involved with someone else (Bartosch, et al., 1989). However, masturbation can be a good choice if practiced by those who are not married or those whose spouses are not available for sexual relations due to absence, disability, or illness. This curriculum states that masturbation is a normal part of growing up.

In regard to a cross-cultural view on masturbation, in ancient Chinese religious thought life was viewed as a balance between the forces of yin and yang. Sex represented this harmonious balance: The essence of sexual **yang** was the male's semen, and the essence of sexual **yin** was the woman's vaginal fluids. Female masturbation was virtually ignored because vaginal fluids (yin) were thought to be inexhaustible. However, semen (yang) was viewed as precious, and masturbation was regarded as a waste of vital yang essence (Tannahill, 1982).

Medicine, Psychotherapy, and Masturbation

The **semen-conservation doctrine** (from early Ayurvedic teachings in India) held that general good health in both sexes depended on conserving the life-giving power of "vital fluids." These fluids, which include both semen and vaginal fluids, were believed to be important for intelligence and memory, and derived from good nutrition. Wastage or depletion of semen (regarded as more important) was discouraged because it might result in a loss of resistance to illness and in a decrease in well-being. The second-century physician Aretaeus the Cappadocian, for example, warned against men losing too much semen, "For it is the semen ... which makes us to be men—hot, well braced in limbs, hairy, well voiced, spirited, strong to think and to act" (quoted in Allen, 2000, p. 83).

Early medicine's negative view of masturbation can also be traced to the fact that for centuries, physicians did not clearly distinguish between masturbation and the sexually transmitted infection, gonorrhea (which in Greek means "flow of seed"). One of the symptoms of gonorrhea in men is the discharge of thick pus from the penis. The failure to differentiate between semen ejaculated during masturbation (or released during spontaneous nocturnal emissions) and the penile discharge associated with gonorrhea led physicians to lump gonorrhea and masturbation into a single pathology until the twentieth century (Allen, 2000). "Additionally, for a medical profession that was increasingly able to recognize problems it could not yet cure, self-abuse [masturbation] was an easy culprit to link with all kinds of diseases nobody could otherwise explain" (Allen, 2000, p. 86).

When Samuel Tissot, a highly respected Swiss doctor, published a book on the diseases produced by masturbation (Tissot, 1758/1766), he added medical credibility to the view that masturbation was harmful. Tissot presented graphic and gruesome case studies depicting the horrific effects of masturbation. Tissot provided drawings of those affected by masturbation, one of which portrays a man who had been reduced by masturbation, as described in the following:

Yang

In Chinese thought, the male force that is viewed as active

Yin

In Chinese thought, the female force that is seen as passive

Semen-conservation doctrine

From early Ayurvedic teachings in India, the belief that general good health in both sexes depends on conserving the life-giving power of "vital fluids" (semen and vaginal fluids)

A being that less resembled a living creature than a corpse … A watery, palish blood issued from his nose; slaver constantly flowed from his mouth. Having diarrhea, he voided his excrement in bed without knowing it. He had a continual flux of semen. … The disorder of his mind was equal to that of his body. … (cited in Allen, 2000, p. 88)

By the mid-nineteenth century, Tissot's admonitions against masturbation had made their way into medical textbooks, journals, and books for parents.

Adding to the medical bias against masturbation was Reverend Sylvester Graham, who also claimed that masturbation resulted in the loss of fluids that were vital to the body. In 1834, Graham wrote that losing an ounce of semen was equal to the loss of several ounces of blood. Graham believed that every time a man ejaculated, he ran the risk of contracting a disease of the nervous system. Among his solutions were "Graham crackers", which would help prevent the development of carnal lust that resulted from eating carnivorous flesh (Graham, 1848). John Harvey Kellogg, M.D., had similar beliefs to Graham and suggested his own cure—corn flakes. Kellogg's Corn Flakes were originally developed as a food to extinguish sexual desire and curb masturbation desires.

In the early twentieth century, psychotherapy joined medicine and religion to convince people of the negative effects of masturbation. In 1893, Sigmund Freud claimed that masturbation caused neurasthenia—a widely diagnosed psychosomatic illness characterized by weakness and nervousness. Freud and other psychotherapists who followed his teachings viewed masturbation as an infantile form of sexual gratification. People who masturbated "to excess" could fixate on themselves as a sexual object and would not be able to relate to others in a sexually mature way. The message was clear: If you want to be a good sexual partner in marriage, don't masturbate. If you do masturbate, don't do it too often.

The result of religious, medical, and therapeutic professions denigrating masturbation was devastating for individuals who succumbed to temptation, causing unnecessary shame, anxiety, fear, and guilt. The burden of these feelings was particularly heavy because there was no one with whom to share the guilt. In the case of a premarital pregnancy, responsibility could be shared. With masturbation, however, the "crime" had been committed alone.

The perceived dangers of masturbation warranted extreme measures to deter children and adults from engaging in this behavior. Physicians recommended mechanical restraints (such as strait jackets and chastity belts), tying children's hands and feet at night, and circumcision as preventive measures (Allen, 2000). Because women who masturbated "could become obsessed with sex and thus unfit for their proper role in society," horseback riding, bicycling, and even using pedal-operated sewing machines ("which could stimulate working women until they became sexually sick") were to be avoided (Allen, 2000, p. 96). If preventive measures did not work, masturbators were often locked up in asylums, treated with drugs (such as sedatives and poisons), or subjected to a range of interventions designed to prevent masturbation by stimulating the genitals in painful ways, preventing genital sensation, or deadening it. These physician-prescribed interventions included putting ice on the genitals; blistering and scalding the penis, vulva, inner thighs, or perineum; inserting electrodes into the rectum and urethra; cauterizing the clitoris by anointing it with pure carbolic acid; circumcising the penis; and surgically removing the clitoris, ovaries, and testicles.

One of the most important developments in reducing inaccurate assumptions about the outcomes of masturbation was the advancement of the germ theory of disease and the recognition of the gonococcus and spirochete as causes of gonorrhea and syphilis in the late nineteenth century (Bullough, 2003). However, sexuality historian Vern Bullough noted that what further promoted changes in attitudes toward masturbation was information provided by modern sex researchers in the twentieth century. Research by Kinsey and his colleagues revealed that 92% of the men in their sample reported having masturbated (Kinsey, Pomeroy, & Martin, 1948). Yet the researchers found no evidence of the dire consequences that had been earlier predicted for those who masturbate. These findings presented a major challenge to the prevailing medical views of masturbation as harmful. In spite of Kinsey's evidence suggesting that masturbation was not physically, emotionally, or socially debilitating, many physicians continued to convey to their patients negative attitudes toward masturbation. More recently, physicians' attitudes toward masturbation have become more positive—in part due to the inclusion of human sexuality courses in medical school curricula. Indeed, sex therapists commonly prescribe masturbation as a treatment for women.

Today, medical concerns about adverse health effects of masturbation are limited to special cases in which masturbation can result in physical harm. One of these special cases is the practice of restricting the flow of blood to the brain by constricting one's neck with a rope or belt during masturbation. This dangerous practice, designed to intensify orgasm, can result in **autoerotic asphyxiation**—accidental death by strangulation. Other types of harmful (or potentially harmful) masturbation behavior include using objects that can harm the genitalia (such as sharp objects) and masturbating excessively to the point of creating abrasions and open sores on the genitalia that can lead to infection. Such harmful masturbatory behavior is not typical among the general population and is more of a concern for caregivers of individuals with mental retardation.

8.3b Social Correlates of Masturbation

Survey research reveals that reported frequency of masturbation tends to be associated with such factors as gender, race, and education. Keep in mind, however, that survey data tell us more about what people *say* they do than what they *actually* do.

1. *Gender*   Men are more likely to report having masturbated than women. Explanations for higher rates of masturbation among men include: greater genital availability; traditional male social scripts that emphasize pleasure aspects of sexuality, independent of relationship factors; and greater social support for sexual expression among men than women. In spite of the high percentage of men who masturbate, some men choose never to masturbate.

National **DATA**

Based on a survey of 5,865 respondents in the U.S., (adults ages 20–29), 84% of men and 68% of women reported having masturbated alone (rather than with a partner) in the past 12 months (Reece, Herbinick, & Fortenberry, 2012).

Autoerotic asphyxiation
Cutting off one's air supply to enhance one's orgasm but misjudging the extent of doing so such that accidental death occurs

2. *Race and Ethnicity*   Reported masturbatory behavior varies by race and ethnicity. The rates for white men are higher than for black men, but the rates for black women are higher than for white women. Possible explanations for the lower rate of masturbation among black men (compared to that of white men) include the following: (1) The black male subculture teaches black men that masturbation is an admission of not being able to find a sexual partner; and (2) black men have more frequent interpersonal sexual relations, which may lower the need to masturbate. The higher rate of reported masturbation among black women compared to white women may be due to the shortage

of available black men. Black women with no regular partner in their lives may find sexual enjoyment through masturbation.

3. *Education* Individuals with higher levels of education are more likely to report having masturbated in the past year than are individuals with lower levels of education. In a national sample of adults, among those with less than a high school education, more than half of the men and more than three-quarters of the women reported that they did not masturbate in the past year (Michael, Gagnon, Laumann, Laumann, & Kolata, 1994). Among those with advanced degrees, only 1 out of 5 men and 6 out of 10 women reported that they did not masturbate (Michael, Gagnon, Laumann, Laumann, & Kolata, 1994).

8.3c Pros and Cons of Masturbation

Some individuals feel very uncomfortable about masturbating, especially when their religious beliefs prohibit masturbation. Deciding whether or not to masturbate is a very personal decision, and opting not to masturbate is just as legitimate a choice as the decision to masturbate. Nevertheless, it may be helpful to consider the pros and cons of masturbation in making one's own choices regarding this form of sexual behavior.

> *The fact that a particular act is unpleasant or bad does not make it a disease; nor does the fact that it is pleasant or good make it a treatment.*
>
> Thomas Szasz, psychiatrist

Pros of Masturbation:

1. *Self-knowledge* Masturbation can provide immediate feedback about what one enjoys. Self-knowledge about what feels good enables a person to know what one needs for sexual pleasure, and what to teach a partner about how to provide pleasure.

2. *Increased body comfort* Masturbation can increase an individual's comfort with her or his own body. Individuals who are comfortable with their bodies are more confident and less anxious during sexual interactions, resulting in more overall sexual satisfaction with one's partner. Not all individuals (particularly women) are comfortable when they begin masturbating, but comfort often develops with repeated experiences. Masturbation may also increase an individual's physical, as well as psychological, body comfort. Students in the authors' classes reported that they masturbate to relieve tension, to get to sleep, and to help abate menstrual cramps.

3. *Orgasm more likely* Carvalheira and Leal (2013) analyzed data on 3,687 Portuguese women, 91% of whom reported that they had masturbated at some point in their lives (29% in the last month.) Greater ease of becoming sexually aroused and having an orgasm were associated with their masturbatory behavior. The probability of an orgasm via masturbation is 90% or greater; 30% via sexual intercourse.

4. *Pressure taken off partner* Inevitably, partners in a relationship will vary in their desire for having interpersonal sex. During such times, the partner wanting more sex may feel frustrated, and the partner wanting less sex may feel guilty for not wanting to accommodate the partner. Masturbation might provide an alternative means of sexual satisfaction for the partner wanting more partner sex while taking the pressure off the other partner. The result may be less interpersonal stress for both people.

5. *No partner necessary* Masturbation provides a way to enjoy a sexual experience or an orgasm when no partner is available.

6. *Avoids risk of STI or pregnancy*   When masturbation is enjoyed as a solo activity, there is no risk of transmitting or acquiring a sexually transmitted infection, nor is there any risk of pregnancy.

7. *Unique, pleasurable experience*   Masturbation is a unique sexual experience, different from intercourse and oral stimulation of the genitals. Some people who have interpersonal sex on a regular basis with their partners may also enjoy masturbation because they regard masturbation as a unique experience that partner sex cannot duplicate.

8. *Helpful in maintaining sexual fidelity*   For individuals in coupled relationships, masturbation can help the partners remain faithful when they are separated. For those who have partners who are ill or disabled, masturbation is also an option.

9. *Useful in treatment of sexual dysfunctions*   Sex therapists routinely recommend masturbation to women who report never having experienced orgasm as a means of learning the place(s), pressure, and rhythm of clitoral/genital stimulation that lead(s) to orgasm. Women who know how to pleasure themselves to orgasm are better able to teach their partners how to do so. As noted in point number 3, women who masturbate to orgasm are more likely to report orgasm during intercourse. Masturbation also can be useful in treatment of hypoactive (low) sexual desire (Zamboni & Crawford, 2003).

Persons who have not masturbated but wish to do so can find explicit directions on the Internet. One can go the search engine http://www.google.com and type in "how to masturbate" to identify several websites devoted to providing specific masturbatory information, including how to masturbate.

Cons of Masturbation

1. *Feeling of being abnormal*   Some people feel they are abnormal because they masturbate "too frequently" or in unusual ways. Although masturbation that is consistently used to avoid the complexities of involvement in an intimate relationship may be symptomatic of a larger interpersonal deficit, frequent masturbation per se is not regarded as a problem; and a person who masturbates frequently is not abnormal.

   Masturbating in unusual ways can be viewed as creative or simply different, without the negative implication of "abnormal." One student in the authors' classes reported feeling abnormal because she could experience orgasm by contracting her abdominal muscles. Another student reported that he wondered if he was "normal" because he masturbated to a particular piece of classical music and tried to time his orgasm to the climax of the music. Earlier we mentioned special cases in which masturbation was harmful, such as the practice of constricting the neck during masturbation, which can lead to autoerotic asphyxiation. Aside from such an example, masturbatory behaviors that are not harmful need not elicit concern about abnormality.

2. *Strengthened attraction to inappropriate stimuli*   Masturbation to an inappropriate stimulus or to fantasies of an inappropriate stimulus may strengthen erotic feelings toward that stimulus. For example, adults who masturbate while fantasizing about sexual interactions with children are strengthening their erotic responses to children. Repeated rehearsal of such sexual fantasies and masturbatory behavior contributes to viewing children as sexual objects.

3. *Guilt*   Because social influences such as religion still communicate disapproval for masturbation, the person who does so is vulnerable to feeling guilty. These feelings may cause the person to have low self-esteem or feel distressed.

personal Choices 8-1

To Use a Vibrator or Not

Vibrators, which are made in many sizes, shapes, and styles, are only one type of sex toy that some individuals use during masturbation and/or lovemaking with their partners. Several considerations may be kept in mind in regard to using a vibrator.

Using a vibrator can provide sexual pleasure and orgasm, especially for women who may have difficulty achieving orgasm through other means of stimulation. Sex pioneer Virginia Johnson warned, however, that if a woman uses intense mechanical stimulation over a long period of time, she might lose her appreciation of the various stages of arousal and diminish her ultimate joy. In other words, because the vibrator will usually produce an orgasm quickly, it may short-circuit erotic fantasies, and slow buildup and eventual release, so that some of the emotional and cognitive aspects of orgasm are lost. The counter position is that women vary in how long it takes them to orgasm using a vibrator and that there is no "short circuiting" of erotic pleasure. Most women benefit from the intense stimulation a vibrator provides, and "getting hooked" is a concept they do not indulge.

Vibrators can also add another pleasurable dimension to interpersonal sexual activity. For example, a woman may stimulate her clitoris during lovemaking with a vibrator while her partner penetrates her vagina, kisses her, and/or caresses her. Whereas some partners are in favor of using a vibrator, others may be threatened by its use. One man, who said that his fiancée had gotten hooked on her vibrator, stated, "I think she prefers it to me." In response, the woman told him, "There is no replacing you … since you are my love/my partner. A vibrator is simply what I need to help me orgasm, enjoy sex, and be an involved sexual partner with you." Some couples shop together for their sex toys and have a drawer full. Others give each other sex toys for special events (e.g., birthdays and Christmas). There are hundreds of sex toys, including sex toys for men, sold in "intimate adult shops" or online (google "sex toys" or "vibrators"). Experimenting with the various options can be an enjoyable adventure. It may be helpful for both partners to openly discuss their feelings regarding the use of a vibrator in their relationship.

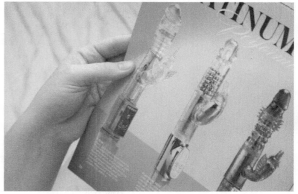

Source: Chelsea Curry

8.3d Masturbation in Relationships

It is sometimes assumed that people who are cohabiting, married, or in established sexual relationships do not masturbate because they have a sexual partner. This assumption is inaccurate because individuals with partners may also report high rates of masturbatory behavior. Masturbation provides a way for partners to experience sexual pleasure when they are not sexually available to each other due to travel, work, hospitalization, military duty, or imprisonment. Some coupled individuals masturbate because their sexual relationship with their partner is unfulfilling or because they desire sexual pleasure at times when their partner is not interested in sexual activity.

When one partner lacks the interest in or ability to participate in sexual activity due to illness or disability, the other partner can find sexual release and pleasure through masturbation. Pregnancy is also a context for masturbation since intercourse may be uncomfortable or not desired.

People in coupled relationships (including marriage) also masturbate for many of the same reasons that single people do. Masturbation can relieve stress and tension, and can also help a person relax and fall asleep. It provides a unique pleasurable experience. Researchers Dekker and Schmidt (2003) observed that, "masturbation is losing its stigma as a substitute for 'the real thing' for both genders. It is acquiring a new status as a separate form of sex behavior in its own right" (p. 41).

Masturbation can have positive effects on a relationship. It can be incorporated into interpersonal sexual activity to increase enjoyment and variety. For example, a woman can stimulate her clitoral area with her fingers or with a vibrator while her partner penetrates her or stimulates her in other ways. Also, a man can masturbate while his partner provides anal penetration or stimulates him in other ways. For some couples, watching each other masturbate can be a turn-on that adds another erotic dimension to the couple's sex life. Separated partners may also masturbate while interacting on Skype.

Women who masturbate are better able to teach their partners how to pleasure them, so they may achieve higher levels of sexual satisfaction in their relationships. Their partners may also derive satisfaction from being able to provide them with pleasure. Finally, masturbation may help some spouses remain faithful by providing a means of experiencing sexual pleasure when the partner is not available, able, and/or interested in sexual activity.

Masturbation can also be problematic in relationships. When a partner's masturbation occurs during interaction with a phone-sex worker or cybersex partner, the other partner might view this as a form of infidelity and feel jealous and angry. More commonly, adults in couple relationships who masturbate do so alone—although they may fantasize about other people and/or view sexually explicit photos or videos. For some couples, solo masturbation is something the partners talk about with each other and accept as normal, healthy sexual behavior. For other couples, one or both partners may masturbate secretly, hiding their behavior from the other partner. In this case, if one partner accidentally discovers that his or her partner masturbates and has done so regularly in secrecy, he or she may feel angry and hurt—not about the masturbation, but about the fact that the partner had not been honest about it. Another potential problem involving masturbation in relationships is that some individuals can interpret their partner's masturbation as evidence that they are not desirable and/or are not satisfying the partner sexually. This interpretation can cause feelings of inadequacy and rejection.

In conclusion, individuals in coupled relationships who masturbate can do so during sexual interaction with their partner, by themselves, with someone outside the relationship (e.g., phone-sex workers or another lover), with or without viewing sexually explicit materials, and with or without the other partner's knowledge. Whether masturbation has positive or negative effects on the couple's relationship depends on the type of situation in which the masturbation occurs, as well as the values and interpretations each partner has of the behavior.

8.3e Masturbation in Groups

Also known as *social masturbation*, group masturbation involves three or more individuals masturbating together. The slang term *circle jerk* refers to a boys' game in which a group of boys form a circle, take out their penises, and masturbate to see who can ejaculate the fastest and who can propel their ejaculate most accurately into the center of a chalk circle on a floor. Variations of the circle jerk include the boys stimulating each other or watching just one boy, the performer, masturbating to ejaculation.

Females may also masturbate in groups. The HBO television series *Real Sex* features the diversity of sexuality. "Masturbation-a-Thon" is one segment that depicted 30 females in a room lying on individual cots with their vibrators. The various participants reported that they solicited donations from their boyfriends and strangers on the street to sponsor them in the competition for who could masturbate the longest. A leader of the group monitored the competition.

8.4 Sexual Fantasies and Sexual Dreams

Both **sexual fantasies** and dreams are part of one's individual sexuality.

8.4a Sexual Fantasies

Sexual fantasies can be thought of as cognitive erotic visual scripts. Sexual fantasies occur in a variety of contexts, one of which is the office. Table 8-2 reveals the sexual fantasies of 774 employed individuals.

> *In my sex fantasy, nobody ever loves me for my mind.*
>
> Nora Ephron

TABLE **8-2**	Sexual Fantasies on the Job (*N* = 774)	
	Fantasized About	Actually Experienced
Sexual Relationship at the Office	41%	24%

Merrill, J. and Knox, D. (2010). *Finding love from 9 to 5: Trade secrets of an office love.* Santa Barbara, CA: Praeger.

In regard to a couple relationship, Santos-Iglesias and colleagues (2013) sampled 195 men and 290 women ages 18 to 81 and found that sexual fantasies predicted sexual desire for one's partner.

8.4b Sexual Dreams

Kai-Ching Yu (2012) studied sex dreams and focused on the degree to which use of pornography affected the frequency. The sample consisted of 52 young male adults who completed a questionnaire concerning their frequencies of sexual fantasy, sexual behaviors, pornography consumption, erotic dreams, and nocturnal emissions. Analysis of the data revealed that the more often the men watched pornography, the more frequently they masturbated to ejaculation, which was associated with fewer nocturnal emissions—hence fewer sex dreams.

> *Sex on television can't hurt you unless you fall off.*
>
> Author unknown

Not all sexual dreams are pleasant and enjoyable; they can also be troubling and even frightening. For example, survivors of sexual abuse often have dreams in which they relive the sexual victimization, after which they wake up in a state of terror. This is a common form of re-experiencing the event—and may be a symptom of post-traumatic stress disorder (PTSD). Counseling and specific therapy to treat PTSD may be helpful and can be accessed through rape crisis centers or hotlines and community or university counseling centers.

Sexual fantasies
Cognitions, or thoughts and/or images, that are sexual in nature

personal Choices 8-2

Sharing Sexual Fantasies with Your Partner

Sharing one's sexual fantasies and dreams with a partner can be an enjoyable experience and add a new dimension to a couple's sexual intimacy. However, doing so can also be a source of jealousy, anger, and conflict—particularly when one's fantasies are about someone other than the partner. In a sample of 349 university students, 98% of the men and 80% of the women reported having sexual fantasies about someone other than the primary partner of the past two months (Hicks & Leitenberg, 2001). When people experience sexual cognitions and dreams that involve prior lovers or anyone other than the primary partner, they often choose not to share their experience with their partner due to discomfort, guilt, concern about hurting the partner's feelings, and fear of the partner's disapproval, jealousy, or anger.

In deciding whether or not to share your sexual fantasies and dreams with your partner, you might consider discussing the issue with your partner. Find out what his or her thoughts and feelings are in regard to having and then sharing sexual cognitions and dreams that do and do not involve other people. Sharing sexual cognitions and dreams is not essential for intimacy and relationship satisfaction.

8.5 Interpersonal Sexual Behaviors

Most adult sexual behavior occurs in the context of a relationship. In the following sections, a variety of interpersonal sexual behaviors from touching to anal intercourse are presented.

> *The secret of a good sexual relationship is making love WITH your partner, not TO your partner.*
>
> Dianna Lowe, Kenneth Lowe

8.5a Sexual Touching

Sexual touching See Foreplay

Foreplay Also referred to as sexual touching, the broad category of activities which are usually undertaken with the goal of increasing one's own and/or one's partner's sexual arousal and pleasure

Sexual touching, also referred to as **foreplay**, is a "broad category of activities which are usually undertaken with the goal of increasing one's own and/or one's partner's sexual arousal and pleasure. These activities can include, but are not limited to, kissing, stroking, massaging, and holding anywhere from one part to the entirety of a partner's body" (Galinsky, 2012, p. 876). Many people regard touching as the most significant aspect of sex. Jenny McCarthy, former Playmate of the Year, said in an interview that she did not care if she ever had an orgasm again. What she needed was to be held.

Both men and women report orgasmic benefits from foreplay. Analysis of data on 1,352 adults revealed that the odds of being "unable to climax were greater by 2.4 times among men and 2.8 times among women who sometimes, rarely, or never engaged in sexual touching, compared to those who always engaged in sexual touching" (Galinsky, 2012).

FIGURE **8-1** ‖ Affectionate Touch Enhances Feelings of Intimacy and Arousal

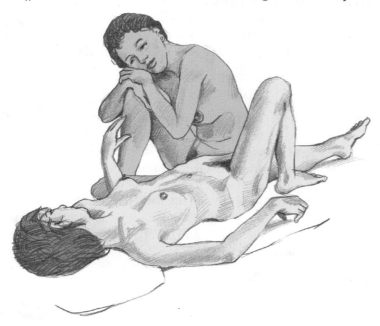

The benefits of sexual touching have been identified by Galinsky (2012). For one, touching is not focused on genital performance, so the lovers can get relaxed and enjoy. Second, there are physiological benefits from touching, which not only decreases stress but also increases a sense of calm and contentment. Third, sexual touching may promote a context of trust and connection, which has been linked to reduced sexual inhibition in women and reduced risk for erectile dysfunction in men. Sexual touching is, in effect, a signal for affection and the desire for greater intimacy (see Figure 8-1).

How often does sexual touching occur? Of the 1,352 respondents, 80% of the men reported "always" (13% usually and 7% sometimes, rarely, never). In contrast, women reported 75% always, 15% usually, and 11% sometimes, rarely, never. Hence, the genders report similar frequencies of sexual touching (Galinsky, 2012). Both genders benefit emotionally from sexual touching in that emotional satisfaction was related to the frequency of sexual touching.

8.5b Kissing

There are different types of kissing. In one style of kissing, the partners gently touch their lips together for a short time with their mouths closed. In another, there is considerable pressure and movement for a prolonged time when the closed mouths meet. In still another, the partners kiss with their mouths open, using gentle or light pressure and variations in tongue movement. Kinsey referred to the latter as *deep kissing* (also known as *soul kissing, tongue kissing,* or *French kissing*). Kissing is included in the concept of sexual touching with attendant benefits in sexual arousal and pleasure.

Wlodarski and Dunbar (2013) analyzed the responses of 308 males and 594 females, ages 18–63, to an internet questionnaire on kissing and found that kissing serves a useful mate-assessment function: women, high mate-value participants, and participants high in sociosexual orientation placed

This is a soul kiss where the partners express intense love feelings for each other.
Source: Mike Jenkins

greater importance on kissing in romantic relationships and stated that an initial kiss was more likely to affect their attraction to a potential mate than did men, low-mate value participants or low sociosexual orientation participants. Kissing also seemed to be important in increasing pair-bond attachments and was found to be related to relationship satisfaction.

Twas not my lips you kissed, but my soul.

Judy Garland, singer/actress

8.5c Oral Penile Stimulation

Oral stimulation of the man's genitals is known as **fellatio**, which comes from the Latin *fellare*, meaning "to suck." Fellatio may be a precursor to intercourse (vaginal or anal), or may be engaged in independently from intercourse.

Although fellatio most often involves sucking the penis, it may also include licking the shaft, glans, frenulum, and scrotum. The partner's hands also may caress the scrotum and perineum during fellatio. If fellatio results in orgasm, the semen may be swallowed without harm (in the absence of HIV or other STIs) if the partner desires to do so. However, to reduce risk of HIV and other STI transmission, the penis should be covered with a condom during fellatio.

National DATA

Based on a survey of 5,865 respondents in the U.S., of (adults ages 20–29), 70% of the men reported that they "received oral sex from a woman" in the past 12 months (Reece, Herbinick, & Fortenberry, 2012).

Some couples engage in oral sex simultaneously, whereby each partner is a giver and receiver at the same time. The term *69* has been used to describe the positions of two partners engaging in mutual oral-genital stimulation.

Fellatio can be used as a means of avoiding intercourse for moral reasons (to preserve virginity) or to avoid pregnancy. Some who engage in unprotected oral sex mistakenly believe it cannot transmit STIs. A primary motivation for fellatio is pleasure. Many men, as well as women, experience physical pleasure and satisfaction from receiving and/or giving fellatio. As is true with all sexual behaviors, positive interpretations of the experience contribute to the pleasure and satisfaction. For example, both the giver and receiver of oral sex can view this behavior as an expression of love and intimacy. Prior to June 26, 2003, sodomy laws made oral and anal sex a criminal acts in 15 states. On that date, the U.S. Supreme Court struck down a Texas state law banning private consensual sex between adults of the same sex. This decision invalidated the sodomy laws of other states as well, with the result that sexual behavior between consenting, same-sex adults in the United States is no longer illegal.

Clinton lied. A man might forget where he parks or where he lives, but he never forgets oral sex, no matter how bad it is.

Barbara Bush

Some men enjoy fellatio because it gives them a feeling of dominance. A common theme in pornographic media involves a man forcing his partner to perform fellatio. In this context, the act implies sexual submission, which may give the male an ego boost. This may also explain why some partners do not find giving fellatio appealing. However, the person providing fellatio can also feel dominant in that he or she is in a more active role than the more passive recipient.

Fellatio
Oral stimulation of a man's genitals

8.5d Oral Clitoral Stimulation

National DATA

Based on a survey of 5,865 respondents in the U.S., of (adults ages 20–29), 71% of the women reported that they "received oral sex from a man" in the past 12 months (Reece, Herbinick, & Fortenberry, 2012)

Cunnilingus, translated from the Latin, means "he who licks the vulva." Specifically, cunnilingus involves the stimulation of the clitoris, labia, and vaginal opening of the woman by her partner's tongue and lips (see Figure 8-2). The technique many women enjoy is gentle teasing by the tongue, with stronger, more rhythmic sucking or tongue stroking movements when orgasm approaches. While the partner's mouth is caressing and licking the clitoral shaft and glans, some women prefer additional stimulation by a dildo, finger, or vibrator in the vagina or anus.

Stock and colleagues (2013) reemphasized that HPV can be transmitted through oral sex—and that HPV can cause throat cancer. To reduce risk of STI transmission during cunnilingus, partners should use a **dental dam**, which is a thin piece of latex that covers the vulva. A latex condom that is cut into a flat piece may act as a substitute for a dental dam. Dental dams can also be purchased over the Internet. (Saran Wrap may also be used.) Some partners also want to use a vibrator. Up Close 8-1 addresses talking with a partner about vibrator use.

> *I like to see oral sex and manual sex and intercourse as foreplay for my vibrator sex.*
>
> Betty Dodson

8.5e Penile-Clitoral Stimulation

In addition to stimulating the clitoral area by mouth, some heterosexual women rub their partner's penis across and around their clitoris. Such stimulation may or may not be followed by penetration. If the man is not wearing a condom, penile-clitoral stimulation carries a risk of causing pregnancy. If the man ejaculates near the woman's vaginal opening during penile-clitoral stimulation, or even if he just emits a small amount of pre-ejaculatory fluid (which may contain sperm), pregnancy is possible.

8.5f Anal Stimulation

Some men enjoy an orgasm via stimulation of the prostate. Others enjoy the sensation of a lover's finger in their anal opening and gently rotating and/or moving in and out.

Cunnilingus
Stimulation of the clitoris, labia, and vaginal opening of the woman by her partner's tongue and lips

Dental dam
Thin piece of latex that covers the vulva during cunnilingus, or the anus during analingus

FIGURE **8-2** ‖ Simultaneous Oral-Genital Stimulation

Close 8-1

Talking with a New Partner About Using a Vibrator

Talking with a new partner about introducing a vibrator into our sex life is always a little tense and anxious. I never know how the guy is going to respond. Some guys love sex toys and like to use them on me. Other guys go along, but I know they don't like it. And, I had one guy tell me that if he wasn't good enough and that if I needed a "machine" maybe something was wrong with me. Needless to say, that guy is history.

Once it is clear that I'm in a stable relationship, I tell my partner flat out, I need clitoral stimulation with a vibrator to have an orgasm. I also make it clear that my using a vibrator does not diminish my love for him or my enjoyment in intercourse. Most guys appreciate my being up front about my enjoyment with sex toys.

Fisting
Insertion of several fingers or an entire closed fist and forearm (typically lubricated with a non-petroleum-based lubricant) into a partner's rectum and sometimes the lower colon; term also used to describe insertion of hand into vagina

Analingus
Licking of and/or insertion of the tongue into the partner's anus (also known as Rimming.)

Sexual intercourse
Sexual union of a man's penis and a woman's vagina (also known as Coitus)

Coitus
Sexual union of a man's penis and a woman's vagina (also known as Sexual intercourse)

Still others may prefer the insertion of a dildo or vibrator beyond the anal opening and short anal canal, into the larger rectum.

Another form of anal stimulation, called **fisting,** involves the insertion of several fingers or an entire closed fist and forearm (typically lubricated with a non-petroleum-based lubricant) into a partner's rectum and sometimes the lower colon. Care during insertion is particularly important, and that it not be abrupt or forceful so as to avoid damage to the rectum, colon, and anal sphincter. Although anyone can perform or receive fisting, this activity is usually associated with male homosexual activity.

Some partners enjoy oral-anal stimulation or **analingus** (also referred to as rimming), which involves the licking of and/or insertion of the tongue into the partner's anus. The idea of this form of sexual activity is disgusting to some people, and others avoid it due to health concerns. For protection, a latex barrier (or Saran Wrap) should be used during analingus.

8.5g Vaginal Intercourse

Sexual intercourse, or **coitus**, refers to the sexual union of a man's penis and a woman's vagina (the woman's vagina encircles or surrounds the penis, and the penis penetrates the vagina) (see Figure 8-3).

Miller and Byers (2004) compared the duration of actual intercourse (men = 8 minutes; women = 7 minutes) and desired intercourse (men = 18 minutes; women = 14 minutes) of heterosexual men and women in long-term relationships with each other. These findings revealed a discrepancy between desired and actual duration of intercourse.

National **DATA**

Based on a survey of 5,865 respondents in the U.S., of (adults ages 20–29), 73% of the men and 84% of the women reported that they experienced sexual intercourse in the past 12 months (Reece, Herbinick, & Fortenberry, 2012).

FIGURE **8-3** ‖ Sexual Intercourse

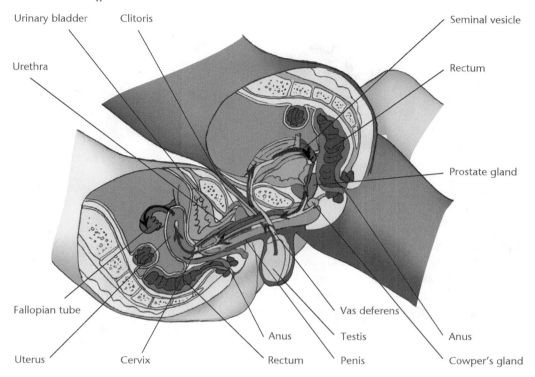

Urinary bladder
Clitoris
Urethra
Fallopian tube
Uterus
Cervix
Anus
Rectum
Penis
Testis
Vas deferens
Seminal vesicle
Rectum
Prostate gland
Anus
Cowper's gland

Positions for Intercourse

There are numerous positions for intercourse. Some of the more common positions follow:

1. *Man-on-Top Position*   The man-on-top position is the most frequently reported position used during intercourse (see Figure 8-4). This position is also referred to as the "missionary position" because the Polynesians observed that the British missionaries had intercourse with the man on top. The woman reclines on her back, bends her knees, and spreads her legs. The man positions himself between her legs, supporting himself on his elbows and knees. The man or woman may guide his penis into her vagina. This position permits maximum male thrusting and facilitates eye contact, kissing, and caressing. Some partners may prefer to be on top or on bottom as an expression of their feelings about gender, dominance, and submission.

> *"Can you … make it different this time?"*
> *"Different, how?"*
> *"Different position, different … something. I want to learn it all."*
> *Whoa, pressure. When Maira's genius brain wanted to learn something, she really applied herself.*
>
> Alisha Rai, *Veiled Seduction*

FIGURE **8-4** ‖ **Man on Top Position**

FIGURE **8-5** ‖ Woman on Top Position

Some women experience pain from the deep penetration. Closing their legs after penetration can reduce this pain. For some women, the man-above position makes clitoral contact and orgasm difficult, although many women find ways of moving their hips and/or positioning their body to achieve clitoral stimulation and/or orgasm. Either the man's or the woman's hand or finger may also stimulate the woman's clitoris during man-on-top intercourse. For some men, the muscle tension produced by supporting their weight and active thrusting hastens ejaculation, which may be problematic for both the woman and man.

A variation of the man-on-top position involves the woman lying on her back, with the man squatting or kneeling between the woman's spread legs. This is often referred to as the "Oceanic position" because it has been described in Pacific cultures. Body contact can be full and intimate, or minimal.

2. *Woman-on-Top Position*   In the woman-on-top position, the woman may either lie lengthwise, so that her legs are between her partner's, or kneel on top with her knees on either side of him (see Figure 8-5). The primary advantage of this position is that it provides the woman with more control so that she can move in ways that provide her with maximum pleasure. Many women report that this position is more likely to lead to orgasm than the man-on-top position. In this position, partners can also touch each other (or themselves), kiss, and maintain eye contact.

Some women report drawbacks to the woman-above position. Some feel too shy in this position and do not enjoy "being on display." Others complain

FIGURE **8-6** ‖ Side-by-Side Position

FIGURE **8-7** || **Rear Entry During Pregnancy**

that the penis keeps falling out because the woman may lift too high before the downward stroke on the penis.

For both women and men, being on the bottom position during intercourse is easier and requires less energy and exertion, whereas being in the top position during intercourse is more work. Some partners' preferences for being on the bottom or the top depend on how tired or energetic they feel.

3. *Side-by-Side Position*   A relaxing position for both partners is the side-by-side position (see Figure 8-6). The partners lie on their sides, facing each other. The top legs are lifted and positioned to accommodate easy entry of the penis. Neither partner bears the strain of "doing all the work," and the partners have relative freedom to move their body as they wish to achieve the desired place of contact and rhythm of movement. This position may be preferred in the latter months of pregnancy.

4. *Rear-Entry Position*   There are several ways to achieve a rear-entry intercourse position. The woman may lie on her side with her back to her partner (see Figure 8-7). She may also support herself on her knees and hands

FIGURE **8-8** || **Rear Entry, Man Kneeling**

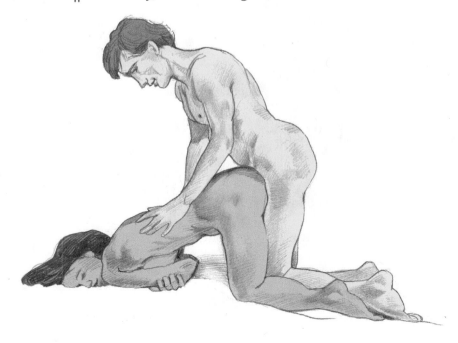

or forearms and elbows (see Figure 8-8), or she may lie on her stomach and tilt her buttocks upward while the man enters her vagina from behind. In another rear-entry variation, the man may lie on his back and the woman may kneel or squat above him with her back toward her partner.

Many of the rear-entry intercourse positions permit the man or the woman to manually stimulate her breasts or clitoris, or caress her legs and buttocks. Many women are unable to achieve orgasm using the rear-entry position. Although some women enjoy the deep penetration that results from rear-entry intercourse, others find it painful. Other disadvantages of rear-entry intercourse include a tendency for the penis to slip out and the loss of face-to-face contact. Sometimes the stigma of bestiality accompanies this position because it is often described with animal names, as in the Chinese "Leaping Tiger," the Marquesan "horse intercourse," and the American term "doggie position" or "doggie style."

5. *Sitting Position*   In the sitting position, the man sits on a chair or the edge of the bed with his partner sitting across his thighs (see Figure 8-9). The woman can lower herself onto his erect penis or insert his penis after she is sitting. She may be facing him, or her back may be turned to him. The face-to-face sitting position involves maximum freedom to stimulate the breasts (manually or orally), to kiss, and to hug. It may allow the man to delay ejaculating because

FIGURE **8-9** ‖ Sitting Position

it doesn't involve pelvic thrusting. Chinese erotic art often depicts coitus in a sitting position, but this is not prominent in other cultures.

6. *Standing Position*   In the standing position, the woman raises one leg, or the man picks hers up and places her onto his erect penis. She puts her legs around his waist and her arms around his neck while he is holding her. Both must be well coordinated and in good physical condition for this position.

    An easier variation of the standing position is for the man to stand while the woman sits or reclines on a raised surface (a high bed, a table, or a chair). The woman's legs are spread, and the man inserts his penis into her vagina while standing between her legs. In most cultures of the world, standing positions are associated with brief (often illicit) encounters.

7. *Variations*   There are innumerable variations to the basic positions described here. For example, in the man-above position the woman's legs may be closed or open, bent or straight, over his shoulders or around his neck. The woman may be on her back or raised on her elbows. The partners may face each other or be head-to-toe. Couples can choose different positions to add variety to their lovemaking and to provide different types of stimulation and pleasure. Sexual intercourse positions may also vary according to pregnancy and health issues.

    Regardless of position, partners may disagree over the frequency of intercourse. Willoughby and colleagues (2013) analyzed data on 1,054 married couples to assess the effect of sexual desire discrepancy (SDD) on relationship satisfaction, stability and conflict during marriage. Results showed that disagreement on the frequency of sexual intercourse was associated with negative relational outcomes, including lower relationship satisfaction, stability, and more couple conflict. Negative associations were particularly strong when the husband reported high discrepancies between desired and actual sexual frequency.

8.5h Anal Intercourse

National DATA

Based on a survey of 5,865 respondents in the U.S., of (adults ages 20–29), 5% of the men and 22% of the women reported having received a penis in the anus in the past 12 months (Reece, Herbinick, & Fortenberry, 2012)

Anal intercourse is one form (not the primary form) of sexual expression enjoyed by some homosexual males. Partners differ in their preference for and comfort in being the active or passive partner. Both partners may have orgasm during anal penetration—the active partner due to stimulation of the penis and the passive partner due to the fact that the partner's penis in his rectum exerts pressure on his prostate gland, which may trigger orgasm.

For couples who enjoy anal intercourse, or who want to try it, care and patience during insertion are critical to avoiding rectal tearing and pain. It is important for the receiving partner to be in control of the timing and depth of penetration. It is best for the receiving partner to be relaxed, specifically for his or her anal sphincter muscles to be relaxed, and for insertion to be slow and gradual. Using a lubricant is recommended for easing entry into the anus and minimizing discomfort.

National **DATA**

Based on a survey of 5,865 respondents in the U.S., of (adults ages 20–29), 19% of the men reported inserting a penis into an anus in the past 12 months (Reece, Herbinick, & Fortenberry, 2012).

The person receiving anal intercourse is at higher risk than the man who inserts his penis into his partner's rectum. The reason is that anal intercourse often tears the rectum, allowing HIV-infected semen to come in contact with the bloodstream. In addition, the first few inches of the anus provide darkness, warmth, and moisture in the mucous membranes, which is a prime host for transmitting HIV. Couples who engage in anal intercourse should always use a condom to protect against transmission of HIV and other STIs. The use of water-based lubrication products, such as K-Y Jelly, may also enable the penis to enter the partner's rectum more easily, and thus minimize tearing of the rectal tissue. If vaginal intercourse or oral contact with the penis follows anal intercourse, the penis should first be thoroughly washed.

Another risk associated with anal intercourse (as well as with manual or oral stimulation of the anus) is **cystitis** (bladder infection). Cystitis may result from bacteria from the anal region being spread to the urethral opening. Symptoms of cystitis may include a persistent urge to urinate, pain during urination, and fever. Cystitis is treated with antibiotics; if left untreated, a serious kidney infection could develop. Women are much more prone to developing cystitis than men. To reduce risk of cystitis, partners should use a condom, clean the anal area before engaging in anal stimulation, urinate immediately after sex, and clean the anal and genital area after sex. Also, after a penis, mouth, or finger has come in contact with the anal area, partners should avoid contact with the vagina and clitoris until the penis, mouth, or finger has been washed thoroughly.

Racial/Ethnic
Diversity

Hall and colleagues (2012) analyzed data on 4,413 young women, ages 15–24, in the U.S. and found a higher incidence of vaginal sex among women of black race/ethnicity. However, in regard to oral and anal sex, white women had higher incidences than nonwhites. Hispanic women had a lower incidence of oral sex; Asian women a lower incidence of anal sex.

Cystitis
Bladder infection

personal Choices   8-3

Considerations for Having Sex with a New Partner

There are several issues you might consider in making the decision to have sexual intercourse with a new partner.

1. *Personal consequences*   How do you predict you will feel about yourself after you have had intercourse with a new partner? An increasing percentage of college students are relativists and feel that the outcome will be positive if they are in love. The following quote is from a student in our classes:

> I believe intercourse before marriage is OK under certain circumstances. I believe that when a person falls in love with another and the relationship is stable, it is then appropriate. This should be thought about very carefully for a long time, so as not to regret engaging in intercourse.

Those who are not in love and have sex in a casual context often report sexual regret about their decision.

> When I have the chance to experience sex with someone new, my first thought is to jump right in, ask questions later. However, my very second thought is, "If we do this, will he think I'm slutty?" followed by "Is it too early to be doing this? What if I regret it?" Looking back at my dating experiences over the past several years, it seems that earlier on, I let a guy talk me into doing something sexual, even though those questions were running circles in my head. However, in the most recent instances, I remained firm that sex wasn't going to happen so soon into dating someone, and I do not regret my decision. In the future, I don't plan on being intimate with anyone until we have gone from "going out on dates" to boyfriend/girlfriend status. (Merrill & Knox, 2010, p. 3)

The effect intercourse will have on you, personally, will be influenced by your personal values, your religious values, and your emotional involvement with your partner. Some people prefer to wait until they are married to have intercourse and feel that this is the best course for future marital stability and happiness. There is often, but not necessarily, a religious basis for this value.

Strong personal and religious values against nonmarital intercourse may result in guilt and regret following an intercourse experience. In a sample of 270 unmarried undergraduates who had had intercourse, 71.9% regretted their decision to do so at least once (for example, they may have had intercourse more than once or with multiple partners and reported regret at least once). Higgins and colleagues (2010) analyzed data on first intercourse behavior from a cross-sectional survey of 1,986 non-Hispanic white and black 18- to 25-year-old respondents from four university campuses. Respondents were asked to rate the degree to which their first vaginal intercourse was physiologically and psychologically satisfying. Women were less likely than men to report a positive first vaginal intercourse experience, particularly physiological satisfaction. Being in a committed relationship was the condition associated with the most positive experience.

2. *Timing* In a sample of over 5,000 unmarried singles, about a third (28%) reported that they had sex by the third date; almost half (46%) had done so by the sixth date (Walsh, 2013). Delaying intercourse with a new partner is important for achieving a positive outcome and avoiding regret. The table below reveals that a third of 429 undergraduates regretted having sexual intercourse "too soon" in a relationship (Merrill & Knox, 2010, p. 2).

TABLE **8-3**	Regret for Engaging in Behavior "Too Soon" or "Too Late" (*N* = 429)			
Behavior	"Too Soon"	"Too Late"	"Perfect Timing"	"Did Not Do"
Sexual Intercourse	33.3%	3.3%	48.4%	15.0%
Spent the night	26.6%	3.7%	58.8%	11.4%
Saying "I love you"	26.1%	3.9%	50.8%	19.2%
Kissing	11.1%	3.1%	82.8%	3.1%

3. *Partner consequences* Because a basic moral principle is to do no harm to others, it is important to consider the effect of intercourse on your partner. Whereas intercourse may be a pleasurable experience with positive consequences for you, your partner may react differently. What is your partner's religious background, and what are your partner's sexual values? A highly religious person with absolutist sexual values will typically have a very different reaction to sexual intercourse than a person with low religiosity and relativistic or hedonistic sexual values.

4. *Relationship consequences* What is the effect of intercourse on a couple's relationship? One's personal reaction to having intercourse may spill over into the relationship. Individuals might predict how they feel having intercourse will affect their relationship before including it in their relationship.

5. *Contraception* Another potential consequence of intercourse is pregnancy. Once a couple decides to have intercourse, a separate decision must be made as to whether intercourse should result in pregnancy. Most sexually active undergraduates do not want children. People who want to avoid pregnancy must choose and plan to use a contraceptive method.

6. *HIV and other sexually transmissible infections* Engaging in casual sex has potentially fatal consequences. Avoiding HIV infection and other STIs is an important consideration in deciding whether to have intercourse in a new relationship. Pflieger and colleagues (2013) analyzed data from a nationally representative sample of 7,015 female young adults and found black and Hispanic young women most at risk for STIs in young adulthood—30% of blacks, 10% of Hispanics, and 6% of whites self-reported or tested positive via biospecimen for an STI.

    More people having an increase in the number of sex partners results in the rapid spread of the bacteria and viruses responsible for numerous varieties of STIs. However, in a sample of 1,071 undergraduate males, 30% reported consistent condom use, and of 3,390 undergraduate females, 27% reported consistent condom use (Hall & Knox, 2013). In one study, women with low GPAs and those who were binge drinkers reported the lowest condom use (Walsh, 2013). OraQuick, available for about $40, is a home test for HIV. A swab of saliva and 20 minutes could reveal antibodies that signal HIV infection.

7. *Influence of alcohol and other drugs*   A final consideration with regard to the decision to have intercourse in a new relationship is to be aware of the influence of alcohol and other drugs on such a decision. Bersamin and colleagues (2013) confirmed that amount of alcohol consumed by undergraduates was associated with having sex with a stranger. The contexts of alcohol consumption included Greek parties, residence hall parties, off-campus parties, and a bar/restaurant—in short, all places where students drink.

8. *It's okay to change your mind about including intercourse in a relationship.*   Although most couples who include intercourse in their relationship continue the pattern, some decide to omit it from their sexual agenda. One female student said, "Since I did not want to go on the pill and would be frantic if I got pregnant, we decided the stress was not worth having intercourse. While we do have oral sex, we don't even think about having intercourse any more."

BVT *Lab*

Visit **www.BVTLab.com** to explore the student resources available for this chapter.

personal choices   8-4

Shaving Pubic Hair

Increasingly, women are shaving their pubic hair. A team of researchers (Herbenick, et al., 2013) analyzed data from diaries/journals of 2,453 women, ages 18 to 68 (mean age 33). Fifteen percent of all days (7,362) involved pubic hair waxing or shaving (99% shaving). Pubic hair removal was significantly associated with younger age, a greater interest in sex, vaginal fingering, finger-clitoral stimulation, having a casual sex partner, using vaginal hygiene products, and applying cream to the genitals.

A continuing trend among men is **manscaping**. While waxing is common among young single women, single men are now shaving, waxing and trimming their body hair since they feel their partners expect and will be pleased at their presentation. Stores such as Kohls and Bed, Bath & Beyond stock body trimmers right next to facial ones. "The Mangroomer Private Body Shaver" is specifically for this.

Manscaping
Removal of body hair by men (mostly single) as a grooming behavior to present one's best sexual self to one's partner

Chapter Summary

Sexuality differs in the same individual and/or couple across time, and between individuals and couples. In this chapter, we examined the range of individual and interpersonal sexual behaviors.

Erotophilia and Erotophobia

The range of feelings toward sexual behavior can be conceptualized according to a continuum known as the *erotophilic-erotophobic continuum*. The propensity to have positive emotional responses to sexuality is referred to as *erotophilia*. The tendency to have negative emotional responses to sexuality is known as *erotophobia*. Individuals who are erotophobic tend to feel uncomfortable about sex and try to avoid sexual partners, contexts, and experiences. Although erotophobic individuals are less likely to be sexually active, those who do engage in sexual relations have a higher risk of pregnancy and HIV or STI transmission because they feel uncomfortable discussing or using contraception or condoms.

Virginity, Chastity, Celibacy, and Abstinence

Virginity refers to not having experienced sexual intercourse. Virgins—may or may not have experienced other forms of sexual interaction, such as manual or oral-genital stimulation. The term *chastity* also refers to not having had sexual intercourse, but it also implies moral purity or virtuousness in both thought and conduct. Individuals who practice chastity probably abstain not only from intercourse but also from all sexual behaviors. *Celibacy* may refer to the condition of being unmarried, especially by reason of religious vows, and also implies refraining from having sexual intercourse although a person who practices celibacy is not necessarily a virgin. The more commonly used term today that refers to refraining from having sexual intercourse is *abstinence*. Like celibacy, the practice of abstinence does not necessarily mean that the person is a virgin; a person who has experienced sexual intercourse can subsequently practice abstinence. For some individuals, abstinence means refraining from sexual intercourse, but not from other forms of sexual interaction. For other individuals, abstinence means refraining from not only sexual intercourse but also from other sexual behaviors as well. Abstinence can be voluntary or involuntary, and can last for short or extended periods of time. Sometimes abstinence is enforced by an institutional structure such as a nursing or retirement home.

Masturbation

Autoerotic behavior, commonly known as *masturbation,* involves touching and stimulating one's self to achieve sexual pleasure and/or orgasm. Due to traditional negative attitudes toward masturbation that originated in religion, medicine, and traditional psychotherapy, shame, guilt, and anxiety continue to be common feelings associated with masturbation in our society. Most healthcare professionals today agree that masturbation is a normal and healthy sexual behavior. Masturbation varies by sex, religion, race/ethnicity, and education. Partnered individuals, as well as singles, engage in masturbation as a solo activity or with a partner. The effects of masturbation on relationships can be positive or negative and largely depend on the situation in which the behavior occurs and the values and interpretations of each partner. Masturbation also occurs in groups, and organized masturbation clubs can be found in large cities throughout the world.

Sexual Fantasies and Sexual Dreams

Sexual fantasies can be thought of as cognitive erotic visual scripts. It is commonly assumed that engaging in sexual fantasy is a pleasant and enjoyable experience that is engaged in deliberately. However, some individuals experience negative reactions to their sexual fantasies, including guilt, embarrassment, and anxiety. In addition, sexual fantasies are not always deliberate and under the control of the individual. Sexual dreams can result in arousal and orgasm in both women and men.

Interpersonal Sexual Behaviors

Most adult sexual behavior occurs in the context of a relationship. These behaviors include sexual touching, kissing, oral penile stimulation, oral clitoral stimulation, anal stimulation, vaginal intercourse, and anal intercourse. There are many variations of these sexual behaviors, many of which can be enjoyed by homosexual male couples, lesbian couples, and heterosexual couples. In deciding whether or not to become sexually active with a person, individuals might consider the following: consequences for one's self, one's partner, and the relationship; contraception and pregnancy issues; the need for protecting against transmission of HIV/ STDs; and the influence of alcohol/ drugs on making this decision.

Web Links

Anal Sex

> http://www.sexuality.org/authors/morin/analrule.html

Bed Sider Birth Control Support Network

> http://bedsider.org/

Sexuality and Aging Today Blog

> http://www.sexualityandaging.com/board/bill-taverner-ma/

Sex Toys

> http://www.sexuality.org/sextoys.html

Key Terms

Additional study resources are available at www.BVTLab.com

CHAPTER 9

Lifespan View of Sexuality

Yesterday you were 17. Tomorrow you'll be 50. Life's a short trip. You'll see.

The late Rodney Dangerfield, comedian

Chapter Outline

Objectives

1. Describe the lifespan perspective of human sexuality.

2. Understand how sexual development begins during infancy and is influenced by parental behaviors.

3. Know how sexuality impacts adolescent development.

4. Review the effect of sex education and the consequences of teen pregnancy.

5. Discuss the various trends in sexuality among singles, cohabitants, married couples, and divorced individuals.

6. Understand extradyadic sexual involvement and the various types of extramarital affairs.

7. Learn how sexuality changes in the middle and later years.

Source: Sara DeGaetano

TRUTH OR FICTION?

T/F   Overweight females are more likely to be sexually active than recommended-weight counterparts.

T/F   National data on adolescents reveals that most are depressed and feel social rejection.

T/F   Most very early sexual debuts (e.g., age 12) are nonconsensual.

T/F   In one study of sexually active adolescents, over 15% reported wanting to get pregnant.

T/F   Most teachers in public schools to use abstinence-only curriculum.

Answers:
1.F 2.F 3.T 4.T 5.T

Sexuality is not the same in all of life's innings. In this chapter we take the long view of one's sexuality across time. We begin with sexuality in the uterus and continue with the various issues individuals face.

In youth we learn, in age we understand.
Marie Ebner von Eschenbach

9.1 Sexuality in Infancy and Childhood

A life-cycle view of sexuality emphasizes that early experiences are important influences in subsequent sexual development.

9.1a Infancy

Infancy is the first year of life following birth. Just as infants are born with digestive and respiratory systems, they also are born with a sexual response system that has already begun to function. Ultrasound on the pregnant woman has been used to document fetal erection of the penis. Such an erection confirms that, with the exception of the reproductive system (which will be delayed until puberty), all the human body systems begin functioning prenatally. Indeed, even in the uterus, boys often have penile erections and girls have clitoral erections or vaginal lubrication.

Because sexual pleasure is an unconditioned positive stimulus, infants are capable of learning associations via classical conditioning processes. Masturbation has been observed in both boys and girls as infants.

Because infants may learn to associate sexual pleasure with their bodies early, it is important for parents not to overreact. Parents who slap their infants for touching their own body parts and label such behaviors as "dirty" may teach their children to associate anxiety and guilt with sexuality. It is crucial to keep in mind that for babies to find pleasure in touching their bodies is developmentally normal. Of course, although parents should be careful to teach children that it is okay to touch themselves, there are societal restrictions such as when to do so (in private). There are also restrictions about touching others (with their consent) and having others touch them (again, with consent).

Although we can assume that touching the genitals results in pleasurable feelings, it is unlikely that infants attach sexual meaning to these experiences in the ways that adults do. It is also important to keep in mind that even though infants are capable of sexual responsiveness, they are not experiencing arousal in the same sense as a young adult. Pedophiles who claim that the child "wanted it" may not be mindful that infants and young children have not learned the social scripting of arousal and sexuality that come as the child gets older and moves toward reproductive age, maturity, and relationships.

9.1b Sexual Behaviors of Children

Childhood extends from age 2 to age 12 and involves physical, cognitive, social, and sexual development. Collecting data on the sexuality of children involves the observations of caretakers. Schoentjes and Deboutte (1999) analyzed data from a 7 page questionnaire completed by caregivers of 917 children ages 2–12 of Belgian or Dutch origin. Children who had been sexually abused were omitted from the analysis. Table 9-1 reveals selected sexual behaviors of various age groups. The researchers noted that the findings are similar to studies of U.S. children (Friedrich, Fisher, Broughton, Houston, & Shafran, 1998).

The selected behaviors in Table 9-1 can be sorted into various categories: exhibitionism, self-stimulation, other focused, gender role behavior, sexual anxiety, sexual interest, and voyeuristic behavior. Notice that the uninhibited behavior of 2- to 5-year-olds quickly abates as socialization takes place. For example, 30% of those children were observed touching their sex parts in public, but only 9% of 10- through 12-year-olds exhibit this behavior. Similarly, 21% of 2- to 5-year-olds touch the sex parts of others, but only 2% of those ages 10–12 years do.

Infancy
First year of life following birth

Childhood
Developmental time frame that extends from age 2 to age 12 and involves physical, cognitive, social, and sexual development

TABLE **9-1**	Sexual Behaviors of 917 Belgian/Dutch Children				
A— No.	B— Item	C—2–5 yrs. (*n* = 470)	D—6–9 yrs. (*n* = 311)	E—10–12 yrs. (*n* = 136)	F— Chi² P
1.	Touches sex parts in public	30.0%	16.1%	8.8%	<0.00001
2.	Masturbates with hands	9.2	6.1	5.2	NS
3.	Masturbates with object	3.2	0.3	1.5	<0.02
4.	Touches other people's sex parts	21.9	7.7	1.5	<0.00001
5.	Touches sex parts at home	78.3	56.0	31.6	<0.00001
6.	Uses words that describe sex acts	3.6	24.4	27.9	<0.00001
7.	Pretends to be opposite sex when playing	13.8	2.9	1.5	<0.00001
8.	Puts objects in vagina/rectum	3.0	0.3	0.0	<0.005
9.	Tries to look at people when they are nude	37.2	28.9	19.1	<0.001
10.	Undresses self in front of others	62.6	48.6	27.2	<0.00001
11.	Kisses other children not in the family	63.4	38.6	23.5	<0.00001
12.	Shows sex parts to children	13.2	7.1	2.2	<0.001
13.	If boy, plays with girl's toys; if girl, plays with boy's toys	59.4	38.3	20.6	<0.00001
14.	Shy about undressing	15.3	30.2	32.4	<0.00001
15.	Plays doctor	53.0	39.2	15.4	<0.00001

Source: Adapted from Schoentjes, E. & Deboutte, D. (1999). Child Sexual Behavior Inventory: A Dutch-speaking normative sample. *Pediatrics, 104:* 885–893.

Personal REFLECTION

Take a moment to express your thoughts about the following question. A favorite game among preschool children is "doctor." This game—which may be played between boys, between girls, or between boys and girls—involves one child assuming the role of patient and the other the role of doctor. The patient undresses, and the doctor examines the patient both by making a visual inspection and by touching his or her body, including the genitals. Some parents, believing such exploration is wrong, punish their children for playing "doctor." Alternatively, parents might respond by saying something nonpunitive, such as, "It is interesting to find out how other people's bodies look, isn't it?" However, developmental psychologists suggest that parents should be concerned, and should intervene, if one child is unwilling or coerced into playing doctor, if the children are not the same age (within a couple of years), or if the activity is potentially harmful—such as inserting objects into themselves or each other. In such situations, parents might say something like, "Your body is wonderful, and it is natural that you are interested in your own body. But it is your body, and only you should touch yourself in private places." What reactions do you recall your parents making to your early sexual behavior?

9.1c Barriers to Parents Talking to Their Children About Sex

Sexual socialization/sexuality education of children is a process by which knowledge, attitudes and values about sex are learned (Stone, Inghamand, & Gibbins, 2013). Parents are typically regarded as the first and most important source of sexual socialization for their children. While children are continually learning from parents about sex (even though parents do not talk about sex), parents are concerned about what and when to talk with their children about sex. That they should say anything at all is accompanied by the fear that doing so will spark experimentation and destroy their child's innocence/nonsexual state. Parents also may be tense when engaging in a conversation about sex due to their own inadequate socialization; and when they do bring up the subject, it is more often about reproduction than relationships. Nevertheless, there is strong evidence that there is a positive link between parental openness about sex and "young people's confidence, competence, and sexual safety" (Stone, Inghamand, & Gibbins, 2013).

Direct information from parents about the process of talking with their children about sex was collected from 20 parents of 44 children, ages 3–7, in five group discussions. The content of the discussions focused on "barriers to communication" (Stone, Inghamand, & Gibbins, 2013). One barrier (referred to above) is the anxiety associated with the desire to protect the innocence of the child. One parent said it was just easier to lie: *"I've completely avoided telling him what periods are, because he's seen blood in the toilet when it hasn't flushed properly and asked. I actually said to him, 'Oh, I had some beetroot at lunchtime and it's colored the water.'"* Commenting on this statement, Stone and colleagues (2013) said, "Parents tended to express their fears through the potential of lost childhood and shielding their children from 'corruption,' noting that children are non-sexual and that they did not want prematurely to assist them to cross over into the 'world of the grown-ups'. In particular, there were fears that children would start thinking and behaving in sexual ways that are regarded as being reserved for adulthood."

BVT *Lab*

Flashcards are available for this chapter at **www.BVTLab.com**.

Another barrier was the uncertainty regarding the best age, for the child, for the parent to be open about sexual information. "Some parents felt that children have little need for any sexuality education before age 8, whereas others had already discussed specific topics and dealt with issues in some detail." Regardless of when, parents struggle with the words. One parent said, "I find it hard using the right words to explain, the right terminology that they can understand." The result of parental struggle on timing and words is to be reactive—and wait till the child asks rather than be proactive with information about sexuality.

Fear of the reactions of other parents was a third barrier for parents in talking with their children about sex. An example is a parent who said:

> I kind of worry, for instance there was an incident lately where (daughter) was convinced that babies come out of your belly button, and so I tried to explain to her like, no they don't come out your belly button and she asked me, 'Well how do they come out?' and I said, 'I squeezed you out of my foofee'. And then she was outside and she was talking to the next door neighbors' kids, they were talking about how they'd had a little baby next door and (daughter) screamed out across three gardens, 'My mummy squeezed me out of her foofee' and I'm just thinking these kids are younger than (daughter) and I'm not sure that their parents want them to hear. You've got to consider other parents. (Stone, Inghamand, & Gibbins, 2013)

Parental discomfort was a fourth barrier to being open and honest about sex with their children. The parents generally felt inadequate in knowledge, skills, and delivery, and their discomfort was often based on their own parents' inadequacies. One parent remarked: "I do get embarrassed talking about any of it because nothing was explained to me as a child and I never asked questions. ... I think more than anything it's knowing where to start and what to say and like getting yourself stuck into a deeper hole when you start answering the questions."

Early and open communication with children about sexuality can have a positive impact in terms of sexual safety and outcomes (Stone, Inghamand, & Gibbins, 2013). Indeed, parent-child sexual communication is most effective when it is initiated prior to first intercourse (**sexual debut**). Parents who create the context with their children that talking about sex is normative have opportunities across time to provide information/teach lessons. Watching sexual content on TV, listening to sexual lyrics, and reacting to a child's stories from school provide "teachable moments" to talk about sexuality. See the Un/Hushed weblink by Karen Rayne for information about how parents can talk with their teens about sex.

Harris and colleagues (2013) confirmed the value of positive parent-child relationships and communication on the sexual decisions and behavior of adolescents. They analyzed data from 134 adolescent African American males and revealed parent-child closeness was positively correlated with amount of parent-child sexual communication with both mothers and fathers. Such closeness was also associated with greater condom use, less permissive sexual attitudes, fewer sexual partners, and less unprotected sex. The findings emphasize the importance of the parent-child relationship and the role of parent-child communication between parents and sons. Of note is that the males noted greater communication with mothers than fathers.

Sexual debut
One's first sexual intercourse

personal choices 9-1

Exposing Children to Parental Nudity

Some parents are concerned about the effects parental nudity may have on their children. "Will it traumatize my children or affect their sexual development negatively if I allow them to see me nude?" parents ask. Others are concerned that they may have already damaged their children because the children have walked in on the parents and observed them having intercourse. (This is known as the "primal scene.") To what degree should parents be concerned about these issues?

Schoentjes and Deboutte (1999) reported 40% of children ages 6–9 and 13% of those 10–12 reported walking around the house without clothes. Of the effects of family nudity on children, Friedrich and colleagues (1998) noted that children so exposed reported higher levels of sexual behavior for children ages 2–12 (but within cultural limits). In general, children who grow up with parents who embrace "nudism" learn positive associations with their bodies. Harm in the form of negative feelings or guilt about one's body would be a result of a parent shaming the child for being nude or for touching his or her own body.

9.2 Sexuality in Adolescence

Adolescence is defined as the developmental period between puberty and adulthood. It is a time when the individual transforms his or her image as a child into that of a young adult with a future adult life. Explorations with sexuality, including same sex sexual behavior, are a usual part of adolescent development (Cartaxo, Peixoto, Rolim, Neto, & deAbreu, 2013). In the United States and most cultures today, adolescence typically begins between the ages of 10 and 13 and ends between the ages of 18 and 22. Adolescence is a time when one becomes increasingly aware of one's own sexuality and that of others.

9.2a Adolescence

Early adolescence (middle school or junior high school ages) includes the time of greatest pubertal change. Late adolescence (the mid to late teen years) involves identity exploration, interacting with romantic partners, and school performance with a career objective in mind. The most noticeable changes in adolescence are physical.

9.2b Physical Changes

The adolescent's body undergoes rapid physiological and anatomical change. The term **puberty** comes from the Latin *pubescere,* which means to be covered with hair. Pubic hair and axillary (underarm) hair in young girls and pubic, axillary, and facial hair in young boys are evidence that the hypothalamus is triggering the pituitary gland

Adolescence
Developmental period in which youths move from childhood to adulthood

Puberty
Developmental stage in which a youth achieves reproductive capacity

to release gonadotropins into the bloodstream. These hormones cause the testes in the male to increase testosterone production, as well as the ovaries in the female to increase estrogen production.

Further physical changes in adolescence include the development of secondary sex characteristics, such as breasts in the female and a deepened voice in the male. A growth spurt also ensues, with girls preceding boys by about two years. Girls growing taller than boys their age characterize this growth spurt. Genitals of the respective sexes also enlarge (the penis and testes in the male and the labia in the female). Internally, the prostate gland and seminal vesicles begin to function, making it possible for the young adolescent male to ejaculate. (Sperm is present in the ejaculate at about age 14.) First ejaculation usually occurs around age 13 or 14, but the timing is variable. The first ejaculation is referred to as **semenarche**.

Girls experience their own internal changes. The uterus, cervix, and vaginal walls respond to hormone changes to produce the first menstruation, or *menarche*. This usually occurs between the ages of 12 and 13, but the timing is highly variable.

Adolescents are particularly concerned about the degree to which their bodies match the cultural image and are unhappy when their bodies do not match that image. Girls are more likely to be dissatisfied with their body image than boys. Since adolescent females are intent on matching the cultural weight ideal for a female, what is the consequence of being overweight on sexual decisions and behavior? Averett and colleagues (2013) analyzed national data on adolescents (National Longitudinal Survey of Adolescent Health) and found that overweight or obese adolescent girls are less likely than their recommended-weight counterparts to be sexually active. However, overweight or obese girls are not less likely to have sex under the influence of alcohol; and once they have had vaginal intercourse, their consistency of condom use is no different from that of their recommended-weight peers. The most striking finding is that overweight or obese girls are at least 15% more likely than their recommended-weight peers to have ever had anal intercourse, regardless of whether they have ever had vaginal sexual intercourse.

Adolescence is a time of stress between parents and adolescence. One issue is money where adolescents want more, but are often dependent on their parents to provide it.
Source: Chelsea Curry

9.2c Psychological Changes

In addition to physical changes, psychological changes also occur in adolescence. Psychological changes include moving from a state of childish dependence to a state of relative independence, resolving sexual identity issues, and feeling secure that one is normal. An example of adolescent ambivalence about growing up is the adolescent female who has a bottle of blow bubbles and a bottle of perfume on her bedroom dresser. Adolescents often want the freedom to play as children along with the freedom/independence of an adult.

Risk taking is normative during adolescence. **Sexting** (sending sexually explicit text or photos via cell phone) is an example of risk-taking behavior. Sexting is associated with substance abuse and high-risk sexual behavior. Benotsch and colleagues (2013) analyzed Internet questionnaire data on 763 young adults, 44% of whom reported sexting. The researchers compared those who sex texted/sent photos with their non-sexting counterparts. The "sexters" were more likely to report recent substance use and high-risk sexual behaviors, such as unprotected sex and sex with multiple partners. Of those who engaged in sexting, a considerable percentage (31.8%) reported having sex with a new partner for the first time after sexting with that person.

Semenarche
A boy's first seminal ejaculation

Sexting
Sending sexually explicit text or photos via cell phone

Strassberg and colleagues (2013) found that 20% of their sample of 606 high school students in the Southwest reported they had sent a sexually explicit image of themselves via cell phone, whereas almost twice as many reported that they had received a sexually explicit picture via cell phone. Of those who received such a photo, 25% forwarded it to others; and of these who forwarded such a photo, 30% said that they were aware of potential serious legal consequences.

Temple and colleagues (2012) analyzed data from 948 public high school students on their dating and sexual behavior (including sexting). Of the sample, 28% reported having sent a naked picture of themselves through text or e-mail (sext), and 31% reported having asked someone for a sext. More than half (57%) had been asked to send a sext, with most being bothered by having been asked. Adolescents who engaged in sexting behaviors were more likely to have begun dating and to have had sex than those who did not sext (all $P < .001$). For girls, sexting was also associated with risky sexual behaviors (e.g., drinking alcohol, having multiple sexual partners, not using a condom). Walker and colleagues (2013) observed that girls often feel coerced by their partners to engage in sexting behavior. Doing so is a risky sexual behavior since the partner may put the nude photos on Facebook to intimidate the girl/punish her.

In spite of their quest for independence and risk taking, adolescents tend to be psychologically healthy. Jenkins and Vazsonyi (2013) studied national data on adolescents and found that, on average, all participants had low levels of depression, perceptions of social rejection that tended to decrease over time, high levels of self-esteem, and happiness that tended to increase over time. These data suggest that heterosexual adolescents transition well into adulthood with positive psychosocial outcomes.

A major focus of adolescent development is the exploration of how emotionally intimate and how sexually intimate of a relationship the adolescent wants (Short, Catallazzi, & Beitkopf, 2013). The adolescent in Sweden sometimes uses the friends-with-benefits context to explore the parameters of intimacy and sexuality (see Cultural Diversity).

Cultural Diversity

Adolescence is a time of emotional/sexual exploration in the U.S. and in other societies, as well. Erlandsson and colleagues (2013) interviewed Swedish adolescents (ages 16–18) involved in "friends-with-benefits" (FWB) relationships. The goal of involvement in a FWB relationship was exploration of physical and psychological intimacy, with no expectations or demands. The eight adolescents revealed that they were ambivalent about the legitimacy of the romantic feelings they had for their partner, used alcohol frequently, and rarely used contraception.

9.2d Sexual Debut of Adolescents

At what age do adolescents first have sexual intercourse and what are the outcomes? Based on analysis of 17,220 New York youth (ages 15 through 19), of those who reported ever having had sex, a quarter of the females and over half of the males (52%) had their first sexual intercourse before age 14 (Kaplan, Jones, Olson, & Yunzal-Butler, 2013). Finer and Philbin (2013) also identified early sexual debuts of adolescents and found that the youngest (e.g., age 12) are often non-consensual. In another study of middle school children in ten states, 20% of the sixth graders and 42% of the eighth graders had engaged in sexual intercourse. Consistent with previous studies, males, minorities, and those who are not likely to complete high school are more likely to have engaged in higher frequencies of sexual behavior and high sexual risk behaviors (Moore, Barr, & Johnson, 2013; R-Almendarez & Wilson, 2013; Lyons, Manning, Giordano, & Longmore, 2013).

Early sexual debut is typically associated with high-risk sexual behavior—including alcohol/drug use, not using condoms, getting pregnant (or causing pregnancy), and violence in the form of being hit/slapped or otherwise hurt by a partner. Sexually active black and Hispanic students were significantly more likely to report early sex than white and API (Asian Pacific Islander) students (42.9% and 38.8%, respectively, versus 25.9% and 30.8%, respectively) (Kaplan, Jones, Olson, & Yunzal-Butler, 2013). In an effort to delay adolescent sexual debut, the researchers emphasized the following:

> Evidence-based interventions in school and community settings must be accompanied by efforts to increase access to sexual and reproductive health services and environmental changes that support healthy relationships, including responsible decision making about sexual activity. Our findings provide strong support for the need to create social environments in schools and neighborhoods that support young people of all races/ethnicities to make healthy and informed decisions about their sexual and reproductive health. (p. 355)

First Sexual Intercourse Experience

The following is a description of a first intercourse experience of a student (name withheld by request) from the authors' classes.

> *I was 15 and my partner was 16. I had two fears. The first was my fear of getting her pregnant the first time. The second was of "parking" in dark and desolate areas. Therefore, once we decided to have intercourse, we spent a boring evening waiting for my parents to go to sleep so we could move to the station wagon in the driveway.*
>
> *After near hyperventilation in an attempt to fog the windows (to prevent others from seeing in), we commenced to prepare for the long-awaited event. In recognition of my first fear, I wore four prophylactics. She, out of fear, was not lubricating well; and needless to say, I couldn't feel anything through four layers of latex.*
>
> *We were able to climax, which I attribute solely to sheer emotional excitement, yet both of us were later able to admit that the experience was disappointing. We knew it could only get better.*

Being Modern-Orthodox adds an additional challenge to the first sexual intercourse experience. Shalev and colleagues (2013) interviewed 36 newlywed men and women about their first intercourse experience. They were Modern-Orthodox (8% of the population) and may not have even held hands prior to the wedding. Both men and women associated the sexual intercourse with emotional and behavioral difficulties, which were rooted in the traditional nature of the religious Modern-Orthodox society in Israel. They had had no sex education, no previous interpersonal sexual experience, and no familiarity with their own bodies. They were in shock and in coping mode. In addition, they were adjusting to living with a person of the opposite sex and sharing the same space (i.e., bedroom, bathroom, etc.). They sought help on the Internet and discovered that their problems were common, given their limited experience and traditional religious upbringing.

Alcohol use (which impairs sexual decisions) in adolescence is common. Livingston and colleagues (2013) interviewed adolescent females (ages 14–17) to investigate the effect of alcohol on sexual choices. While reducing social anxiety and excusing unsanctioned sexual behavior were identified as advantages of using alcohol, the respondents also noted that it impaired their judgment and increased the chance of sexual regret and coercion. Hence, any educational/preventative attempt to delay sexual debut and increase responsible decision-making must include attention to decisions about alcohol use.

Think About It

Take a moment to answer the following questions. What do you think is the ideal "first" sexual intercourse or sexual experience? What would be the nature of the relationship? How long would the partners have known each other? Would there be alcohol or not? How does your own reality differ from your answers?

Cultural *Diversity*

In late 2013, France's senate voted to ban beauty pageants for children under 16 in an effort to protect girls from being sexualized too early. Anyone who enters a child into such a contest would face up to 2 years in prison and €30,000 in fines. The senate approved the measure 197–146.

9.2e Teen Pregnancy

The mention of a teenage mom may sometimes carry the implication that the mother did not want to get pregnant and is trying to cope with early motherhood; however, some sexually active adolescent females want to get pregnant. Cavazos-Rehg and colleagues (2013) discovered that 16% of their sample of teenage girls, ages 15–18, reported that they would be "a little pleased" or "very pleased" if they were to become pregnant. Factors associated with wanting to become pregnant included having had a prior pregnancy, being "older" in contrast to "being younger," and having parents with a high school education or less.

Medical risks to teen mothers are greatest for younger teens. Although maternal mortality rates for adolescent women are low, they are twice the rate for adult women. The neonatal death rate for babies born to adolescent women is three times higher than for those born to those in their 20s and the risks of low birth weight and preterm birth are more than double. Access to prenatal care, poverty, unmarried status, smoking, and drug use are contributors to the health risks.

In addition to health risks, there are developmental and social complications of teen pregnancy as well. Unless supportive interventions are in place, these complications include interruption of the teen's educational and vocational opportunities, separation or divorce from the child's father, poverty, and repeat pregnancies. Children who are born to teen mothers do not fare as well as those born to adult mothers.

Plan B for Adolescents?

The over-the-counter morning after pill is available, without a prescription, to females of any age. **Plan B** (also sold as Next Choice and My Way) is a high dose progestin pill that acts to prevent ovulation or fertilization of an egg. Taking it 72 hours after unprotected sex, condom failure, or a missed period can reduce the chance of pregnancy by 89%. The morning after pill is most effective if taken 24 hours after exposure. Plan B is not the "abortion pill" (RU-486), which requires a prescription.

The argument for making Plan B,—which costs $40 to $60 for one pill and is available without a prescription—is that it will help to reduce pregnancy for the 1 in 5 adolescent females who report unprotected sexual intercourse. Ten percent of teens are forced to have sex, and Plan B provides the option of not becoming pregnant with a partner who used force. The argument against Plan B being available without a prescription is that some teens will be more willing to have sex since they can "take a pill in the morning." In addition, some parents do not want their children to have the Plan B option since they feel it "encourages promiscuity."

Content of Sex Education in Public Schools

Since sex education provided by parents is limited (Mauras, Grolnick, & Friendly, 2013), sex education is provided in most public school systems and is usually taught as part of another subject, such as health education, home economics, biology, or physical education. Because each state, rather than the federal government, is responsible for sex education in the public school system, there is considerable variation among the states in terms of the sex education offered. The prevailing model for sex education has been "abstinence only." More recently, comprehensive sex education has involved abstinence plus information about condoms, HIV, STIs, etc. Three-fourths of the teachers in one study reported using the abstinence-only curricula (Einsenberg, Madsen, Oliphant, & Sieving, 2013).

How do teachers feel about teaching sex education? Einsenberg and colleagues (2013) analyzed data from 368 middle and high school sex education teachers in Minnesota. Almost two-thirds reported structural barriers; 45% were concerned about parent, student, or administrator response; and one-fourth reported restrictive policies. What is needed is more structural support for teachers to teach a wide variety of topics, not only abstinence, but contraception, STIs, sexual violence, sexual orientation, etc., as well. Agreement on the content of the curriculum becomes the problem. Some parents do not want their child exposed to any sex education since they fear liberal teachers will teach permissive values or that students will be prompted to become sexually active as a result of classroom instruction.

In response to more limited sex education programs, Planned Parenthood Los Angeles developed and launched a teen-centered sexuality education program based on critical thinking, human rights, gender equality, and access to health care. The program included

Plan B
A high dose progestin pill that acts to prevent ovulation or fertilization of an egg

a 12-session classroom sexuality education curriculum for ninth grade students, workshops for parents, a peer advocacy training program, and access to sexual health services (Marques & Ressa, 2013).

How effective is sex education when effectiveness is defined as "delaying early sexual debut of young adolescents"? Erkut and colleagues (2013) compared sixth graders exposed to a nine-lesson sex education program "Get Real: Comprehensive Sex Education That Works" with a control group. Participants were 548 boys and 675 girls who completed surveys in both sixth grade (baseline) and seventh grade (follow-up). 30% of those not exposed to the sex education program were more likely to initiate sex by follow-up when controlling for having had sex by sixth grade, demographic variables, and a tendency to give socially desirable responses.

Sex education is not just what happens in public schools in the U.S. Rogow and colleagues (2013) discussed sex education on a broad international scale. "It's All One" is one such program with the theme of integrating gender and rights into sexuality education that is used in various countries. Hence, sex education is focused not on encouraging individuals to "use a condom" but to internalize empowerment and equality in dyadic relationships.

9.3 **Sexuality in Adulthood**

National **DATA**

By age 75, only 3.9% of American women and 3.5% of American men have never married *(Statistical Abstract of the United States,* 2012–2013, Table 57). Between the ages of 25 and 29, 47.8% of females and 62.2% of males are not married (Table 57).

9.3a **Sexuality Among Singles**

TABLE **9-2**	Reasons for Remaining Single
Table 9-2 reflects some of the reasons young adults choose to remain single and to avoid marriage.	
Benefits of Singlehood	**Limitations of Marriage**
Freedom, including sexual variety	Restrictions from spouse or children
Responsible for one's self only	Responsible for spouse and children
Close friends of both sexes	Pressure to avoid other relationships
Spontaneous lifestyle	Routine, predictable sex/lifestyle
Feeling of self-sufficiency	Potential to feel dependent
Freedom to spend money as one wishes	Money spent in reference to spouse/children
Freedom to move as career dictates	Restrictions on career mobility
No control/influence from spouse	Potential to be controlled/influenced by spouse
No emotional or financial loss caused by divorce	Possibility of divorce

The primary advantage of remaining single is freedom and control over one's life. This freedom translates into being available to have a variety of sex partners since there is no spouse to disappoint; and unless a couple is polyamorous, commitment means giving up other sex partners.

However, singles have intercourse less frequently than those who are married or living together. Not only may singles be having less sex and achieving less sexual satisfaction (Michael, Gagnon, Laumann, & Kolata, 1994), they may also be more vulnerable to engaging in high-risk sexual behavior. The following self-assessment allows you to determine the degree to which you engage in behavior that involves a high risk for HIV infection.

SELF-ASSESSMENT 9-1: STUDENT SEXUAL RISKS SCALE (SSRS)

The following self-assessment allows you to evaluate the degree to which you may be at risk for engaging in behavior that exposes you to HIV. Safer sex means sexual activity that reduces the risk of transmitting the AIDS virus. Using condoms is an example of safer sex. Unsafe, risky, or unprotected sex refers to sex without a condom, or to other sexual activity that might increase the risk of AIDS virus transmission. For each of the following items, check the response that best characterizes your belief:

A = Agree   U = Undecided   D = Disagree

1. If my partner wanted me to have unprotected sex, I would probably give in.
   A   U   D
2. The proper use of a condom could enhance sexual pleasure.
   A   U   D
3. I may have had sex with someone who was at risk for HIV/AIDS.
   A   U   D
4. If I were going to have sex, I would take precautions to reduce my risk of HIV/AIDS.
   A   U   D
5. Condoms ruin the natural sex act.
   A   U   D
6. When I think that one of my friends might have sex on a date, I ask him/her if he/she has a condom.
   A   U   D
7. I am at risk for HIV/AIDS.
   A   U   D
8. I would try to use a condom when I had sex.
   A   U   D
9. Condoms interfere with romance.
   A   U   D
10. My friends talk a lot about safer sex.
    A   U   D
11. If my partner wanted me to participate in risky sex, and I said that we needed to be safer, we would still probably end up having unsafe sex.
    A   U   D
12. Generally, I am in favor of using condoms.
    A   U   D
13. I would avoid using condoms if at all possible.
    A   U   D

14. If a friend knew that I might have sex on a date, he/she would ask me whether I was carrying a condom.

    A   U   D

15. There is a possibility that I have HIV/AIDS.

    A   U   D

16. If I had a date, I would probably not drink alcohol or use drugs.

    A   U   D

17. Safer sex reduces the mental pleasure of sex.

    A   U   D

18. If I thought that one of my friends had sex on a date, I would ask him/her if he/she used a condom.

    A   U   D

19. The idea of using a condom doesn't appeal to me.

    A   U   D

20. Safer sex is a habit for me.

    A   U   D

21. If a friend knew that I had sex on a date, he/she wouldn't care whether I had used a condom or not.

    A   U   D

22. If my partner wanted me to participate in risky sex, and I suggested a lower risk alternative, we would have the safer sex instead.

    A   U   D

23. The sensory aspects (smell, touch, etc.) of condoms make them unpleasant.

    A   U   D

24. I intend to follow "safer sex" guidelines within the next year.

    A   U   D

25. With condoms, you can't really give yourself over to your partner.

    A   U   D

26. I am determined to practice safer sex.

    A   U   D

27. If my partner wanted me to have unprotected sex, and I made some excuse to use a condom, we would still end up having unprotected sex.

    A   U   D

28. If I had sex and I told my friends that I did not use condoms, they would be angry or disappointed.

    A   U   D

29. I think safer sex would get boring fast.

    A   U   D

30. My sexual experiences do not put me at risk for HIV/AIDS.

    A   U   D

31. Condoms are irritating.

    A   U   D

32. My friends and I encourage each other before dates to practice safer sex.

    A   U   D

33. When I socialize, I usually drink alcohol or use drugs.

    A   U   D

34. If I were going to have sex in the next year, I would use condoms.

    A   U   D

35. If a sexual partner didn't want to use condoms, we would have sex without using condoms.

    A   U   D

36. People can get the same pleasure from safer sex as from unprotected sex.

    A   U   D

37. Using condoms interrupts sex play.

    A   U   D

38. It is a hassle to use condoms.

    A   U   D

Scoring

Begin by giving yourself eighty points. Subtract one point for every undecided response. Subtract two points every time that you disagreed with odd-numbered items or with item number 38. Subtract two points every time you agreed with even-numbered items 2 through 36.

Interpreting Your Score

Research shows that students who make higher scores on the SSRS are more likely to engage in risky sexual activities, such as having multiple sex partners and/or failing to consistently use condoms during sex. In contrast, students who practice safer sex tend to endorse more positive attitudes toward safer sex, and tend to have peer networks that encourage safer sexual practices. These students usually plan on making sexual activity safer, and they feel confident in their ability to negotiate safer sex even when a dating partner may press for riskier sex. Students who practice safer sex often refrain from using alcohol or drugs, which may impede negotiation of safer sex. They also often report having engaged in lower-risk activities in the past. How do you measure up?

(Below 15) Lower Risk

(Of 200 students surveyed by DeHart and Birkimer (1997), 16% were in this category.) Congratulations! Your score on the SSRS indicates that, relative to other students, your thoughts and behaviors are more supportive of safer sex. Is there any room for improvement in your score? If so, you may want to examine items for which you lost points and try to build safer sexual strengths in those areas. You can help protect others from HIV by educating your peers about making sexual activity safer.

(15 to 37) Average Risk

(Of 200 students surveyed by DeHart and Birkimer, 68% were in this category.) Your score on the SSRS is about average in comparison with those of other college students. Although you don't fall into the higher-risk category, be aware that "average" people can get HIV, too. In fact, a recent study indicated that the rate of HIV among college students is 10 times that in the general heterosexual population. Thus, you may want to enhance your sexual safety by figuring out where you lost points and working toward safer sexual strengths in those areas.

(38 and Above) Higher Risk

(Of 200 students surveyed by DeHart and Birkimer, 16% were in this category.) Relative to other students, your score on the SSRS indicates that your thoughts and behaviors are less supportive of safer sex. Such high scores tend to be associated with greater HIV-risk behavior. Rather than simply giving in to riskier attitudes and behaviors, you may want to empower yourself and reduce your risk by critically examining areas for improvement. On which items did you lose points? Think about how you can strengthen your sexual safety in these areas. Reading more about safer sex can help, and sometimes colleges and health clinics offer courses or workshops on safer sex. You can get more information about resources in your area by contacting the CDC's HIV/AIDS Information Line at 1-800-342-2437.

Source: DeHart, D. D., & Birkimer, J. C. (1997). The Student Sexual Risks Scale (modification of SRS for popular use; facilitates student self-administration, scoring, and normative interpretation). Developed for this text by Dana D. DeHart, College of Social Work at the University of South Carolina; John C. Birkimer, University of Louisville. Used by permission of Dana DeHart and John C. Birkimer.

9.3b Sexuality Among Cohabitants

Cohabitants often can't keep their hands off each other.
Source: Chelsea Curry

Cohabitation, also known as living together, involves two adults—unrelated by blood or by law and involved in an emotional and sexual relationship—who sleep in the same residence at least 4 nights a week for 3 months. Willoughby and Carroll (2012) surveyed 1,036 young adult college students and found that the endorsement of cohabitation is strongly associated with having more sexual partners, being permissive in sexual attitudes, and being less religious. Cohabitants also tend to have a higher frequency of sex since the partners are often relatively new to each other.

Not all cohabitants are college students. Indeed, only 18% of all cohabitants are under the age of 25. The largest percentage (36%) are between the ages of 25 and 34 (Jayson, 2012). Reasons for the increase in cohabitation include career or educational commitments; increased tolerance of society, parents, and peers; improved birth control technology; desire for a stable emotional and sexual relationship without legal ties; avoiding loneliness; and greater disregard for convention (Kasearu, 2010).

The couple living in a cohabitation relationship precedes virtually all marriages in Sweden (Thomson, E. & Bernhardt, 2010); however, only 12% of first marriages in Italy are preceded by cohabitation (Kiernan, 2000). Italy is primarily Catholic, which helps to account for the low cohabitation rate. Religious affiliation is also associated with lower rates of cohabitation in the United States (Gault-Sherman & Draper, 2012).

9.3c Sexuality Among the Married

In spite of the perceived benefits of singlehood or cohabitation, marriage remains the lifestyle most Americans choose.

Marital sex is characterized by its social legitimacy, declining frequency, and superiority in terms of sexual and emotional satisfaction.

> *Marital sex is less of a negotiation and an adventure, and more of a routine.*
> Randall Collins and Scott Coltran, sociologists

Cohabitation
Living situation in which two heterosexual adults involved in an emotional and sexual relationship share a common residence for 4 nights a week for 3 months

1. *Social Legitimacy*   In our society, marital intercourse is the most legitimate form of sexual behavior. Premarital, extramarital, and homosexual intercourse do not enjoy as high a level of social approval as does marital sex. It is not only okay to have intercourse when married, it is expected. People assume that married couples make love and that something is wrong if they do not.

2. *Declining Frequency*   Sexual intercourse between spouses occurs about six times a month, and declines in frequency as the spouses age. Pregnancy also decreases the frequency of sexual intercourse (Lee, Lin, Wan, & Liang, 2010). In addition to biological changes due to aging and pregnancy, satiation also contributes to the declining frequency of intercourse between spouses and partners in long-term relationships. Psychologists use the term **satiation** to refer to the repeated exposure of a particular stimulus (in this case, the partner), which results in the loss of its ability to reinforce. The 500th time that a person has intercourse with the same partner is not as new and exciting as the first few times.

   A change in hormone levels may also be related to the decline in frequency of sexual intercourse between spouses. Testosterone levels (associated with interest in sex) are lower in men who are in committed or married relationships, as well as in women who are mothers (Barrett, et al., 2013).

   Some spouses do not have intercourse at all. In a nationwide study of sexuality, 1% of husbands and 3% of wives reported that they had not had intercourse in the past 12 months (Michael, Gagnon, Laumann, & Kolata, 1994). Health, age, sexual orientation, stress, depression, and conflict were some of the reasons given for not having intercourse with one's spouse. Such an arrangement may be accompanied by either limited or extensive affection.

3. *Sexual and Emotional Satisfaction*   Despite declining frequency over time, marital sex remains a richly satisfying experience. Contrary to the popular belief that unattached singles have the best sex, married and pair-bonded adults enjoy the most satisfying sexual relationships. In the national sample referred to earlier, 88% of married people said they received great physical pleasure from their sexual lives, and almost 85% said they received great emotional satisfaction (Michael, Gagnon, Laumann, & Kolata, 1994). Individuals least likely to report being physically and emotionally pleased in their sexual relationships are those who are not married, not living with anyone, or not in a stable relationship with one person. Hence, the categories from most to least sexually satisfied are the marrieds, cohabitants, and the uninvolved.

9.3d Sexuality Among the Divorced

Of the almost 2 million people getting divorced annually, most will have intercourse within 1 year of being separated from their spouses. The meanings of intercourse for separated or divorced individuals vary. For many, intercourse is a way to reestablish—indeed, repair—their crippled self-esteem. Questions such as "What did I do wrong?" "Am I a failure?" and "Is there anybody out there who will love me again?" loom in the minds of the divorced. One way to feel loved, at least temporarily, is through sex. Being held by another and being told that it feels good give people some evidence that they are desirable.

Because divorced individuals are usually in their mid-30s or older, they may not be as sensitized to the danger of contracting HIV as are people in their 20s. Divorced individuals should always use a condom to lessen the risk of an STI, including HIV infection, and AIDS.

Satiation
A stimulus loses its value with repeated exposure

9.3e Extradyadic Sexual Involvement

About a one-fourth of husbands and 20% of wives have sex with someone outside the marriage at some time during their marriage (Russell, Baker, & Mcnulty, 2013).

After all the things you told me
And the promises you made
Why can't you behave?

Cole Porter, "Why Can't You Behave"?

Types of Extradyadic Encounters

The term **extramarital affair** refers to a spouse's sexual involvement with someone outside the marriage. Affairs are of different types and include the following:

1. *Brief encounter*   A spouse meets and hooks up with a stranger. In this case, the spouse is usually out of town, and alcohol is often involved.

2. *Paid sex*   A spouse seeks sexual variety with a prostitute who will do whatever that spouse wants (e.g., former New York governor Eliot Spitzer). These encounters usually go undetected unless there is an STI, the person confesses, or the prostitute exposes the client.

3. *Instrumental or utilitarian affair*   This is sex in exchange for a job or promotion, to get back at a spouse, to evoke jealousy, or to transition out of a marriage.

4. *Coping mechanism*   Sex can be used to enhance one's self-concept or feeling of sexual inadequacy, compensate for failure in business, cope with the death of a family member, or test one's sexual orientation.

5. *Paraphiliac affairs*   In these encounters, the on-the-side sex partner acts out sexual fantasies or participates in sexual practices that the spouse considers bizarre or abnormal, such as sexual masochism, sexual sadism, or transvestite fetishism.

6. *Office romance*   Two individuals who work together may drift into an affair. David Petraeus (former CIA director) and John Edwards (former presidential candidate) became involved in affairs with women they met on the job.

After being married for over 37 years, I showed extremely poor judgment by engaging in an extramarital affair.

David Petraeus, former CIA Director

7. *Internet use*   Internet users now tops 1.6 billion people (Hertlein & Piercy, 2012). Although an extramarital affair does not exist, legally, unless two people (one being married) have intercourse, Internet use can be disruptive to a marriage or a couple's relationship. While men and women agree that offline kissing, touching breasts/genitals, and sexual intercourse constitute infidelity they disagree about the degree to which online behaviors constitute cheating. Based on data collected by Hines (2012), men are less likely than women to view a partner emailing a person online for relationship advice (27% versus 51%), having a friendly conversation with someone in a chat room called "Married and Lonely" (64% versus 84%), and creating a pet name for a person he/she met in an Internet chat room (40% versus 70%) as cheating. Males also are less likely to view online pornography as cheating (27% versus 64%).

Computer friendships may evolve to feelings of intimacy; involve secrecy (one's partner does not know the level of involvement); include sexual tension (even though there is no overt sex); and take time, attention, energy, and

Extramarital affair Sexual intercourse between a spouse and someone other than the person he or she is married to

Former CIA Director David Petraeus met the woman with whom he had an affair in the workplace.
Source: AP Wide World Photo

affection away from one's partner. Cavaglion and Rashty (2010) noted the anguish embedded in 1,130 messages on self-help chat boards from female partners of males involved in cybersex relationships and pornographic websites. The females reported distress and feelings of ambivalent loss that had impact on the individual, couple, and their sexual relationship. Cramer and colleagues (2008) also noted that women become more upset when their man is emotionally unfaithful with another woman (although men become more upset when their partner is sexually unfaithful with another man). The Self-Assessment 9-2 section allows you to measure your attitude toward infidelity.

SELF-ASSESSMENT 9-2: ATTITUDES TOWARD INFIDELITY SCALE

Infidelity can be defined as "unfaithfulness in a committed monogamous relationship." Infidelity can affect anyone, regardless of race, color, or creed; it does not matter whether you are rich or attractive, where you live, or how old you are. The purpose of this survey is to gain a better understanding of what people think and how they feel about issues associated with infidelity. There are no right or wrong answers to any of these statements; we are interested in your honest reactions and opinions.

Please read each statement carefully, and respond by using the following scale:

1	2	3	4	5	6	7
Strongly Disagree						Strongly Agree

1. ___ Being unfaithful never hurt anyone.
2.* ___ Infidelity in a marital relationship is grounds for divorce.
3. ___ Infidelity is acceptable for retaliation of infidelity.
4. ___ It is natural for people to be unfaithful.
5.* ___ Online/Internet behavior (for example, visiting sex chat rooms, porn sites) is an act of infidelity.
6.* ___ Infidelity is morally wrong in all circumstances, regardless of the situation.
7.* ___ Being unfaithful in a relationship is one of the most dishonorable things a person can do. ·
8.* ___ Infidelity is unacceptable, under any circumstances, if the couple is married.
9. ___ I would not mind if my significant other had an affair as long as I did not know about it.
10. ___ It would be acceptable for me to have an affair, but not my significant other.
11. ___ I would have an affair if I knew my significant other would never find out.
12.* ___ If I knew my significant other was guilty of infidelity, I would confront him/her.

Scoring

Selecting a 1 reflects the least acceptance of infidelity; selecting a 7 reflects the greatest acceptance of infidelity. Before adding the numbers you selected, reverse the scores for item numbers 2*, 5*, 6*, 7*, 8*, and 12*. For example, if you responded to item 2 with a "6," change this number to a "2"; if you responded with a "3," change this number to "5," and so on. After making these changes, add the numbers. The lower your total score (12 is the lowest possible), the less accepting you are of infidelity; the higher your total score (84 is the highest possible), the greater your acceptance of infidelity. A score of 48 places you at the midpoint between being very disapproving and very accepting of infidelity.

Scores of Other Students Who Completed the Scale

The scale was completed by 150 male and 136 female student volunteers at Valdosta State University. The average score on the scale was 27.85 (SD = 12.02). Their ages ranged from 18 to 49, with a mean age of 23.36 (SD = 5.13). The ethnic backgrounds of the sample consisted of 60.8% white, 28.3% African American, 2.4% Hispanic, 3.8% Asian, 0.3% American Indian, and 4.2% other. The college classification level of the sample included 11.5% freshmen, 18.2% sophomores, 20.6% juniors, 37.8% seniors, 7.7% graduate students, and 4.2% post baccalaureate. Male participants reported more positive attitudes toward infidelity (mean = 31.53; SD = 11.86) than did female participants (mean = 23.78; SD = 10.86; $p < 0.05$). White participants had more negative attitudes toward infidelity (mean = 25.36; SD = 11.17) than did nonwhite participants (mean = 31.71; SD = 12.32; $p < 0.05$). There were no significant differences in regard to college classification.

Source: "Attitudes toward Infidelity Scale" 2006 by Mark Whatley, Ph.D., Department of Psychology, Valdosta State University, Valdosta, Georgia 31698-0100. Used by permission. Other uses of this scale by written permission of Dr. Whatley only (mwhatley@valdosta.edu). Information on the reliability and validity of this scale is available from Dr. Whatley.

Extradyadic sexual involvement or extrarelational involvement refers to the sexual involvement of a pair-bonded individual with someone other than the partner. Extradyadic involvements are not uncommon. Of 1,099 undergraduate males, 21% agreed with the statement, "I have cheated on a partner I was involved with"; of 3,459 undergraduate females, 25% were cheated on by a partner they were involved with (Hall & Knox, 2013).

Researcher Pam Druckerman (2007) wrote *Lust in Translation*, in which she reflects how affairs are viewed throughout the world. First, terms for having an affair vary. For the Dutch, it is called, "pinching the cat in the dark"; in Taiwan, it is called "a man standing in two boats"; and in England, "playing off sides." Second, how an affair is regarded differs by culture. In America, the script for discovering a partner's affair involves confronting the partner and ending the marriage. In France, the script does not involve confronting the partner and does not assume that the affair means the end of the marriage; rather, "letting time pass to let a partner go through the experience without pressure or comment" is the norm. In America, presidential candidate John Edwards's disclosure of his affair with an office worker ended his political career.

Motivations for Extradyadic Sexual Encounters

Individuals in pair bonded relationships report a number of reasons why they become involved in a sexual encounter outside their relationship. The top three identified reasons, in an Internet sample of spouses, included sexual needs, emotional needs, and falling in love—with no differences between women and men (Omarzu, Miller, Shultz, & Timmerman, 2012). Other reasons for an affair include the following:

1. *Variety, novelty, and excitement*   Most spouses struggle with the transition of moving from a context where one has multiple sexual partners to having only one sexual partner. Most spouses enter marriage having had numerous sexual partners. Traditional marriage scripts fidelity. Indeed, traditional wedding vows state, "Hold myself only unto you as long as we both should live."

Extradyadic sexual involvement
Sexual relationship that occurs outside the couple, as when an individual of a dyad (couple) becomes sexually involved with someone other than the partner or mate

Table 9-3 identifies the lifestyle alternatives for resolving the transition from multiple to one sexual partner at marriage.

TABLE 9-3	Sexual Lifestyle Alternatives		
Monogamy	**Cheating**	**Swinging**	**Polyamory**
Spouse is only sex partner.	Husband and/or wife cheats.	Souses agree to multiple sex partners.	Spouses agree to multiple love and sex partners.

Extradyadic sexual involvement may be motivated by the desire for variety, novelty, and excitement. One of the characteristics of sex in long-term, committed relationships is the tendency for sex to become routine. Early in a relationship, the partners cannot seem to have sex often enough. However, with constant availability, partners may achieve a level of satiation; and the attractiveness and excitement of sex with the primary partner seem to wane.

The **Coolidge effect** is a term used to describe this waning of sexual excitement and the effect of novelty and variety on sexual arousal:

> One day President and Mrs. Coolidge were visiting a government farm. Soon after their arrival, they were taken off on separate tours. When Mrs. Coolidge passed the chicken pens, she paused to ask the man in charge if the rooster copulated more than once each day. "Dozens of times," was the reply. "Please tell that to the President," Mrs. Coolidge requested. When the President passed the pens and was told about the rooster, he asked, "Same hen every time?" "Oh no, Mr. President, a different one each time." The President nodded slowly and then said, "Tell that to Mrs. Coolidge." (Bermant, 1976, pp. 76–77)

Whether or not individuals are biologically wired for monogamy continues to be debated. Monogamy among mammals is rare (from 3% to 10%), and monogamy tends to be the exception more often than the rule (Morell, 1998). Pornography use, which involves viewing a variety of individuals in sexual contexts, is associated with extramarital sex (Wright, 2013). Even if such biological wiring for plurality of partners does exist, it is equally debated whether such wiring justifies non-monogamous behavior—or whether individuals are responsible for their decisions.

My second husband was married and I was engaged to be married when we met at a Sunday lunch party in Rockland County. Our connection was so electrifying that all didn't seem to matter. As we spoke, the other people at the party fell away.

Susan Cheever, author

2. *Workplace friendships* A common place for extramarital involvements to develop is the workplace (Merrill & Knox, 2010). Neuman (2008) noted that 4 in 10 of the affairs that men reported began with a woman they met at work. Coworkers share the same world 8 to 10 hours a day and over a period of time may develop good feelings for each other that eventually lead to a sexual relationship. Tabloid reports regularly reflect that romances develop between married actors making a movie together (e.g., Brad Pitt and Angelina Jolie met on a movie set). Arnold Schwarzenegger's housekeeper was "at work" when she had sex with him (which produced their child and prompted the end of Schwarzenegger's marriage upon disclosure 10 years later).

Coolidge effect
The effect of novelty and variety on sexual arousal— such as when a novel partner is available, a sexually satiated male regains capacity for arousal

3. *Relationship dissatisfaction*   It is commonly believed that people who have affairs are not happy in their marriage. Spouses who feel misunderstood, unloved, and ignored sometimes turn to another who offers understanding, love, and attention. Neuman (2008) confirmed that being emotionally dissatisfied in one's relationship is the primary culprit behind an affair.

4. *Sexual dissatisfaction*   Some spouses engage in extramarital sex because their partner is not interested in sex. Others may go outside the relationship because their partners will not engage in the sexual behaviors they want and enjoy. The unwillingness of the spouse to engage in oral sex, anal intercourse, or a variety of sexual positions sometimes results in the other spouse's looking elsewhere for a more cooperative and willing sexual partner.

5. *Revenge*   Some extramarital sexual involvements are acts of revenge against one's spouse for having an affair. When partners find out that their mate has had, or is having an affair, they are often hurt and angry. One response to this hurt and anger is to have an affair to get even with the unfaithful partner.

6. *Homosexuality*   Some individuals marry as a front for their homosexuality. Cole Porter, known for such songs as "I've Got You Under My Skin," "Night and Day," and "Every Time We Say Goodbye," was a homosexual who feared no one would buy his music if his sexual orientation were known. He married Linda Lee Porter (alleged to be a lesbian), and their marriage lasted until Porter's death 30 years later.

   Other gay individuals marry as a way of denying their homosexuality. These individuals are likely to feel unfulfilled in their marriage and may seek involvement in an extramarital homosexual relationship. Other individuals may marry and then discover later in life that they desire a homosexual relationship. Such individuals may feel that (1) they have been homosexual or bisexual all along, (2) their sexual orientation has changed from heterosexual to homosexual or bisexual, (3) they are unsure of their sexual orientation and want to explore a homosexual relationship, or (4) they are predominantly heterosexual but wish to experience a homosexual relationship for variety. The term **down low** typically refers to African American married men who have sex with men and hide this behavior from their spouse.

7. *Aging*   A frequent motive for intercourse outside marriage is the desire to return to the feeling of youth. Ageism, which is discrimination against the elderly, promotes the idea that being young is good and being old is bad. Sexual attractiveness is equated with youth, and having an affair may confirm to older partners that they are still sexually desirable. Also, people may try to recapture the love, excitement, adventure, and romance associated with youth by having an affair.

8. *Absence from partner*   One factor that may predispose a spouse to an affair is prolonged separation from the partner. Some wives whose husbands are away for military service report that the loneliness can become unbearable. Some husbands who are away say that remaining faithful is difficult. Partners in commuter relationships may also be vulnerable to extradyadic sexual relationships.

9. *High androgen levels*   Men who have high levels of androgen (male hormone) have an increased likelihood of extrapartner involvement (Fisher, et al., 2012a).

Down low
Behavior of keeping one's activity private; term used to describe men who have sex with men but do not label themselves as gay or bisexual

personal Choices 9-2

An Affair?

An affair has both negative and positive consequences. An affair may end the marriage. Allen and Atkins (2012) surveyed 16,090 U.S. individuals and found that more than half of the men and women who had engaged in extramarital sex were also separated or divorced from their spouse. Traeen and Thuen (2013) identified reasons for divorce in a sample of 1,001 Norwegians. Of those age 50 or older, infidelity was the top reason. More men (44%) than women (33%) reported infidelity.

Even if the marriage does not end, there is the potential to contract a sexually transmitted infection (HPV being the most common). The HIV epidemic has increased the concern over this possibility. Spouses who engage in extradyadic sex may not only contract a sexually transmitted infection but may also transmit the infection to their partners (and potentially their unborn offspring). In some cases, an affair may prove deadly.

Finally, spouses who have an affair risk the possibility of their partner finding out and going into a jealous rage. Jealousy may result in violence and even the death of the unfaithful spouse or the lover involved. Another possible tragic outcome of extramarital relationships is that a spouse who "cheats" or has been "cheated on" becomes depressed and commits suicide.

Partners who decide to avoid an affair might focus on the small choices that lead to a sexual encounter. Because an affair occurs in an identifiable sequence of behaviors (e.g., eye contact, flirting, sex references, touching, etc.) and contexts (e.g., away from spouse, presence of alcohol/drugs, etc.), the person can choose to avoid them. Avoiding intimate conversations and drinking with someone to whom you are attracted helps ensure that a sexual encounter will not occur. Not to make these choices ("not to decide is to decide") is to increase the chance that extradyadic sex will occur.

There are some potential positive outcomes from an affair. Some spouses who have had an affair do not regret doing so. One woman, known to the authors, said that while her husband constantly criticized her, the man with whom she had had the extramarital relationship "needed me and made me feel loved and important again." This woman eventually divorced her husband and said that she never regretted moving from an emotionally dead and abusive relationship to one in which she was loved and nurtured. In this case, the extramarital affair served as a bridge out of the marriage.

For some spouses who have an affair and stay married, the marriage may benefit. Some partners become more sensitive to the problems in their marriage. "For us," one spouse said, "the affair helped us to look at our marriage, to know that we were in trouble, and to seek help." Couples need not view the discovery of an affair as the end of their marriage; to the contrary, it can be a new beginning.

One husband said his wife had an affair because he was too busy with his work and did not spend enough time with her. Her affair taught him that she had alternatives—other men who would love her emotionally and sexually. To ensure that he did not lose his wife, he cut back on his work hours and spent more time with her.

Think About It

Take a moment to answer the following question. The spouse who chooses to have an affair is often judged as being unfaithful to the vows of the marriage, as being deceitful to the partner, and as inflicting enormous pain on the partner (and children). What is often not considered is that when an affair is defined in terms of giving emotional energy, time, and economic resources to something or someone outside the primary relationship, other types of "affairs" may be equally devastating to one's partner and relationship. Spouses who choose to devote their lives to their careers, parents, friends, or recreational interests may deprive the partner of significant amounts of emotional energy, time, money, and create a context in which the partner may choose to become involved with a person who provides more attention and interest. What relationships are you aware of in which a spouse felt neglected by the partner who was excessively focused on someone or something external to the marriage?

9.4 Sexuality in the Middle and Later Years

Middle age is commonly thought to occur between the ages of 40 and 60. Family life specialists define middle age as beginning when the last child leaves home and continuing until retirement or the death of either spouse. Middle age is a time of transition for women, men, and their sexuality. In general, beginning at age 50, there appears to be a gradual continuous decline in sexual interest and activity. The decline in sexual interest may also be due to the physiology of aging or age-related disease processes. A major change in the sexuality of women is the experience of going through menopause. For men, sexual changes are associated with a decrease in testosterone.

9.4a Women, Menopause and Hormone Replacement Therapy

Menopause is a primary physical event for middle-aged women. Defined as the permanent cessation of menstruation, menopause is caused by the gradual decline of estrogen produced by the ovaries. It occurs around age 50 for most women but may begin much earlier or later. Signs that the woman may be nearing menopause include decreased menstrual flow and a less predictable cycle. After 12 months with no period, the woman is said to be through menopause. However, a woman who is sexually involved with a man and does not want to risk a pregnancy should use some form of contraception until her periods have stopped for 2 years because she may not know until the second year whether periods have really ceased.

Although the term **climacteric** is often used synonymously with menopause, it refers to changes that both men and women experience. The term *menopause* refers only to the time when the menstrual flow permanently stops, whereas *climacteric* refers to the whole process of hormonal change induced by the ovaries or testes, pituitary gland, and hypothalamus. Reactions to such hormonal changes may include hot flashes, in which the woman feels a sudden rush of heat from the waist up. Hot flashes are often accompanied by an increased reddening of the skin surface and a drenching perspiration. Other symptoms may include heart palpitations, dizziness, irritability, headaches, backache, and weight gain.

For most women, the symptoms associated with decreasing levels of estrogen will stop within 1 year of their final period. Some women find estrogen replacement therapy (ERT) or hormone replacement therapy (HRT)—estrogen plus progestin—helpful to

Middle age
Time in a person's life that begins when the last child leaves home and continues until retirement or the death of either spouse.

Menopause
Permanent cessation of menstruation that occurs in middle age

Climacteric
Term often used synonymously with menopause, refers to changes that both men and women experience at midlife

control hot flashes, night sweats, and vaginal dryness. The use of hormone replacement therapy continues to be debated and researched. Davies and colleagues (2013) reported the collective thinking of the Society for Women's Health research roundtable of 18 of the foremost experts within the field who discussed the collective evidence related to the risks and benefits of hormone therapy. Regarding the quality of life, the panel noted that HRT initiated in midlife women (around age 50) would significantly increase one's quality of life. However, HRT started in later years would not significantly improve one's quality of life or life expectancy. Details of the recommendations of the experts are provided in Table 9-4. Any woman considering using either estrogen or HRT for treatment of menopausal symptoms is encouraged to review her individual health history and medical goals with her health-care provider.

Think About It

Take a moment to answer the following questions. How is the sexuality of aging women and men affected by cultural stereotypes and expectations? How might a generation of today's young women, who have grown up in a sexually open and permissive era, differ when they become elderly (in terms of their sexuality) from elderly women of today who were reared in a more conservative, restrictive era?

9.4b Men and Testosterone Replacement Therapy

Some researchers suggest that men go through their own menopause because there is also a drop in sex hormones similar to that in women. However, the drop in testosterone is highly variable. In some men, the level can drop so low that men may experience depression, anxiety, hot flashes, decreased libido, difficulty achieving/maintaining an erection, and diminished memory. Yet other men experience no profound drop, and those who do may or may not respond to hormonal intervention.

Indeed, the changes most men experience as they age occur over a long period of time, and the depression and anxiety seem to be as much related to their life situation (for example, lack of career success) as to hormonal alterations. A middle-aged man who is not successful in his career is often forced to recognize that he will never achieve what he had hoped but instead will carry his unfulfilled dreams to the grave. This knowledge may be coupled with his awareness of diminishing sexual vigor. For the man who has been taught that masculinity is measured by career success and sexual prowess, middle age may be particularly difficult.

Nevertheless, "low testosterone level" and "testosterone replacement therapy" are frequent television advertisement phrases reflecting the $5 billion market promising renewed sexual energy, renewed mental clarity, an upbeat mood and erections. Testosterone is available in gels, patches or injections. The most reliable change is an improved libido for 80% of men.

There is disagreement among physicians, however, in regard to the risk of heart disease and prostate cancer. Most physicians agree that "testosterone does not instigate prostate cancer," but they do not give testosterone to men who have prostate cancer. The range of testosterone levels is from 250 to 890. The FDA defines low testosterone level at 300, but some physicians will treat men with higher levels. The best advice to men considering testosterone replacement is to "consult with a physician who works with testosterone issues on a regular basis and ask a lot of questions" (Harvard Health Letter, 2013).

TABLE **9-4**	Consensus Clinical Statements on Hormone Replacement Therapy[a]		
Clinical Recommendation		Vote	Difference from the USPTF recommendations[8,9]
Overall health benefits			
1. The benefit–risk profile of HT is more favorable for younger, newly menopausal, women.		Unanimous	The SWHR roundtable recommendation provides guidance on duration that is acceptable based on literature. USPTF did not address HT for symptom management.
2. In younger, symptomatic postmenopausal women, the benefits of E+P for at least 5 years outweigh the risks.		2 abstain	The SWHR Roundtable recommendation provides guidance on duration that is acceptable based on literature.
3. In younger, postmenopausal women with hysterectomy, the benefits of unopposed estrogen treatment for at least 10 years outweigh the risks.		Unanimous	The SWHR Roundtable recommendation provides risk information for younger individuals.
4. Patients with premature ovarian insufficiency benefit from hormone therapy and should be treated until at least the age of menopause, based on expert opinions and available observational data.		Unanimous	The SWHR Roundtable recommendation applies to women less than 50 years old.
5. There is consistent evidence that in early postmenopausal women, hormone therapy reduces total mortality.		5 opposed[b]	The SWHR Roundtable recommendation provides guidance on total mortality and age difference with respect to the effects of HT initiation and effect
Quality of life			
6. Hormone therapy is the most effective treatment for vasomotor symptoms.		Unanimous	
7. Hormone therapy provides a significant benefit on MS-QOL (HRQOL) in early postmenopausal women, mainly through the relief of symptoms, but treatment also may result in a global increase in sense of wellbeing (GQOL).		Unanimous	The SWHR Roundtable recommendation shows improvement in QOL for younger women.
Osteoporosis			
8. Estrogen can be used for the prevention of osteoporosis (an FDA approved indication) in early postmenopausal women at increased risk of fracture. The optimal duration for treatment is not known. However, if HT is discontinued the benefits dissipate. Therefore, in patients at high risk for osteoporotic fractures, continued estrogen treatment or other alternative treatments should be considered.		2 abstain	The SWHR Roundtable recommendation advocates for the use of HT for the prevention of a chronic disease, osteoporosis.
Breast cancer			
9. Available evidence suggests that unopposed estrogen appears not to increase the risk of breast cancer and may possibly reduce the risk in postmenopausal women with hysterectomy.		Unanimous	
Dementia			
10. There is insufficient evidence to recommend hormone therapy after menopause for the prevention of dementia or enhancement of cognition.		Unanimous	
Vascular disease			
11. HT in early postmenopausal women does not increase the risk for CHD, and may reduce it. However, there is insufficient evidence for the use of HT in the primary prevention of CHD.		1 opposed[c]	The SWHR Roundtable recommendation provides guidance concerning CHD in younger women.
12. Hormone therapy should not be used for the secondary prevention of CHD or stroke.		3 abstain	
13. HT in early postmenopausal women may slightly increase the risk of stroke although the absolute increase in risk, if present, is very small.		3 opposed[d]	

[a]Roundtable participants were asked to draw up consensus statements, based on the best evidence available, which includes both observational and clinical trial data. Unanimous agreement was reached on several topic areas, however, where necessary, the dissenting opinions are presented as well. Most of the consensus statements are based on studies of estrogen (conjugated equine estrogen) alone or with medroxyprogesterone acetate as continuous combined therapy. Each of the consensus statements is based on available data concerning the relationship between HT and a particular chronic condition. More research is necessary in each area. When considering the use of the following, a benefit–risk evaluation should be performed to include the entirety of a woman's health history.

[b]All present agreed that HT does not pose a risk on total mortality. However, 10 members wanted the stronger wording that HT "reduces" total mortality, while 5 members wanted to state that HT "may reduce" total mortality.

[c]The opposing vote supported a stronger statement and did not want the inclusion of "insufficient" in this statement.

[d]The three opposing votes wanted a stronger statement that the risk, if present, is "rare" as opposed to "very small."

HT, hormone therapy; USPTF, U.S. Preventative Services Task Force; E+P, estrogen and progestogen; SWHR, Society for Women's Health Research; MS-QOL, menopause-specific quality of life; HRQOL, health-related quality of life; GQOL, global quality of life; FDA, U.S. Food and Drug Administration; CHD, coronary heart disease.

Source: Davies, E., N. P. Mangongi and C. L. Carter. (2013). Is timing everything? A meeting report of the Society for Women's Health research roundtable on menopausal hormone therapy. *Journal of Women's Health,* 22: 303–311. Used with permission of *Journal of Women's Health.*

9.4c Sexuality in the Later Years

There are numerous changes in the sexuality of women and men as they age (Vickers, 2010). Frequency of intercourse drops from about once a week for those 40 to 59 to once every 6 weeks for those 70 and older. Changes in men include a decrease in the size of the penis from an average of 5 to about 4 ½ inches. Elderly men also become more easily aroused by touch rather than visual stimulation, which was arousing when they were younger. Erections take longer to achieve, are less rigid, and it takes longer for the man to recover so that he can have another erection. "It now takes me all night to do what I use to do all night" is the motto of the aging male.

Levitra, Cialis, and Viagra (prescription drugs that help a man obtain and maintain an erection) are helpful for about 50% of men in their late 60s. Others with erectile dysfunction may benefit from a pump that inflates two small banana-shaped tubes that have been surgically implanted into the penis. Still others benefit from devices placed over the penis to trap blood so as to create an erection.

Women also experience changes including menopause, which is associated with a surge of sexual libido, an interest in initiating sex with her partner, and greater orgasmic capacity. Not only are they free from worry about getting pregnant, estrogen levels drop and testosterone levels increase. Her vaginal walls become thinner and less lubricating. (Lubricants like KY Jelly can resolve the latter issue.)

> *Sex at age 90 is like trying to shoot pool with a rope.*
>
> George Burns

Chao and colleagues (2011) studied the sexuality of 283 individuals ages 45 to over 75. While sexual intercourse decreased as the respondent aged (to once a month), the respondents rated themselves more interested in sex than others their age. The National Institute on Aging surveyed 3,005 men and women ages 57 to 85 and found that sexual activity decreases with age (Lindau, et al., 2007). Almost three-fourths (73%) of those 57 to 64 reported being sexually active in the last 12 months. This percentage declined to about half (53%) for those 65 to 74 and to about a fourth (26%) for those ages 75 to 80. An easy way to remember these percentages is three-fourths of those around 60, half of those about 70, and a fourth of those around 80 report being sexually active.

As noted above, the most sexually active individuals are in good health. Diabetes and hypertension are major causes of sexual dysfunction. Incontinence (leaking of urine) is particularly an issue for older women and can be a source of embarrassment. The most frequent sexual problem for men is erectile dysfunction; for women, the most frequent sexual problem is the lack of a partner.

> *My intention—for the remaining years of my life—is to embrace my aging body, honoring its limitations, challenging its capabilities, and celebrating its accomplishments.*
>
> Pam Lewis, mental health consultant

Some spouses are sexually inactive. Karraker and DeLamater (2013) analyzed data on 1,502 men and women ages 57 to 85 and found that 29% reported no sexual activity for the past 12 months or more. The longer the couple had been married, the older the spouse, and the more compromised the health of the spouse, the more likely the individual was to report no sexual activity. Syme and colleagues (2013) studied a sample of older adults ages 63–67 to identify conditions under which respondents were not satisfied with their sexual relationship. Having a spouse in poor health, a history of diabetes, and feeling fatigued were the primary culprits. In contrast, those who were satisfied with their sexual relationship were male, reported positive marital support, and had a spouse in good health.

BVT *Lab*

Visit **www.BVTLab.com** to explore the student resources available for this chapter.

Chapter Summary

Sexuality in Infancy and Childhood

Sexuality begins early. In the uterus, boys often have penile erections and girls have clitoral erections and vaginal lubrication. Masturbation has been observed in both boys and girls as infants. Parents might be mindful of not reacting negatively to their infant's self-pleasuring. The sexual behaviors of children can be categorized into various areas including exhibitionism, self-stimulation, and voyeuristic behavior.

Parents are reluctant to talk with their children about sex. Not only do they feel inadequate in terms of their own knowledge (their parents taught them nothing), they fear that sexual discussions will spark experimentation and destroy their child's innocence/nonsexual state. Regarding family nudity, children who grow up in this context tend to feel very positive about their bodies/sexuality.

Sexuality in Adolescence

Adolescence is defined as the developmental period between puberty and adulthood. It is a time when the individual transforms his or her image as a child into a young adult with a future adult life. Adolescence involves identity exploration, interacting with romantic partners, and school performance with a career objective in mind. The most noticeable changes in adolescence are the physical and anatomical changes. Psychological changes include moving from a state of childish dependence to a state of relative independence, resolving sexual identity issues, and feeling secure that one is normal.

Over half of adolescent males and a quarter of adolescent females have had their first intercourse by age 14. Early sexual debut is typically associated with high-risk sexual behavior including alcohol/drug use, no condom use, getting pregnant (or causing pregnancy) and violence. The first sexual experience is usually one of anxiety. About 15% of teens would be "okay" with getting pregnant.

Sexuality in Adulthood

While most individuals eventually marry, singlehood is a time of sexual freedom. About 60% of U.S. adults will live together. In general, cohabitants have permissive sexual attitudes and behavior. They are not as emotionally or sexually happy as spouses.

About 25% of husbands and 20% of wives report having had sexual intercourse outside the marriage. Reasons include the desire for variety, sexual unhappiness in the marriage, and drifting into a sexual relationship with a coworker. While an affair may strengthen a relationship, divorce or separation is the more frequent outcome.

Sexuality in the Middle and Later Years

Physiological and psychological changes occur among women and men in the middle/late years. Women experience the end of their periods; men experience the loss of testosterone. Hormone replacement therapy and testosterone therapy are indicated. However, the decision to use hormone/testosterone therapy is complex and should be undertaken with the advice of a specialist in elder sexuality.

Web Links

Talk about Sex

http://www.seriouslysexuality.com/index.cfm?fuseaction=Page.
ViewPage&pageId=1080

Un/Hushed (Talking with Adolescents about Sex)

http://www.unhushed.net/

Sex and the Elderly

http://www.caring-for-aging-parents.com/sex-and-the-elderly.html

Key Terms

Additional study resources are available at www.BVTLab.com

CHAPTER
10

Sexual Orientation and Sexuality

Who am I to judge?

Pope Francis

Chapter Outline

Objectives

1. Differentiate the terms sexual orientation and sexual preference.
2. Identify the three conceptual models of sexual orientation
3. Know the prevalence of heterosexuality, homosexuality, and bisexuality.
4. Review the theories of sexual orientation.
5. Identify the stages of gay and bisexuality identity development.
6. Understand the process of "coming out" including risks and benefits.
7. Identify the different types of homosexual and bisexual relationships.
8. Know the relationship between sexual orientation and HIV infection.
9. Differentiate between heterosexism, homonegativity, and homophobia.
10. Review how heterosexuals are affected by homophobia.

Source: David Knox

Truth *OR* Fiction?

T/F Self-identified sexual orientation is often incongruent with preference and behavior.

T/F Most (over half) U.S. adults believe that the legalization of same sex marriage is inevitable.

T/F Bisexual women report the worst mental health in terms of anxiety, anger, and depressive symptoms.

T/F Heterosexuals are twice as likely as homosexuals to have a mood disorder.

T/F Lesbian relationships are happier than heterosexual relationships.

Answers:
1.T 2.T 3.T 4.F 5.T

Mainstream acceptance of gay individuals and their relationships has turned the corner. The Supreme Court has recognized same-sex marriage, President Obama has approved gay marriage, 16 states and the District of Columbia have legalized same sex marriage (as of November 2013), and television media (e.g., *Glee*) regularly feature gay characters/themes. Gay individuals feel the shift in public opinion. Of the 1,197 adults in a study of the LGBT (lesbian, gay, bisexual, transgender) community, 92% reported that they saw society becoming more accepting of them in the last decade (Drake, 2013). In this chapter, we review definitions and conceptions of heterosexuality, homosexuality, and bisexuality. We also examine theories of how sexual orientation develops, characteristics of homosexual and bisexual relationships, and the causes and consequences of homonegativity/ homophobia. We end with why it is important for heterosexuals to care about gay issues.

10.1 Terms of Sexual Orientation

Sexual orientation

Classification of individuals as heterosexual, bisexual, or homosexual based on their emotional, cognitive, and sexual attractions as well as their self-identity and lifestyle

Heterosexuality

Sexual orientation whereby the predominance of emotional and sexual attraction is to persons of the other sex

Homosexuality

Sexual orientation that involves the predominance of emotional and sexual attractions to persons of the same sex

Bisexuality

Emotional and sexual attraction to members of both sexes

Transgender

Term that refers to individuals who express some characteristics other than their assigned gender, which is usually based on their biological sex (male or female)

Sexual orientation refers to the classification of individuals as heterosexual, bisexual, or homosexual based on their emotional and sexual attractions, relationships, self-identity, and lifestyle. **Heterosexuality** refers to the predominance of emotional and sexual attraction to persons of the other sex. **Homosexuality** refers to the predominance of emotional and sexual attractions to persons of the same sex, and **bisexuality** is the emotional and sexual attraction to members of both sexes. **Transgender**

> *If advances in the understanding of sexual orientations are to be made, it is critical that definitions and measures of sexual orientation be standardized.*
>
> Randall Sell, researcher

is a generic term for a person of one biological sex who displays characteristics of the other sex. Kuper and colleagues (2012) identified 292 transgendered individuals online. Most self-identified as gender queer (their gender identity was neither male nor female) and pansexual/queer (they were attracted to men, women, bisexuals) as their sexual orientation. **Transgendered individuals** include cross-dressers and transsexuals. **LGBT** is a term that has emerged to refer collectively to lesbians, gays, bisexuals, and transgendered individuals.

Think About It

Take a moment to answer the following question. Although the terms *sexual preference* and *sexual orientation* are often used interchangeably, many sexuality researchers and academicians (including the authors of this text) prefer to use the term *sexual orientation*. The former term implies one is consciously choosing to whom one will be attracted. The latter term suggests that one's sexual orientation (whether heterosexual or homosexual) is innate (as is handedness) or may be influenced by multiple factors. What is your feeling about using the respective terms, and what meaning does each have for you?

National DATA

An estimated 3% of adults in the U.S., or about 700,000 individuals, self-identify as transgender (Gates, 2011).

Transgendered individuals

Persons who do not fit neatly into either the male or female category, or their behavior is not congruent with the norms and expectations of their sex

LGBT

Lesbian, gay, bisexual, transgender

10.2 Conceptual Models of Sexual Orientation

There are three models of sexual orientation: the dichotomous model, in which people are either heterosexual or homosexual; the unidimensional continuum model, in which sexual orientation is viewed on a continuum; and the multidimensional model, which views sexuality as a function of degrees of various components such as emotions, behaviors, and cognitions.

FIGURE **10-1** ‖ The Heterosexual-Homosexual Rating Scale

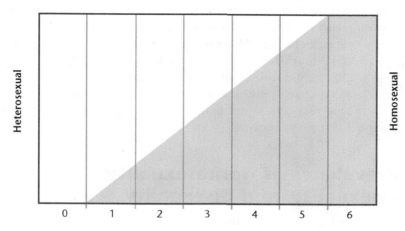

Based on both psychologic reactions and overt experience, individuals rate as follows:

0. Exclusively heterosexual with no homosexual factors

1. Predominantly heterosexual, only incidentally homosexual

2. Predominantly heterosexual, but more than incidentally homosexual

3. Equally heterosexual and homosexual

4. Predominantly homosexual, but more than incidentally heterosexual

5. Predominantly homosexual, but incidentally heterosexual

6. Exclusively homosexual factors

Source: Kinsey, A. C., Pomeroy, W. B., Martin, C. E., & Gebhard, P. H. (1953). Sexual behavior in the human female (p. 470, Figure 93). Philadelphia: W. B. Saunders. Reproduced by permission of The Kinsey Institute for Research in Sex, Gender, and Reproduction, Inc.

10.2a Dichotomous Model

The **dichotomous model** (also referred to as the "either-or" model of sexuality) takes the position that one is either gay or not. The major criticism of the dichotomous model of sexual orientation is that it ignores the existence of bisexuality and does not allow for any gradations or viewing sexual orientation as being on a continuum.

10.2b Unidimensional Continuum Model

In early research on sexual behavior, Kinsey and his colleagues (Kinsey, Pomeroy, & Martin, 1948; Kinsey, Pomeroy, Martin, & Gebhard, 1953) found that a substantial proportion of respondents reported having had same-sex sexual experiences. Yet, very few of the individuals in Kinsey's research reported exclusive homosexual behavior. These data led Kinsey to conclude that, contrary to the commonly held dichotomous model of sexual orientation, most people are not exclusively heterosexual or homosexual. Thus, Kinsey suggested a **unidimensional continuum model** of sexual orientation and developed the Heterosexual-Homosexual Rating Scale to assess where on the continuum of sexual orientation an individual is located (see Figure 10-1).

The unidimensional continuum model recognizes that the heterosexual and homosexual orientations are not mutually exclusive and that an individual's sexual orientation may have both heterosexual and homosexual elements. The criticism of the Kinsey scale is that it does not account for some important aspects of sexuality—such as self-identity, lifestyle, and social group preference. One could place himself or herself on the continuum, but the criteria for doing so is not clear.

Dichotomous model
(Also referred to as the "either-or" model of sexuality) Way of conceptualizing sexual orientation that prevails not only in views on sexual orientation but also in cultural understandings of biological sex (male vs. female) and gender (masculine vs. feminine)

Unidimensional continuum model
Identification of one's sexual orientation on a scale from 0 (exclusively heterosexual) to 6 (exclusively homosexual) suggesting that most people are not on the extremes but somewhere in between

10.2c Multidimensional Model

The **multidimensional model** of sexual orientation suggests that orientation consists of various independent components (including emotional and social preferences, behavior, self-identification, sexual attraction, fantasy, and lifestyle) and that these components may change over time. The most important contribution of the multidimensional model is its incorporation of self-identity as a central element of sexual orientation. For example an individual may have engaged in same-sex sexual behavior but maintained the self-concept of being heterosexual.

I'm not even kind of a lesbian.

Oprah Winfrey

Multidimensional model
Way of conceptualizing sexual orientation which suggests that a person's orientation consists of various independent components (including emotions, lifestyle, self-identification, sexual attraction, fantasy, and behavior) and that these components may change over time

Sexual fluidity
Capacity for variation in one's erotic responses depending on the situation

10.3 Prevalence of Homosexuality, Heterosexuality, and Bisexuality

The prevalence of homosexuality, heterosexuality, and bisexuality is difficult to determine. Due to embarrassment, a desire for privacy, or fear of social disapproval, many individuals do not identify themselves as homosexual. Korchmaros and colleagues (2013) confirmed that self-identified sexual orientation is often incongruent with preference and behavior. Hence, how one defines one's sexual orientation can be different from one's actual behavior; thus, individuals can engage in same-sex behavior, but self-identify as heterosexual.

Estimates of the prevalence of sexual orientations also vary due to differences in the way researchers define and measure homosexuality, bisexuality, and heterosexuality. Definitional problems arise due to the considerable overlap between people with different sexual orientation self-identities and the fact that sexual attractions, behavior, and self-identity may or may not change over time.

National DATA

Of adults in the U.S., about 1% of females self-identify as lesbian, 2% of males self-identify as gay, and 1.5% of adults self-identify as bisexual. Hence, about 3.5% (or about 10 million individuals in the U.S.) are LGB (Mock & Eibach, 2012).

WOMEN'S STUDIES PROGRAM
&
THE LGBT RESOURCE CENTER
COME ON IN!
★★★★★

Dr. Marieke Van Willigen
Women's Studies Director

Ms. Summer Wisdom
Director LGBT Resource Center

Lesbian Gay Bisexual
Transgender Resource Office

Director Summer Wisdom
252-737-4451
wisdoms@ecu.edu
www.ecu.edu/lgbt

Increasingly, college and university campuses are embracing sexual diversity by providing space for offices and meetings of gay individuals and organizations.
Source: Chelsea Curry

Sexual fluidity, or the capacity for variation in one's erotic responses depending on the situation, is another way to characterize sexual orientation. It is not fixed but subject to context, experiences, age, etc. Nevertheless, research data have yielded rough estimates of prevalence rates of self-identified homosexuals.

10.4 Theories of Sexual Orientation

One of the prevailing questions raised regarding homosexuality centers on its origin or "cause." Gay people are often irritated by the fact that heterosexual people seem overly concerned about finding "the cause" of homosexuality. However, the same question is rarely asked about heterosexuality because it is assumed that this sexual orientation is normal and needs no explanation. Questions about the cause of homosexuality imply that something is "wrong" with homosexuality.

Nevertheless, considerable research has been conducted on the origin of homosexuality and whether its basis is derived from nature (genetic, hormonal, innate) or nurture (learned through social experiences and cultural influences). Most researchers agree that an interaction of biological (nature) and social/cultural (environmental) forces is involved in the development of one's sexual orientation.

10.4a Biological Explanations

Biological explanations of the development of sexual orientation usually focus on genetic, neuroanatomical, or hormonal differences between heterosexuals and homosexuals. Several lines of evidence suggest that biological factors play a role (Dupree, Mustanski, Bocklandt, Nievergelt, & Hamer, 2004). A discussion of three biological explorations of sexual orientation follows.

> *No, I've never thought that I was gay. And that's not something you think. It's something you know.*
>
> Robert Plant, English musician

Genetic Theories

Is sexual orientation an inborn trait that is transmitted genetically, like eye color? There does seem to be a genetic influence, although unlike eye color, a single gene has not been confirmed. In the United States, a study of a national probability sample of twin and nontwin siblings concluded that "Familial factors, which are at least partly genetic, influence sexual orientation" (Kendler, Thomton, Gilman, & Kessler, 2000). In this sample, 3.1% of the men and 1.5% of the women reported non-heterosexual sexual orientation. The concordance rate in monozygotic twins was 31.6% for non-heterosexual sexual orientation (so if one identical twin was gay or lesbian, in 31.6% of the pairs, the co-twin was also gay or lesbian).

Further support for a genetic influence on homosexuality has been provided by Cantor and colleagues (2002), who noted that men with older homosexual brothers are more likely to be homosexual themselves: "[R]oughly one gay man in seven owes his sexual orientation to the fraternal birth order effect" (p. 63).

How much of the link in sexual orientation between twins is accounted for by genetic inheritance? One large population-based twin study used the Australian National Health and Medical Research Council Twin Registry (Kirk, Bailey, Dunne, & Martin, 2000). Behavioral and psychological aspects of sexual orientation were measured. Of the 4,901 respondents, 2.6% of the women rated themselves as bisexual and 0.7% as homosexual; 3.2% of the men rated themselves as bisexual and 3.1% as homosexual. The researchers concluded that genetic influences were linked to homosexuality in both women and men, with estimates of 50%–60% heritability for women and about 30% for men. So genetic inheritance accounted for much more of the variance in women than in men.

Perinatal Hormonal Theories

In his discussion of prenatal influences on sexual orientation, Diamond (1995) discussed the effects of the maturation of the testes or ovaries and their release (or lack) of hormones. These hormones affect the structural development of the genitalia and other structures. At the gross and microscopic levels, they also organize the developing nervous system and influence sex-linked behaviors (biasing the individual toward male- or female-typical behaviors).

Ellis and Ames (1987) concluded that hormonal and neurological factors operating prior to birth, between the second and fifth month of gestation, are the "main determinants of sexual orientation" (p. 235). Fetal exposure to hormones such as testosterone is believed to impact the developing neural pathways of the brain. Money (1987) suggested that sexual orientation is programmed into the brain during critical prenatal periods and early childhood.

Postpubertal Hormonal Theories

Endocrinology (the study of hormones) research to determine whether the levels of sex hormones of gay men and lesbians resemble the other sex has yielded mixed results

We struggled against apartheid because we were being blamed and made to suffer for something we could do nothing about. It is the same with homosexuality. The orientation is a given, not a matter of choice. It would be crazy for someone to choose to be gay, given the homophobia that is present.

Desmond Tutu, South African social activist

(Ellis, 1996). Although some studies of circulating testosterone levels in men found slightly lower levels in gay men, most studies have not found significant differences. About half of the studies of women found no differences; the other half found higher levels of testosterone in lesbians (although the levels are still well below the normal level for men). Ellis concluded that the connection between postpubertal sex hormone levels and homosexuality is complex and is probably applicable only to some subgroups of gay men and lesbians.

The belief in biological determinism of sexual orientation among homosexuals is strong. In a national study of homosexual men, 90% believe that they were born with their homosexual orientation; only 4% believe that environmental factors are the sole cause (Lever, 1994). Although the general public believes that homosexuality is more of a choice, acceptance of a biological explanation is increasing.

10.4b Social/Cultural Explanations

Although adrenal androgens provide the fuel for the sex drive (around age 10), they do not provide the direction or sexual orientation that is determined by sociocultural forces such as one's peer group, parents, and mass media—according to social/cultural explanations of sexual orientation. Because these forces encourage heterosexuality, unique environmental influences help account for homosexuality. Sociocultural theories of homosexuality suggest that parent-child interaction, sexual experiences, and adoption of sex roles and self-labels are especially influential.

Parent-Child Interaction Theories

Freud's psychoanalytic theory has been described as one of the first scientific explanations of homosexuality (Ellis, 1996). His theories suggested that the relationship individuals have with their parents might predispose them toward heterosexuality or homosexuality. Whereas heterosexual men identified closely with their fathers and had more distant relationships with their mothers, homosexual men had close emotional relationships with their mothers and were distant with their fathers (Freud had little to say about the development of sexual orientation in women).

The presumed script for the development of a homosexual male follows: The overprotective mother seeks to establish a binding emotional relationship with her son. However, this closeness also elicits strong sexual feelings on the part of the son toward the mother, which are punished by her and blocked by the society through the incest taboo. The son is fearful of expressing sexual feelings for his mother. He generalizes this fear to other women with the result that they are no longer viewed as potential sexual partners.

The son's distant relationship with his father prevents identification with a male role model. For example, the relationship between playwright Tennessee Williams and his father was one of mutual rejection—the father was contemptuous of his "sissy" son, and Williams was hostile to his father because of his father's arrogance.

BVT *Lab*

Flashcards are available for this chapter at **www.BVTLab.com**.

The scientific community does not support Freud's theory of male homosexuality. First, it does not resolve the question, "Is the absent or distant father relationship a result or a cause of the child's homosexuality?" Second, sons with overprotective mothers and rejecting fathers also grow up to be heterosexual, just as those with moderate mothering and warm fathering grow up to be homosexual. Third, two sons growing up in the same type of family may have different sexual orientations.

Sexual Interaction Theories

Sexual interaction theories propose that such factors as availability of sexual partners, early sexual experiences, imprinting, and sexual reinforcement influence subsequent sexual orientation. Because homosexuality is more prevalent among men than women, shortages of women and an emphasis on the chastity of women have been hypothesized to be conducive to male homosexuality (Ellis, 1996). The degree to which early sexual experiences have been negative or positive has been hypothesized as influencing sexual orientation. Having pleasurable same-sex experiences would be likely to increase the probability of a homosexual orientation. By the same token, early sexual experiences that are either unsuccessful or traumatic have been suspected as causing fear of heterosexual activity. One lesbian in the authors' classes explained her attraction to women as a result of being turned off to men—her uncle molested her regularly and often over 4 years. However, one study that compared sexual histories of lesbian and heterosexual women found no difference in the incidence of traumatic experiences with men (Brannock & Chapman, 1990).

I don't think homosexuality is a choice. Society forces you to think it's a choice, but in fact, it's in one's nature. The choice is whether one expresses one's nature truthfully or spends the rest of one's life lying about it.

Marlo Thomas, actress

Sex-Role Theories

Sex-role theories include self-labeling theory and inappropriate (or nontraditional) sex-role training. How people perceive themselves and the reactions of others to their sex-role behavior are important in a child's development. The self-labeling theory is supported by research showing that gay men, when compared to heterosexual men, were more likely to dislike athletics and to have played with dolls (Strong, Devendra, & Randall, 2000). In a study comparing the recalled childhood experiences of heterosexual and lesbian women, lesbian women were much more likely to have imagined themselves as male characters, to have a preference for boys' games, and to have considered themselves tomboys as children (Phillips & Over, 1995). According to labeling theorists, "through a process of socialization, lesbians and gays incorporate ideas about what it means to be lesbian or gay into their own identities. The labeling of an individual's acts as homosexual—both by other lesbians and gays and by the straight world—and the stigmatization of that identity, over time, lead to the adoption of a homosexual identity" (Esterberg, 1997, p. 20). Although labeling theory is useful in emphasizing the fact that the labels "homosexual" and "heterosexual" are socially constructed categories, "it does not appear that individuals become lesbian or gay simply by a process of labeling by others" (Esterberg, 1997, p. 21).

The Exotic Becomes Erotic (EBE) theory provides an explanation of the development of sexual orientation that combines biological and environmental components (Bem, 1996). Bem suggested that a child's biological inheritance influences temperament (including characteristics such as aggressiveness and activity level), which predisposes him or her to prefer some activities to others. Gender-conforming children (who enjoy sex-typical activities) will feel different from peers of the other sex and perceive them as dissimilar and exotic. Likewise, gender-nonconforming children (who enjoy atypical activities for their sex) will perceive same-sex peers as unfamiliar and exotic. These feelings result in autonomic arousal, which is transformed into erotic or romantic attraction. Bem observed that as natives of a gender-polarizing culture, we have learned to view the world through the lens of gender. He also noted that culture influences the way biological and behavioral scientists think about sexual orientation.

10.5 Gay and Bisexual Identity Development

Gay and bisexual identity development is usually a gradual process that progresses through various stages.

10.5a Stages of Development

In a review of six theories of gay identity development, Sophie (1985/1986) synthesized four essential stages of identity development:

- *Stage 1: First awareness or realization that one is "different"*   This awareness often begins before puberty. Girls and boys may feel different in their lack of interest in the other sex. An awareness of being different from others may also involve a vague feeling of not fitting in with one's peers, without knowing why.

- *Stage 2: Test and exploration*   At this stage, which often occurs in the teenage years, individuals may suspect they are homosexual but may not be sure. This stage involves exploring one's feelings and attractions, as well as initiating limited contact with other non-heterosexual individuals.

- *Stage 3: Identity acceptance*   In this stage, individuals come to define themselves as homosexual or bisexual. For women, developing a homosexual identity often occurs after developing an emotionally intimate, loving same-sex relationship. For men, identity acceptance often occurs after having an initial same-sex sexual experience. Troiden (1989) reported that gay men arrive at homosexual self-definitions between the ages of 19 and 21, whereas women arrive at homosexual self-definitions between the ages of 21 and 23. Bisexual self-identification typically occurs at later ages due to the difficulties bisexual women and men have in arriving at an identity that is not affirmed in either the heterosexual or homosexual community.

- *Stage 4: Identity integration*   The final stage of developing a gay or bisexual identity involves developing pride in and commitment to one's sexual orientation. This stage also involves disclosing one's sexual orientation to others. Figure 10-2 summarizes the stages involved in developing a gay identity.

Not all homosexual and bisexual individuals go through identity development stages in an orderly, predictable fashion. In their interviews with young sexual-minority youth, Diamond and Savin-Williams (2000) found that the developmental trajectories, or course of sexual identity development, differed radically among their interviewees. In recalling their first same-sex attraction, only one-third of the young women recalled an explicit sexual context for the attraction; it was more often emotional. Women whose first same-sex sexual contact occurred within a relationship were more likely to self-identify as sexual minorities prior to or soon after this experience. In contrast, the majority of sexual-minority men did not self-label until several years after their first same-sex sexual contact.

FIGURE **10-2** ‖ Synthesized Model of Gay Identity Development

This model is based on the theory and research of Sophie (1985/1986) and Troiden (1989). Although not all gay or lesbian individuals follow this sequence, the model is helpful in showing commonly reported stages of gay identity development.

Stage-identity models might be criticized on the basis of their small samples, their narrow focus on sexuality, and their lack of attention to the larger sociohistorical context. A more comprehensive model of identity development would put sexual identity into a context that includes other important facets of identity, such as gender, race, and class. Such personal characteristics as personality variables, sexual attitudes, social skills, and appearance may be influential. Family relationships, access to sexuality information, friendships, and romantic relationships may also be important (Diamond & Savin-Williams, 2000).

Personal ~~REFLECTION~~

Take a moment to express your thoughts about the following question. Can you describe the development of your own sexual identity as a process consisting of various stages? For example, when did you first become aware of and define your own sexual orientation?

10.5b Conversion Therapy

Individuals who believe that homosexual people choose their sexual orientation tend to think that homosexuals can and should change their sexual orientation. While about 2% of U.S. adults report that there has been a change in their sexual orientation (Mock & Eibach, 2012), **conversion therapy** (also known as reparative therapy) is focused on changing homosexuals' sexual orientation. Fjelstrom (2013) interviewed 15 former participants in sexual orientation change efforts (SOCE), who currently identify as gay or lesbian. While the participants noted that they sometimes identified as heterosexual during SOCE, they also reported that they never changed their underlying homosexual orientation.

Critics of reparative therapy and ex-gay ministries take a different approach—gay people are not the problem; social disapproval is the problem. The National Association for the Research and Therapy of Homosexuality (NARTH) has been influential in moving public opinion from "gays are sick" to "society is judgmental." The American Psychiatric Association, the American Psychological Association, the American Academy of Pediatrics, the American Counseling Association, the National Association of School Psychologists, the National Association of Social Workers, and the American Medical Association agree that homosexuality is not a mental disorder and needs no cure—that efforts to change sexual orientation do not work and may, in fact, be harmful.

Conversion therapy
Therapy designed to change the sexual orientation of a person, usually homosexual to heterosexual

Some research brings into question that reparative therapies "never work." Karten and Wade (2010) reported that the majority of 117 men who were dissatisfied with their sexual orientation and who sought sexual orientation change efforts (SOCE) were able to reduce their homosexual feelings and behaviors and increase their heterosexual feelings and behaviors. The primary motivations for their seeking change were religion ("homosexuality is wrong") and emotional dissatisfaction with the homosexual life-style. Being married, feeling disconnected from other men prior to seeking help, and feeling able to express nonsexual affection toward other men—all were factors predictive of greatest change. Developing nonsexual relationships with same-sex peers was also identified as helpful in change.

10.6 Coming Out

Gay and bisexual identity development also occurs through the process of "coming out." The term **coming out** (a shortened form of "coming out of the closet") refers to the sequence of defining one's self as homosexual in sexual orientation and disclosing one's self-identification to others. Coming out helps to solidify commitment to a homosexual or bisexual identity. Most individuals/couples are very slow to make public their homosexuality

Let's get one thing straight, I'm not.

bumper sticker

Personal REFLECTION

Take a moment to express your thoughts about the following question. Resolving sexual identity issues requires becoming comfortable with one's sexual orientation. Adolescents are already concerned about fitting in, so being homosexual or questioning one's sexuality may add to the burden adolescents feel when they discover that they are not part of the heterosexual mainstream. Part of this concern is the fear of rejection. What would be your reaction to someone coming out to you?

Coming out
(Shortened form of "coming out of the closet") Sequence of defining one's self as homosexual in sexual orientation and disclosing one's self-identification to others

10.6a Coming Out to One's Self and Others

Defining one's self as a homosexual and coming out to one's self can be a frightening and confusing experience. Coming out to others involves disclosing one's homosexual or bisexual identity to parents and other family members, friends and peers, employers, partners or spouses, and children. The Personal Choices 10-1 section examines the risks and benefits of coming out.

personal *C*hoices 10-1

The Risks and Benefits of Coming Out

In a society where heterosexuality is expected and considered the norm, heterosexuals do not have to choose whether or not to tell others that they are heterosexual. However, decisions about "coming out," or being open and honest about one's sexual orientation and identity (particularly to one's parents) create anxiety for most gay individuals. Rossi (2010) studied the coming out experiences of 53 young adults and noted that most came out to a friend first, then their mothers, and then their fathers.

Risks of Coming Out

Whether or not LGBT individuals come out is influenced by the degree to which they are tired of hiding their sexual orientation, the degree to which they feel more "honest" about being open, their assessment of the risks of coming out, and their prediction of how others will respond. Some of the overall risks involved in coming out include disapproval and rejection by parents and other family members, harassment and discrimination at school, discrimination and harassment in the workplace, and hate crime victimization.

1. *Parental and family members' reactions* Rothman and colleagues (2012) studied 177 LBG individuals who reported that two-thirds of the parents to whom they first came out responded with social and emotional support. Researchers Mena and Vaccaro (2013), who interviewed 24 gay and lesbian youth about their coming out experience to their parents reported a less than 100% affirmative "we love you"/"being gay is irrelevant" reaction which resulted in varying degrees of sadness/depression (three became suicidal). Padilla and colleagues (2010) found that parental reaction to a son or daughter coming out had a major effect on the development of their child. Acceptance had an enormous positive effect. When LGBT individuals in their study come out to their parents, parental reactions range from "I already knew you were gay and I'm glad that you feel ready to be open with me about it" to "Get out of this house, you are no longer welcome here." We know of a father who responded to the disclosure of his son that the son was gay, "I'd rather have a dead son than a gay son." Parental rejection of LGBT individuals is related to suicide ideation and suicide attempts (van Bergen, Bos, Lisdonk, Keuzenkamp, & Sandfort, 2013).

   Because black individuals are more likely than white individuals to view homosexual relations as "always wrong," African Americans who are gay or lesbian are more likely to face disapproval from their families (and straight friends) than are white lesbians and gays (2003). *The Resource Guide to Coming Out for African Americans* (2011) is a useful guide. Because most parents are heavily invested in their children, they find a way to not make an issue of their son or daughter being gay. "We just don't talk about it," said one parent.

   Parents and other family members can learn more about homosexuality from the local chapter of Parents, Families, and Friends of Lesbians and Gays (PFLAG) and from books and online resources, such as those found at Human Rights Campaign's National Coming Out Project (http://www.hrc.org/). Mena and Vaccaro (2013) emphasized the importance of parents educating themselves about gay/lesbian issues and knowing the importance of their loving and accepting their son or daughter at this most difficult time.

2. *Harassment and discrimination at school*   LGBT students are more vulnerable to being bullied, harassed, and discriminated against. The negative effects are predictable and include a wide range of health and mental health concerns, including sexual health risk, substance abuse, and suicide, compared with their heterosexual peers (Russell, Ryan, Toomey, Diaz, & Sanchez, 2011). The U.S. Department of Health (2012) published new guidelines to be sensitive to the needs of and to protect LGBT youth.

3. *Discrimination and harassment in the workplace*   The workplace continues to be a place where the 8 million LGBT individuals experience discrimination and harassment. However, in November 2013, the Senate approved the Employment Non-Discrimination Act banning discrimination against gays and transgender people in the workplace.

4. *Hate crime victimization*   Another risk of coming out is that of being victimized by antigay hate crimes against individuals or their property that are based on bias against the victims because of their perceived sexual orientation. Such crimes include verbal threats and intimidation, vandalism, sexual assault and rape, physical assault, and murder. "Homosexuals are far more likely than any other minority group in the United States to be victimized by violent hate crime" (Potok, 2010, p. 29).

Benefits of Coming Out

Coming out to parents is associated with decided benefits. D'Amico and Julien (2012) compared 111 gay, lesbian, and bisexual youth who disclosed their sexual orientation to their parents with 53 who had not done so. Results showed that the former reported higher levels of acceptance from their parents, lower levels of alcohol and drug consumption, and fewer identity and adjustment problems. Similarly, Rothman and colleagues (2012) noted that for lesbian and bisexual females (not males), higher levels of illicit drug use, poorer self-reported health status and being more depressed were associated with non-disclosure to parents.

Beyond disclosing to parents, individuals who come out feel a sense of relief from no longer having to hide. Cheryl Jacques, a Massachusetts state senator who came out publicly in the *Boston Globe*, noted:

> Coming out is a risk worth taking because it is one of the *most* powerful things any of us can do. I've yet to meet anyone who regretted the decision to live life truthfully … That's why while coming out may be just one step in the life of a gay, lesbian, bisexual or transgender person, it contributes to a giant leap for all LGBT people.

McLaren and colleagues (2013) also noted that persons who join LGBT groups report less depression. In effect they have come out both to themselves and others.

This gay male reports complete approval/support from his parents.
Source: Chelsea Curry

10.6b Coming Out to a Heterosexual Partner or Spouse and Children

Gay and bisexual people marry for reasons similar to heterosexuals—genuine love for a spouse, desire for children in a socially approved context, family pressure to marry, the desire to live a socially approved heterosexual lifestyle, and belief that marriage is the only way to achieve a happy adult life. In a probability sample of gay and bisexual men, 42% reported that they were currently married (Harry, 1990). Other researchers estimate that 20% of gay men are married (Strommen, 1989). Some individuals do not realize that they are gay or bisexual until after they are married.

Many homosexuals and bisexuals in heterosexual relationships do not disclose their sexual identity to their partners out of fear that their partners will reject them and that there may be legal consequences (getting custody of the children would be jeopardized). The immediate and long-term consequences for coming out to one's partner vary from couple to couple. Some who disclose are able to work though the event. Buxton (2001) analyzed survey responses of 56 self-identified bisexual husbands and 51 heterosexual wives of bisexual men who maintained their marriage after disclosure. Honest communication, peer support, therapy, and "taking time" were identified as factors associated with positive coping. In addition, the couples were able to deconstruct not only traditional concepts of marriage but dichotomous views of sexual orientation.

There are about a half million gay dads in the United States. Dr. Jerry Bigner, himself a gay dad, provided several suggestions for coming out to one's children—including becoming comfortable with one's own gayness before coming out to one's children, discussing it with one's children when they are young before they find out from someone external to the family, ensuring one's child that "you won't be gay just because your dad is gay," and helping them with what they tell their friends (be selective) (Knox, 2000).

BVT *Lab*

Improve your test scores. Practice quizzes are available at **www.BVTLab.com**.

Up Close 10-1

A Coming Out Letter to Parents

The following recommendations for coming out to one's parents are made by a 21-year-old lesbian college student who came out to her parents in a letter:

1. *Avoid speaking from a defensive point of view.* Too often, gay people are forced to defend their lifestyle, as if it were wrong. If you approach your parents with the view that your homosexuality is a positive aspect of your personality, you will have a better chance of evoking a positive response from them.

2. *Avoid talking about your current relationship.* Homosexuality is often labeled as a phase rather than a permanent facet of one's life. Your parents may feel, as mine did, that your current partner is the cause of your lifestyle. Thus, when your relationship ends (so they hope), so will your homosexuality. Deal with the subject as it affects you as an individual.

3. *Try to maintain a constant flow of positive reinforcement toward your parents.* Reiterate your love for them, as you would like them to do to you.

4. *Be confident in your views and outlook on homosexuality.* Before you begin to explain your position to anyone else, you must have it clear in your own mind. (authors' files)

10.7 **Homosexual and Bisexual Relationships**

In a review of literature on relationship satisfaction and sexual orientation, Kurdek (1994) concluded, "The most striking finding regarding the factors linked to relationship satisfaction is that they seem to be the same for lesbian couples, gay couples, and heterosexual couples" (p. 251). These factors include having equal power and control, being emotionally expressive, perceiving many attractions and few alternatives to the relationship, placing a high value on attachment, and sharing decision-making. Kamen and colleagues (2011) also noted that commitment, trust, and support from one's partner were related to relationship satisfaction in same-sex relationships. In a comparison of relationship quality of cohabitants over a 10-year period involving both partners from 95 lesbian, 92 gay male, and 226 heterosexual couples living without children, and both partners from 312 heterosexual couples living with children, the researcher found that lesbian couples showed the highest level of relationship quality. (Kurdek, 2008). Issues unique to gay couples include if, when, and how to disclose their relationships to others and how to develop healthy intimate relationships in the absence of same-sex relationship models.

10.7a Gay Male Relationships

A common stereotype of gay men is that they prefer casual sexual relationships with multiple partners versus monogamous, long-term relationships. However, although gay men report greater interest in casual sex than do heterosexual men (Gotta, et al., 2011), most gay men prefer long-term relationships; and sex outside the primary relationship is usually infrequent and not emotionally involved (Green, Bettinger, & Zacks, 1996).

The degree to which gay males engage in casual sexual relationships is better explained by the fact that they are male than by the fact that they are gay. In this regard, gay and straight men have a lot in common—including that they both tend to have fewer barriers to engaging in casual sex than do women (heterosexual or lesbian). One way that gay men meet partners is through the Internet. Blackwell and Dziegielewski (2012) studied men who seek men for sex on the Internet and noted that these sites promote higher-risk sexual activities. "Party and play" (PNP) is one such activity and involves using crystal methamphetamine and having unprotected anal sex. More scholarly inquiry is needed on the extent of this phenomenon.

Such nonuse of condoms results in the high rate of human immunodeficiency virus (HIV) infection and acquired immunodeficiency syndrome (AIDS). Approximately 50,000 new cases of HIV are reported annually, and male-to-male sexual contact is the most common mode of transmission in the United States with 29,700 infections reported annually (Centers for Disease Control and Prevention, 2012). Women who have sex exclusively with other women have a much lower rate of HIV infection than do men (both gay and straight) and women who have sex with men. Many gay men have lost a love partner to HIV infection or AIDS; some have experienced multiple losses.

Approximately 50% of gay men describe themselves as single (i.e., without a committed relationship). Hostetler (2009) interviewed 94 single middle-class gay men (over 30% were men of color) between the ages of 35 and 70. Just over a fifth (20.2%) viewed their singlehood as a potentially permanent choice. Various reasons for remaining unattached included the following:

1. *Personal Past*   Attributing one's single status to events or circumstances in one's childhood, adolescence, and/or early-adult years, including growing up in a home where one's parents were viewed as having a stale marriage and not wanting to model this experience

2. *Collective Past*   Attributing one's single status to membership in a particular historical cohort, such as belonging to a group who served in the military in Iraq or Afghanistan, being traumatized by war, and feeling "unfit to marry anybody"

3. *Previous Relationship*   Attributing one's single status to past relationship experiences, such as being burned in a previous relationship and wanting to steer clear of new romances/commitments

4. *Particular Tastes*   Attributing one's single status to sexual tastes that are seen as incompatible with the establishment and/or maintenance of a long-term relationship, such as feeling that one could never be faithful due to the need for constant sexual variety or being gay and not having the option to marry

5. *Still Searching*   The conviction that one has not yet met the right person

6. *Loner*   Attributing one's single status to seeing oneself as a loner or attributing one's single status to preferences and/or behavioral patterns acquired as a result of long-term singlehood, such as feeling that one is set in one's ways and not willing to adapt to a relationship

The majority (80%) of Hostetler's respondents reported that they were not happy being single and that it was not their preference. A common revelation was that the "decision" to be single was made in retrospect—after awhile they just noticed that they were not partnered. Of respondents, 61.7% felt that they would be happier if they had a relationship.

Lyons and colleagues (2013) reported on 840 Australian gay men over the age of 60. They were more likely to be living alone than men in their 40s/50s. Having good physical health, a satisfying sex life, feeling supported, and fewer experiences of discrimination were key factors in the self-esteem and subjective well-being of these men.

10.7b Lesbian Relationships

Like many heterosexual women, most gay women value stable, monogamous relationships that are emotionally as well as sexually satisfying. Gay and heterosexual women in U.S. society are taught that sexual expression should occur in the context of emotional or romantic involvement.

There are stereotypes and assumptions about what sexual behaviors various categories of lesbians engage in. Walker and colleagues (2012) studied a sample of 214 women who self-identified as lesbian to explore the relationship between lesbian labels (butch, soft butch, butch/femme, femme, and high femme) and attraction to sexual behavior (being on top, etc.). They found no relationship between the label and the sexual behavior. The researchers emphasized that sexual behaviors in the lesbian community are fluid across labels.

Women in our society, gay and "straight," are taught that sexual expression "should" occur in the context of emotional or romantic involvement. Of 94 gay women in one study, 93% said their first homosexual experience was emotional; physical expression came later (Corbett & Morgan, 1983). Hence, for gay women, the formula is love first; for gay men, it's sex first—just as for their straight counterparts. Indeed, a joke in the lesbian community is that the second date of a lesbian couple involves getting a U-Haul together so that they can move in and "nest" together.

My lesbianism is an act of Christian charity. All those women out there praying for a man, and I'm giving them my share.

Rita Mae Brown

Kurdek (1995) reviewed the literature on lesbian and gay couples and concluded that the factors associated with relationship satisfaction were the same for all couples regardless of sexual orientation. These factors include having equal power and control,

This couple plans a life together.
Source: Mary Mills

being emotionally expressive, perceiving many attractions and few alternatives to the relationship, placing a high value on attachment, and sharing decision-making. Green and colleagues (1996) compared 52 lesbian couples with 50 gay male couples and 218 heterosexual married couples. They found that the lesbian couples were the most cohesive (closest), the most flexible in terms of their roles, and the most satisfied in their relationships.

10.7c Bisexual Relationships

Individuals who identify as bisexual have the ability to form intimate relationships with both sexes. However, research has found that the majority of bisexual women and men tend toward primary relationships with the other sex (McLean, 2004). Contrary to the common myth that bisexuals are non-monogamous, by

I'm bisexual.

Lady Gaga

definition, some bisexuals prefer monogamous relationships (especially in light of the widespread concern about HIV). In another study of 60 bisexual women and men, 25% of the men and 35% of the women were in exclusive relationships; 60% of the men and 53% of the women were in "open" relationships in which both partners agreed to allow each other to have sexual or emotional relationships, or both, with others, often under specific conditions or rules about how such relationships would occur (McLean, 2004). Some gay and bisexual men have monogamous relationships in which both men have agreed that any sexual activity with casual partners must happen when both members of the couple are present and involved,— 'threeways' or group sex (Parsons, Starks, DuBois, Grov, & Golub, 2013).

Bisexuality is one of the least understood aspects of sexual orientation. So strong is the tendency to dichotomize sexual orientation that many people simply do not believe it exists.

Margaret Nichols

10.8 Sexual Orientation and HIV Infection

Most worldwide HIV infection occurs through heterosexual transmission. However, in the United States, HIV infection remains the most threatening STI for male homosexuals and bisexuals. Men who have sex with men account for more new cases of AIDS in the United States than do persons in any other transmission category. While the exchange of semen in men who have unprotected anal intercourse (bareback) may meet emotional needs for the men, it remains a dangerous practice from the point of view of healthcare professionals.

Women who have sex exclusively with other women have a much lower rate of HIV infection than men (both gay and straight) and women who have sex with men. However, since female-to-female transmission of HIV is theoretically possible through exposure to cervical and vaginal secretions of an HIV-infected woman, following safer sex guidelines is recommended. Lesbians and bisexual women are most at risk for HIV if they have sex with men who have been exposed to HIV or if they share needles to inject drugs.

10.9 Heterosexism, Homonegativity, and Homophobia

Attitudes toward same-sex sexual behavior and relationships vary across cultures and across historical time periods. Today, most countries throughout the world, including the United States, are predominantly heterosexist. **Heterosexism** is the belief, stated or implied, that heterosexuality is superior (e.g., morally, socially, emotionally, and behaviorally) to homosexuality. It involves the systematic degradation and stigmatization of any nonheterosexual form of behavior, identity, or relationship. Heterosexism involves the belief that heterosexuality is superior to homosexuality and results in prejudice and discrimination against homosexuals and bisexuals. Heterosexism assumes that all people are or should be heterosexual. Heterosexism is so pervasive that public space is controlled and heterosexualized in the sense that most tourism choices are assumed to be heterosexual. Indeed, gay individuals going on vacation often look for specific "gay friendly" towns (e.g., Key West, San Francisco), tourist spots, and bed & breakfast establishments.

Gilla and colleagues (2010) found evidence that gays are subjected to negative comments and name calling in contexts such as physical education classes or physical activities where they are perceived to be small or gay. The fact that the "don't ask, don't tell" policy of the military changed, and then changed again in 2010, implies that being gay is "bad and we don't want to hear about it." (Both the president and military brass supported the repeal.) Before reading further, you may wish to complete the Self-Assessment 10-1: Sexual Prejudice Scale.

Heterosexism
Belief, stated or implied, that heterosexuality is superior (e.g., morally, socially, emotionally, and behaviorally) to homosexuality

SELF-ASSESSMENT 10-1: SEXUAL PREJUDICE SCALE

Directions:

The items below provide a way to assess one's level of prejudice toward gay men and lesbians. For each item, identify a number from 1 to 6 that reflects your level of agreement, and write the number in the space provided.

1 = strongly disagree
2 = disagree
3 = mildly disagree
4 = mildly agree
5 = agree
6 = strongly agree

Gay Men Scale

1.   ___ You can tell a man is gay by the way he walks.
2.   ___ I think it's gross when I see two men who are clearly "together."
3.* ___ Retirement benefits should include the partners of gay men.
4.   ___ Most gay men are flamboyant.
5.   ___ It's wrong for men to have sex with men.
6.* ___ Family medical leave rules should include the domestic partners of gay men.
7.   ___ Most gay men are promiscuous.
8.   ___ Marriage between two men should be kept illegal.
9.* ___ Health care benefits should include partners of gay male employees.
10. ___ Most gay men have HIV/AIDS.
11. ___ Gay men are immoral.
12.* ___ Hospitals should allow gay men to be involved in their partners' medical care.
13. ___ A sexual relationship between two men is unnatural.
14. ___ Most gay men like to have anonymous sex with men in public places.
15.* ___ There's nothing wrong with being a gay man.

Scoring:

*Reverse score items 3, 6, 9, 12, and 15. For example, if you selected a 6, replace the 6 with a 1. If you selected a 1, replace it with a 6, etc. Add each score of the 15 items. The lowest possible score is 15, suggesting a very low level of prejudice against gay men; the highest possible score is 90, suggesting a very high level of prejudice against gay men. The midpoint between 15 and 90 is 52. Scores lower than 52 reflect less prejudice against gay men, while scores higher than this reflect more prejudice against gay men.

Participants:

Both undergraduate and graduate students enrolled in social work courses comprised a convenience sample ($N=851$). The sample was predominantly women (83.1%), white (65.9%), heterosexual (89.8%), single (81.3%), non-parenting (81.1%), 25 years of age or under (69.3%), and majoring in social work (80.8%).

Results:

The range of scores for the gay men scale was 15 to 84. The M = 31.53, SD = 15.30. The sample had relatively low levels of prejudice against gay men.

Lesbian Scale

1. ___ Most lesbians don't wear make-up.
2. ___ Lesbians are harming the traditional family.
3.* ___ Lesbians should have the same civil rights as straight women.
4. ___ Most lesbians prefer to dress like men.
5.* ___ Being a lesbian is a normal expression of sexuality.
6. ___ Lesbians want too many rights.
7. ___ Most lesbians are more masculine than straight women.
8. ___ It's morally wrong to be a lesbian.
9.* ___ Employers should provide retirement benefits for lesbian partners.
10. ___ Most lesbians look like men.
11. ___ I disapprove of lesbians.
12.* ___ Marriage between two women should be legal.
13. ___ Lesbians are confused about their sexuality.
14. ___ Most lesbians don't like men.
15.* ___ Employers should provide health care benefits to the partners of their lesbian employees.

Scoring:

*Reverse score items 3, 5, 9, 12 and 15. For example, if you selected a 6, replace the 6 with a 1. If you selected a 1, replace it with a 6, etc. Add each score of the 15 items. The lowest possible score is 15, suggesting a very low level of prejudice against lesbians; the highest possible score is 90, suggesting a very high level of prejudice against lesbians. The midpoint between 15 and 90 is 52. Scores lower than 52 would reflect less prejudice against lesbians, while scores higher than this would reflect more prejudice against lesbians.

Participants:

Both undergraduate and graduate students enrolled in social work courses comprised a convenience sample (N =851). The sample was predominantly women (83.1%), white (65.9%), heterosexual (89.8%), single (81.3%), non-parenting (81.1%), 25 years of age or under (69.3%), and majoring in social work (80.8%).

Results:

The range of the scores for the lesbian scale was 15 to 86. M = 30.41, SD = 15.60. The sample had relatively low levels of prejudice against lesbians.

Scale is used with the permission of Jill Chonody, School of Psychology, Social Work and Public Policy. University of South Australia, Magill, South Australia, Australia jill.chonody@unisa.edu.au. The scale is used with the permission of the *Journal of Homosexuality*.

Adolfsen and colleagues (2010) noted that there are multiple dimensions to attitudes about homosexuality and identified five:

1. *General attitude*   Is homosexuality considered to be normal or abnormal? Do people think that homosexuals should be allowed to live their lives just as freely as heterosexuals?

2. *Equal rights*   Should homosexuals be granted the same rights as heterosexuals in regard to marriage and adoption?

3. *Close quarters*   Feelings in regard to having a gay neighbor or a lesbian colleague

4. *Public display*   Reactions to a gay couple kissing in public

5. *Modern homonegativity*   Feeling that homosexuality is accepted in society and that various special attention are unnecessary

10.9a Homonegativity and Homophobia

The term **homophobia** is commonly used to refer to negative attitudes and emotions toward homosexuality and those who engage in homosexual behavior. Persons who have had little contact with gays, who are male, and who believe that homosexuality is a choice are most likely to have negative attitudes towards homosexuals (Chonody, 2013). Other factors associated with intolerance toward lesbians and gays include Christian religious values, being a first-year college student, and selecting a major other than in College of Arts and Sciences (Holland, Matthews, & Schott, 2012). Gay and lesbian college students looking to find support might assess the existence of an LGBT student organization on campus (Kane, 2013).

Do not follow where the path may lead. Go, instead, where there is no path and leave a trail.

Ralph Waldo Emerson, American poet

Homophobia is not necessarily a clinical phobia (that is, one involving a compelling desire to avoid the feared object despite recognizing that the fear is unreasonable). Other terms that refer to negative attitudes and emotions toward homosexuality include **homonegativity** (attaching negative connotations to being gay) and antigay bias. Dysart-Gale (2010) noted that these prejudicial negative attitudes exert a negative impact.

Cultural Diversity

Fifteen countries have legalized same sex marriage: Argentina, Belgium, Brazil, Canada, Denmark, France, Iceland, The Netherlands, New Zealand, Norway, Portugal, South Africa, Spain, Sweden, and Uruguay.

Homophobia
Negative emotional responses toward, and aversion to, homosexuals

Homonegativity
Construct that refers to antigay responses including negative feelings (fear, disgust, anger), thoughts, and behavior

The Sex Information and Education Council of the United States notes that "individuals have the right to accept, acknowledge, and live in accordance with their sexual orientation, be they bisexual, heterosexual, gay or lesbian. The legal system should guarantee the civil rights and protection of all people, regardless of sexual orientation" (SIECUS, 2013). Nevertheless, negative attitudes toward homosexuality continue (Rutledge, Siebert, & Chonody, 2012).

Characteristics associated with positive attitudes toward homosexuals and gay rights include younger age, advanced education, no religious affiliation, liberal political party affiliation, and personal contact with homosexual individuals (Lee & Hicks, 2011). In one study, heterosexual women who kissed other women had more positive attitudes toward homosexuality (Beaver, Knox, & Kiskute, 2010).

> *I know what it feels like to try to blend in so that everybody will think that you are OK and they won't hurt you.*
>
> Ellen DeGeneres, comedian

There are several sources for homonegativity and homophobia in the United States:

1. *Religion* Although some religious groups (such as the Quakers) accept homosexuality, many religions teach that homosexuality is sinful and prohibited by God. "God made Adam and Eve, not Adam and Steve" is a phrase commonly cited by individuals whose homophobia is rooted in religion. The Roman Catholic Church rejects all homosexual expression (just as it rejects all sex outside marriage) and resists any attempt to validate or sanction the homosexual orientation. The Catholic Church regards homosexuality as a "disorder," a "condition." Homosexuality is not sinful; same-sex sexual behavior is the culprit, and gay Catholics are encouraged to be abstinent. Some fundamentalist churches regard AIDS as God's punishment for homosexuality.

   On the other hand, some religious organizations are very accepting of gay relationships. In the Episcopal Church, delegates to the 2003 General Convention confirmed the consecration of Bishop Gene Robinson as bishop of New Hampshire. He is in a long-term, committed relationship with another man.

2. *Marital and procreative bias* Many societies have traditionally condoned sex only when it occurs in a marital context that provides for the possibility of reproducing and rearing children. Sixteen states have now legalized same-sex marriage: Connecticut, Delaware, Iowa, Maine, Maryland, Minnesota, New Hampshire, New York, Rhode Island, Vermont, Washington, New Jersey, California, Maine, Illinois, Hawaii, and the District of Columbia. Other states are still debating the issue (see Social Choices 10-1).

3. *Concern about HIV and AIDS* Although most cases of HIV and AIDS worldwide are attributed to heterosexual transmission, the rates of HIV and AIDS in the United States are much higher among gay and bisexual men than among other groups. Because of this, many people in the United States associate HIV and AIDS with homosexuality and bisexuality. Lesbians, incidentally, have a very low risk for sexually transmitted HIV—a lower risk than heterosexual women.

4. *Rigid gender roles* Antigay sentiments also stem from rigid gender roles. Lesbians are perceived as "stepping out of line" by relinquishing traditional female sexual and economic dependence on men. Both gay men and lesbians are often viewed as betrayers of their gender who must be punished.

5. *Psychiatric labeling* Prior to 1973, the American Psychiatric Association defined homosexuality as a mental disorder. When the third edition of the *Diagnostic and Statistical Manual of Mental Disorders*, or *DSM-III* (1980), was published, homosexuality was no longer included as a disorder. Hence, homosexuality

itself is not regarded as a psychiatric disorder, but persistent and marked distress over being homosexual is a concern that warrants the label.

6. *Myths and negative stereotypes*   Homonegativity may also stem from some of the unsupported beliefs and negative stereotypes regarding homosexuality. For example, many people believe that gays are child molesters, even though the ratio of heterosexual to homosexual child molesters is approximately 11:1 (Moser, 1992). Further, lesbians are stereotyped as women who want to be (or at least look and act like) men, whereas gay men are stereotyped as men who want to be (or at least look and act like) women. In reality, the gay population is as diverse as the heterosexual population, not only in appearance, but also in social class, educational achievement, occupational status, race, ethnicity, and personality.

> *I've just concluded that for me personally it is important for me to go ahead and affirm that I think same-sex couples should be able to get married.*
>
> Barack Obama

Same-Sex Marriage

By a 5–4 decision, the Supreme Court declared DOMA (The Defense of Marriage Act) unconstitutional on equal protection grounds, thus giving same-sex married couples federal recognition and benefits (Wolf & Heath, 2013). Over half (51%) of U.S. adults favor same sex marriage. Almost three quarters (72%) of 1,504 adults in a Pew Research Center survey say that legal same sex marriage is "inevitable." This percentage includes 85% of gay marriage supporters, as well as 59% of its opponents (Pew Research Center, 2013). Hence, even those against gay marriage feel that it will be a legal option for gay couples. In 2013, with the Supreme Court ruling, 800,000 legally married same-sex couples were no longer denied access to federal marriage benefits.

As of November 2013, 16 states (identified in the previous section) offered civil marriage licenses to same-sex couples. Thirty-four states have expressly prohibited same sex marriage by amending their constitution: "marriage between one man and one woman is the only domestic legal union that shall be valid or recognized in this state." Hence, a same sex couple married in one of the 16 states or the District of Columbia is no longer married when they move to one of the states that has not legalized same sex marriage.

With the Supreme Court ruling in 2013, the federal government recognizes same sex marriages (i.e., the survivor of a legal same-sex marriage can collect social security benefits as is true of a spouse in a traditional heterosexual marriage). The **Defense of Marriage Act** (DOMA)—passed in 1996, which states that marriage is a "legal union between one man and one woman" and in effect denies federal recognition of same-sex marriage—is no more.

However, same-sex marriage remains a hotly contested issue in many states, and political candidates are careful about their position in regard to same-sex relationship for fear of losing votes. After Obama announced his support for gay marriage, a quarter (25%) of Americans reported that they felt less favorable toward Obama because of this, while 19% felt more favorably toward him (Pew Research Center, 2012a).

Arguments in Favor of Same-Sex Marriage

A major argument for same-sex marriage is that it would promote relationship stability among gay and lesbian couples. "To the extent that marriage provides status, institutional support, and legitimacy, gay and lesbian couples, if allowed to marry, would likely experience greater relationship stability" (Amato, 2004, p. 963).

Defense of Marriage Act

Legislative act that denied federal recognition of homosexual marriage and allowed states to ignore same-sex marriages licensed elsewhere

Advocates of same-sex marriage argue that banning or refusing to recognize same-sex marriages granted in other states is a violation of civil rights that denies same-sex couples the many legal and financial benefits that are granted to heterosexual married couples. Rights and benefits accorded to married people (and legally married same-sex couples) include the following:

- The right to inherit from a spouse who dies without a will
- The benefit of not paying inheritance taxes upon the death of a spouse
- The right to make crucial medical decisions for a spouse and to take care of a seriously ill spouse or a parent of a spouse under current provisions in the federal Family and Medical Leave Act
- The right to collect Social Security survivor benefits
- The right to receive health insurance coverage under a spouse's insurance plan

Other rights bestowed on married (or once-married) partners include assumption of a spouse's pension, bereavement leave, burial determination, domestic violence protection, reduced-rate memberships, divorce protections (such as equitable division of assets and visitation of partner's children), automatic housing lease transfer, and immunity from testifying against a spouse. As noted earlier, same-sex couples are taxed on employer-provided insurance benefits for domestic partners, whereas married spouses receive those benefits tax-free. Finally, just as 17 other countries recognize same-sex couples for immigration purposes, the United States now recognizes same-sex partners. So if a gay individual travels to another country and falls in love, the new partner is now eligible for sponsorship to become an American citizen in the same way a heterosexual who falls in love can move to America.

Positive outcomes for being married as a gay couple have been documented. Ducharme and Kollar (2012) evaluated a sample of 225 lesbian married couples in Massachusetts who reported physical, psychological, and financial well-being in their relationships. The researchers noted that these data support the finding in the heterosexual marriage literature that healthy marriage is associated with distinct wellbeing benefits for lesbian couples. Wright and colleagues (2013) found that same-sex married lesbian, gay, and bisexual persons were significantly less distressed than lesbian, gay, and bisexual persons not in a legally recognized relationship. However, Ocobock (2013) studied 32 gay men who were married to same sex partners and found that while the legitimacy of marriage often led to positive family outcomes, it also commonly had negative consequences, including new and renewed experiences of family rejection. Hence, negative attitudes toward gay marriage may continue even when the marriage is "legal."

Children of loving parents flourish whether the parents are gay or straight.
Source: Chelsea Curry

Children of same sex parents would also benefit from legal recognition of same sex marriage. Children living in gay- and lesbian-headed households are no longer denied a range of securities that protect children of heterosexual married couples. These include the right to get health insurance coverage and Social Security survivor benefits from a nonbiological parent Chonody et al., 2012).

Children of gay parents are thought to be disadvantaged. Lick and colleagues (2013) reported data from 91 adults reared by gay and lesbian parents who reported on their recalled social experiences, as well as current depressive symptoms, positive and negative affect, and life satisfaction. Participants reported no significant differences in long-term psychological adjustment. It could be the case that children of gay and lesbian parents learn to cope with difficult social experiences, leading to positive adjustment overall.

In some cases, children in same-sex households lack the automatic right to continue living with their nonbiological parent should their biological mother or father die (Tobias & Cahill, 2003). It is ironic that the same pro-marriage groups that stress that children are better off in married-couple families disregard the benefits of same-sex marriage to children.

Finally, there are religion-based arguments in support of same-sex marriage. Although many religious leaders teach that homosexuality is sinful and prohibited by God, some religious groups, such as the Quakers and the United Church of Christ (UCC), accept homosexuality; and other groups have made reforms toward increased acceptance of lesbians and gays.

Arguments Against Same-Sex Marriage

The primary reason for disapproval of same sex marriage is morality. Gay marriage is viewed as "immoral, a sin, against the Bible." Opponents of same-sex marriage who view homosexuality as unnatural, sick, and/or immoral do not want their children to view homosexuality as socially acceptable.

Opponents of gay marriage also suggest that gay marriage leads to declining marriage rates, increased divorce rates, and increased nonmarital births. However, data in Scandinavia reflect that these trends were occurring 10 years before Scandinavia adopted registered same-sex partnership laws, liberalized alternatives to marriage (such as cohabitation), and expanded exit options such as no-fault divorce (Pinello, 2008).

Opponents of same-sex marriage commonly argue that such marriages would subvert the stability and integrity of the heterosexual family. However, Sullivan (1997) suggests that homosexuals are already part of heterosexual families:

> [Homosexuals] are sons and daughters, brothers and sisters, even mothers and fathers, of heterosexuals. The distinction between "families" and "homosexuals" is, to begin with, empirically false; and the stability of existing families is closely linked to how homosexuals are treated within them. (p. 147)

In previous years, opponents of gay marriage have pointed to public opinion polls that suggested that the majority of Americans are against same-sex marriage. However, public opposition to same-sex marriage is decreasing. A 2012 Pew Research Center national poll found that 43% of U.S. adults oppose legalizing gay marriage, down from 51% in 2008 (Pew Research Center, 2012a).

10.9b Discrimination Against Homosexuals

Behavioral homonegativity involves **discrimination**, or behavior that involves treating categories of individuals unequally. Discrimination against lesbians and gays can occur at the individual level. The most severe form of behavioral homonegativity is antigay violence, in which gay men and lesbians are physically attacked, injured, tortured, and even killed because of their sexual orientation. Matthew Shepard was a 21-year-old gay college student at the University of Wyoming who was murdered by two assailants. Shepard's death has drawn attention to hate crimes and the harm caused by prejudice. His mother created the Matthew Shepard Foundation, which supports educational projects that increase awareness of issues involving discrimination and diversity.

The consequences of homophobia may not be death but poor mental health, instead. Kerr and colleagues (2013) investigated selected mental health characteristics of lesbians and bisexual undergraduate college women as compared with heterosexual college women. Results revealed that bisexual women reported the worst mental health in terms of anxiety, anger, depressive symptoms, self-injury, and suicidal ideation and attempts. Both bisexual women and lesbians had a far greater likelihood of having these mental health issues when compared with heterosexual women.

Further evidence is from Hequembourg and Dearing (2013) who analyzed data on 389 gay, lesbian, and bisexuals and found a tendency toward their feeling shame and guilt as well as abusing drugs as a function of internalizing heterosexism. Hence, a relentless sea of disapproval surrounds these individuals for who they are and what they do; it is not unexpected that there would be negative psychological outcomes.

Discrimination
Behavior that involves treating categories of individuals unequally

Take a moment to answer the following question. Judges are given enormous latitude to rule against homosexual parents. The first author of this text served as an expert witness in a trial whereby a lesbian mother petitioned the court for custody of her children in a divorce from her husband. She was denied custody. The lawyer defending the lesbian mother said, "No judge in this town can keep his job if he gives a child to a gay parent." What is the political climate in your area for supporting the rights of gay individuals to rear children?

10.9c Biphobia

Just as the term *homophobia* is used to refer to negative attitudes and emotional responses and discriminatory behavior toward gay men and lesbians, **biphobia** refers to similar reactions and discrimination toward bisexuals. Eliason (2001) noted that bisexual men are viewed more negatively than bisexual women, gay men, or lesbians. Bisexuals are thought to be really homosexuals afraid to acknowledge their real identity or homosexuals maintaining heterosexual relationships to avoid rejection by the heterosexual mainstream. In addition, bisexual individuals are sometimes viewed as heterosexuals who are looking for exotic sexual experiences. Bisexuals may experience double discrimination in that neither the heterosexual nor homosexual community accepts them.

Gay women seem to exhibit greater levels of biphobia than do gay men. The reason is that many lesbian women associate their identity with a political stance against sexism and patriarchy. Some lesbians view heterosexual and bisexual women who "sleep with the enemy" as traitors to the feminist movement.

10.10 How Heterosexuals Are Affected by Homophobia

The antigay and heterosexist social climate of our society is often viewed in terms of how it victimizes the gay population. However, heterosexuals are also victimized by heterosexism and antigay prejudice and discrimination. Some of these effects follow:

1. *Heterosexual victims of hate crimes*   Extreme homophobia contributes to instances of violence against homosexuals—acts known as **hate crimes**. Such crimes include verbal harassment (the most frequent form of hate crime experienced by victims), vandalism, sexual assault and rape, physical assault, and murder. Hate crimes also target transsexuals (more so than gay individuals).

   Because hate crimes are crimes of perception, victims may not be homosexual; they may just be perceived as being homosexual. The National Coalition of Anti-Violence Programs (2012) reported that, in 2011, heterosexual individuals in the United States were victims of antigay hate crimes, representing 15% of all antigay hate crime victims.

2. *Concern, fear, and grief over well-being of gay or lesbian family members and friends*   Many heterosexual family members and friends of homosexual people experience concern, fear, and grief over the mistreatment of their gay or lesbian friends and/or family members. In 2011, there were 30 murders

Biphobia
Fearful, negative, discriminatory reactions toward bisexuals

Hate crimes
Bringing harm to an individual because he or she is viewed as belonging to a group of which one does not approve

of LGBTQH, or lesbian, gay, bisexual, transgender, queer, HIV-infected, individuals (National Coalition of Anti-Violence Programs, 2012). Heterosexual parents who have a gay or lesbian teenager often worry about how the harassment, ridicule, rejection, and violence experienced at school might affect their gay or lesbian child. Will their child be traumatized, make bad grades, and/or drop out of school to escape the harassment, violence, and alienation they endure there? Will the gay or lesbian child respond to the antigay victimization by turning to drugs or alcohol or by committing suicide, as there is an increased risk in this population (van Bergen, Bos, Lisdonk, Keuzenkamp, & Sandfort, 2013)? Higher rates of anxiety, depression, and panic attacks are associated with being gay (Oswalt & Wyatt, 2011). Four gay teens (Billy Lucas, Tyler Clementi, Asher Brown, and Seth Walsh) committed suicide in 2010 in response to being bullied about their sexuality. The suicides generated media attention and started an online video campaign called the "It Gets Better Project" (http://www.itgetsbetter.org/).

Prejudice and discrimination toward gays and lesbians also have negative outcomes in other countries. Canadian data confirm that gay men and women report higher incidences of mood disorders than heterosexuals. Among adult respondents in a national study, respondents who identified as LGB, 17.1% self-reported having a current mood disorder while 6.9% of heterosexuals reported having a current mood disorder (Pakula & Shoveller, 2013).

To heterosexuals who have lesbian and gay family members and friends, lack of family protections such as health insurance and rights of survivorship for same-sex couples can also be cause for concern. Finally, heterosexuals live with the painful awareness that their gay or lesbian family member or friend is a potential victim of antigay hate crime. Jamie Nabozny was a gay high school student in Ashland, Wisconsin, who was subjected to relentless harassment and abuse over a 4-year period. He attempted suicide and dropped out of school. With his parents' help he sued the school, lost, and appealed in federal court. The school administration was held liable for his mistreatment, and the case was settled for close to a million dollars (see the documentary *Bullied*).

3. *Restriction of intimacy and self-expression*   Because of the antigay social climate, heterosexual individuals—especially males are hindered in their own self-expression and intimacy in same-sex relationships. Males must be careful about how they hug each other so as not to appear gay. Homophobic scripts also frighten youth who do not conform to gender role expectations, leading some youth to avoid activities—such as arts for boys, athletics for girls—and professions such as elementary education for males. A male student in the authors' class revealed that he always wanted to work with young children and had majored in early childhood education. His peers

teased him relentlessly about his choice of majors, questioning both his masculinity and his heterosexuality. Eventually, this student changed his major to psychology, which his peers viewed as an acceptable major for a heterosexual male.

4. *Dysfunctional sexual behavior*   Some cases of rape and sexual assault are related to homophobia and compulsory heterosexuality. For example, college men who participate in gang rape, also known as "pulling train," entice each other into the act "by implying that those who do not participate are unmanly or homosexual" (Sanday, 1995, p. 399). Homonegativity also encourages early sexual activity among adolescent men. Adolescent male virgins are often teased by their male peers: "You mean you don't do it with girls yet? What are you, a fag or something?" Not wanting to be labeled and stigmatized as a "fag," some adolescent boys "prove" their heterosexuality by having sex with girls.

5. *School shootings*   Antigay harassment has also been a factor in many of the school shootings in recent years. For example, 15-year-old Charles Andrew Williams fired more than 30 rounds in a San Diego, California, suburban high school, killing 2 and injuring 13 others. A woman who knew Williams reported that the students had teased him and called him gay.

6. *Loss of rights for individuals in unmarried relationships*   The passage of state constitutional amendments that prohibit same-sex marriage can also result in denial of rights and protections to opposite-sex unmarried couples. For example, Judge Stuart Friedman of Cuyahoga County (Ohio) agreed that a man who was charged with assaulting his girlfriend could not be charged with a domestic violence felony because the Ohio state constitutional amendment granted no such protections to unmarried couples. Some antigay marriage measures also threaten the provision of domestic partnership benefits to unmarried heterosexual couples.

BVT *Lab*

Visit **www.BVTLab.com** to explore the student resources available for this chapter.

Chapter Summary

Gay, lesbian, and bisexual individuals and their concerns are receiving increased visibility in our society. This chapter defined terms, models, prevalence, relationships, and homonegativity/homophobia.

Terms of Sexual Orientation

Sexual orientation refers to the classification of individuals as heterosexual, bisexual, or homosexual based on their emotional and sexual attractions, relationships, self-identity, and lifestyle. Heterosexuality refers to the predominance of emotional and sexual attraction to persons of the other sex; homosexuality, to persons of the same sex; bisexuality, to both sexes. Transgendered individual do not fit neatly into either the male or female category, or their behavior is not congruent with the norms and expectations of their sex in the society in which they live. Examples of transgendered individuals include homosexuals, bisexuals, cross-dressers, and transsexuals. LGBT is a term that has emerged to refer collectively to lesbians, gays, bisexuals, and transgendered individuals.

Conceptual Models of Sexual Orientation

The three models of sexual orientation are the dichotomous model (people are either heterosexual or homosexual); the unidimensional continuum model (sexual orientation is viewed on a continuum from heterosexuality to homosexuality); and the multidimensional model (sexuality involves the factors of emotions, behaviors, and cognitions).

Prevalence of Homosexuality, Heterosexuality, and Bisexuality

The prevalence of homosexuality, heterosexuality, and bisexuality is difficult to determine. This is due to fear of social disapproval and changing sexual attractions, behaviors, and identities over time. Of adults in the U.S., about 1% of females self identify as lesbian, 2% of males self identify as gay, and 1.5% of adults self-identify as bisexual. Hence, about 3.5% or about 10 million individuals in the U.S. are LGB.

Theories of Sexual Orientation

Basic theories of sexual orientation are biological (genetic, chromosomal, hormonal) and social/cultural (parent-child interactions, early sexual experiences). Most researchers agree that an interaction of biological and social/cultural forces is involved in the development of one's sexual orientation.

Gay and Bisexual Identity Development

The development of a gay or bisexual identity often involves four stages: awareness or realization that one is "different," test and exploration, identity acceptance, and identity integration.

Two percent of U.S. adults report that there has been a change in their sexual orientation. Conversion therapy is focused on changing homosexuals' sexual orientation. It is rare that such therapy "works." Even changes toward heterosexuality are short term and occur under conditions of strong religious influence; one's yearning for same sex contact does not disappear. It is society's attitude toward homosexuality that is seen as the problem, in many cases, not same-sex orientation itself." or something similar.

Coming Out

"Coming out" refers to the recognition of a homosexual or bisexual orientation to one's self, parents, siblings, heterosexual partner or spouse and children, friends, and employers. The reactions are unpredictable. Coming out is especially difficult for bisexuals because both heterosexuals and homosexuals may reject them. Most gays who come out report positive consequences for doing so.

Homosexual and Bisexual Relationships

Homosexual, bisexual, and heterosexual relationships are more similar than different. However, unlike heterosexual couples (who receive social support for long-term relationships), same-sex couples receive little social support. The literature on lesbian and gay couples reveals that the factors associated with relationship satisfaction are the same for all couples regardless of sexual orientation.

Gay male relationships are stereotyped as short-term and lacking closeness and intimacy. In reality, most gay men prefer long-term, close relationships. Lesbians value monogamous, emotionally and sexually satisfying relationships. Some bisexuals prefer monogamous relationships; others prefer "open" relationships that permit emotional and sexual involvement with more than one partner.

Sexual Orientation and HIV Infection

Most HIV infection occurs worldwide through heterosexual transmission and in the United States through male-to-male transmission. Women who have sex exclusively with other women have a much lower rate of HIV infection than men (both gay and "straight") and women who have sex with men. However, lesbians and bisexual women may also be at risk for HIV if they have sex with high-risk male partners (bisexuals) and inject drugs.

Heterosexism, Homonegativity, and Homophobia

Heterosexism is the belief that heterosexuality is superior (e.g., morally, socially, emotionally, and behaviorally) to homosexuality and involves the systematic degradation and stigmatization of any nonheterosexual form of behavior, identity, or relationship. Homonegativity includes negative feelings (fear, disgust, anger); thoughts (homosexuals are HIV carriers); and behavior (homosexuals deserve a beating). Homophobia refers to emotional responses toward and aversion to homosexuals. Homophobia may be cultural (stereotypes include that lesbian/gay individuals are inherently bad, evil, immoral, abnormal, perverted, unhealthy, dangerous, sick, contagious, and/or predatory); social (dread that one will be perceived by others as gay); or psychological (irrational fear of lesbian/gay individuals and phobic reaction to them).

How Heterosexuals Are Affected by Homophobia

Heterosexuals *hhh* affected by how homosexuals are treated. For example, hate crimes directed toward gays may hurt heterosexuals. Beating up gays because they are seen as "helpless fags" may also include gentle heterosexuals who are perceived as gay. The National Coalition of Anti-Violence Programs reported that heterosexual individuals in the United States were victims of antigay hate crimes, representing 15% of all antigay hate crime victims.

Family and friends of homosexual people experience concern, fear, and grief over the mistreatment of their gay or lesbian friends and/or family members. In 2011, there were 30 murders of lesbian, gay, bisexual, transgender, queer, and HIV-infected individuals (LGBTQH). These individuals have parents and friends who love them and fear for their safety because they are gay. Higher rates of anxiety, depression, and panic attacks are associated with being gay.

Web Links

Human Rights Campaign

http://www.hrc.org

Lesbian and Gay Community Centers

http://www.gaycenter.org

Matthew Shepard Foundation

http://www.matthewshepard.org

Parents, Families, and Friends of Lesbians and Gays

http://www.pflag.org

Key Terms

Biphobia   283

Bisexuality   260

Coming out   268

Conversion therapy   267

Defense of Marriage Act   280

Dichotomous model   261

Discrimination   282

Hate crimes   283

Heterosexism   275

Heterosexuality   260

Homonegativity   278

Homophobia   278

Homosexuality   260

LGBT   260

Multidimensional model   262

Sexual fluidity   262

Sexual orientation   260

Transgender   260

Transgendered individuals   260

Unidimensional continuum
   model   261

Additional study resources are available at www.BVTLab.com

CHAPTER 11

Illness, Disability, Drugs, and Sexuality

It is normal and natural for every person with a body to express their sexuality regardless of their handicap condition or functional ability level.

Rebecca Koller, University of Utah

Chapter Outline

Objectives

1. Identify the effects of illness and disability on one's self-concept/body image.
2. Understand the effects of impaired sensory-motor function on sexuality.
3. Discuss the impact of diabetes on sexuality.
4. Review the effects of impaired cognitive function on sexuality.
5. Explain the effects of mental illness on sexuality.
6. Learn how pain and fatigue impact sexuality.
7. Know the effect of various medical treatments on sexuality.
8. Identify how alcohol and other drugs impact sexuality.

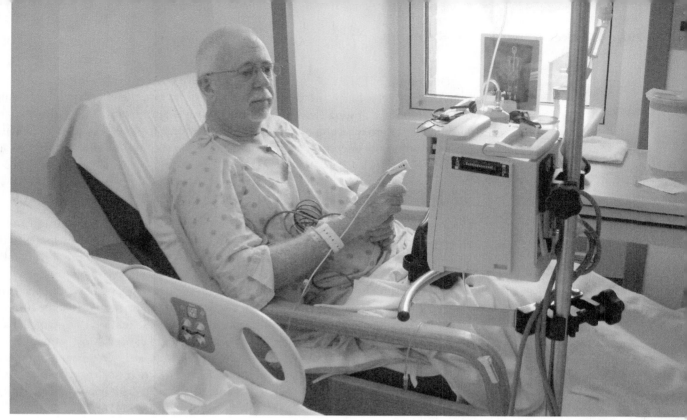

Source: E. Fred Johnson Jr.

TRUTH OR FICTION?

T/F   Less than 10% of over 810 students reported that they would date or marry a person in a wheelchair.

T/F   Antidepressant medications are widely recognized as affecting sexual desire and arousal.

T/F   Intellectually disabled women think of sex in very positive terms.

T/F   Persons with a stoma view it as an irrelevant inconvenience since they are happy to be alive.

T/F   Marijuana has now surpassed alcohol as the most frequently used drug in college.

Answers: 1.F 2.T 3.F 4.F 5.F

*T*he movie *The Sessions* (on DVD in 2013) gave renewed cultural visibility to the fact that the disabled have sexual needs. The plot featured a virgin male in an iron lung who hired a sex surrogate to talk, touch, and have sex with him. The number of adults with a **disability** (health condition that involves functional deficits in performing activities of daily living) is staggering.

Disability
Health condition that involves functional deficits in performing activities of daily living

National DATA

Thirty-three million adults (18 years and over) have a chronic disability (*Statistical Abstract of the United States,* 2012–2013, Table 191).

One need not have a physical disability to have one's sexuality impaired. Having a physical illness is likely and common for most of us, and the effect on our sexuality can be temporary or long term. In this chapter we examine how illness, disease, and disability interfere with the quality of life in relationships and sexuality. We include information on the effects of alcohol and drugs on sexuality.

11.1 Illness, Disability, and Effect on Sexuality

The disabled are assumed to be asexual—to have no interest in sexual expression and no capacity for experiencing physical pleasure and intimacy. This belief contributes to the fact that physicians and healthcare professionals ignore the sexuality of the ill or disabled. In a study of 137 females with multiple sclerosis, only 2% reported that they had ever discussed sexual concerns with a physician (Lew-Starowicz & Rola, 2013). Furthermore, some illnesses have a dramatic impact on the patient's sexuality. Demirgoz Bal and colleagues (2013) interviewed women with gynecologic cancer. Most women noted severe decreases in sexual desire, arousal, the frequency of intercourse, and orgasm; yet they felt they could not talk about these issues with their healthcare professional. Sexuality is vital in regard to "quality of life, self-esteem, self image and quality of interpersonal relationships". (Lew-Starowicz & Rola, 2013, p. 141)

> *It is only when the rich are sick that they fully feel the impotence of wealth.*
>
> Benjamin Franklin

11.2 Effects of Illness and Disability on Self-Concept/Body Image

In general, persons with chronic illness or disability are vulnerable to developing a negative self-concept and body image, and view themselves as undesirable or inadequate romantic and sexual partners. The paraplegic in *The Sessions* was fearful that no female would be willing to touch him, let alone have sex with him. All too often, individuals with disabilities internalize negative social attitudes, which lead them to retreat from intimate relations and adopt a nonsexual lifestyle.

Persons with disabilities or disease may also view themselves as physically flawed and sexually unattractive. Erbil (2013) analyzed data on 193 women and revealed that positive body image was related to their sexual functioning. Their Body Mass Index scores were negatively correlated with their body image. The more weight on the women, the less positively they viewed their bodies.

This person has had several love relationships, including marriage, since his spinal cord injury.
Source: David Knox

> *It is a waste of time to be angry about my disability. One has to get on with life, and I haven't done badly. People won't have time for you if you are always angry or complaining.*
>
> Stephen Hawking

personal choices   11-1

Would You Date/Marry a Person in a Wheelchair?

Access to public places has become law for those in wheelchairs with the result of increasing their numbers and visibility. It is common for individuals in wheelchairs to be seen on campus or in one's class. Because of stigma and stereotypes, the able bodied may be reluctant to engage the person in a wheelchair. Do I speak to the person? Would I date the person? Would marriage be an option?

A team of researchers (Marini, Wang, Etzbach, & Del Castillo, 2013) surveyed 810 undergraduates regarding their interest in being friends with, dating, or marrying a wheelchair user. Almost two-thirds (66%) reported that they would have no problem dating or marrying a wheelchair user. Those having the personal traits of intelligence, humor, kindness, and pleasing physical appearance were rated most highly as potential dates/marriage partners. Students who were unwilling to date or marry an individual in a wheelchair noted that they feared the partner would require too much caregiving, would not be able to perform sexually, or would be sick too often.

Think About It

Take a moment to answer the following question. Illness and disability can also enhance one's self-concept. For example, some childhood cancer survivors feel stronger and more confident as a result of surviving cancer. What are some other ways in which illness and/or disability might enhance one's self-concept?

11.3 Impaired Sensory-Motor Function and Sexuality

A number of neurological diseases and injuries can result in impaired sensory-motor functioning, including spinal cord injury. The effects of sensory-motor impairment on sexuality are varied and depend, in part, on the type and severity of the illness or injury.

11.3a Spinal Cord Injury

The effect of spinal cord injury on sexual functioning depends on the level of injury and whether it is "complete" or "incomplete." A complete injury means that there is no function below the level of the injury, no sensation, and no voluntary movement. An incomplete injury means that there is some functioning below the primary level of the injury.

Cervical (neck) injuries usually result in **quadriplegia** paralysis from the neck down. Very high cervical injuries can result in a loss of many involuntary functions including the ability to breathe, necessitating breathing aids such as mechanical ventilators. Injuries at the thoracic level and below result in **paraplegia** paralysis of the lower half of the body.

Parker and Yau (2012) interviewed four women who revealed the challenges of sustaining themselves as a sexual individuals, despite societal stereotypes of the disabled. Their struggle was to be perceived as a sexual being, not just as a woman with a disability in a wheelchair. Two of the women noted:

> You think that because you are in a wheelchair that nobody will want you … You have still got feelings and you still want to experience your sexuality. But they [society and potential romantic partners] don't see you like that, because you are in a wheelchair. Which makes it very hard because you still feel like a woman. (Ms. C)

> When you are trying to meet new people, the reality is they see you in the chair … After a few years I resorted to the fact that I was going to be alone for the rest of my life. (Ms. D)

Nevertheless, the respondents reported that they had "regained their sexual life and positive feelings regarding their sexuality." Peer support, masturbation, use of the Internet to meet new partners, and communication were important in regaining their sexuality.

In persons with spinal cord injury, orgasm may occur by direct stimulation of the genitals, by mentally reassigning sensations that can be felt in other areas of the body to the genitals, and/or by erotic imagery (i.e., fantasizing).

For men with spinal cord injury who are able to achieve erection, intercourse may take place with the partner sitting down on the erect penis. If erection is not achieved, some couples use the "stuffing technique," in which partners push the soft penis into the woman's vagina, which she then contracts to hold the penis inside her. For some men with spinal cord injury, sildenafil citrate (Viagra) or an inflatable penile prosthesis implant can be helpful in achieving erection. Up Close 11-1 reveals the experience of a man with a a spinal cord injury (car accident) and the effect on his marriage.

Kaiser and colleagues (2013) interviewed parents with spinal cord injury and noted that while they could still have children, they were not immune to the stress and sexual dysfunctions that sometimes accompanies SCI. Hence, SCI involves enormous challenges, which are often overcome with support, patience and perseverance.

Quadriplegia
Paralysis from the neck down

Paraplegia
Paralysis of the lower half of the body

Close 11-1

Effect of Spinal Cord Injury on Marriage and Sexuality

I was a happily married 25-year-old man with two children. I was in a car accident that left me paralyzed from the waist down and partially paralyzed from the waist up. I had a terrible time adjusting to the fact that I was in a wheelchair. Plus, the accident messed up my marriage completely. My wife stayed with me for five years, but only because she felt sorry for me. As soon as I went to a rehabilitation center and began to manage for myself, she left me.

It has been very hard for me to find a woman who doesn't have hang-ups about men in wheelchairs unless they are in one, too. Because I'm not in an environment where there are a lot of disabled people, it has been difficult finding female companionship. The exception has been a nurse I met at the rehabilitation center. We had a great time together. After I left, we stayed in touch for awhile; and then I just stopped hearing from her.

While women don't want me as a permanent companion/partner/husband, they are curious. I find that women try to pick me up in bars. They want to know what sex is like with a guy in a wheelchair. What they like me to do is drive them wild orally, but eventually they want intercourse and that's something I can't do. It is a major problem.

11.3b Multiple Sclerosis and Cerebral Palsy

International DATA

About 2.1 million individuals are affected by multiple sclerosis worldwide (National Multiple Sclerosis Society, 2013).

Multiple sclerosis (MS) is a progressive disease that attacks the central nervous system. Onset of MS usually occurs between the ages of 20 and 40, and the incidence of MS is two to three times higher in women than men (Sahay, Haynes, Rao, & Pirko, 2012). Symptoms of MS, which vary from person to person, may include lack of muscle coordination; weakness and fatigue; tremors; spasms; stiffness; slurred speech; bladder and bowel dysfunction; impaired genital sensation; pain (stabbing pain in the face or down the spine, burning, aching, cramping, or "pins and needles" sensation); numbness in the face, body, or extremities; and cognitive impairment. Sahay and colleagues (2012) reported bladder (38%) and bowel (48%) problems in a sample of 144 MS females.

Sexual dysfunction is common among women and men with MS, and may involve reduced genital sensation, genital pain, vaginal dryness, loss of libido, erection problems, difficulty or inability to ejaculate, and difficulty reaching orgasm. Because of the progressive nature of the disease, symptoms of sexual dysfunction in women and men with MS tend to increase in severity and number over time. However, individuals with MS and their partners can improve marital and sexual satisfaction through counseling, communication about sexual issues with healthcare providers, and interventions to improve sexual functioning such as sildenafil citrate (Viagra) for men and personal lubricating products for women.

> *One's dignity may be assaulted, vandalized and cruelly mocked, but cannot be taken away unless it is surrendered.*
>
> Michael J. Fox

Multiple sclerosis
Progressive disease that attacks the central nervous system

Cerebral palsy (CP)—a condition caused by brain damage that occurs before or during birth or in infancy also involves symptoms that can interfere with sexual expression. Infancy symptoms that can vary according to the area and degree of brain damage but generally include uncontrollable movement, lack of coordination, spasms, and speech impairment. Problems with sight and hearing may also occur. Cerebral palsy may also result in cognitive impairment (e.g., learning disabilities, intellectual/developmental disabilities).

Adults with CP often require counseling and assistance in achieving sexual satisfaction. For example, one woman with severe spasticity due to cerebral palsy used her mouth to operate a specially designed vibrator that enabled her to reach orgasm (Donnelly, 1997).

11.4 Diabetes and Sexuality

Diabetes mellitus is a chronic disease in which the pancreas fails to produce sufficient insulin, which is necessary for metabolizing carbohydrates and fats. The symptoms—which may be controlled through injections of insulin—include excess sugar in the blood and urine; excessive thirst, hunger, and urination; and weakness. Nearly 6% of the population, or 20.5 million Americans, have diabetes *(Statistical Abstract of the United States*, 2012–2013, Table 196). Most have type 2 diabetes (associated with obesity in later life). Type 2 diabetes is increasing dramatically in the United States and worldwide as populations become more sedentary and obese.

Hintistan and Cilingir (2013) studied the sexuality of 80 men and 80 women who had type 2 diabetes. Of the men, 65% reported male sexual dysfunction (erectile dysfunction); and 68% of the women reported female sexual dysfunction such as lack of sexual desire and orgasmic dysfunction. Psychogenic factors were more operative in women than men. In another study, Kucuk and colleagues (2013) analyzed data on 100 patients with type 2 diabetes (70 women/30 men) and found that over half (53%) reported that the diabetes had affected their sex life adversely. The greater the sexual dissatisfaction, the greater the depression; women were more depressed than men.

11.5 Impaired Cognitive Function and Sexuality

Many illnesses and injuries result in impaired cognitive functioning—such as memory loss, language comprehension problems, learning disabilities, and confusion. Some illnesses and injuries, such multiple sclerosis and cerebral palsy (discussed in the

Cerebral palsy
Condition often caused by brain damage that occurs before or during birth or in infancy, resulting in muscular impairment and sometimes speech and learning disabilities

Diabetes mellitus
Chronic disease in which the pancreas fails to produce sufficient insulin, which is necessary for metabolizing carbohydrates and fats

previous sections), may involve both sensory-motor impairment as well as cognitive impairment. Next, we examine impaired cognitive function and its effects on sexuality more closely, focusing on Alzheimer's disease and other forms of dementia, traumatic brain injury, and intellectual/developmental disabilities.

11.5a Alzheimer's Disease and Other Forms of Dementia

National DATA

In 2013, 5.2 million Americans have Alzheimer's (Alz.org, 2013).

Dementia is a brain disorder involving memory impairment and at least one of the following: **aphasia** (impaired communicative ability); **agnosia** (loss of auditory, sensory, or visual comprehension); **apraxia** (inability to perform coordinated movements); or loss of ability to think abstractly and to plan, initiate, sequence, monitor, and stop complex behavior. Other symptoms of dementia include depression, personality changes, sleep disturbances, psychosis and agitation, and incontinence.

I think I'm getting a little bit of Alzheimer's. Just a little.

Christopher Walken, celebrity

Causes of dementia include stroke, Parkinson's disease, head trauma, brain tumor, infectious disease (HIV and syphilis), and long-term alcohol abuse. The most common cause of dementia, accounting for two-thirds of all dementia cases, is **Alzheimer's disease**—a progressive and degenerative brain disease that typically progresses through stages from mild memory loss, through significant cognitive impairment, to very serious confusion and the loss of ability to manage activities of daily living, such as dressing, eating, and bathing. A person with end-stage Alzheimer's may be incontinent, unable to speak, and unable to walk.

It is not uncommon for persons with dementia to exhibit inappropriate sexual and social behavior, such as uninvited and intrusive touching and inappropriate sexual comments. For example, a hospitalized man diagnosed with Alzheimer's disease asked a female nurse, who was giving him a bath, if she would "jack him off." The nurse simply told him that she was giving him a bath, not performing a sexual service. Joller and colleagues (2013) reviewed the literature on how to manage inappropriate sexual behavior in persons with dementia and found that there is no clear management protocol.

Think About It

Spouses or partners of individuals with Alzheimer's disease face a number of sexual concerns—such as whether to have sex with a partner "who has become a stranger," how to respond when the partner "does not remember we just had sex," and the appropriateness of having an affair to meet one's own sexual needs since the partner is "no longer there." What decisions would you make about our own sexuality if your partner had Alzheimer's and no longer recognized you?

Dourado and colleagues (2010) assessed the sexual behavior of 36 Alzheimer's patients and their spouses. Both patients and spouses reported sexual dissatisfaction. Common causes of sexual dissatisfaction included erectile dysfunction and lack of

Dementia
Brain disorder involving multiple cognitive deficits, including memory impairment and at least one of the following: aphasia, agnosia, apraxia, or loss of ability to think abstractly and to plan, initiate, sequence, monitor, and stop complex behavior

Aphasia
Impaired communicative ability

Agnosia
Loss of auditory, sensory, or visual comprehension

Apraxia
Inability to perform coordinated movements

Alzheimer's disease
Progressive and degenerative brain disease progressing from mild memory loss, through significant cognitive impairment, to very serious confusion and the loss of ability to manage activities of daily living, such as dressing, eating, and bathing

female sexual desire. Men associated sexual dissatisfaction with sadness, and women reported feelings of lack of intimacy and increased anxiety.

11.5b Traumatic Brain Injury

National **DATA**

1.7 million Americans sustain a brain injury annually (Brainline.org, 2013 Brain concussion due to football is a culturally visible topic.

Traumatic brain injury (TBI) is a closed head injury that results from an exterior force and creates a temporary or enduring impairment in brain functioning. The nature of impairment varies according to the severity of the injury and the specific area of the brain that is affected. Brain concussion due to football is a culturally visible topic.

Moreno and colleagues (2013) noted that brain injury can directly and indirectly affect important aspects related to sexuality and sexual function. Following a traumatic brain injury, individuals may experience some type of problem in sexual functioning, such as reduced sexual drive and self-control, decreased erectile ability, inability to become aroused, or the development of new sexual interests (e.g., masochism). They may also experience changes that affect their social interactions: mood swings, depression, social withdrawal, and problems with anger control. Since TBI is most commonly experienced by those ages 15 to 25, those affected are often in a life stage of beginning to form and maintain intimate relationships. (See Up Close 11-2 for how a brain injury affected the sex life of one of our students.)

Traumatic brain injury
Closed head injury that results from an exterior force and creates a temporary or enduring impairment in brain functioning

My Brain Injury Changed My Sex Life

At 18, I was almost killed in a car wreck. I emerged from the wreckage with a traumatic brain injury. Everything changed … my personality, likes, dislikes, and my sex life. Besides the confusion and emotional turmoil, most of the changes were easy to adapt to. The changes in my sex life and what turns me on have been the most surprising.

Even before the wreck, I was atypical in terms of what turned me on—sexual masochism. Pain is what I enjoyed. My clitoris and boobs were insensitive (no pleasure) and I did not like light touching, kissing on my neck (or anywhere else on my body,) making out, or what most people would view as foreplay. I wanted pain—being hit with riding crops, whipped, restrained, choked, scratched, bitten, cut, and burned.

Source: Cherie Buchanan

After the wreck what turned me on was less predictable. I realized I had to start back at square one and figure out what I liked. My boobs and clit were now sensitive and elicited pleasure. I now liked light touch, lingerie outfits, kissing and making out as well as mild to moderate pain, force/dominance, choking, anal … Actually it's safe to say that there isn't much I have found I am opposed to sexually.

The brain injury has led to a much better sex life. I am now dating a guy who finds experimenting in the bedroom just as exciting. Combine all of this with the emotional connection and a wonderful relationship, and this has all led to the best sex I could have ever imagined.

11.5c Intellectual and Developmental Disability

National **DATA**

6.5 million people in the U.S. have an intellectual disability (Nichcy.org, 2013).

Intellectual disability involves subaverage intellectual functioning (with onset prior to age 18) and three functional deficits in adaptive behavior (e.g., needs assistance with bathing). In 2010, President Obama signed Rosa's Law, officially changing the term *mental retardation* to *intellectual disability* or ID. A person's severity of disability can be described as *mild, moderate, severe,* or *profound*. Increasingly, the emphasis in defining intellectual disability is focused on adaptive behavior; individuals are categorized in terms of their need for supportive services (e.g., intermittent, limited, extensive, and pervasive). Opinion is divided on attitudes toward sexuality of the disabled (see Self-Assessment 11-1 scale).

Ward and colleagues (2013) noted that the intellectually and developmentally disabled are vulnerable to abuse in their interpersonal relationships. The Friendships and Dating Program (FDP) was designed to teach the social skills needed to develop healthy, meaningful relationships and to prevent violence in dating and partnered relationships. Thirty-one participant adults revealed that the program was successful in increasing social networks and reducing interpersonal violence. Kijak and colleagues (2013) emphasized the importance of sexuality (e.g., sense of self, sexual role, sexual preference, eroticism, pleasure, intimacy etc.) in the life of everyone, including the intellectually disabled. The researchers surveyed 133 individuals with mild intellectual disability and emphasized that while "people with intellectual disability don't form a homogenous group as regards their psychological and sexual development," sexual development was delayed by an average of 3 years. Autoerotic behavior was the most common sexual behavior, which sometimes occurred in inappropriate places—schools, parks, squares, public toilets, shops, trams, buses, and forests, as well as healthcare facilities.

Petting and sexual intercourse also occurred, but less frequently and later than in a control group of adolescents. The petting/intercourse was typically initiated by the male, and with another intellectually disabled partner. One of the male respondents commented on his experience:

> When Ann and I touched each other on the bottom—that was a cool feeling. I was seventeen when I had sex with a girl for the first time. She was the same age as me. I did it out of curiosity. She was very scared and even cried. I thought that something bad had happened to her. It was not too good. But now, we have sex and it is really cool.

Sexual knowledge of the respondents was limited with only 10% understanding the notion of contraception. Balancing the rights of the intellectually disabled against the social norms of propriety and preventing pregnancy/STIs remains a challenge.

There are two basic models for viewing the disabled: the medical model and the social model (Parchomiuk, 2013). The **medical model** (also called the biological model) views the individual as coping with a personal tragedy, which implies adjusting to limited functioning. The sexual needs of the individual are viewed as nonexistent. In contrast, the **social model** views the intellectual disability as the product of specific social definitions that involve oppression and discrimination of disabled persons. The focus of the social model is encouraging the disabled to get control over their own lives by rejecting the social definitions.

Intellectual disability
Condition that involves subaverage intellectual functioning and deficits in adaptive behavior (also referred to as *mental retardation*)

Medical model view of intellectual disability
View that the individual is coping with a personal tragedy—which implies adjusting to limited functioning—and that his/her sexual needs are nonexistent

Social model view of intellectual disability
Views the intellectually disabled person as the product of specific social definitions which involve oppression and discrimination of disabled persons

SELF-ASSESSMENT 11-1: ATTITUDES TOWARDS SEXUALITY OF PERSONS WITH AN INTELLECTUAL DISABILITY

Directions

The items below provide a way to assess one's attitudes and beliefs toward the sexuality of persons with an intellectual disability. For each item, identify a number from 0 to 5 that reflects your level of agreement, and write the number in the space provided.

5 = I completely agree.

4 = I mostly agree.

3 = I mildly agree.

2 = I mildly disagree.

1 = I mostly disagree.

0 = I completely disagree.

X = I am not able to tell.

1. ___ Intellectual disability eliminates sexual needs.
2. ___ Individuals with intellectual disability are, in most cases, "forever children" and require constant care.
3. ___ Individuals with intellectual disability are, in most cases, incapable of forming marital relationships.
4. ___ Individuals with intellectual disability usually express their sexual needs in pathological forms.
5. ___ Due to deficits in the cognitive and the emotional spheres, individuals with intellectual disability are usually incapable of fidelity in a partnership.
6. ___ Intellectual disability is always inherited; hence individuals with disability should not be allowed to have children.
7. ___ Love in a partnership of individuals with intellectual disability is, in most cases, only an attempt to copy observed models and not a genuine feeling.
8. ___ Sterilization would protect individuals with intellectual disability from sexual harassment.
9. ___ Individuals with intellectual disability tend to commit sex-related crimes.
10. ___ Bringing up issues related to sexuality during school education may "arouse dormant sexual needs".
11. ___ Individuals with intellectual disability are very unlikely to form happy relationships with each other.

Scoring

Add each of the 11 items (each ranges from 0 to 5). Total scores ranged from 0 to 55, with lower scores reflecting more positive views. The lowest possible score is 0 suggesting a very high level of acceptance of sexuality among the intellectually disabled. The highest possible score is 55 suggesting a very low level of acceptance of sexuality among the disabled. The midpoint between 0 and 55 is 27.5. Scores lower than 27.5 would reflect greater approval for sexuality of the intellectually disabled; scores higher than this would reflect greater disapproval for sexuality of the intellectually disabled.

Source: Adapted from the work of Monika Parchomiuk and used with her permission (2013) . Dr. Parchomiuk is on the Faculty of Pedagogy and Psychology, Institute of Pedagogy, University of Maria Curie Sklodowska in Lublin, Narutowicza Street 12, 20-004 Lublin, Poland. mparchomiuk@o2.pl

A sample of 181 students responded to various scales to reveal their belief in the respective models. The respondents most frequently endorsed the social model of intellectual disability, which suggests that they were largely focused on normalizing the life of the disabled. "They recognized the civil status of these persons, granting them the opportunity to exercise their rights and fulfill certain duties." However, acceptance of sexual intercourse leading to parenthood is more tenuous. This issue along with potential victimization and STIs are challenges in regard to sexuality of people with intellectual or developmental disabilities (IDD) (Basler-Francis, 2013).

Wilkenfeld and Ballan (2011) found that educators of people with intellectual or developmental disabilities view their sexuality as a basic human right. However, these educators have concerns about the capacity of this population to consent to and facilitate sexual behavior without negative consequences (e.g., pregnancy and STIs). People with intellectual disabilities often require extensive assistance performing activities of daily living. Becoming pregnant and having a child as an adolescent or adult with an intellectual disability becomes a very complicated endeavor—and one that sexuality educators think requires serious consideration. While parents are the logical choice as sex educators for their children with intellectual disabilities, they often lack the specialized skills or choose not to fulfill this role. There is agreement that the school system should be a major source of socialization.

A great deal is known about what professionals think about the sexuality of the intellectually disabled. But what do the intellectually disabled themselves think about sex and sexuality? Fitzgerald and Withers (2013) conducted semi-structured interviews with 10 women with intellectual disabilities. Many of the women could not conceptualize themselves as sexual beings, and they tended to regard sex as a dirty and inappropriate activity for them. They generally believed that other people prohibited them from engaging in sexual activity. The women often considered themselves to be of little value, and the majority had no clear sense of identity. There is also a prevalence of sexual abuse and assault of people with intellectual disabilities. The percentages range from 63–86%, with a high likelihood of repeat victimization. Statistics have also shown that most perpetrators of sexual violence are caregivers, family, and other staff (Muccigrasso, 1991; Tyiska, 1998; Cambridge, Beadle-Brown, Milne, Mansell, & Whelton, 2011).

11.6 **Mental Illness and Sexuality**

Everyone experiences problems in mental functioning that are not necessarily considered mental illness, unless they meet specific criteria (such as level of intensity and duration) specified in the *Diagnostic and Statistical Manual of Mental Disorders* (American Psychiatric Association, 2013). **Mental disorders** are characterized by mild to severe disturbances in thinking, mood, and/or behavior associated with distress and/or impaired functioning. Mental illness refers collectively to all mental disorders. There are more than 300 classified forms of mental illness.

11.6a Mental Illness and Sexual Dysfunction

Some mental illnesses and their treatments (e.g., medication) are associated with problems in sexual functioning. For example, major depression is associated with a higher risk of erectile dysfunction in men and lower sexual desire in both women and men. Antidepressant medications are widely recognized as affecting sexual desire and arousal. Patients sometimes stop taking their much-needed medications due to the side effects (Quinn, Happell, & Browne, 2012).

Mental disorders
Mental states characterized by mild to severe disturbances in thinking, mood, and/or behavior associated with distress and/or impaired functioning (sometimes called mental illness)

Schizophrenia is a mental disorder characterized by social withdrawal and disturbances in thought, motor behavior, and interpersonal functioning. José Acuna and colleagues (2010) compared the sexual functioning of institutionalized patients with schizophrenia with noninstitutionalized adults and found that 71.2% of males and 57.1% of females in the institutionalized group experienced sexual dysfunction compared with 10% of males and 50% of females in the noninstitutionalized group. These dysfunctions include erectile dysfunction, ejaculatory difficulties, and difficulty achieving orgasm. Persons with untreated schizophrenia may also report decreased sexual desire and thoughts, and are likely to experience interference in their sexual communication and relationships with others. Schizophrenic women are often women of childbearing age and potential mothers who need to be informed by healthcare professionals about intimate relationships and contraception (Seeman, 2013).

11.6b Mental Illness and Barriers to Sexual Expression, Safer Sex, and Contraception

In residential settings for mentally ill persons, such as group homes, lack of privacy and "no sex between residents" policies limit opportunities for sexual expression. Among the noninstitutionalized mentally ill population, the formation of intimate relationships is hindered by the stigma associated with mental illness and by the impaired social skills associated with some disorders. For example, individuals with schizophrenia tend to have fewer sexual relationships than the normal population because of deficits in their social and relational abilities.

A major barrier to the practice of safer sex and the use of contraception among individuals with mental illness is lack of knowledge and information. The families of mentally ill patients may disapprove of their relative's sexual activity, resulting in a lack of support from family members in communicating with the mentally ill about contraception and safer sex. Persons with mental illness may also have limited incomes and cannot afford the most effective methods of contraception, such as birth control pills.

Some individuals with mental illness may lack the knowledge and the social skills needed to negotiate safer sex, such as persuasion or limit setting. Not only may they not know what contraception is, but they may also lack the skills to discuss contraceptive use with a potential partner. The result may be an unintended pregnancy or STI.

Finally, women with serious mental illness often have histories of physical and sexual assault, and are at risk for repeated victimization. Quinn and colleagues (2013) noted a reluctance of nurses working in mental health to discuss sexual issues with their patients. Mental health and healthcare professionals are encouraged to be mindful of the need for education in this area.

11.7 Effects of Pain and Fatigue on Sexuality

Persons with illness or disability often experience pain and fatigue. Both of these impact sexuality negatively.

11.7a Pain and Sexuality

Pain can result from a disease or injury and/or treatments for the disease or injury. Pain is associated with a number of health problems, including arthritis, migraine headaches, back injuries, multiple sclerosis, and cancer.

Schizophrenia
Mental disorder characterized by social withdrawal and disturbances in thought, motor behavior, and interpersonal functioning

Most people with chronic pain have pain-related difficulty with sexual activity. Painful conditions can impair range of motion or make vigorous movement difficult during sexual activity. Pain decreases sexual desire and contributes to emotional distress, anxiety, fatigue, and depression, which interfere with sexual functioning. Bahouq and colleagues (2013) found that 81% of their sample of chronic low back pain patients complained about sexual difficulties. Libido decrease and painful intercourse position were reported respectively in 14.8% and 97.5% of cases. The sexual quality of life reported by the patients was also affected.

To minimize the effects of pain on sexual functioning, couples can explore alternative positions for comfort and substitute noncoital sexual activity. Some sexual positions involve less physical exertion, place little or no weight on painful areas, and permit more control of depth of penetration during intercourse. When pain makes intercourse uncomfortable, couples can explore the pleasures of kissing, massage, cuddling, and oral and/or manual genital stimulation.

Various medications can relieve pain, which can have a positive effect on sexuality. However, pain is often under-treated with inadequate doses of pain medication. Pain medication may have a negative effect on sexual desire.

Personal REFLECTION

Take a moment to express your thoughts about the following question. Has pain ever prevented you from having sex? If so, to what degree did your partner respond with understanding?

11.7b Fatigue and Sexuality

In addition to pain, chronic illness and disability are often accompanied by fatigue. Persons with fatigue feel exhausted, weak, and depleted of energy. Fatigue may result from the effects of an illness or disease on the various body organs. Syme and colleagues (2013) noted that one of the factors that impacts sexuality during aging is fatigue. The researchers analyzed longitudinal data and found that low sexual satisfaction was associated with reported fatigue.

Fatigue may also be related to a specific illness. For example, individuals with **chronic obstructive pulmonary disease** (COPD)—a collective term for diseases that affect the flow of air into the body (such as asthma, bronchitis, and emphysema)—often experience fatigue due to decreased oxygen intake and the effort involved in breathing. Because breathing is difficult for COPD patients (some require an oxygen tank), any activity that increases respiration rate, including sexual activity, may be beyond the person's physical capability.

Fatigue may also result from medication or other medical treatments. The emotional and psychological stress that accompanies chronic illness and disability also produces fatigue, not only for patients, but for their intimate partners as well. Patients and their partners may spend a great deal of emotional energy trying to cope with the illness or disability.

When fatigue interferes with sexual interest and/or functioning, several interventions may be helpful. First, the fatigued person might engage in sexual behavior at a time when he or she feels most rested and has the most energy. Second, the person may

Chronic obstructive pulmonary disease (COPD)
Collective term for diseases that affect the flow of air into the body, such as asthma, bronchitis, and emphysema (Individuals with COPD often experience fatigue due to decreased oxygen intake and the effort involved in breathing.)

explore different positions for sexual activity and noncoital sexual behaviors that are less demanding. Third, counseling may help a person work through the conflicts of accepting the illness or disability in an effort to reduce psychological fatigue.

11.8 Effects of Medical Treatment on Sexuality

Although medical treatments, such as medication, radiation, and surgery, can improve sexual functioning, they can also reduce sexual desire, produce erectile dysfunction or vaginal dryness, cause difficulty in reaching orgasm, and/or lead to ejaculation problems.

11.8a Effects of Surgery on Sexuality

Surgery can have positive effects on sexuality when it alleviates a condition that interferes with sexual functioning. For example, a man who lacks interest in sex due to chronic back pain may find renewed libido following successful back surgery. Or, a woman who avoids sexual activity because she has **endometriosis**—the growth of endometrial tissue outside the uterus (in the Fallopian tubes or abdominal cavity)—may be free of pain and able to enjoy intercourse again following surgery to remove the endometrial tissue.

However, surgical treatment of medical problems may have a negative impact on sexuality. Carter and colleagues (2013) emphasized that surgery for gynecologic cancer can affect sexuality, reproductive function, and overall quality of life. Indeed, surgery can affect sexuality by removing a part of the body involved in sexual activity and causing negative changes in body image and self-concept.

Hysterectomy

Surgical removal of the uterus, known as a **hysterectomy**, is the second most common surgery performed on women in the United States (after the C-section). Surgical removal of the ovaries (**oophorectomy**) alters the estrogen levels of women, resulting in what is known as **surgical menopause**. The sudden decrease in estrogen can lead to decreased desire, vaginal dryness, and dyspareunia. Hormone replacement therapy can alleviate these sexual dysfunction symptoms.

Lermann and colleagues (2013) surveyed 258 women who had undergone one of five types of hysterectomy—abdominal hysterectomy (AH), vaginal hysterectomy (VH), laparoscopy-assisted vaginal hysterectomy (LAVH), laparoscopic supracervical hysterectomy (LASH), and total laparoscopic hysterectomy (TLH)—to assess the prevalence of loss of sexual desire. No differences were observed in change in sexual desire among the various types of hysterectomy.

Mastectomy and Lumpectomy

Women with breast cancer may have **breast-conserving therapy** (BCT, commonly known as lumpectomy), **mastectomy** (surgical removal of the breast), or **double mastectomy** (removal of both breasts). Women who have a mastectomy commonly struggle to accept their body image and may choose to wear prosthetic breasts that are inserted into a bra or glued onto the body. Alternatively, they may choose to undergo reconstruction surgery to form a new breast (or two new breasts if they have had a double mastectomy). In a reconstructed breast, feelings of pleasure from touching the breast and nipple are largely lost because the nerve that supplies feeling to the nipple is cut during surgery.

Endometriosis
Growth of endometrial tissue outside the uterus, in the Fallopian tubes or abdominal cavity, which may cause pain

Hysterectomy
Surgical removal of the uterus

Oophorectomy
Surgical removal of the ovaries

Surgical menopause
Sudden decrease in estrogen resulting from removal of the ovaries that can lead to decreased desire, vaginal dryness, and dyspareunia

Breast-conserving therapy
Removal of the cancerous lump rather than the whole breast (also called Lumpectomy.)

Mastectomy
Surgical removal of one breast

Double mastectomy
Removal of both breasts

Kedde and colleagues (2013) determined the prevalence of sexual dysfunction in young women with breast cancer in the Netherlands. Of women who were still undergoing treatment, 64% had a sexual dysfunction. In women who had completed treatment, 45%. Radical mastectomy was associated with female orgasmic disorder and early menopause dyspareunia.

Radical Prostatectomy, Orchiectomy, and Penectomy

Treatment for prostate cancer may involve surgical removal of the prostate (a procedure known as a **radical prostatectomy**) and/or surgical removal of the testicles (known as an **orchiectomy**). Removal of both testicles stops the production of the hormone testosterone which nourishes the cancer. These surgical procedures result in infertility. Other sexual effects of these surgeries include erection problems; low sexual desire; and lack of orgasm, dry orgasm, and weaker orgasm. Up Close 11-3 reflects the experience of a husband with prostate cancer who had a radical prostatectomy.

Radical prostatectomy
Surgical removal of the prostate

Orchiectomy
Surgical removal of the testicles)

Radical Prostatectomy—My Sex Life Is Ruined, but I'm Alive

Since my father had prostate cancer, I was warned that it is genetic and to be alert as I reached age 50. At the age of 56, I noticed that I was getting up more frequently at night to urinate. My doc said it was probably just one of my usual prostate infections, and he prescribed the usual antibiotic. When the infection did not subside, a urologist did a transrectal ultrasound (TRUS) needle biopsy. The TRUS gives the urologist an image of the prostate while he takes about 10 tissue samples from the prostate with a thin, hollow needle.

Treatment Options *Two weeks later I learned the bad news (I had prostate cancer) and the good news (it had not spread). Since the prostate is very close to the spinal column, failure to act quickly can allow time for cancer cells to spread from the prostate to the bones. My urologist outlined a number of treatment options, including traditional surgery, laparoscopic surgery, radiation treatment, implantation of radioactive "seeds," cryotherapy (in which liquid nitrogen is used to freeze and kill prostate cancer cells), and hormone therapy, which blocks production of the male sex hormones that stimulate growth of prostate cancer cells. He recommended traditional surgery ("radical retro pubic prostatectomy"), in which an incision is made between the belly button and the pubic bone to remove the prostate gland and nearby lymph nodes in the pelvis. This surgery is generally considered the "gold standard" when the disease is detected early. Within three weeks I had the surgery.*

Physical Effects Following Surgery *Every patient awakes from radical prostate surgery with urinary incontinence and impotence—which can continue for a year, two years, or forever. Such patients also awake from surgery hoping that they are cancer-free. This is determined by laboratory analysis of tissue samples taken during surgery. The patient waits for a period of about two weeks, hoping to hear the medical term "negative margins" from his doctor. That finding means that the cancer cells were confined to the prostate and did not spread past the margins of the prostate. A finding of negative margins should be accompanied by a PSA [prostate specific antigen] score of zero, confirming that the body no longer detects the presence of cancer cells. I cannot describe the feeling of relief that accompanies such a report, and I am very fortunate to have heard those words.*

Psychological Effects Following Surgery *The psychological effects have been devastating—more for me than for my partner. I have only been intimate with one woman—my wife—and having intercourse with her was one of the greatest pleasures in my life. For a year, I was left with no erection and an inability to have an orgasm. Afterwards I was able to have an erection (via the use of a vacuum pump) and an orgasm. Dealing with urinary incontinence (I refer to myself as Mr. Drippy) is a "wish it were otherwise" on my psyche.*

Evaluation *When faced with the decision to live or die, the choice for most of us is clear. In my case, I am alive, cancer free, and enjoying the love of my life (now in our 44th year together).*

Orchiectomy is also performed for testicular cancer, although in this case, the surgeon usually removes only the affected testicle, leaving the man with one testicle. Fertility, sexual desire, and sexual functioning are rarely affected when only one testicle is removed. After undergoing surgical removal of a testicle, a man can have a silicone gel-filled prosthesis surgically implanted in his scrotum to regain a more natural look.

When a man has cancer of the penis or of the bottom part of the urethra, treatment may involve **penectomy**—surgical removal of part of or the entire penis. Following a partial penectomy, in which only the end of the penis is removed, the remaining shaft still becomes erect with excitement, and sexual penetration can usually be achieved. Even though the most sensitive area of the penis (the glans or "head") is gone, a man can still experience orgasm and ejaculation. A total penectomy involves removing the entire penis. The surgeon creates a new opening for the urethra, and the man expels urine from a tube between his scrotum and his anus. The man can experience pleasure by stimulating the area between the anus and the scrotum. He can pleasure his partner through manual or oral stimulation, or by stimulation with a vibrator.

Ostomy Surgery

During ostomy surgery, a portion of the large or small intestine or urinary system is rerouted and brought to the skin surface of the abdomen. The resulting protruding portion of bowel is called a **stoma** (also referred to as an ostomy) and has a moist reddish appearance similar to the lining inside the mouth. Depending on the type of surgery, urine or stool leaves the body through the stoma and is collected in a pouch adhered to the abdomen and worn under clothing. The most common reason for **ostomy surgery** is cancer, usually of the colon, rectum, bladder, cervix, or ovaries.

Ostomy surgery affects sexuality primarily through its negative effects on sexual self-concept and body image. A person with a stoma cannot control the elimination of urine, gas, or stool from the body. Functions previously conducted in private (urination, defecation, and passage of gas) are now out of control in public situations. This loss of control can be unnerving. However, these inconveniences are viewed in context. Neuman and colleagues (2012) assessed the quality of life and changes in sexuality of patients with rectal cancer who had an ostomy. In depth interviews with 26 patients (both male and female) revealed difficulty related to exercise, sleep, social activities and sexuality. However, patients' perception of the quality of life with a stoma "appears to have undergone a response shift through recalibration of their standards for measuring quality of life" in the sense that these difficulties were viewed as less important in comparison with cancer-related mortality.

11.8b Effects of Medication and Radiation on Sexuality

Medication can improve sexual functioning either by (a) directly affecting sexual response (e.g., Viagra/Levitra/Cialis improve erectile functioning) or (b) alleviating the health problem that underlies the sexual dysfunction (e.g., aspirin relieves pain that interferes with sexual desire). However, many commonly prescribed medications, including antidepressants, antihypertensives (for high blood pressure), and drugs for heartburn, interfere with sexual desire and functioning. Some prescription pain medications produce sedation, constipation, and nausea—symptoms that diminish interest in sexual activity.

Chemotherapy medication and radiation treatment for cancer patients produce nausea and fatigue, which reduce sexual desire. Hair loss, weight loss, and paleness—other common effects of cancer treatment—can reduce sexual desire by creating feelings of unattractiveness.

Penectomy
Surgical removal of part or all of the penis

Stoma
Protruding portion of the large or small intestine (bowel) or urinary system that is rerouted and brought to the skin surface of the abdomen during ostomy surgery (also called ostomy.)

Ostomy surgery
Surgery whereby a portion of the large or small intestine or urinary system is rerouted and brought to the skin surface of the abdomen where the contents are collected in a bag (Cancers of the colon, rectum, bladder, cervix, or ovaries are typical causes of ostomy surgery.)

When a medication has a negative sexual side effect, a doctor may suggest that the patient wait to see if the problem subsides, change the drug's schedule or dosage, switch to a different drug, or take another drug to counteract or neutralize the first drug's side effect. Alternative therapies that can relieve pain without the sexual side effects associated with medication include biofeedback, hypnosis, yoga, meditation, Pilates, and acupuncture.

Medications and radiation can also interfere with fertility and reproduction. For example, women who must take medication regularly to control a health condition (such as anti-seizure medicine for epilepsy) are advised to avoid getting pregnant because the medication they must take could result in birth defects. Chemotherapy drugs and radiation used to treat cancer to the pelvic area can either temporarily or permanently damage ovaries, affecting fertility in women, and can slow semen production, affecting fertility in men.

11.9 Alcohol, Other Drugs, and Sexuality

Use of alcohol or other drugs is considered mental illness when it meets the criteria for substance dependence or **substance abuse**—the person no longer fulfills vital roles in work, relationships, and health (see Table 11-1.) Alcohol is the most frequently used recreational drug in our society and on college and university campuses (see Social Choices 11-1).

TABLE **11-1** | Criteria for Substance Dependence and Abuse

Substance Dependence	Substance Abuse
Drug tolerance (more and more of the drug is needed to experience the effects)	Failure to fulfill role obligations at work, school, or home due to substance use
Persistent desire or failed efforts to reduce or control substance use	Substance use in situations that are hazardous (e.g., driving while impaired)
Giving up important social, occupational, or recreational activities because of substance use	Recurrent substance-related legal problems
Continued substance use despite knowledge that such use contributes to a physical or psychological problem	Continued substance use despite its negative effect on social or interpersonal relationships

Substance abuse
Overuse or overdependence on drugs or chemicals that results in a failure to fulfill role obligations at work, school, or home, the effects of which include danger (e.g., driving while impaired), recurrent substance-related legal problems, and continued substance use despite its negative effect on social or interpersonal relationships. (also called substance dependence.)

Alcohol Abuse on Campus

While some college students do not drink, most do (Herman-Kinney & Kinney, 2013). Even in a private, conservative religious college, 53.6% of a sample of undergraduates reported drinking an average of five or more beers at a time (Coll, Draves, & Major, 2008), and 43.1% reported drinking beer at least once a week. Of 1,084 undergraduate males, 12% agreed that, "I have a problem with alcohol" (of 3,438 undergraduate females, 7% agreed) (Hall & Knox, 2013). Bulmer and colleagues (2010) reported that, in general, alcohol consumption patterns have remained stable. However, patterns vary by campus.

This male is watching and waiting patiently as this female gets liquored up. Alcohol is available, legal, and normative on the college campus.
Source: Chelsea Curry

At a northeastern university, increases in both frequency and volume were noted over a 6-year period—particularly in females, those over 21, those living off campus, and those performing well academically. Individuals with personalities characterized by urgency and sensation-seeking also drink more, have more binges, and more alcohol problems (Shin, Hong, & Jeon, 2012). Alcohol and other drug use (Pedrelli, et al., 2013), including with high-energy drinks (Snipes & Benotsch, 2013), are correlated—as is the greater likelihood of cohabitation, early marriage, and divorce (Williams, Wray-Lake, Loken, & Maggs, 2012).

Campus policies throughout the United States include alcohol-free dorms; alcohol bans, enforcement, and sanctions; peer support; alerting parents; and education. Most colleges and universities do not ban alcohol or its possession on campus. Indeed, some sell alcohol at football games to boost revenue. Administrators fear that students will attend other colleges where they would be allowed to drink. Some attorneys think colleges and universities can be held liable for not stopping dangerous drinking patterns, but others argue that college is a place for students to learn how to behave responsibly. Should sanctions be used (for example, expelling a student or closing down a fraternity)? If policies are too restrictive, drinking may go underground, where detecting use may be more difficult.

Substance-related disorders are sometimes associated with mental illness. See Table 11-2 for use of various drugs by age group.

TABLE **11-2** | Current Drug Use by Type of Drug and Age Group

Type of Drug Used	Ages 12 to 17	Ages 18 to 25	Ages 26 to 34
Marijuana and hashish	6.7%	18.5%	8.8%
Cocaine	0.4%	1.5%	1.5%
Alcohol	14.8%	61.2%	no data
Cigarettes	9.1%	36.7%	no data

Source: Adapted from *Statistical Abstract of the United States (2012–2013),* 131st ed. Washington, DC: U.S. Bureau of the Census, Table 207.

11.9a Alcohol and Sexuality

Alcohol is a central nervous system depressant that physiologically suppresses sexual response for both women and men; it can interfere with sexual arousal, penile erection, and ability to achieve orgasm. The Self-Assessment 11-2 feature allows you to identify your motives for drinking alcohol.

SELF-ASSESSMENT 11-2: MOTIVES FOR DRINKING ALCOHOL SCALE

Read the list of reasons people sometimes give for drinking alcohol. Thinking of all the times you drink, how often would you say you drink for each of the following reasons? (Write the appropriate number after reading each item.)

1 = never/almost never
2 = some of the time
3 = half of the time
4 = most of the time
5 = almost always

1. ___ Because it helps me to enjoy a party
2. ___ To be sociable
3. ___ To make social gatherings more fun
4. ___ To improve parties and celebrations
5. ___ To celebrate a special occasion with friends
6. ___ To forget my worries
7. ___ To help my depression or nervousness
8. ___ To cheer me up
9. ___ To make me feel more self-confident
10. ___ To help me forget about problems
11. ___ Because the effects of alcohol feel good
12. ___ Because it is exciting
13. ___ To get high
14. ___ Because it gives me a pleasant feeling
15. ___ Because it is fun
16. ___ Because of pressure from friends
17. ___ To avoid disapproval for not drinking
18. ___ To fit in with the group
19. ___ To be liked
20. ___ To avoid feeling left out

Scoring

The four basic drinking motives are social, coping, enhancement, and conformity. The items for these and the average scores from 1,243 respondents follow. The lowest score reflecting each motive would be 1 = never; the highest score reflecting each motive would be 5 = always. The most frequent motive for women and men is to be sociable. The least frequent motive for women and men is to conform. To compare your score with other respondents, add the numbers you circled for each of the following social, coping, enhancement, and conformity reasons identified. For example, to ascertain the degree to which your motivation for drinking alcohol is to be sociable, add the numbers you circled for items 1 and 5.

Again, the basic reasons for drinking are social, coping, enhancement, and conformity. Items 1, 2, 3, 4, 5 pertain to social drinking; items 6, 7, 8, 9, 10 pertain to coping drinking; items 11, 12, 13, 14, 15 pertain to enhancement drinking; and items 16, 17, 18, 19, 20 pertain to conformity drinking. In this study, female respondents scored 2.29 for social drinking; 1.61 for coping drinking; 1.99 for enhancement drinking; and 1.34 for conformity drinking. Male respondents scored 2.63 for social drinking; 1.59 for coping drinking; 2.33 for enhancement drinking; and 1.43 for conformity drinking.

Source: © 1994 by the American Psychological Association. Adapted with permission. Cooper, M. Lynne. (1994) Motivations for Alcohol Use Among Adolescents: Development and Validation of a four-factor model. *Psychological Assessment, 6:* 117–128.

Drink the first. Sip the second slowly. Skip the third.

Knute Rockne, legendary football coach

Whereas some partners consume alcohol to enhance sexual intimacy, others drink to suppress their negative feelings toward sex and/or toward their partner and to tolerate sexual relations. Long-term alcohol use in high doses can lead to cirrhosis and other diseases of the liver, and a number of other health problems that affect sexual functioning and relationships. In men, alcoholism can lead to decreases in testosterone, loss of facial hair, breast enlargement, decreased libido, and erectile dysfunction. In women, alcoholism can interfere with menstruation and ovulation, leading to early menopause.

11.9b Other Recreational Drugs and Sexuality

Fazio and colleagues (2010) assessed drug use at dance clubs/raves and found men and non-heterosexuals consume more drugs than women and heterosexuals. Recreational drugs are often used with the intention of enhancing sexual pleasure. For example, some individuals report that marijuana use enhances their experience of sexual pleasure. However, this impact seems to be affected by one's expectations, personality, age, setting, and relationship of the users. Desire may be indirectly affected in some users, with some describing mild aphrodisiac effects. There is not a direct effect on the sexual response phases, except for preliminary data that regular use may inhibit orgasm response for some women.

Another drug sometimes used to enhance sexual pleasure is **ecstasy**, also known as *MDMA, X,* or *E.* Ecstasy has both stimulant and psychedelic effects that can result in increased energy; enhanced sense of pleasure and self-confidence; and feelings of peacefulness, acceptance, and closeness with others. Although these effects of ecstasy can enhance sexual pleasure, ecstasy is also associated with a number of dangerous risks, including dehydration, hyperthermia, seizures, and heart or kidney failure.

Cocaine (snorted or injected) or crack (smoked) use has significant negative effect on sexual function and overall health. Although new users of cocaine may perceive a positive effect, this is not specifically a sexual effect but is likely a function of the overall feeling of confidence and energy associated with the drug use. However, regular or long-term use results in diminished sexual desire, erective ability, and decreased ability to have an orgasm. In addition, using cocaine increases one's risk of heart attack, sudden death, and other cardiovascular conditions.

Crystal methamphetamine is a stimulant that decreases inhibitions, enhances libido, and heightens perceptions of sexual intensity. Although it constricts the blood vessels, interfering with prolonged erection, some users counter that effect by using Viagra or another similar drug. The hazards of crystal meth are great, and the drug is highly addictive. Its use promotes risky sexual behaviors, and especially among gay men, is substantially linked with HIV and other STDs. It causes long-term damage to

Ecstasy
Drug which has both stimulant and psychedelic effects that can result in increased energy; enhanced sense of pleasure and self-confidence; and feelings of peacefulness, acceptance, and closeness with others; also known as MDMA, X or E (Use of the drug is also associated with dangerous risks such as heart failure.)

the brain (to all users, not just addicts), and can result in heart failure, stroke, memory loss, paranoia, anorexia, malnutrition, and dehydration (see Table 11-3).

TABLE 11-3	Illicit and Abused Drugs Associated with Sexual Disorders
Substance	Sexual Disorder
Alcohol	Acute effects: erectile disorder,*** desire disorder,*** delayed orgasm*** Chronic effects: erectile disorder,*** desire disorder***
Amphetamines	Low doses: may increase desire and delay orgasm* High doses and chronic use: *delayed or no ejaculation,*** erectile disorder,** inhibition of orgasm (men and women)*
Amyl nitrate	Decrease in arousal and lubrication; erectile disorder; delayed orgasm or ejaculation*
Barbiturates	Decreased desire, erectile disorder, inhibited ejaculation***
Cocaine	Erectile disorder,***spontaneous or delayed ejaculation, priapism*
Diazepam (Valium)	Decreased desire, delayed ejaculation, retarded or no orgasm in women*
Marijuana	Decreased desire, hormonal alteration*
MDMA	Erectile disorder,****inhibited ejaculation and orgasm,**** decreased desire**
Methaqualone	Erectile disorder, inhibited ejaculation, decreased desire in women*
Morphine	Decreased desire, erectile disorder, hormonal alteration*
Tobacco	Erectile disorder**

*Case reports, package insert, or uncertain frequency
** Infrequent side effect
*** Frequent side effect
**** Very frequent side effect

Note: Medications and their accompanying side effects that have been cited frequently as causing sexual disorders are in *italics*.

Source: Reprinted with permission from Finger, W. W., Lund, M., & Slagle, M. A. (1997). Medications that may contribute to sexual disorders: A guide to assessment and treatment in family practice. *Journal of Family Practice, 44,* 33–43. Dowden Health Media.

11.9c Alcohol, Drugs, and Unsafe Sex

Use of alcohol and other drugs is associated with having unprotected sex. High-risk sexual behavior associated with substance use may result from the disinhibiting effects of the substance, the effect of the substance on judgment, or from the exchange of sex for drugs (or for money to buy drugs).

Chapter **Summary**

In this chapter, we examined the effects of physical and mental illness, disability and substance use on sexuality. This chapter identifies some of the sexual issues and concerns facing individuals with health problems, their partners, and their healthcare providers.

Illness, Disability and Effect on Sexuality

The disabled are assumed to be *asexual* and their sexuality is often ignored by healthcare professionals. In one study, women with gynecologic cancer noted severe decreases in sexual desire, arousal, the frequency of intercourse and orgasm. Yet they felt they could not talk about these issues with their physician.

Effects of Illness and Disability on Self-Concept and Body Image

Persons with chronic illness or disability are vulnerable to developing a negative self-concept and body image and to viewing themselves as undesirable or inadequate romantic and sexual partners. Being obese is associated with a negative body image and a decrease in sexual behavior.

Impaired Sensory-Motor Function and Sexuality

A number of neurological diseases and injuries—including spinal cord injury, multiple sclerosis (MS), and cerebral palsy—can result in impaired sensory-motor functioning. The effects of sensory-motor impairment on sexuality are varied and depend, in part, on the type and severity of the illness or injury.

Diabetes and Sexuality

Diabetes mellitus is a chronic disease in which the pancreas fails to produce sufficient insulin, which is necessary for metabolizing carbohydrates and fats. In women, diabetes can result in lack of libido, diminished clitoral sensation, vaginal dryness and discomfort, and orgasmic dysfunction. Diabetic men may notice a progressive softening of the penis, eventually leading to the inability to perform vaginal penetration.

Impaired Cognitive Function and Sexuality

Many illnesses and injuries—such as Alzheimer's disease and other forms of dementia, traumatic brain injury, and intellectual disability—result in impaired cognitive functioning, such as memory loss, language comprehension problems, learning disabilities, and confusion. Inappropriate sexual behavior is common among persons with cognitive impairment. Issues of pregnancy and STIs for the intellectually disabled are challenges to healthcare professionals.

Mental Illness and Sexuality

Mental disorders are characterized by mild to severe disturbances in thinking, mood, and/or behavior associated with distress and/or impaired functioning. Some mental illnesses and their treatments (e.g., medication) are associated with problems in sexual functioning. Major depression is associated with a higher risk of erectile dysfunction in men and lower sexual desire in both women and men, and some antidepressant medications used to treat depression interfere with sexual desire and arousal. In addition, individuals with mental illness face barriers to sexual expression, safer sex, and contraception.

Effects of Pain and Fatigue on Sexuality

Persons with illness or disability often experience pain and fatigue. Pain can impair range of motion or make vigorous movement difficult during sexual activity. Pain decreases sexual desire and contributes to emotional distress, anxiety, fatigue, and depression. To minimize the effects of pain on sexual functioning, couples can explore alternative positions for comfort and substitute noncoital sexual activity. Various medications can relieve pain, which can have a positive effect on sexuality. However, pain medication often has negative sexual side effects.

Effects of Medical Treatment on Sexuality

Although medical treatments (e.g., medication, radiation, and surgery) can improve sexual functioning, they can also reduce sexual desire, produce erectile dysfunction or vaginal dryness, cause difficulty in reaching orgasm, and/ or lead to ejaculation problems. Surgery can also affect sexuality by removing a part of the body involved in sexual activity, causing negative changes in body image and self-concept, affecting hormonal levels, and causing infertility.

Alcohol, Other Drugs, and Sexuality

Alcohol is the most frequently used recreational drug in our society, including college and university campuses. Alcohol is a central nervous system depressant that physiologically suppresses sexual response for both women and men, and can interfere with sexual arousal, penile erection, and ability to achieve orgasm. However, the belief or expectancy that alcohol consumption increases sexual desire and response has a strong effect on sexual arousal. Some partners drink to suppress their negative feelings toward sex and/or toward their partner and to tolerate sexual relations.

Long-term alcohol use in high doses can lead to cirrhosis and other diseases of the liver, and a number of other health problems that affect sexual functioning and relationships. Recreational drugs, such as marijuana and ecstasy, are often used with the intention of enhancing sexual pleasure. Ecstasy is associated with a number of dangerous risks, including dehydration, hyperthermia, seizures, and heart or kidney failure. Use of alcohol and other drugs is associated with having unprotected sex.

Web Links

Key Terms

Additional study resources are available at www.BVTLab.com

CHAPTER 12

Contraception and Pregnancy

You cannot have maternal health without reproductive health. And reproductive health includes contraception and family planning and access to legal, safe abortion.

Hillary Clinton

Chapter Outline

Objectives

1. Define contraception and list the various methods.
2. Review the meaning and methods of sterilization for women and men.
3. Identify the different types of abortion.
4. Know the divergent attitudes and political positions in regards to abortion.
5. Recognize and understand the physical and physiological effects of abortion.
6. Learn the signs of pregnancy and the methods of testing for pregnancy.
7. Review the physical and psychological changes that occur during pregnancy.
8. Know what options are available for prenatal care and prenatal testing.
9. Understand the effects of miscarriage.

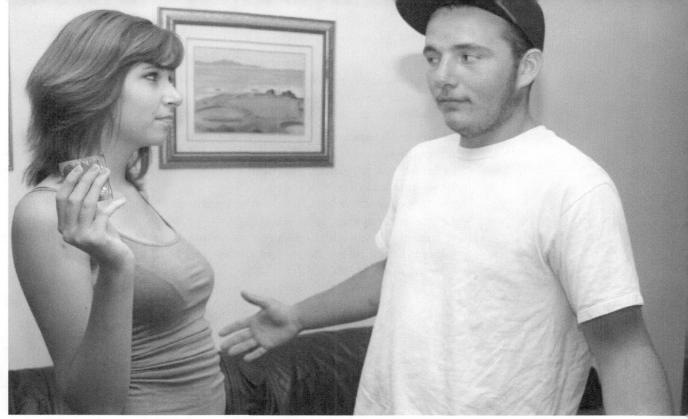

Source: Chelsea Curry

TRUTH *OR* FICTION

T/F New data confirms that the damage to a woman's body from taking the pill is no longer worth the benefit of the very high protection against pregnancy.

T/F Women do not trust men to take a male birth control pill.

T/F Plan B One Step is available in the U.S. for purchase without a prescription as long but the woman must prove she is age 16 or above.

T/F A quarter of the U.S. public believe abortion is morally wrong and want *Roe v. Wade* overturned.

T/F Most women who access a health service about being pregnant have already decided whether they want to have an abortion before they contact the service: "counseling about what to do may have limited benefits."

Answers:
1.F 2.T 3.F 4.T 5.T

Various forms of contraception preceded modern day methods. Records exist of women in ancient Rome and Greece relying on dances and amulets to prevent pregnancy. Other examples of early contraception include (Cheuang, 2010):

1. *Lemons (mentioned in the Talmud)* Jewish women were to soak sponges in lemon juice before inserting them vaginally. Casanova, the great lover, was said to insert the rind of half a lemon into his lovers as a primitive diaphragm.

2. *Cotton (identified in Ebers Papyrus, a scroll from 1550 BC)* It was recommended that cotton be soaked in ground up dates and honey, and inserted vaginally as a barrier.

3. *Papaya seeds (in both South and Southeast Asia)*   Papaya seeds were used to reduce a man's sperm count to zero. The procedure was reversible; thus when the man stopped taking the seeds, his sperm count would return.

In early America (in addition to abstinence), methods included prolonged lactation, male withdrawal, suppositories, and douching solutions that were made from household substances. During the Depression, Lysol douche—although ineffective—was sold as a contraceptive.

In this chapter, we look at the various methods of contemporary contraception, sometimes referred to as *family planning, fertility regulation,* or *birth control.* All methods have one of three goals: to suppress ovulation, to prevent the male sperm from fertilizing the female egg (to prevent conception), or to keep the fertilized egg from implanting in the uterus.

National **DATA**

The cost to parents of rearing one child born in 2012 to age 18 is estimated to be $241,080 (United States Department of Agriculture, 2013).

For moral and/or religious reasons, some women and their partners find only contraception methods (those that prevent conception) acceptable, and not methods that prevent implantation. The barrier methods discussed in the first section prevent conception. The terms *contraception* and *birth control* are often used interchangeably, but some interventions that are in a literal sense a form of birth control (i.e., abortion methods) are not types of contraception and do not prevent pregnancy.

12.1 **Contraception***

Both religion and one's psychological state impact the choice of contraception. In regard to religion, Moreau and colleagues (2013) analyzed survey data in France on 7,495 women and 5,634 men ages 15 to 44. Three quarters of respondents (73%) reported no religious practice, 20% practiced occasionally, and 7% regularly. Regular practice was associated with later sexual debut, regardless of religious denomination. Among participants less than 30 years old, religious respondents were less likely to have used a condom at first sexual intercourse. At the time of the survey, sexually experienced adolescents who reported regular religious practice were less likely to use contraception (84.7% vs. 98.1%, p < 0.001). A Catholic background was particularly associated with nonuse of effective contraception: regular Catholic religious practice was associated with a 50% decrease in the odds of using very effective methods of contraception.

Depression and psychological stress also impact contraceptive use. Hall and colleagues (2013) analyzed 8,877 weekly journals kept for a year by 689 women (ages 18–20) and found that approximately one quarter of the women exhibited moderate/severe depression (27%) and stress (25%) symptoms at baseline. In regard to contraception use, women with moderate/severe stress symptoms had more than twice the odds of contraception nonuse than women without stress. Hence, the greater the stress, the less the use of contraception and the contraception that was used was less effective.

Before discussing the various forms of contraception, you might take the Contraceptive Behavior Scale to assess your use of contraception.

*Appreciation is expressed to Beth Credle Burt, MAEd, CHES, a health education specialist for her review/input into this section.

SELF-ASSESSMENT 12-1:
CONTRACEPTIVE BEHAVIOR SCALE (CBS)

In taking the CBS, participants respond according to the degree of consistency between their actual practice and the statement of the item, which is rated from 0 (totally no correspondence) to 4 (total correspondence). Higher scores (4 is the top score) indicate better contraceptive behaviors.

1. ___ I practice contraception each time when I have sex.
2. ___ I have a preferred contraceptive method used to prevent pregnancy (e.g., safe period combined with condom or coitus interruptus combined with condom).
3. ___ I pay attention to any contraceptive information that enables me to have good contraceptive practice.
4. ___ When I am doubtful about the safety of contraceptive method after having sex with my partners, I will take other compensatory methods (e.g., take emergency contraceptive pills or consult friends to take action).
5. ___ I use a contraceptive method accurately.

Scoring

Add the numbers you gave for each item and divide by five. Four is the top score indicating a high level of contraceptive behavior. Zero is the lowest possible score.

Norms

Five hundred and twenty-five sexually active adolescents completed the CBS. The mean score was 2.72 with a standard deviation of 2.11?

Validity and Reliability:

See article.

Source: Wang, R.-H., Jian, S. Y., and Yang, Y. M. (2013). Psychometric testing of the Chinese version of the Contraceptive Behavior Scale: a preliminary study. *Journal of Clinical Nursing, 22:* 1066–1072. Used by permission.

12.1a Hormonal Methods

Hormonal methods of contraception currently available to women include the "pill," Implanon® or Nexplanon/Implanon NXT®, Depo-Provera® or Depo-subQ Provera 104®, NuvaRing®, and Ortho Evra®.

Oral Contraceptive Agents (Birth Control Pill)

The birth control pill is the most commonly used method of all the nonsurgical forms of contraception. Although some women who take the pill still become pregnant, it remains a desirable birth control option.

Oral contraceptives are available in basically two types: the combination pill, which contains varying levels of estrogen and progestin, and the minipill, which is progestin only. Combination pills work by raising the natural level of hormones in a woman's body, inhibiting ovulation, and creating an environment where sperm cannot easily reach the egg.

The second type of birth control pill, the minipill, contains the same progesterone-like hormone found in the combination pill but does not contain estrogen.

Progestin-only pills are taken every day with no hormone-free interval. The progestin in the minipill provides a hostile environment for sperm and does not allow implantation of a fertilized egg in the uterus; unlike the combination pill, however, the minipill does not always inhibit ovulation. For this reason, the minipill is somewhat less effective than other types of birth control pills. The minipill has also been associated with a higher incidence of irregular bleeding.

Neither the combination pill nor the minipill should be taken unless prescribed by a healthcare provider who has detailed information about the woman's previous medical history. Contraindications—reasons for not prescribing birth control pills—include hypertension, impaired liver function, known or suspected tumors that are estrogen-dependent, undiagnosed abnormal genital bleeding, pregnancy at the time of the examination, and a history of poor blood circulation or blood clotting. The major complications associated with taking oral contraceptives are blood clots and high blood pressure. Also, the risk of heart attack is increased for those who smoke or have other risk factors for heart disease. If they smoke, women over age 35 should generally use other forms of contraception. The progestin in some birth control pills that contain drospirenone—which can raise potassium levels in the blood—may be linked to a higher risk for blood clots and heart problems than other birth control pills. It is important for women to consult/inform their doctor if they have ever had disease of the kidneys, liver, or adrenal glands and to make their healthcare provider aware of all medications they are taking (Planned Parenthood Federation of America Inc., 2013).

Although the long-term negative consequences of taking birth control pills are still the subject of research, 25% of all women who use them experience short-term negative effects. These side effects include increased susceptibility to vaginal infections, nausea, slight weight gain, vaginal bleeding between periods, breast tenderness, headaches, and mood changes (some women become depressed and experience a loss of sexual desire). Women should also be aware of situations in which the pill is not effective, such as the first month of use, when combined with certain prescription medications, and when pills are missed. The pill is also not as effective if it is not taken at the same time every day. On the positive side, pill use reduces the incidence of ectopic pregnancy and offers noncontraceptive benefits: regular menses, less dysmenorrhea, and reduced incidence of ovarian and endometrial cancers.

Finally, women should be aware that pill use is associated with an increased incidence of chlamydia and gonorrhea. One reason for the association of pill use and a higher incidence of STIs is that sexually active women who use the pill sometimes erroneously feel that because they are protected from becoming pregnant, they are also protected from contracting STIs. The pill provides no protection against STIs; the only methods that provide some protection against STIs are the male and female barrier methods, especially condoms.

Hannaford (2013) summarized decades of research on OC (oral contraceptives): The accumulated evidence does not suggest that oral contraception causes a major public health problem, indeed there may be important long-term benefits ... For most women using the contraceptive pill for birth control, the chances of experiencing adverse effects are greatly outweighed by the very high protection against pregnancy, as well as other short- and possibly long-term health benefits. (p. 3)

Nexplanon/Implanon NXT or Implanon

Nexplanon/Implanon NXT or Implanon
Nexplanon/Implanon NXT is a single flexible plastic rod implant the size of a matchstick that releases a progestin hormone called etonogestrel

There have been various subdermal implants (e.g., Norplant and Jadelle), but only Implanon and its newer replacement **Nexplanon/Implanon NXT** is currently on the market in the U.S. Nexplanon/Implanon NXT is a single flexible plastic rod implant the size of a matchstick that releases a progestin hormone called etonogestrel. A healthcare provider inserts the implant just under the skin of the inner side of a woman's upper arm and the implant provides pregnancy protection for up to 3 years—although it may be removed at any time. The main difference between Implanon and Nexplanon/ Implanon NXT (other than an improved applicator for placement), is the small amount of barium sulfate that is added to the newer implant, which allows the implant to be seen by X-ray, computed tomography (CT) scan, ultrasound scan, or magnetic resonance imaging (MRI). This helps doctors confirm the implant is correctly in place and also aids them in locating it for removal. The implant contains no estrogen, which makes it a viable contraceptive solution for some women who have contraindications to estrogen use. Irregular bleeding is the most common side effect, especially in the first 6–12 months of use (Michielson and Merck FDA-Approved Patient Labeling, 2012).

Depo-Provera® or Depo-subQ Provera 104®

Depo-Provera, also known as "Depo" and "the shot," is a long acting, reversible, hormonal contraceptive birth control drug that is injected every 3 months. Side effects of Depo-Provera include menstrual spotting, irregular bleeding, and some heavy bleeding the first few months of use, although 8 out of 10 women using Depo-Provera will eventually experience amenorrhea, or the absence of a menstrual period. Mood changes, headaches, dizziness, and fatigue have also been observed. Some women report a weight gain of 5–10 pounds. Also, after the injections are stopped, it takes an average of 18 months before the woman will become pregnant at the same rate as women who have not used Depo-Provera.

Depo-Provera has been associated with significant loss of bone density, which may not be completely reversible after discontinuing use. The FDA recommends that Depo-Provera only be used for longer than 2 years if other methods are inadequate (hence a 'black box' warning).

Similarly, Depo-subQ Provera 104® is an injection method that offers a 30% lower hormone dosage than Depo-Provera. While Depo-Provera is injected deep into the muscle, Depo-subQ Provera 104 is injected just beneath the skin. Depo-subQ Provera 104 has similar benefits, risks, and side effects—and the same black box warning for risk of significant loss of bone density, as described for Depo-Provera. However, the lower amount of hormone may mean slightly less progestin-related side effects. Less long-term information is available about its effectiveness although short-term studies show similar results to Depo-Provera. Depo-subQ Provera 104 injection is also FDA-approved for the treatment of endometriosis-related pain (Mayo Foundation for Medical Education and Research, 1998–2013).

Vaginal Rings

NuvaRing®, which is a soft, flexible, and transparent ring approximately 2 inches in diameter that is worn inside the vagina, provides month-long pregnancy protection. NuvaRing has two major advantages. One, because the hormones are delivered locally rather than systemically, very low levels are administered (the lowest dose of any of the hormonal contraceptives). Second, unlike oral contraceptives, in which the hormone levels rise and fall depending on when the pill is taken, the hormone level from the NuvaRing remains constant. The NuvaRing is a highly effective contraceptive when used according to the labeling. Out of 100 women using NuvaRing for a year, 1 or 2 will become pregnant. This method is self-administered. NuvaRing is inserted into the vagina and is designed to release hormones that are absorbed by the woman's body for 3 weeks. The ring is then removed for a week, at which time the menstrual cycle will occur; afterward a new ring is inserted.

Depo-Provera
A synthetic compound similar to progesterone injected into the woman's arm or buttock that protects her against pregnancy for 3 months by preventing ovulation

NuvaRing
Soft, flexible, and transparent ring approximately 2 inches in diameter that is worn inside the vagina and provides month-long pregnancy protection

Transdermal Applications

Ortho Evra® is a contraceptive transdermal patch that delivers hormones to a woman's body through skin absorption. The contraceptive patch is worn for 3 weeks (anywhere on the body except the breasts) and is changed on a weekly basis. The 4th week is patch-free and the time when the menstrual cycle will occur. Ortho Evra is the only contraceptive patch available in the U.S.

An alternative to Ortho Evra is being developed: the **NEA-TDS** (norethindrone acetate transdermal system) which is a contraceptive patch worn continuously for 7 days and then replaced with a new patch (rotating sites on the abdomen, buttocks or hips). The patch delivers 0.4 mg each day. Through daily paper diaries kept by 689 women ages 18–47, Simon and colleagues (2013) evaluated its use. While application site reactions (5%) and menstrual disturbances (6%) were the most common adverse reactions, the researchers found that there are no "major safety concerns" evident following treatment for up to 1 year of use and that the NEA patch offers a once-weekly, user-controlled, readily reversible, estrogen-free option for contraception.

Male Hormonal Methods

There is still no "male pill" available, anywhere. Research to date suggests that the success rate of a male hormonal contraception using injectable testosterone alone in clinical trials is actually high and comparable to methods for women. Current studies are attempting to optimize the method of delivery of the hormones and the progestin to use in combination with testosterone (Wang & Swerdloff, 2010).

While efforts to develop hormonal methods for males continue, Campo-Englestein (2013) emphasized that women may not trust men to use these new male contraceptives. Three reasons are cited:

First, there is a cultural belief that men have an uncontrollable sex drive, which interferes with their willingness to use contraception. Second, there is a commonly held idea that men are incompetent in domestic tasks, which impairs their ability to correctly use contraception. Third, there is a social perception that men are not committed to pregnancy prevention, or at least not to the degree that women are (p. 283).

12.1b Barrier Methods

Some women reject the use of hormonal contraceptives on the basis of not wanting to introduce monthly chemicals into their body. Barrier methods provide several alternatives: the male and female condom, **spermicides**, diaphragm, and cervical cap.

Male Condom

The condom is a thin sheath made of latex, polyurethane, or natural membranes. Latex condoms, which can be used only with water-based lubricants, have been more popular historically. However, the polyurethane condom, which is thinner but just as durable as latex, is growing in popularity. Polyurethane condoms can be used with oil-based lubricants, are an option for some people who have latex-sensitive allergies, provide some protection against the HIV virus and other sexually transmitted infections, and allow for greater sensitivity during intercourse. Condoms made of natural membranes (sheep intestinal lining) are not recommended because they are not effective in preventing transmission of HIV or other STIs. Individuals are more likely to use condoms with casual than with stable partners. Ma and colleagues (2013) found that condom use appears to increase the "good" bacteria in the vagina that may protect against bacterial vaginosis as well as HIV.

Ortho Evra
Contraceptive transdermal patch, worn for 3 weeks (anywhere on the body except the breasts) and changed on a weekly basis, that delivers hormones to a woman's body through skin absorption

NEA-TDS
(Norethindrone acetate transdermal system) a contraceptive patch worn continuously for 7 days and then replaced with a new patch (rotating sites on the abdomen, buttocks or hips)

Spermicide
Chemical that kills sperm

FIGURE **12-1** ‖ How to Put on a Condom

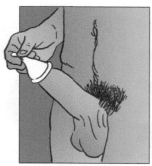

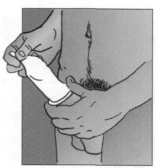

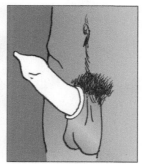

Place condom over head of the erect penis. If condom does not have reservoir tip, pinch the top of the condom to leave room for semen.

While holding the top, unroll the condom.

Continue unrolling the condom to the base of the penis.

The condom works by being rolled over and down the shaft of the erect penis before intercourse (see Figure 12-1). When the man ejaculates, sperm are caught inside the condom. When used in combination with a spermicidal lubricant that is placed inside the reservoir tip of the condom as well as a spermicidal or sperm-killing agent that the woman inserts inside her vagina, the condom is a highly effective contraceptive. Care should be taken *not* to use nonoxynol-9 as a contraceptive lubricant because it has been shown to provide no protection against STIs or HIV. In addition, nonoxynol-9 products, such as condoms that have N-9 as a lubricant, should not be used rectally because doing so could *increase* one's risk of getting HIV or other STIs.

Like any contraceptive, the condom is effective only when used properly. It should be placed on the penis early enough to avoid any seminal leakage into the vagina. In addition, polyurethane or latex condoms with a reservoir tip are preferable because they are less likely to break. (Even if the condom has a reservoir tip, air should be squeezed out of the tip as it is being placed on the penis to reduce the chance of breaking during ejaculation.) Such breakage does occur, however. (Tip: If the condom breaks, immediately insert a spermicide into the vagina to reduce the risk of pregnancy.) Finally, the penis should be withdrawn from the vagina immediately after ejaculation, before the man's penis returns to its flaccid state. If the penis is not withdrawn and the erection subsides, semen may leak from the base of the condom into the labia. Alternatively, when the erection subsides, the condom will come off when the man withdraws his penis if he does not hold onto the condom. Either way, the sperm will begin to travel up the vagina to the reproductive tract, and fertilization may occur.

To what degree are both the condom AND hormonal methods used? Goldstein and colleagues (2013) studied a sample of 1,194 women ages 15–24 who attended public family planning clinics. When the female respondents first came to the clinic, 36% reported condom use and 5% reported using a dual method (hormonal contraception plus condom). Once the woman began to use hormonal contraception, there was a reduction in condom use (to 27%); and condom use stayed at this lower level throughout the 12-month study. Women who believed their main partner thought condoms were "very important," regardless of perceived sexually transmitted infection risk or participant's own views of condoms, had higher odds of dual method use.

Whenever a condom is used, a spermicide may also be used. In addition to furnishing extra protection, spermicides also provide lubrication, which permits easy entrance of the condom-covered penis into the vagina. If no spermicide is used and the condom is not of the prelubricated variety, a sterile lubricant (such as K-Y Jelly)

FIGURE **12-2** ‖ The Female Condom

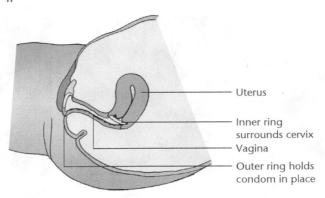

- Uterus
- Inner ring surrounds cervix
- Vagina
- Outer ring holds condom in place

may be needed. Vaseline or other kinds of petroleum jelly should not be used with condoms because vaginal infections and/or condom breakage may result. Even though condoms should also be checked for visible damage and for the date of expiration, this is rarely done.

Female Condom

The female condom resembles the male condom except that it fits in the woman's vagina to protect her from pregnancy, HIV infection, and other STIs. The **female condom** is a lubricated, polyurethane adaptation of the male version. It is about 6.5 inches long and has flexible rings at both ends. It is inserted like a diaphragm, with the inner ring fitting behind the pubic bone against the cervix; the outer ring remains outside the body and encircles the labial area (see Figure 12-2). Like the male version, the female condom is not reusable. Female condoms have been approved by the FDA and are being marketed under the brand names Femidom and Reality. The one-size-fits-all device is available without a prescription.

Female condoms are durable and may not tear as easily as latex male condoms. Some women may encounter some difficulty with first attempts to insert the female condom. A major advantage of the female condom is that, like the male counterpart, it helps protect against transmission of the HIV virus and other STIs, giving women an option for protection if their partner refuses to wear a condom. Placement may occur up to 8 hours before use, allowing greater spontaneity.

There are problems with the female condom. It can slip out of the woman's vagina, and it is more expensive when compared to the male condom.

Vaginal Spermicides

A spermicide is a chemical that kills sperm. Vaginal spermicides come in several forms, including foam, cream, jelly, film, and suppository. Previously, in the United States, the active agent in most spermicides was nonoxynol-9, which had been previously recommended for added STI protection. However, research has shown that women who used nonoxynol-9 became infected with HIV at approximately a 50% higher rate than women who used a placebo gel. Hence, nonoxynol-9 as a spermicide actually *increases* HIV and offers no protection against gonorrhea/chlamydia infections. Current data suggest that spermicidal creams or gels should be used with a diaphragm. Spermicidal foams, creams, gels, suppositories, and films may be used alone or with a condom. Nonoxynol-9 should *not* be used.

Spermicides must be applied before the penis enters the vagina, no more than 20 minutes before intercourse. Appropriate applicators are included when the product is purchased. (See Figure 12-3.) Foam is effective immediately. However, suppositories,

Female condom
Lubricated, polyurethane adaptation of the male condom that is about 6.5 inches long and has flexible rings at both ends—one inserted vaginally, which covers the cervix, and one external, which partially covers the labia

FIGURE **12-3** ‖ Vaginal Spermicides

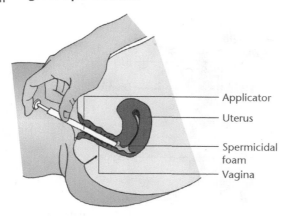

- Applicator
- Uterus
- Spermicidal foam
- Vagina

creams, or jellies require a few minutes to allow the product to melt and spread inside the vagina (package instructions describe the exact time required). Each time intercourse is repeated more spermicide must be applied. Spermicide must be left in place for at least 6–8 hours after intercourse; the vagina should not be douched or rinsed during this period.

One advantage of using spermicides is that they are available without a prescription or medical examination. They also do not manipulate the woman's hormonal system and have few side effects. It was believed that a major noncontraceptive benefit of some spermicides is that they offer some protection against sexually transmitted infections. However, guidelines for prevention and treatment of STIs from the Centers for Disease Control (CDC) suggest that spermicides are not recommended for STI/HIV protection. Furthermore, the CDC emphasizes that condoms lubricated with spermicides offer no more protection from STIs than other lubricated condoms. Finally, spermicidal-lubricated condoms may have a shorter shelf life, cost more, and be associated with increased urinary tract infections in women.

Think About It

Take a moment to answer the following question. Individuals rarely use one method of birth control throughout their fertile years. Which methods seem most suitable for you, and why, for each stage of your life?

Contraceptive Sponge

The Today **Sponge** contraceptive is a disk-shaped polyurethane device that contains spermicide. This small device is dampened with water to activate the spermicide and then inserted into the vagina before intercourse begins. The sponge protects for repeated acts of intercourse for 24 hours without the need for supplying additional spermicide. It cannot be removed for at least 6 hours after intercourse, but it should not be left in place for more than 30 hours. Possible side effects that may occur with use include irritation, allergic reactions, or difficulty with removal; and the risk of toxic shock syndrome, a rare but serious infection, is greater when the device is kept in place longer than recommended. The sponge provides no protection from sexually transmitted infections.

Sponge
Disk-shaped polyurethane device containing the spermicide nonoxynol-9 that protects for repeated acts of intercourse over 24 hours, without the need for supplying additional spermicide

FIGURE **12-4** ‖ The IUD, as It Is Inserted by a Healthcare Practitioner

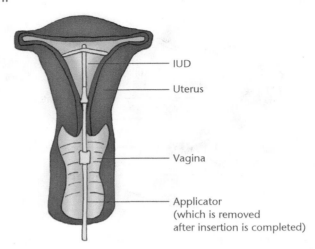

IUD

Uterus

Vagina

Applicator
(which is removed
after insertion is completed)

The Today Sponge was taken off the market for 11 years due to manufacturing concerns. These problems were eliminated, and national distribution resumed.

Intrauterine Device (IUD)

Although not technically a barrier method, the IUD is a structural device that prevents implantation and may interfere with sperm and egg transport. The **intrauterine device**, or IUD, is an object inserted into the uterus by a physician to prevent the fertilized egg from implanting on the uterine wall or to dislodge the fertilized egg if it has already implanted (see Figure 12-4). The IUD is only recommended for women who have had at least one child, are in a mutually monogamous relationship, and have no risk or history of ectopic pregnancy or pelvic inflammatory disease. Two common IUDs sold in the United States are ParaGard (copper IUD) and Mirena (hormonal IUD). The copper IUD is partly wrapped in copper and can remain in the uterus for 10 years. The hormonal IUD contains a supply of progestin, which it continuously releases into the uterus in small amounts; after 5 years, a new IUD must be inserted (American College of Obstetricians and Gynecologists, 2012).

As a result of infertility and miscarriage associated with the Dalkon Shield IUD, and subsequent lawsuits against its manufacturer by persons who were damaged by the device, use of all IUDs in the United States declined in the 1980s. However, other IUDs do not share the rates of pelvic inflammatory disease (PID) or resultant infertility associated with the Dalkon Shield. Nevertheless, other manufacturers voluntarily withdrew their IUDs from the U.S. market. The IUD was reintroduced in the United States in 2001. The IUD is often an excellent choice for women who do not anticipate future pregnancies, yet do not wish to be sterilized or for women who are unable to use hormonal contraceptives. However, it is not recommended for women who have multiple sex partners or whose partner has multiple partners (the IUD does not protect against STIs or HIV).

Diaphragm

Another barrier method of contraception is the **diaphragm**—a shallow rubber dome attached to a flexible, circular steel spring. Varying in diameter from 2–4 inches, the diaphragm covers the cervix and prevents sperm from moving beyond the vagina into the uterus. This device should always be used with a spermicidal jelly or cream.

To obtain a diaphragm, a woman must have an internal pelvic examination by a healthcare provider, who will select the appropriate size and instruct the woman on

Intrauterine device
(IUD) Object inserted into the uterus by a physician to prevent the fertilized egg from implanting on the uterine wall

Diaphragm
Shallow rubber dome attached to a flexible, circular steel spring, 2–4 inches in diameter, that can be inserted vaginally to cover the cervix and prevent sperm from entering the uterus

FIGURE **12-5** ‖ The Diaphragm

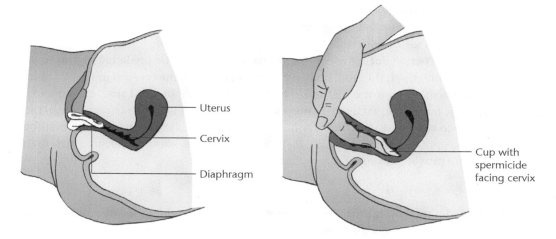

Uterus

Cervix

Diaphragm

Cup with spermicide facing cervix

how to insert the diaphragm. The woman will be told to apply spermicidal cream or jelly on the inside of the diaphragm and around the rim before inserting it into the vagina (no more than 2 hours before intercourse). The diaphragm must also be left in place for 6 to 8 hours after intercourse to permit any lingering sperm to be killed by the spermicidal agent (see Figure 12-5).

After the birth of a child, a miscarriage, abdominal surgery, or the gain or loss of 10 pounds, a woman who uses a diaphragm should consult her physician or health-care practitioner to ensure a continued good fit. In any case, the diaphragm should be checked every 2 years for fit.

A major advantage of the diaphragm is that it does not interfere with the woman's hormonal system and has few, if any, side effects. Also, for those couples who feel that menstruation diminishes their capacity to enjoy intercourse, the diaphragm may be used to catch the menstrual flow for a brief time.

On the negative side, some women feel that use of the diaphragm with the spermicidal gel is a messy nuisance, and it is possible that use of a spermicide may produce an allergic reaction. Furthermore, some partners feel that spermicides make oral genital sex less enjoyable. Finally, if the diaphragm does not fit properly or if it is left in place too long (more than 24 hours), pregnancy or toxic shock syndrome can result.

Cervical Cap

The **cervical cap** is a thimble-shaped contraceptive device made of rubber or polyethylene that fits tightly over the cervix and is held in place by suction. FemCap is the only brand of cervical cap available in the United States today. Like the diaphragm, the cervical cap—which is used in conjunction with spermicidal cream or jelly—prevents sperm from entering the uterus. Cervical caps have been widely available in Europe for some time and were approved for marketing in the United States in 1988. The cervical cap cannot be used during menstruation because the suction cannot be maintained. The effectiveness, problems, risks, and advantages are similar to those of the diaphragm (Planned Parenthood Federation of America Inc., 2013).

12.1c Natural Family Planning Methods

Also referred to as **periodic abstinence**, *rhythm method*, and *fertility awareness*, natural family planning involves refraining from sexual intercourse during the 1–2 weeks each month when the woman is thought to be fertile. Women who use periodic

Cervical cap
Thimble-shaped contraceptive device made of rubber or polyethylene that fits tightly over the cervix and is held in place by suction

Periodic abstinence
Refraining from sexual intercourse during the 1 to 2 weeks each month when the woman is thought to be fertile; also known as *rhythm method, fertility awareness,* and *natural family planning*

abstinence must know their time of ovulation and avoid intercourse just before, during, and immediately after that time. Calculating the fertile period involves three assumption: (1) ovulation occurs on day 14 (plus or minus 2 days) before the onset of the next menstrual period; (2) sperm typically remain viable for 2–3 days; and (3) the ovum survives for 24 hours.

The time period during which the woman is fertile can be predicted in four ways: the calendar method, the basal body temperature method, the cervical mucus method, and the hormone-in-urine method. These methods may be used not only to avoid pregnancy, but also to facilitate conception if the woman wants to become pregnant. We provide only basic instructions here for using periodic abstinence as a method of contraception. Individuals considering this method should consult with their healthcare provider for more information.

Calendar Method

The calendar method is the oldest and most widely practiced method of avoiding pregnancy through periodic abstinence. The calendar method allows women to calculate the onset and duration of their fertile period. When using the calendar method to predict when the egg is ready to be fertilized, the woman keeps a record of the length of her menstrual cycles for 8 months. The menstrual cycle is counted from day one of the menstrual period through the last day before the onset of the next period. She then calculates her fertile period by subtracting 18 days from the length of her shortest cycle and 11 days from the length of her longest cycle. The resulting figures indicate the range of her fertility period. It is during this time that the woman must abstain from intercourse if pregnancy is not desired.

For example, suppose that during an 8-month period, a woman had cycle lengths of 26, 32, 27, 30, 28, 27, 28, and 29 days. Subtracting 18 from her shortest cycle (26) and 11 from her longest cycle (32), she knows the days that the egg is likely to be in the Fallopian tubes. To avoid getting pregnant, she must avoid intercourse on days 8 through 21 of her cycle.

The calendar method of predicting the "safe" period may be unreliable for two reasons. First, the next month the woman may ovulate at a different time than any of the previous 8 months. Second, sperm life varies; they may live up to 5 days, long enough to meet the next egg in the Fallopian tubes.

Basal Body Temperature (BBT) Method

The BBT method is based on determining the time of ovulation by measuring temperature changes that occur in the woman's body shortly after ovulation. The basal body temperature is the temperature of the body, at rest, on waking in the morning. To establish her BBT, the woman must take her temperature before she gets out of bed for 3 months. Shortly before, during, or right after ovulation, the woman's BBT usually rises about 0.4–0.8°F. Some women notice a temperature drop about 12 to 24 hours before it begins to rise after ovulation. Intercourse must be avoided from the time the woman's temperature drops until her temperature has remained elevated for 3 consecutive days. Intercourse may be resumed on the night of the third day after the BBT has risen and remained elevated for 3 consecutive days. Advantages include being "natural" and avoiding chemicals. Disadvantages include the higher pregnancy rate for persons using this method.

Cervical Mucus Method

The cervical mucus method, also known as the *Billings method* of natural family planning, is based on observations of changes in the cervical mucus during the woman's monthly cycle. The woman may observe her cervical mucus by wiping herself with toilet paper. **Spinbarkeit** refers to the slippery, elastic, raw egg white consistency of the cervical mucus that becomes evident at the time of ovulation. When the cervical mucus becomes this consistency, it is likely that the woman has ovulated.

The woman should abstain from intercourse during her menstrual period because the mucus is obscured by menstrual blood and cannot be observed, and ovulation can occur during menstruation. After menstruation ceases, intercourse is permitted on days when no mucus is present or thick mucus is present in small amounts. Intercourse should be avoided just prior to, during, and immediately after ovulation if pregnancy is not desired. Before ovulation, mucus is cloudy, yellow or white, and sticky. During ovulation, cervical mucus is thin, clear, slippery, and stretchy and resembles raw egg white. This phase is known as the *peak symptom*. During ovulation, some women experience ovulatory pain referred to as **Mittelschmerz**. Such pain may include feelings of heaviness, abdominal swelling, rectal pain or discomfort, and lower abdominal pain or discomfort on either side. Mittelschmerz is useful for identifying ovulation but not for predicting it. Intercourse may resume 4 days after the disappearance of the peak symptom and continue until the next menses. During this time, cervical mucus may be either clear and watery, or cloudy and sticky, or there may be no mucus noticed at all.

Advantages of the cervical mucus method include that it requires the woman to become familiar with her reproductive system, and it can give early warning about some STIs (which can affect cervical mucus). However, the cervical mucus method requires the woman to distinguish between mucus and semen, spermicidal agents, lubrication, and infectious discharges. Also, the woman must not douche because she will wash away what she is trying to observe.

Hormone-in-Urine Method

A hormone (LH, luteinizing hormone) is released in increasing amounts in the ovulating woman 12 to 24 hours prior to ovulation. Women can purchase over-the-counter ovulation tests, such as First Response and Ovutime. These are designed to ascertain the surge of LH into the urine (signaling ovulation), so the couple will know to avoid intercourse to maximize the chance of preventing pregnancy. Some test kits involve the woman exposing a test stick during urination, whereas others involve collecting the urine in a small cup and placing the test stick in the cup. In practice, the woman conducts a number of urine tests over a period of days because each test kit comes supplied with five or six tests. Some women experience the LH hormone surge within a 10-hour span, so the woman may need to test herself more than once a day. Of course, this method can also be used to predict the best time to have intercourse to maximize chances of becoming pregnant.

12.1d Non-methods: Withdrawal and Douching

Because withdrawal and douching are not effective in preventing pregnancy, we call them *non-methods* of birth control (some may argue that *natural family planning methods* are also non-methods because a high rate of pregnancies results). Also known as **coitus interruptus**, **withdrawal** is the practice whereby the man withdraws his penis from the vagina before he ejaculates. The advantages of coitus interruptus are that it requires no devices or chemicals, and it is always available. The disadvantages of withdrawal are that it does not provide protection from STIs, it may interrupt the sexual response cycle and diminish the pleasure for the couple, and it is very ineffective in preventing pregnancy. (Coitus interruptus is also known as withdrawal).

Spinbarkeit
The slippery, elastic, raw egg white consistency of the cervical mucus that becomes evident at the time of ovulation and signals that it is likely the woman has ovulated

Mittelschmerz
Ovulatory pain

Coitus interruptus
Practice whereby the man withdraws his penis from the vagina before he ejaculates (Coitus interruptus is also known as withdrawal)

Withdrawal is not a reliable form of contraception for two reasons. First, a man can unknowingly emit a small amount of pre-ejaculatory fluid, which may contain sperm. One drop can contain millions of sperm. In addition, the man may lack the self-control to withdraw his penis before ejaculation, or he may delay his withdrawal too long and inadvertently ejaculate some semen near the vaginal opening of his partner. Sperm deposited there can live in the moist labia and make their way up the vagina.

Although some women believe that douching is an effective form of contraception, it is not. Douching refers to rinsing or cleansing the vaginal canal. After intercourse, the woman fills a syringe with water, any of a variety of solutions, or a spermicidal agent that can be purchased over the counter, and then flushes (so she assumes) the sperm from her vagina. But in some cases, the fluid will actually force sperm up through the cervix. In other cases, a large number of sperm may already have passed through the cervix to the uterus, so the douche may do little good.

Sperm may be found in the cervical mucus within 90 seconds after ejaculation. In effect, douching does little to deter conception and may even encourage it. In addition, douching is associated with an increased risk for pelvic inflammatory disease and ectopic pregnancy.

12.1e Emergency Contraception

Also called **postcoital contraception**, **emergency contraception** refers to various types of combined estrogen-progesterone morning-after pills or post-coital IUD insertion used primarily in three circumstances: when a woman has unprotected intercourse, when a contraceptive method fails (such as condom breakage or slippage), and when a woman is raped. Emergency contraception methods should be used in emergencies for those times when unprotected intercourse has occurred and medication can be taken within 5 days (120 hours of exposure).

Combined Estrogen-Progesterone

The most common morning-after pills are the combined estrogen-progesterone oral contraceptives routinely taken to prevent pregnancy. Common names include Plan B One Step, Next Choice One Dose, My Way, and Ella. Known as the *Yuzpe method* after the physician who proposed it, this method involves ingesting a certain number of tablets of combined estrogen-progesterone. In higher doses, they serve to prevent ovulation, fertilization of the egg, or transportation of the egg to the uterus. They may also make the uterine lining inhospitable to implantation. *Emergency contraception must be taken within 120 hours of unprotected intercourse to be effective.* Common side effects of combined estrogen-progesterone emergency contraception pills include nausea, vomiting, headaches, and breast tenderness, although some women also experience abdominal pain, headache, and dizziness. Side effects subside within 1 to 2 days after treatment is completed. Table 12-1 suggests a much lower rate of ending the pregnancy (75%), but this percentage includes a wide range of when the pills are taken. In 2013, the FDA approved the availability of the morning-after pill, Plan B One Step, over the counter for purchase without a prescription regardless of age. Some other two-pill brands are available behind the pharmacy counter with age-restrictions for purchase for age 17 or older, and available to younger women by prescription only. Ella is restricted "by prescription only" (Planned Parenthood Federation of America Inc., 2013; Office of Population Research & Association of Reproductive Health Professionals, 2013).

Postcoital IUD Insertion

Insertion of a copper IUD within 5 days after ovulation in a cycle when unprotected intercourse has occurred is very effective for preventing pregnancy. This option,

Postcoital contraception
See Emergency contraception

Emergency contraception
Contraceptive administered within 72 hours following unprotected intercourse; referred to as the "morning-after pill"

TABLE **12-1**	Methods of Contraception and STI Protection, Typical Use® and Effectiveness				
Method	Rates[1]	STI Protection	Benefits	Disadvantages	Cost[2]
Oral contraceptive (the pill)	92%	No	High effectiveness rate, 24-hour protection, and menstrual regulation	Daily administration, side effects possible, medication interactions	$10–42 per month
Nexplanon/Implanon NXT® or Implanon® (3-year implant)	99.95%	No	High effectiveness rate, long-term protection	Side effects possible, menstrual changes	$400–600 insertion
Depo-Provera® (3-month injection) or Depo-subQ Provera 104®	97%	No	High effectiveness rate, long-term protection	Decreases body calcium, not recommended for use longer than 2 years for most users, side effects likely	$45–75 per injection
Ortho Evra® (transdermal patch)	92%	No	Same as oral contraceptives except use is weekly, not daily	Patch changed weekly, side effects possible	$15–32 per month
NuvaRing® (vaginal ring)	92%	No	Same as oral contraceptives except use is monthly, not daily	Must be comfortable with body for insertion	$15–48 per month
Male condom	85%	Yes	Few or no side effects, easy to purchase and use	Can interrupt spontaneity	$2–10 a box
Female condom	79%	Yes	Few or no side effects, easy to purchase	Decreased sensation and insertion takes practice	$4–10 a box
Spermicide	71%	No	Many forms to choose, easy to purchase and use	Can cause irritation, can be messy	$8–18 per box/tube/can
Today® Sponge[3]	68–84%	No	Few side effects, effective for 24 hours after insertion	Spermicide irritation possible	$3–5 per sponge
Diaphragm & Cervical cap[3]	68–84%	No	Few side effects, can be inserted within 2 hours before intercourse	Can be messy, increased risk of vaginal/UTI infections	$50–200 plus spermicide
Intrauterine device (IUD): *Paraguard or Mirena*	98.2–99%	No/little maintenance, longer term protection	Risk of PID increased, chance of expulsion		$150–300
Withdrawal	73%	No	Requires little planning, always available	Pre-ejaculatory fluid can contain sperm	
Periodic abstinence	75%	No	No side effects, accepted in all religions/cultures	Requires a lot of planning, need ability to interpret fertility signs	$0
Emergency contraception	75%	No	Provides an option after intercourse has occurred	Must be taken within 72 hours, side effects likely	$10–32
Abstinence	100%	Yes	No risk of pregnancy or STIs	Partners both have to agree to abstain	

1 Effectiveness rates are listed as percentages of women not experiencing an unintended pregnancy during the first year of typical use. Typical use refers to use under real-life conditions. Perfect use effectiveness rates are higher.

2 Costs may vary. The Affordable Care Act healthcare legislation passed by Congress and signed into law by President Obama on March 23, 2010, requires health insurance plans to cover preventive services and eliminate cost sharing for some services, including "All Food and Drug Administration approved contraceptive methods, sterilization procedures, and patient education and counseling for all women with reproductive capacity" (U.S. Department of Health and Human Services Health Resources and Services Administration, Women's Preventive Services Guidelines, http://www.hrsa.gov/womensguidelines/, August 2013).

3 Lower percentages apply to parous women (women who have given birth). Higher rates apply to nulliparous women (women who have never given birth).

Source: Beth Credle Burt, MAEd, CHES, a health education specialist. Education Services Project Manager, Siemens Healthcare. Appreciation is expressed to Beth Credle Burt for her review/editing/contribution to the content of this table and the preceding section.

however, is used much less frequently than hormonal treatment because women who need emergency contraception often are not appropriate IUD candidates.

12.2 Sterilization

Unlike the temporary and reversible methods of contraception discussed in Section 12.1, **sterilization** is a permanent surgical procedure that prevents reproduction (Bartz & Greenberg, 2008). Sterilization may be a contraceptive method of choice when the woman should not have more children for health reasons or when individuals are certain about their desire to have no more children or to remain childfree. Most couples complete their intended childbearing in their late 20s or early 30s, leaving more than 15 years of continued risk of unwanted pregnancy. Because of the risk of pill use at older ages and the lower reliability of alternative birth control methods, sterilization has become the most popular method of contraception among married women who have completed their families.

Think About It

Take a moment to answer the following questions. Some college students feel certain that they do not want to have a child—ever. Do you think that one should be a certain age before physicians can legally perform sterilization procedures because the person may change his or her mind? Or, do you feel this right belongs to the individual?

Slightly more than half of all sterilizations are performed on women. In addition to men being fearful of a vasectomy (which they sometimes equate with castration and the removal of their manhood), women may be more open to sterilization—"I'm the one that ends up being pregnant and having the baby," said one woman. "So I want to make sure that I never get pregnant again."

12.2a Female Sterilization

Although a woman may be sterilized by removal of her ovaries (**oophorectomy**) or uterus (**hysterectomy**), these operations are not normally undertaken for the sole purpose of sterilization because the ovaries produce important hormones (as well as eggs) and because both procedures carry the risks of major surgery.

The usual procedures of female sterilization are the salpingectomy and a variant of it, the laparoscopy. **Salpingectomy**, also known as tubal ligation, or tying the tubes, is often performed under a general anesthetic while the woman is in the hospital (Figure 12-6). Many women elect to have this procedure performed just after they have delivered a baby. An incision is made in the lower abdomen, just above the pubic line, and the Fallopian tubes are brought into view one at a time. A part of each tube is cut out; the ends are tied, clamped, or cauterized (burned). The operation takes about 30 minutes. About 700,000 such procedures are performed annually. The average national cost is cost is around $9,200.

A less expensive and quicker (about 15 minutes) form of salpingectomy, which is performed on an outpatient basis, is the **laparoscopy**. Often using local anesthesia, the surgeon inserts a small, lighted viewing instrument (laparoscope) through the woman's abdominal wall just below the navel through which the uterus and

Sterilization
Permanent surgical procedure that prevents reproduction

Oophorectomy
Surgical removal of the ovaries

Hysterectomy
Surgical removal of the uterus

Salpingectomy
Tubal ligation or "tying of the tubes"; sterilization procedure whereby the woman's Fallopian tubes are cut out and the ends are tied, clamped, or cauterized so that eggs cannot pass down the Fallopian tubes to be fertilized

Laparoscopy
Surgery using a laparoscope; sometimes used for tubal ligation

FIGURE **12-6** ‖ Female Sterilization: Tubal Sterilization

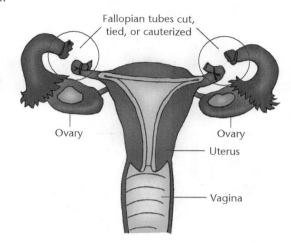

the Fallopian tubes can be seen. The surgeon then makes another small incision in the lower abdomen and inserts a special pair of forceps that carry electricity to cauterize the tubes. The laparoscope and the forceps are then withdrawn, the small wounds are closed with a single stitch, and small bandages are placed over the closed incisions. (Laparoscopy is also known as "the Band-Aid operation.") The cost varies from $1,500 to $5,000. As an alternative to reaching the Fallopian tubes through an opening below the navel, the surgeon may make a small incision in the back of the vaginal barrel (vaginal tubal ligation).

In late 2002, the FDA approved **Essure**, a permanent sterilization procedure that requires no cutting and only a local anesthetic in a 0.5 hour procedure to thread small metal coils that block the Fallopian tubes. Women typically may return home within 45 minutes (and to work the next day). During the first 3 months, the woman cannot rely on the Essure system and must use another type of birth control. After 3 months, she will undergo an x-ray procedure to confirm that her fallopian tubes are blocked. If this shows successful blockage, she can stop using her back-up birth control (US Department of Health & Human Services Food and Drug Administration. Medical Devices Essure™ System—P020014, 2012).

These procedures for female sterilization are more than 95% effective, but sometimes they have complications. In rare cases, a blood vessel in the abdomen is torn open during the sterilization and bleeds into the abdominal cavity. When this happens, another operation is necessary to find the bleeding vessel and tie it closed. Occasionally, injury occurs to the small or large intestine, which may cause nausea, vomiting, and loss of appetite. The fact that death may result, if only rarely, is a reminder that female sterilization is surgery and involves some risks, like all surgery.

In addition, although some sterilization for women may be reversed, a woman should become sterilized only if she does not want to have a biological child. Hillis and colleagues (2000) reported that women who were age 30 or younger at the time they were sterilized were twice as likely to report feelings of regret than women who were older than 30.

12.2b Male Sterilization

The most frequent form of male sterilization is the **vasectomy** (Figure 12-7). There are two different ways for men to be sterilized. Both occur with local anesthetic in the physician's office. With incision methods, the health care provider then makes an incision on each side of the scrotum to reach each vas deferens—the tubes that carry

Essure
Permanent sterilization procedure that requires no cutting and only a local anesthetic in a 0.5 hour procedure that blocks the Fallopian tubes

Vasectomy
Minor surgical procedure whereby the vas deferens are cut so as to prevent sperm from entering the penis

FIGURE **12-7** ‖ Male Sterilization: Vasectomy

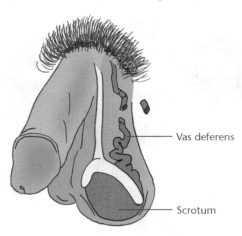

Vas deferens

Scrotum

sperm. Each tube is blocked and a small section of each tube is removed, in most proce-dures. Tubes may be tied off or blocked with surgical clips, or they may be closed using an instrument with an electrical current. With the no-incision ("no-scalpel") method, the skin is not cut; rather, one tiny puncture is made to reach both tubes. The tubes are then tied off, cauterized, or blocked. The tiny puncture heals quickly. No stitches are needed, and no scarring takes place. The no-scalpel method reduces bleeding and decreases the possibility of infection, bruising, and other complications. Either procedure takes about 15–20 minutes and costs vary from $350 to $1,000. The man can leave the physician's office within a short time (Planned Parenthood Federation of America Inc., 2013). (See Personal Experience 12-1).

PERSONAL
Experience   *12-1*

My Experience with Vasectomy

After my divorce and three children, I knew that I never wanted to father another child. Getting a vasectomy would eliminate the discussion of additional children with a future partner and ensure that contraception was always present. But I was hesitant. Getting "cut" didn't sound very enticing; and I feared I would be less horny, ejaculate less, and become effeminate.

I began to read research on guys who had been "cut," talked with guys who had had a vasectomy, and with a urologist. The research said that the "operation" was a cake-walk and that the only problem was potential for infection—but this risk was low. The fears of no longer being horny, less ejaculate, and becoming effeminate turned to be just that—unwarranted fears with no basis. I still wasn't sure and put it off for six months before finally making the appointment.

The procedure took about 10 minutes and except for the needle to "deaden the cutting" was relatively painless. It did take much longer (six weeks) to heal than I had been led to believe (two weeks), but this was not a major issue. It's been years now and I'm glad I had it done—no regrets. However, I've got a buddy who got "cut" and then fell in love with a gal who wanted a family. He tried but was not able to have his vasectomy reversed, so it is important to think of the procedure as a permanent one.

Take a moment to answer the following questions. If you are in a stable relationship and do not want any children (or any more children), at what age do you think it appropriate to become sterilized or to ask your partner to become sterilized? Most men are reluctant. Why?

Because sperm do not disappear from the ejaculate immediately after a vasectomy (some remain in the vas deferens below the severed portion), a couple should use another method of contraception until the man has had about 20 ejaculations. In about 1% of the cases, the vas deferens grows back, and the man becomes fertile again.

A vasectomy does not affect the man's desire for sex, ability to have an erection or an orgasm, amount of ejaculate (sperm comprise only a minute portion of the seminal fluid), health, or chance of prostate cancer. Although in some instances a vasectomy may be reversed, a man should get a vasectomy only if he does not want to have a biological child.

Abortion
Deliberate termination of a pregnancy through chemical or surgical means

12.3 Abortion

National DATA

Among American women, half will have an unintended pregnancy and 30% will have an abortion. About 60% of women having an abortion are in their 20s and unmarried (Guttmacher Institute, 2012).

An **abortion** may be either an **induced abortion**, which is the deliberate termination of a pregnancy through chemical or surgical means, or a **spontaneous abortion** (miscarriage), which is the unintended termination of a pregnancy. Miscarriages often represent a significant loss that is associated with depression/anxiety (Geller, Psaros, & Kornfield, 2010) and marital unhappiness (Sugiura-Ogasawara, Suzuki, Ozaki, Katano, Suzumori, & Kitaori, 2013).

Induced abortion
The deliberate termination of a pregnancy through chemical or surgical means.

Spontaneous abortion
the unintended termination of a pregnancy

Suction curettage
Abortion procedure performed the first 6 to 8 weeks of pregnancy whereby a hollow plastic rod is inserted into the woman's uterus where the fetal tissue is evacuated

Vacuum aspiration
See Suction curettage

12.3a Methods of Abortion

Prior to the availability of modern surgical techniques, abortion in the late eighteenth and early nineteenth centuries was performed by flushing the uterus with caustic substances (such as gunpowder, quinine, or oil of juniper) or by inserting sticks of silver nitrate into the cervix. In this section, we look at modern-day methods of abortion. The procedure used to perform an abortion depends largely on the stage of the pregnancy, as measured from the first day of the last menstrual period.

Suction Curettage

Pregnancy may be terminated during the first 6 to 8 weeks through a procedure called **suction curettage**, also referred to as **vacuum aspiration**. After the administration of a local anesthetic (a general anesthetic may be used at the patient's request), a hollow plastic rod attached to a suction aspirator is inserted into the woman's

FIGURE **12-8** ‖ Suction Curettage

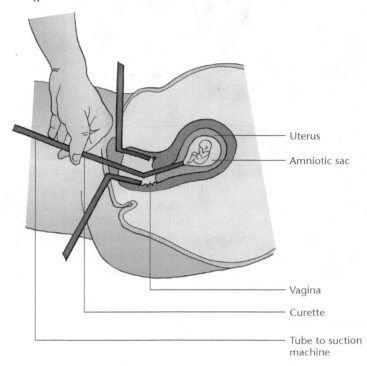

- Uterus
- Amniotic sac
- Vagina
- Curette
- Tube to suction machine

uterus through the cervix. The device suctions the fetal tissue out of the uterus into a container. Following the suction procedure, the physician may explore the uterine cavity with a small metal instrument (curette) to ensure that all the tissue has been removed. The procedure, which takes about 10 to 20 minutes, can be performed on an outpatient basis in a clinic or a physician's office. Following this procedure, the patient usually experiences some bleeding and cramping, which is normal (see Figure 12-8).

Dilation and Suction

Dilation and suction (D & S), a method of abortion used during the first 12 weeks of pregnancy, is essentially the same as suction curettage, except that the cervix is dilated before the suction procedure. Cervical dilation may be achieved by inserting laminaria into the cervix the day before the abortion is performed. Laminaria are dried, sterile rods of compressed seaweed stems that, when inserted into the cervix, absorb moisture and increase in diameter, thereby dilating the cervix. Cervical dilation may also be achieved by using a metal device designed to dilate the cervix just prior to the abortion. After suctioning the contents of the uterus, a physician uses a metal surgical instrument to scrape any remaining fetal tissue and placenta from the uterine walls. This method is also known as **dilation and curettage**, or **D & C**. A local or general anesthetic may be used.

Dilation and Evacuation

Dilation and evacuation (D & E), an abortion procedure used in the second trimester of pregnancy (13–24 weeks' gestation), involves dilating the cervix and dismembering the fetus inside the uterus so that the body parts can be more easily suctioned out. Extraction instruments called *ringed forceps* are also used to remove the fetal tissue. A local or general anesthetic may be used.

Dilation and suction (D & S)
Abortion procedure during the first 12 weeks whereby the cervix is dilated before the suction procedure occurs

Dilation and curettage (D & C)
Abortion procedure whereby a metal surgical instrument is used to scrape any remaining fetal tissue and placenta from the uterine walls after suctioning the contents of the uterus

Dilation and evacuation (D & E)
Abortion procedure during the second trimester (13–24 weeks' gestation) whereby the cervix is dilated and the fetal parts inside are dismembered so they can be suctioned out

Intact Dilation and Extraction

An alternative to D & E is a procedure called **intact dilation and extraction (D & X)**, which results in the whole fetus being aborted. After dilating the cervix, a physician pulls the fetus down into the birth canal, feet first. Then, with the rest of the body delivered and the head still lodged against the cervix, the physician inserts an instrument to make an opening in the base of the skull, inserts a suction catheter into this hole, evacuates the contents, and removes the fetus. An advantage of this procedure, if the fetus is malformed, is that certain types of testing can be more easily performed on an intact fetus to assess the woman's chances for a normal pregnancy in the future.

Abortion opponents have labeled dilation and extraction abortions **partial-birth abortions** because the limbs and torso are typically delivered before the fetus has died. When D & X abortions are performed, it is typically because the fetus has a serious defect, the pregnancy jeopardizes the woman's health, or both. Abortions are rarely performed by dilation and extraction.

Induced Abortions

Another abortion method used late in the second trimester involves inducing premature labor by injecting either saline or prostaglandins through the abdomen into the amniotic sac around the fetus. Prostaglandins may also be administered through vaginal suppositories. The injection or suppositories induce contractions that cause the cervix to dilate. An intravenous drip of oxytocin continues the labor contractions. The contractions are painful and can continue for several hours before the woman expels the fetus and placenta. Painkillers and local anesthesia are used to ease the woman's discomfort. This procedure is major surgery and must be performed in a hospital.

Pharmaceutical Abortion

Also called a **medical abortion**, a **pharmaceutical abortion** involves the intentional termination of pregnancy through the use of pharmaceutical drugs. In 1997, the drug **Mifepristone** became available in the United States after being approved by the U.S. Food and Drug Administration (see Figure 12-9). This drug was originally known by its French name, **RU-486**; it is now sold as Mifeprex and is known as the "abortion pill." Actual use of the drug to induce abortion involves several steps. A physician determines the length of pregnancy to make sure the woman is less than 7 weeks' pregnant. The permitted length of gestation varies, however. In France Mifepristone is approved for use up to 40 days since the onset of the last menstrual period, and up to 63 days in Great Britain and Sweden. Current FDA approval in the United States is for up to 49 days.

Mifepristone is an antiprogestin, which interferes with the uterine development that would support implantation of the fertilized egg. Two days after the Mifepristone is administered, a prostaglandin (misoprostol) is administered, which causes stimulation of uterine contractions that help to dislodge and expel the embryo. A heavy menstrual flow follows. The woman makes a final visit to the physician to confirm that the abortion has been completed and to make sure the bleeding has stopped.

When women are offered a choice of surgical or medical abortion, most choose the medical method. The primary reasons for preferring medical abortions include greater privacy and autonomy (it can be done at home), less invasiveness, and greater naturalness. Another advantage of selecting a medical abortion is that a physician can dispense such drugs in the privacy of an office, which means women can avoid antiabortion forces that target abortion clinics. A decade of experience with Mifepristone in France, Great Britain, and Sweden has not shown that its availability has caused an increase in the number of abortions, but it has influenced their timing at earlier gestation.

Intact dilation and extraction (D & X)
Abortion procedure involving breech delivery of fetus (except for the head) and partial evacuation of the brain, resulting in the vaginal delivery of a dead fetus

Partial-birth abortions
Nonmedical term used by abortion opponents to describe abortions performed very late in pregnancy in which the terminated fetus is delivered (See Intact dilation and extraction.)

Medical abortion
Intentional termination of pregnancy through the use of pharmaceutical drugs

Pharmaceutical abortion
See Medical abortion

Mifepristone
Synthetic steroid that effectively inhibits implantation of a fertilized egg by making the endometrium unsuitable for implantation which, in effect, aborts the fetus; may be used within the first 7 weeks of pregnancy (See also RU-486.)

RU-486
Known as the "abortion pill" and approved for use up to 49 days since the onset of the last menstrual period.

FIGURE **12-9** ‖ How Early Medical Abortion Works

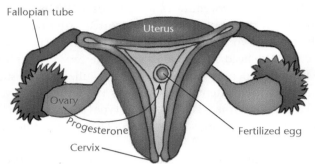

Progesterone is the hormone that supports changes in the uterine lining, allowing a fertilized egg to implant and develop in the uterus.

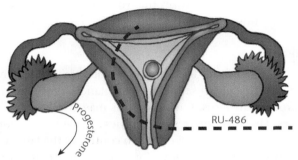

Mifepristone is an antiprogestin, and when administered early in pregnancy, prevents the uterus from supporting the fertilized egg.

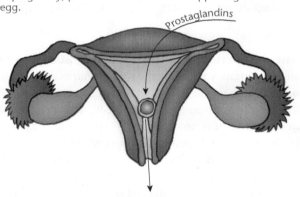

Two days later, prostaglandin is administered, which stimulates contractions of the uterus, expelling the products of conception.

12.3b Abortion Court Rulings and Legislation in the United States

One of the most controversial political issues in U.S. society is abortion legislation. After a brief look at the historical background of abortion court rulings and legislation, we will discuss the landmark *Roe v. Wade* case and more recent judicial and legislative action regarding abortion in the United States.

In the colonial United States, abortion was neither prohibited nor uncommon. During this time, the states were governed by English common law, which permitted abortion until *quickening*—the time when the woman could feel movement of the fetus inside her (usually in the fourth or fifth month of pregnancy). Even if an abortion was performed after quickening, the woman was immune from prosecution.

The legal control of abortion by statute began in 1821. Because thousands of women had died taking medically prescribed poisons to induce abortions, Connecticut passed a law prohibiting the use of poisons to induce post-quickening abortions. This statute existed primarily to protect the lives of women. In 1828, New York enacted a law making abortion of a non-quickened fetus a misdemeanor crime and abortion of a quickened fetus second-degree manslaughter, unless the abortion was necessary to preserve the woman's life.

In the mid-nineteenth century, the American Medical Association led the campaign to criminalize abortion. Their concerns were both economic and moral. Formally trained physicians competed economically with midwives, who assisted not only in births but also in abortions. Moral concerns in the medical community over abortion resulted, in part, from advances in the scientific understanding of human development as a continuous process. These concerns led physicians to question the relevance of the distinction between quickened and non-quickened fetuses.

By 1900, abortion was illegal in all U.S. jurisdictions. In most states, the sole legal reason an abortion could be performed was if continuation of the pregnancy threatened the life of the woman. Women who sought abortions for personal, social, or economic reasons were forced to seek more dangerous illegal abortions. In spite of the criminalization of abortion during this era, it is estimated that as many as 1 in 3 pregnancies was terminated by induced abortion (Rubin, 1987).

Roe v. Wade: A Landmark Decision

The twentieth century movement to legalize abortion was led by advocates of women's rights and family planning. The abortion rights movement did not gain ground until 1973, however, when the U.S. Supreme Court ruled in the famous *Roe v. Wade* case that any restriction on abortions during the first trimester of pregnancy was unconstitutional. This ruling declared that during the first 3 months of pregnancy, the decision to have an abortion would be between the pregnant woman and her physician. In the second trimester (the fourth through the sixth month of pregnancy), the state might regulate the abortion procedure (by requiring that the abortion take place in a hospital, for example) so as to protect the woman's health. During the last trimester, the state would have an interest in protecting the viable fetus, so the state might restrict or prohibit abortion. In effect, the Supreme Court ruled that the fetus is a potential life and not a "person" until the third trimester. The *Roe v. Wade* decision was based on the right to privacy; government intrusion in the doctor-patient relationship and a woman's reproductive decisions were seen as violations of that right. The current abortion debate is a conflict between two fundamental values: the right of a fetus to live and the right of a woman to control her own body.

Abortion Court Rulings and Legislation Since *Roe v. Wade*

In spite of *Roe v. Wade*, the Guttmacher Institute (2013) noted various legal restrictions on abortion:

Physician and Hospital Requirements

Thirty-nine states require an abortion to be performed by a licensed physician. Twenty states require an abortion to be performed in a hospital after a specified point in the pregnancy, and 18 states require the involvement of a second physician after a specified point.

Gestational Limits

Forty-one states prohibit abortions—generally except when necessary to protect the woman's life or health—after a specified point in pregnancy, most often fetal viability.

"Partial-Birth" Abortion

Nineteen states have laws in effect that prohibit "partial-birth" abortion. Three of these laws apply only to postviability abortions.

Public Funding

Seventeen (17) states use their own funds to pay for all or most medically necessary abortions for Medicaid enrollees in the state. Thirty-two states and the District of Columbia prohibit the use of state funds except in those cases when federal funds are available: where the woman's life is in danger or the pregnancy is the result of rape or incest. In defiance of federal requirements, South Dakota limits funding to cases of life endangerment only.

Coverage by Private Insurance

Eight states restrict coverage of abortion in private insurance plans, most often limiting coverage to only when the woman's life would be endangered if the pregnancy were carried to term. Most states allow the purchase of additional abortion coverage at an additional cost.

Refusal

Forty-six states allow individual healthcare providers to refuse to participate in an abortion. Forty-three states allow institutions to refuse to perform abortions, 16 of which limit refusal to private or religious institutions.

State Mandated Counseling

Seventeen states mandate that women be given counseling before an abortion that includes information on at least one of the following: the purported link between abortion and breast cancer (5 states), the ability of a fetus to feel pain (12 states), or long term mental health consequences for the woman (8 states).

Waiting Periods

Twenty-six states require a woman seeking an abortion to wait a specified period of time, usually 24 hours, between when she receives counseling and the procedure is performed. Nine of these states have laws that effectively require the woman make two separate trips to the clinic to obtain the procedure.

Parental Involvement

Thirty-eight states require some type of parental involvement in a minor's decision to have an abortion. Twenty-one states require one or both parents to consent to the procedure, while 12 require that one or both parents be notified and 5 states require both parental consent and notification.

12.3c Attitudes Toward Abortion

Few issues in human sexuality are as controversial as abortion. Attitudes toward abortion range from fierce opposition to approval of abortion under certain circumstances (including rape and endangerment of a woman's life) to staunch support for legal and affordable access to abortion on request.

Private Attitudes Toward Abortion

Attitudes toward abortion vary according to the circumstances. For example, abortion is more likely to be viewed as an acceptable option if continuing the pregnancy endangers the mother's health, if a severe birth defect exists, or if the pregnancy is the result of rape or incest.

Pro-Life Abortion Position

A dichotomy of attitudes toward abortion is reflected in two opposing groups of abortion activists. Individuals and groups who oppose abortion are commonly referred to as "pro-life" or "antiabortion."

It is a poverty to decide that a child must die so that you may live as you wish.

Mother Teresa

Of 1,091 undergraduate males, 22% disagreed that abortion is acceptable under certain conditions (of 3,449 undergraduate females, 25% disagreed) (Hall & Knox, 2013). Pro-life groups favor abortion policies or a complete ban on abortion. They essentially believe the following:

1. The unborn fetus has a right to live, and that right should be protected.
2. Abortion is a violent and immoral solution to unintended pregnancy.
3. The life of an unborn fetus is sacred and should be protected, even at the cost of individual difficulties for the pregnant woman.

Reproductive freedom is critical to a whole range of issues. If we can't take charge of this most personal aspect of our lives, we can't take care of anything. It should not be seen as a privilege or as a benefit, but a fundamental human right.

Faye Wattleton

National DATA

A quarter of the U.S. public (25%) sees abortion as morally wrong and would like to have Roe v. Wade completely overturned (Pew Research Center, 2013).

Foster and colleagues (2013) studied the effect of pro-life protesters outside of abortion clinics on those individuals who came to the clinic to get an abortion. The researchers interviewed 956 women, 16% of which said that they were very upset by the protesters. However, exposure to the protesters was not associated with differences in emotions one week after the abortion.

Pro-Choice Abortion Position

In the sample of 1,099 undergraduate males, 64% agreed that, "abortion is acceptable under certain conditions" (of 3,449 undergraduate females, 63%) (Hall & Knox, 2013). Pro-choice advocates support the legal availability of abortion for all women. They essentially believe the following:

1. Freedom of choice is a central value—the woman has a right to determine what happens to her own body.
2. Those who must personally bear the burden of their moral choices ought to have the right to make these choices.
3. Procreation choices must be free of governmental control.

National **DATA**

Forty-two percent of the U.S. public do not see abortion as morally wrong and do not think *Roe v. Wade* should be overturned (Pew Research Center, 2013).

People most likely to be pro-choice are female, are mothers of one or two children, have some college education, are employed, and have annual income of more than $50,000. Although many self-proclaimed feminists and women's organizations, such as the National Organization for Women (NOW), have been active in promoting abortion rights, not all feminists are pro-choice.

Contrary to common notion, however, not all religious groups oppose the legal availability of abortion. For example, Catholics for Free Choice, a pro-choice organization established in the 1970s, supports the right to legal abortion and promotes family planning. This organization disagrees with the notion that abortion is necessarily sinful in all circumstances.

Labeling the opposing groups in the abortion controversy is problematic. Some pro-choice advocates object to the use of the term *pro-life* when referring to their opponents because it implies that *pro-choice* advocates do not value life. They argue that restricting or banning legal abortion lessens the quality of life for women by forcing them to either bear unwanted children or to obtain an illegal and perhaps unsafe abortion. The quality of life for children born unwanted is also a concern of pro-choice advocates. Pro-choice advocates do not view abortion as desirable but as a necessary evil, and they often combine their efforts to make and keep abortion available with efforts to reduce abortion by family planning and the use of effective contraception.

Some pro-choice advocates also object to the label *pro-abortion* because some who are pro-choice are personally opposed to abortion. Indeed, some individuals feel that they can be antiabortion and pro-choice at the same time.

12.3d Physical and Psychological Effects of Abortion

Women who have experienced or are contemplating abortion may be concerned about the potential physical and psychological effects. Legal abortions, performed under safe conditions in such countries as the United States, are as safe as continuing a pregnancy. The earlier in the pregnancy the abortion is performed, the safer it is.

1. *Rates of Mortality and Complications*   Mortality rates associated with legal abortion are 0.6 per 100,000 abortions. The mortality rate of childbirth is 8.8 maternal deaths per 100,000 live births. Women are 9 times more likely to die from childbirth than from abortion. (Raymond & Grimes, 2012).

    Post abortion complications include the possibility of incomplete abortion, which occurs when the initial procedure misses the fetus and a repeat procedure must be done. Other possible complications include uterine infection; excessive bleeding; perforation or laceration of the uterus, bowel, or adjacent organs; and an adverse reaction to a medication or anesthetic.

2. *Long-Term Effects*   Vacuum aspiration abortions, comprising most U.S. abortions, do not increase the risks to future childbearing. However, late-term abortions do increase the risks of subsequent miscarriages, premature deliveries, and low birth-weight babies.

BVT *Lab*

Improve your test scores. Practice quizzes are available at **www.BVTLab.com**.

Of equal concern are the psychological effects of abortion. The American Psychological Association reviewed all outcome studies on the mental health effects of abortion and concluded, "Based on our comprehensive review and evaluation of the empirical literature published in peer-reviewed journals since 1989, this Task Force on Mental Health and Abortion concludes that the most methodologically sound research indicates that among women who have a single, legal, first-trimester abortion of an unplanned pregnancy for nontherapeutic reasons, the relative risks of mental health problems are no greater than the risks among women who deliver an unplanned pregnancy" (Major, Appelbaum, & West, 2008, p. 71).

What about the partner? Jones and colleagues (2011) examined data from 9,493 women who had obtained an abortion to find out the degree to which their male partners knew of the abortion and the partners' feelings about the abortion. The overwhelming majority of women reported that the men with whom they got pregnant knew about the abortion, and most perceived these men to be supportive. Cohabiting men were particularly supportive. The researchers concluded that most women obtaining abortions are able to rely on male partners for social support.

personal Choices **12-2**

Deciding Whether to Have an Abortion

Women who are faced with the question of whether to have an abortion may benefit by considering the following guidelines:

- Consider all the alternatives available to you, realizing that no alternative may be all good or all bad. As you consider each alternative, think about both the short- and long-term consequences of each course of action.
- Obtain information about each alternative course of action. Inform yourself about the medical, financial, and legal aspects of abortion, childbearing, parenting, and adoption.
- Talk with trusted family members, friends, or unbiased counselors. Talk with the man who participated in the pregnancy. If possible, also talk with women who have had abortions, as well as women who have kept and reared their babies or placed their babies in adoptive homes. If you feel that someone is pressuring you in your decision-making, look for help elsewhere.
- Consider your own personal and moral commitments in life. Understand your own feelings, values, and beliefs concerning the fetus, and weigh those against the circumstances surrounding your pregnancy.

To what degree might women benefit from counseling? Brown (2013) interviewed 24 women between the ages of 16 and 20 who were waiting for, or had recently had, a surgical abortion to identify the process involved in making a decision regarding an abortion. All but one of the women had been offered counseling, but only two accepted. The women had decided that they wanted an abortion before accessing health services to request one. In making the decision, they had discussed their decision with someone close to them and did not feel the need to have further discussions with counselors.

12.4 **Pregnancy**

In this last section of the chapter, we discuss the physiology of becoming pregnant. Most important is that a pregnancy be planned.

> *Love is all fun and games until someone loses an eye or gets pregnant.*
>
> Anonymous

12.4a **Pregnancy Intention**

Children that are born to parents who do not want the pregnancy report negative outcomes later (e.g., preschool and kindergarten). The specific pregnancy factors associated with negative outcomes include the mother not wanting the pregnancy, the father feeling that now is not the time for the pregnancy, and the parents

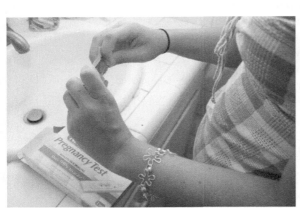

Source: Chelsea Curry

being discordant about wanting the baby. Saleem and Surkan (2013) analyzed a nationally representative U.S. sample from the Early Childhood Longitudinal Study Birth Cohort and found that these characteristics of parents predicted children with poorer social-emotional development in preschool and kindergarten, especially in the areas of concentration and attention.

The mother wanting to get pregnant is not only important for her but also for the child. While drinking alcohol, smoking, and drug abuse are behaviors more often true of women who do not want to become pregnant, these same women (when compared to women who wanted to get pregnant) also had lower scores for physical and mental health status; less prenatal care; and lower scores for self-care behaviors such as use of supplements, vaccination and nutrition (Khajehpour, Simbar, Jannesari, Ramezani-Tehrani, & Majd, 2013). The point

> *The condom broke. I know how stupid that sounds. It's the reproductive version of the dog ate my homework.*
>
> Jennifer Weiner, *Little Earthquakes*

is that the timing of pregnancy is critical to the well being of the child, the mother, the father, and the relationship between the couple. Younger mothers (e.g., ages 17 to 19) and older mothers (age 35 and above) are more likely to have low birth weight babies (below 5 lbs., 8 ounces). In the U.S., 1 in 12 babies is a LBW baby (da Silva, Hernandez, & Agranonik, 2013).

Some couples think of prenatal genetic testing before getting pregnant. Pivetti and Melotti (2013) assessed the degree to which various populations were comfortable with prenatal genetic testing. Results showed that less religious women tended to be more in favor of taking prenatal tests. Beyond genetic testing, a number of other issues should be considered before getting pregnant. Self-Assessment 12-2 assesses your knowledge of various issues to consider before getting pregnant.

12.4b **Beginning of Pregnancy**

Immediately after the egg and sperm unite, typically in the Fallopian tube, the egg begins to divide and is pushed by hairlike cilia down the tube into the uterus, where it attaches itself to the inner wall. The placenta forms in the endometrium of the woman's uterus and its blood vessels. The **umbilical cord** connects the developing fetus and the placenta; this flexible cord contains the two arteries and the vein that facilitate this exchange. Furnished with a rich supply of blood and nutrients, the developing organism is called an **embryo** for the first 8 weeks, and a **fetus** thereafter (see Figure 12-10).

Umbilical cord
Flexible cord that connects the developing fetus and the placenta; this cord contains two arteries and a vein that facilitate this exchange

Embryo
Developing organism from conception to the 8th week of pregnancy

Fetus
Developing organism from the 8th week of pregnancy forward

SELF-ASSESSMENT 12-2: DO YOU NEED PRECONCEPTION COUNSELING?

To determine whether you might benefit from preconception counseling, ask yourself the following questions:

- Do you have a major medical problem, such as diabetes, asthma, anemia, or high blood pressure?
- Do you know of any family members who have had a child with a birth defect or mental retardation?
- Have you had a child with a birth defect or mental retardation?
- Are you concerned about inherited diseases, such as Tay-Sachs disease, sickle cell anemia, hemophilia, or thalassemia?
- Are you 35 years of age or older?
- Do you smoke, drink alcohol, or take illegal drugs?
- Do you take prescription or over-the-counter medications regularly?
- Do you use birth control pills?
- Do you have a cat?
- Are you a strict vegetarian?
- Are you dieting or fasting for any reason?
- Do you run long distances or exercise strenuously?
- Do you work with chemicals, toxic substances, radiation, or anesthesia?
- Do you suspect that you or your partner may have a sexually transmitted disease?
- Have you had German measles (rubella) or a German measles vaccination?
- Have you ever had a miscarriage, ectopic pregnancy, stillbirth, or complicated pregnancy?
- Have you recently traveled outside the United States?

If your answer to any of these questions is yes, you definitely should seek counseling from an obstetrician, nurse midwife, or family practitioner 3 to 6 months before you hope to conceive a child.

Source: From *Instructor's Guide for Hale's An Invitation to Health,* 7th ed., by Diane Hales. Copyright # 1997. Reprinted with permission of Wadsworth, a division of Thomson Learning: www.thomsonrights.com. Fax: 800-730-2215

FIGURE **12-10** ‖ The Developing Fetus

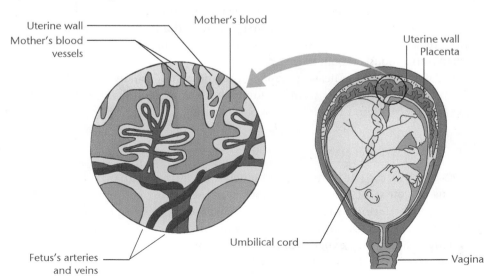

Detecting pregnancy as early as possible is important. Early detection not only enables the woman to begin prenatal precautions and medical care during the most vulnerable stage of fetal development, it also allows a woman with an unintended pregnancy time to consider whether she wants to have an abortion, which may then be performed when it is safest (early in pregnancy). Finally, early diagnosis may permit early detection of an **ectopic pregnancy**. Such a pregnancy involves the baby developing outside the uterus, such as in the cervix, abdominal area, or ovary. Most ectopic pregnancies occur in the Fallopian tube. The increase in tubal pregnancies in the past few years has been attributed to the rise in sexually transmitted infections because infection that results in the formation of scar tissue may interfere in the passage of the fertilized egg to the uterus.

An ectopic pregnancy is potentially dangerous because the tubal wall can be ruptured and cause severe bleeding, which can be lethal to the mother. Signs of such a pregnancy should be taken seriously. These signs include sudden intense pain in the lower abdomen, irregular bleeding, or dizziness that persists for more than a few seconds.

New treatments for ectopic pregnancy include microsurgery incisions that allow the physician to remove the embryo while leaving the reproductive system intact. In some cases, methotrexate may be prescribed to destroy the pregnancy-related tissue.

12.4c Pregnancy Testing

Signs of pregnancy may include a missed period, morning sickness, enlarged and tender breasts, frequent urination, and excessive fatigue. However, pregnancy is best confirmed by laboratory tests and a physical examination.

Several laboratory tests for pregnancy have a high degree of accuracy. All of them depend on the presence of a hormone produced by the developing embryo, human chorionic gonadotropin (HCG), which appears in the pregnant woman's urine. One procedure, formally known as the lutex agglutination inhibition immunologic slide test, detects HCG in about 2.5 hours and can reveal within 14 days after the first missed menstrual period whether the woman is pregnant. All commercially available pregnancy tests use the lutex agglutination principle and are reasonably reliable in providing information about the existence of a pregnancy. The most common error in the home pregnancy tests is that the woman takes the test too early in pregnancy and concludes that she is not pregnant when, in fact, she is (false negative).

HCG also appears in the bloodstream of the pregnant woman. A radioimmuno-assay test, a laboratory examination of the blood, can determine whether the woman is pregnant within 8 days of conception. A new test, radioreceptor assay, also analyzes the blood and is 100% accurate on the first day after the first missed period. These tests have replaced pregnancy tests in which urine of the presumed pregnant woman is injected into a mouse, rabbit, or frog.

If the laboratory test indicates pregnancy, the physician usually conducts a pelvic examination to find out if the woman's uterus has enlarged or changed color. These changes take place around the sixth week of pregnancy.

12.4d Physical Changes During Pregnancy

Figure 12-11 shows the size of the fetus as it develops during pregnancy.

The usual course of a typical 266-day pregnancy is divided into trimesters, or 3-month periods, during which the woman may experience some discomfort due to physical changes (see Table 12-2). Women vary in the degree to which they experience these changes. Some may experience few or none of the related symptoms, whereas others may experience many of them.

Ectopic pregnancy
Condition in which a fertilized egg becomes implanted in a site other than the uterus

FIGURE **12-11** || **Growth of the Embryo and Fetus from 2 to 15 Weeks after Conception**

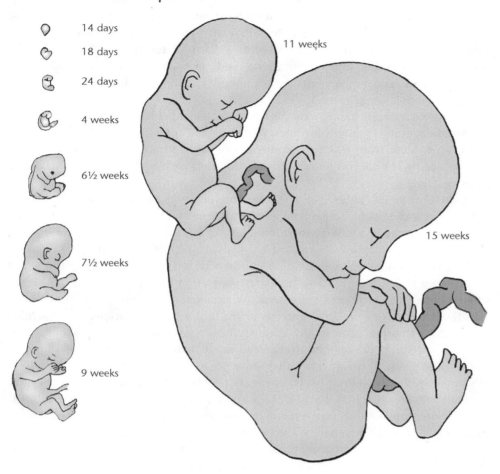

TABLE **12-2**	Side Effects of Pregnancy		
	First Trimester Weeks 0–14	Second Trimester Weeks 15–26	Third Trimester Weeks 27–40
Nausea	X		
Vomiting	X		
Frequent urination	X		X
Leg cramps	X		
Vaginal discharge	X	X	X
Fatigue	X	X	X
Constipation	X	X	X
Swelling		X	X
Varicose veins		X	X
Backache		X	X
Heartburn		X	
Shortness of breath		X	

12.4e Prenatal Care and Prenatal Testing

Some women seek preconception care to help ensure a healthy pregnancy and baby, whereas others do not receive pregnancy-related healthcare until after they become pregnant. Like preconception care, prenatal care involves receiving adequate nutrition; achieving adequate weight gain; and avoiding harmful substances such as alcohol, nicotine, illegal drugs, some medications, and toxic chemicals in the workplace. Vitamin and mineral supplements are commonly recommended, especially iron and folate (or folic acid) supplements.

In general, exercise in pregnancy is beneficial. Guendelman and colleagues (2013) compared data on 344 cases of women who delivered their babies preterm (less than 37 weeks) to data from 698 term controls and found that moderate and vigorous exercise during the second trimester was associated with reduced odds of having a preterm delivery.

Exercise is beneficial in that it reduces the incidence of muscle cramps, fatigue, and shortness of breath. It also reduces the increase in baseline maternal heart rate that occurs in pregnancy. Women who undertake regular exercise have a lower incidence of third- and fourth-degree vaginal tears. In addition, children of exercising mothers have similar birth weights to children of sedentary mothers; and mental performance at age 5 is higher—this latter correlation may be due to the fact that active mothers may promote more interactive games/activities for their children than sedentary moms. If no specific obstetric or medical contraindications exist (such as anemia, hypertension, pain of any kind, fetal distress, heart palpitations, or vaginal or uterine bleeding), fit pregnant women can safely maintain the same level of fitness during pregnancy, although they may have to reduce the frequency with which they exercise. Amezcua-Prieto and colleagues (2013) collected data on 1,175 healthy pregnant women and found that just 27.5% and 19.4%, respectively, of women fulfilled LTPA (leisure time physical activity) recommendations prior to pregnancy and during pregnancy. Across the pregnancy, the researchers noted that there was a decrease in LTPA, not only regarding frequency, but also duration and intensity.

Pregnant women are advised to eliminate their alcohol intake to avoid **fetal alcohol syndrome** (FAS), which refers to the possible negative consequences for the fetus and infant of the mother who drinks alcohol. Possible negative consequences for the developing infant include increased risk of low birth weight, growth retardation, facial malformations, and intellectual retardation. Avoiding alcohol intake during the early weeks of pregnancy (and before pregnancy if no reliable method of birth control is being used) is particularly critical; and alcohol consumed in the later months may impede organ growth and cognitive ability.

Fetal alcohol syndrome (FAS)
Possible negative consequences (e.g., facial malformation, low birth weight) for the fetus and infant of the mother who drinks alcohol during pregnancy

In one study on alcohol consumption during pregnancy, half of 127 women who were currently pregnant reported that they had stopped drinking when they learned that they were pregnant. Of 425 women who were previously pregnant, slightly over a third (37%) reported that they had stopped drinking when they learned they were pregnant. The researchers (Parackal, Parackal, & Harraway, 2013) noted that women who were categorized as "risky drinkers" and those aged 16–24 years were more likely to drink and to binge drink in early pregnancy.

National **DATA**

The most conservative annual estimate for attributing maternal binge drinking to the number of preterm births (PTBs) is 8,701 and 5,627 low birth weight babies (below 5 lbs, 8 ounces). The estimated rate of PTBs due to maternal binge drinking was 1.57% among all PTBs to white women, 0.69% among black women, 3.31% among Hispanic women, and 2.35% among other races. Compared to other (pre term) age groups, women ages 40–44 had the highest adjusted binge drinking rate and highest PTB rate due to maternal binge drinking at 4.33% (Truong, Reifsnider, Mayorga, & Spitler, 2013).

Smoking cigarettes during pregnancy is also associated with harm to the developing fetus. Negative consequences include lower birth-weight babies, premature babies, and higher fetal or infant deaths. Hauge and colleagues (2013) studied the smoking behavior of 10,890 women who had had one child and who were pregnant with a second child. Smoking is a behavior most of the women tried to avoid during pregnancy: most did not smoke in either pregnancy and were least likely to relapse in the second pregnancy. Of those who smoked during their first pregnancy, almost a third (30.9%) had quit by their second pregnancy. Factors associated with not smoking were a shorter interval between births, lower stress, high education, and living with a partner who did not smoke. Only 2.3% of those who did not smoke during their first pregnancy did so during their second pregnancy.

Paternal smoking may be equally hazardous. Tobacco smoke contains many mutagenic compounds that are easily absorbed into the blood and reach the testes. Paternal smoking is also associated with greater risk of perinatal mortality, lower birth weight, congenital malformation, and childhood cancers.

Concerned about the health of their babies, some pregnant women avoid not only alcohol and nicotine but also caffeine. Boylan and colleagues (2013) reviewed the literature on caffeine and pregnancy outcomes and reaffirmed that caffeine during pregnancy increases the odds of fetal growth restriction.

Prescription drugs may have negative consequences for the developing fetus. Medications for depression, such as selective serotonin reuptake inhibitors and newer antidepressants used by pregnant women, have been associated with the birth of children small for their gestational age, SGA (Jensen, Gron, Lidegaard, Dedersen, Andersen, & Kessing, 2013).

Illegal drugs, such as marijuana and cocaine, and also nonprescription drugs should also be avoided. Cocaine has been associated with preterm labor and delivery, lower birth-weight babies, limb defects, lower IQ, and oversensitivity to stimulation. These "crack" or "cocaine" babies may enter the world disadvantaged; however, because their mothers may have used various substances, it is difficult to isolate the specific effects of cocaine from malnutrition and lack of prenatal care. Social Choices 12-1 introduces the question of whether or not women should be prosecuted for abusing substances that may harm their fetuses.

Social Choices   12-1

Criminal Prosecution for Fetal Abuse?

Should pregnant women who abuse alcohol, crack cocaine, and other drugs harmful to a fetus be prosecuted? Even though more than 100,000 infants have been exposed to such drugs while they were developing *in utero,* the courts have been reluctant to prosecute their mothers. Arguments against such prosecution are based on several issues: defining when the fetus becomes a person whose rights have been violated, the lack of warning to women that drug abuse during pregnancy may be a prosecutable offense, the vagueness of what exactly constitutes "the crime," and the fact that fetal abuse is a lifestyle issue. Regarding the latter, many women who take drugs during their pregnancy live in poverty, which means they often lack prenatal care and have nutritional deficiencies. Indeed, prenatal care, drug treatment, and general health services are least accessible for poor and minority women. An additional problem is that sending pregnant women to jail or prison for drug abuse interferes with their ability to receive treatment during pregnancy.

Prenatal care may also involve prenatal testing. Such tests range from screening measures routinely used in prenatal care to invasive prenatal diagnostic tests. The National Institutes of Health (NIH) now recommend routine prenatal genetic screening for cystic fibrosis, the most common inherited disease.

An **ultrasound scan** involves looking at sound waves being intermittently beamed at the fetus, producing a detailed image on a video screen. This noninvasive test immediately provides pictures of the maternal and fetal outlines and inner organs. Although its long-term effects are still being studied, it appears to be one of the safest procedures for the amount of information it provides. Ultrasound allows the physician to determine the length of gestation (the age of the fetus) and assess the presence of structural abnormalities. High-resolution ultrasound has been shown to allow detection of risk of trisomy 21 (Down's syndrome).

Other prenatal tests are used to identify fetuses with chromosomal and biochemical defects. These procedures are usually offered to women who have a child with a birth defect or some other risk factor (such as advanced maternal age, now defined at around age 35). Their purpose is to detect defects early enough so that if the test is positive, the woman can either be prepared for the birth of a child with health problems or terminate the pregnancy. Their availability has provided to many people the confidence to initiate a pregnancy despite familial history of serious genetic disease or prior birth of affected children.

Amniocentesis (which is performed after the 15th week of pregnancy) involves inserting a slender needle through the abdomen into the amniotic sac and taking about 1 ounce of fluid (see Figure 12-12). Fetal cells, which are present in this amniotic fluid, are sent to a laboratory where they are cultured (permitted to multiply in a special medium) and then analyzed for defects.

Amniocentesis involves some risk. In rare cases (about 0.5% of the time, or 1 in 200 cases), the needle may damage the fetus, even though an ultrasound scan has been used to identify its position. Congenital orthopedic defects, such as clubfoot, and premature birth have been associated with amniocentesis. Also, even if no specific abnormality is detected (as is the case 97.5% of the time), this does not guarantee that

Ultrasound scan
Procedure whereby sound waves are used to project an image of the developing fetus on a video screen; used in prenatal testing

Amniocentesis
Prenatal test in which a needle is inserted (usually in the 16th or 17th week of pregnancy) into the pregnant woman's uterus to withdraw fluid, which is analyzed to see if the cells carry XX (female) or XY (male) chromosomes, and to identify chromosomal defects

FIGURE **12-12** || Amniocentesis

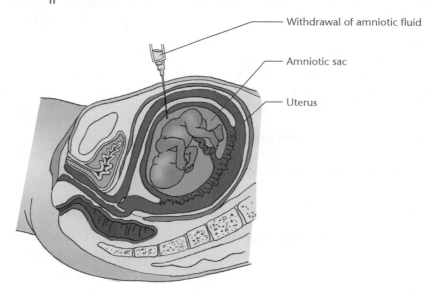

Withdrawal of amniotic fluid

Amniotic sac

Uterus

the baby will be normal and healthy. Cleft palate, cleft lip, and most heart defects are not detected by amniocentesis.

Unfortunately, after the amniocentesis procedure at 16 to 17 weeks of gestation, an additional 3 or 4 weeks is required for cell tissue culture. By this time, the woman may be 20 to 22 weeks pregnant, the pregnancy is publicly visible, and she has probably felt fetal movement. Terminating a pregnancy at this juncture may be quite traumatic. To terminate a pregnancy that has progressed to 20 or 22 weeks, a saline or prostaglandin (induced miscarriage) abortion procedure is frequently used, which involves the delivery of the fetus.

Chorionic villus sampling (CVS) may be performed at 10 to 12 weeks of gestation. Villi are the threadlike edges of the chorion, or membrane, surrounding the fetus. A small sample of the chorion can be obtained by passing a thin catheter, using ultrasound guidance, through the cervix and into the placenta. Sometimes, due to the placement of the placenta, the villi must be extracted through the abdomen, as in amniocentesis. The villi can then be analyzed directly or cultured and the chromosomes studied. CVS does not test for neural tube defects (such as spina bifida); amniocentesis is used to detect these problems. A woman may choose CVS if she wants test results during the first 3 months of pregnancy. The risk of pregnancy interruption is slightly greater with CVS than amniocentesis (about 1.0% to 1.5% risk of spontaneous abortion).

Deciding to undergo prenatal diagnosis can cause significant emotional strain to pregnant women; waiting for results can cause depression and feelings of guilt and helplessness.

12.4f Miscarriage

A **miscarriage**, also known as spontaneous abortion, is the unintended loss of an embryo or fetus that occurs before the 20th week of pregnancy. Toffol and colleagues (2013) analyzed national data and concluded that a miscarriage may have a sustained negative effect on the mental health of the mother. Indeed, a diagnosis of depressive disorder and the presence of depressive symptoms were more prevalent among women with a history of miscarriage: the higher the number of miscarriages, the worse the current state of mood was and the higher the frequency of a psychiatric diagnosis.

Chorionic villus sampling (CVS)
Prenatal diagnostic test of cells from the chorion (membrane surrounding the fetus) (performed at 10 to 12 weeks gestation) to identify chromosomal abnormalities and some other diseases

Miscarriage
Unintended termination of a pregnancy.

Women who experience a miscarriage often feel intense grief. They may also feel guilt, anger, a sense of failure, and jealousy of other pregnant women or women with children. They may blame themselves for the miscarriage. Some feel that they are being

I am not functioning very well. Living with the knowledge that the baby is dead is painful. I feel so far away from you, God.

Christine O'Keeffe Lafser, *An Empty Cradle, a Full Heart: Reflections for Mothers and Fathers after Miscarriage, Stillbirth, or Infant Death*

punished for something they have done in the past—frequent, casual, anonymous premarital sex; an abortion; an extramarital affair. Others feel that they have failed, not only as a woman or mother, but also in living up to the expectations of their partner, parents, and other children. (Women who have a miscarriage are often inappropriately urged to "try again" rather than focus on their grief.) Others are hurt or angry at the insensitivity of their friends who show little empathy

for their feelings of sadness and emptiness at the loss of "their baby." Friends and family can help by acknowledging the loss instead of attempting to minimize it.

12.4g Psychological Changes During Pregnancy

Affonso and Mayberry (1989) assessed the stresses of 221 women during and after pregnancy. Stress related to physical issues was the most frequently reported problem. "The total group identified fatigue, disturbed sleep, feeling physically restricted, and nausea or vomiting as the most common physical distresses" (p. 46). The second most frequently experienced stressor was associated "with 'weight gain' and feelings of being 'fat,' 'unattractive,' and 'distorted'" (p. 48).

The third most frequently reported concern during pregnancy was for the "baby's welfare and dealing with changes relative to household arrangements and restrictions in physical activities, especially as the woman nears childbirth" (Affonso & Mayberry, 1989, p. 49). Some of the women reported that they were plagued by frequent thoughts: "Something might happen to my baby." "Am I doing the right thing to protect my baby?" "I shouldn't have done this because now I'm worried about how it affected my baby" (p. 49). As women near the end of pregnancy, fears of pain, complications, and the threat of a cesarean section are high-intensity stressors.

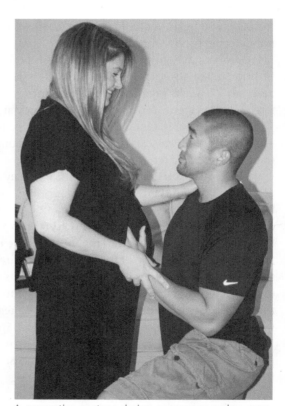

A supportive partner during pregnancy makes pregnancy an easier transition for the woman.
Source: Andrea Howard

12.4h Intimate Partner Violence During Pregnancy

Pregnancy is a stressful time for couples and has been associated with intimate partner violence (IPV). Scribano and colleagues (2013) analyzed data on a national sample of women enrolled in the Nurse Family Partnership. The respondents provided data before, during, and following their pregnancy. The percentage of women reporting interpersonal violence before the pregnancy was 8.1%, during the first 36 weeks of pregnancy was 4.7%, and in the 12 months following pregnancy was 12.4%. Hence, the lowest IPV was during the pregnancy. Whether the partner did not want to inflict violence on a pregnant woman or whether pregnancy was a relatively stress free time is unknown. We suspect that the chaos created by the presence of an infant and the demands of the infant accounted for the increased incidence of IPV after the delivery.

12.4i Sex During Pregnancy

Lowenstein and colleagues (2013) reviewed the literature on sex and pregnancy and noted that the findings are contradictory. While some studies have shown a loss of sexual interest during the first trimester (attributed to physiological factors, such as nausea and vomiting) and that this drop off continues into the second semester, other studies have shown an increase in sexual activity. The researchers make clear that sexual activity does not cause harm in pregnancy and that sexual function during the postpartum period may be influenced by pain disorders, hypoactive sexual desire, the method used in delivery, obstetric perineal damage, breastfeeding, and postpartum mood changes.

Are there conditions under which a pregnant woman should forgo intercourse and orgasmic activity? Yes. Women who are experiencing vaginal bleeding or abdominal pain, those whose amniotic membrane has ruptured, and those whose cervix has begun to efface or dilate after 24 weeks should abstain from sexual intercourse. Also, those with a history of premature delivery or a history of miscarriage should consult their physician or midwife about intercourse during pregnancy.

What about the relationship of expectant couples who sign up for relationship help during this period? Engsheden and colleagues (2013) compared the characteristics of 89 expectant couples who self-selected into a Prevention and Relationship Education Program (PREP) with 52 expectant couples who did not attend. Those who enrolled in the program had known each other for a shorter period of time, reported lower levels of relationship adjustment, and had higher depressive symptoms.

BVT *Lab*

Visit **www.BVTLab.com** to explore the student resources available for this chapter.

Chapter **Summary**

The decision to become a parent is one of the most important an individual or couple will make. In this chapter we reviewed the various methods to ensure one's desired family size, sterilization, abortion and pregnancy.

Contraception

Hormonal methods of contraception currently available to women include the "pill," Implanon® or Nexplanon/Implanon NXT®, Depo-Provera® or Depo-subQ Provera 104®, NuvaRing®, and Ortho Evra®. Barrier methods include the male and female condom, spermicides, diaphragm, and cervical cap. Natural family planning methods involve refraining from sexual intercourse during the 1 to 2 weeks each month when the woman is thought to be fertile. Non-methods include withdrawal and douching.

Emergency contraception refers to various types of morning-after pills or the insertion of a postcoital IUD that are used when a woman has unprotected intercourse, when a contraceptive method fails (such as condom breakage or slippage), or when a woman is raped.

Sterilization

Sterilization is a surgical procedure that prevents fertilization, usually by blocking the passage of eggs or sperm through the Fallopian tubes or vas deferens, respectively. The procedure for female sterilization is called salpingectomy, or tubal ligation. Laparoscopy is a variation of tubal ligation. The most frequent form of male sterilization is vasectomy.

Abortion

Abortion methods include suction curettage (vacuum aspiration) during the first 6 to 8 weeks of pregnancy, dilation and suction during the first 12 weeks, dilation and evacuation from 13 to 24 weeks' gestation, and intact dilation and extraction, which results in the whole fetus being aborted (also known as "partial-birth abortion"). An abortion may also be induced by the use of the drug RU-486 (Mifepristone, sold as Mifeprex and known as "the abortion pill") if the woman is less than 9-weeks pregnant.

The United States is deeply divided over the issue of abortion. Abortion is more likely to be viewed as an acceptable option if continuing the pregnancy endangers the mother's health, if a severe birth defect exists, or if the pregnancy is the result of rape or incest. Although "pro-life" and "pro-choice" groups dominate public discourse on abortion, most people have views that are mixed. For most women, elective abortion does not pose a risk to their physical or mental health. The concept of **post abortion syndrome** has little to no validity in the scientific community. Much of the evidence of PAS is anecdotal and not supported by scientific studies. Of women who have had an abortion, 1% meet the criteria for post-traumatic stress disorder.

Pregnancy

Post abortion syndrome
Purportedly, the range of adverse psychological effects women who have had an abortion experience

Early signs of pregnancy include lack of menstruation, nausea and vomiting (morning sickness), enlarged and tender breasts, frequent urination, and fatigue. Pregnancy is best confirmed by laboratory tests and a physical examination. In the early stages of pregnancy, some women experience leg cramps, constipation, backache, varicose veins, swelling, heartburn, increased vaginal discharge, and shortness of breath. Prenatal care helps to ensure a healthy pregnancy and healthy baby. Miscarriages, or spontaneous abortions, are not uncommon in early pregnancy.

Web Links

Abortion and Reproductive Rights

http://www.naral.org/

Abortion Clinics Online

http://www.gynpages.com/

National Right to Life

http://www.nrlc.org/

Population Council

http://www.popcouncil.org

Key Terms

Abortion   341

Amniocentesis   350

Cervical cap   327

Chorionic villus sampling (CVS)   351

Coitus interruptus   329

Depo-Provera   321

Diaphragm   326

Dilation and curettage (D & C)   336

Dilation and evacuation (D & E)   336

Dilation and suction (D & S)   336

Ectopic pregnancy   346

Embryo   344

Emergency contraception   330

Essure   333

Female condom   324

Fetal alcohol syndrome (FAS)   348

Fetus   344

Hysterectomy   332

Induced abortion   335

Intact dilation and extraction (D & X)   337

Intrauterine device   326

Laparoscopy   332

Medical abortion   337

Mifepristone   337

Miscarriage   351

Mittelschmerz   329

NEA-TDS   322

Nexplanon/Implanon NXT or Implanon   320

NuvaRing   321

Oophorectomy   332

Ortho Evra   322

Partial-birth abortions   337

Periodic abstinence   327

Pharmaceutical abortion   337

Post abortion syndrome   354

Postcoital contraception   330

RU-486   337

Salpingectomy   332

Spermicide   322

Spinbarkeit   329

Sponge   325

Spontaneous abortion   335

Sterilization   332

Suction curettage   335

Ultrasound scan   350

Umbilical cord   344

Vacuum aspiration   335

Vasectomy   333

Additional study resources are available at www.BVTLab.com

CHAPTER 13

Sexual Dysfunctions and Sex Therapy

My therapist says I have an obsession with revenge. We'll see about that.

Unknown

Chapter Outline

Objectives

1. Identify the various elements which comprise the definition of sexual dysfunction.

2. Understand the various causes and contributing factors to sexual dysfunctions.

3. Review the various interest/arousal dysfunctions.

4. Explain the two major male sexual dysfunctions.

5. Discuss the two orgasm dysfunctions.

6. Learn the two genito-pelvic pain/penetration disorders.

7. Describe the various approaches used in sex therapy and their effectiveness.

Source: David Knox

TRUTH *OR* FICTION?

T/F   Men out-earned by their wives are more likely to use erectile dysfunction medication than their male breadwinner counterparts.

T/F   Males who have a sexual dysfunction (e.g., erectile failure) also tend to report low libido (e.g., low interest in sex).

T/F   Over 90% of men with erectile dysfunction can become erect with Viagra.

T/F   A higher percentage of women in Asia than the U.S. report female orgasmic disorder.

T/F   Over half of women taking SSRIs (e.g., Paxil) report difficulty in achieving orgasm.

Answers: 1.T 2.T 3.F 4.T 5.T

A common belief among sex therapists is that when a couple's sex life is good, it is about 15% of the relationship; but when the sex is bad, it becomes a focus of the relationship. Psychiatrist Robert Sammons confirms that among the couples he sees for sexual dysfunction, a common belief is that "the only thing that's important is that which is missing." So regardless of how good everything else is in a couple's relationship, if they view their sex life as bad, they see their whole relationship as unhappy and in trouble. Although Sammons's statement may be an oversimplification of the complexity of relationships and an overstatement of the importance of sex in relationships, it emphasizes the association between sexual function and relationship satisfaction. There is also a connection between sexual function and sexual satisfaction. Lo and Kok (2013), in their study of menopausal women, concluded, "sexual dysfunction is the main contributor to sexual dissatisfaction" (p. 190).

Personal REFLECTION

Take a moment to express your thoughts about the following question. Persons vary in regard to their value of the importance of a good sexual relationship. For some it is the prerequisite for a quality relationship; for others it is irrelevant. On a 10-point scale, with 10 as the top, what value do you place on your sexual relationship with your partner? What number do you feel your partner would select? How discrepant can the numbers be before they impact the relationship?

In one study, about a fourth of the husbands and a third of the wives reported sexual problems (e.g., dealing with actual, desired, or intended sexual behaviors; feelings of closeness; or displays of verbal and physical affection in the relationship). One hundred married couples (husbands and wives) kept a diary for 15 days of marital conflict. Average ages of the husbands and wives were 39 and 37 respectively, and they had been married an average of 12 years. Most had between two and three children, with the range between one child and six. (Papp, Goeke-Morey, & Cummings, 2013). Notice that this study did not focus on sexual dysfunctions but on general sexual issues in the relationship instead.

> *The obsessive focus on getting the genitals to perform properly, if not perfectly, results in the neglect of much of what makes sexual problems so complex—personally and theoretically. First on the list would be the relational aspects of sexual experience.*
>
> Lenore Tiefer, psychologist

13.1 Definitions of Sexual Dysfunctions

Sexual dysfunctions are a heterogeneous group of disorders that are typically characterized by a clinically significant disturbance in a person's ability to respond sexually or to experience sexual pleasure (American Psychiatric Association, 2013, p. 423). A person may have several sexual dysfunctions at once. The term sexual dysfunction is not appropriate if the sexual problem exists due to inadequate sexual stimulation.

One way to discuss sexual dysfunctions is to do so in terms of the stages in which sexual problems occur across the sexual response cycle. However, doing so emphasizes the physical processes within the genitals (the **medicalization of sexual dysfunctions**) rather than one person's or couple's overall emotional relationship and sexual satisfaction. An example of the degree to which sexual dysfunctions have been medicalized is the research by Leeners and colleagues (2013) which quantified satisfaction levels of female orgasm in reference to the pituitary hormone prolactin (PRL). More about this follows in the section on female orgasmic disorder.

Throughout the discussion of each sexual dysfunction, it is important to keep in mind the cognitions and feelings of the individuals and their partners. From this point of view, a couple may have various sexual issues (including being asexual), yet still be happy with one another and their sexual relationship.

Sexual problems have been medicalized in that medical causes and treatments have been paramount. If a male loses his interest in sex and/or is not capable of getting and keeping an erection, the cause (we are reminded of regularly on television and in print ads) is "low testosterone." A woman's libido drop is seen as an issue of "hormones." What is missing are the emotional and psychological factors as they impact sexual feelings and sexual interaction.

In this chapter, we will review sexual dysfunctions as they are classified in the *Diagnostic and Statistical Manual of Mental Disorders, 5th edition* (commonly referred to

Sexual dysfunctions
A heterogeneous group of disorders that are typically characterized by a clinically significant disturbance in a person's ability to respond sexually or to experience sexual pleasure

Medicalization of sexual dysfunctions
Emphasizes that sexual dysfunctions have a medical or biological basis rather than an emotional or relationship cause

as *DSM-5™*) (APA, 2013). Although its title implies that mental disorders are distinct from physical disorders, there is much overlap between them; the term *mental disorders* is used because an appropriate substitute has not been found. Although there are problems with this conceptualization, the *DSM-5* remains a widely used resource and is the standard diagnostic reference among health and mental health professionals in the United States.

According to the *DSM-5*, each of the sexual dysfunctions identified may also be classified as being lifelong or acquired. A **lifelong dysfunction** (also referred to as a **primary dysfunction**) is one that a person has always experienced; for example, a person may have always lacked sexual desire. An **acquired dysfunction**, or **secondary dysfunction**, is one that a person is currently experiencing but has not always experienced. One may also have a **situational dysfunction**, in that it occurs only with certain types of stimulation, situations, or partners, or a **generalized dysfunction**, which identifies sexual difficulties that are not limited to certain types of stimulation (American Psychiatric Association, 2013). Basic causes may be organic, psychogenic, mixed, or unknown.

International **DATA**

Of 61,000 males in a National Health Insurance Database in Taiwan, 2% reported experiencing a sexual dysfunction (Chen, et al., 2013).

How a sexual dysfunction is conceptualized and treated has changed across time—human sexuality has been a focus of academic/scientific interest for 70 to 80 years (Atwood & Klucinec, 2011). Berry (2013) reviewed the treatment of sexual dysfunction in the historical perspective and noted that the various treatments have "regularly" claimed to be "revolutionary," (p. 21). Over the years, erectile dysfunction has been seen as primarily psychological, then biopsychological, and today the focus is biochemical with pharmacotherapy (e.g., Viagra) as the treatment of choice. Berry (2013) recommends caution in accepting any one conceptualization or treatment plan and points out that when selecting a chemical treatment for erectile failure that "Viagra and similar drugs, may not present broadly efficacious stand-alone cures" and that there is no "magic bullet" solution to sexual dysfunctions (p. 21). Today a broad approach, encompassing biopsychosocial factors, is indicated since any sexual dysfunction has a biological basis and a psychological (e.g., anxiety) component, and occurs in a social (e.g., interpersonal) context.

13.2 **Causes and Contributing Factors in Sexual Dysfunctions**

Building on Berry's observations above, we examine the numerous causes of sexual dysfunctions.

13.2a Organic Factors

As noted in the chapter on illness, disease, etc., the organic and neurophysiological factors are important causes to consider for sexual dysfunctions. Such factors include physical illness, disease, or disability and its treatment (such as surgery, medication, or chemotherapy). A physical condition (such as diabetes, arthritis, pituitary tumors, or

Lifelong dysfunction
Sexual dysfunction that a person has always experienced; for example, a person may have always lacked sexual desire

Primary dysfunction
See Lifelong dysfunction

Acquired dysfunction
Sexual dysfunction that a person is currently experiencing but has not always experienced

Secondary dysfunction
See Acquired dysfunction

Situational dysfunction
Sexual dysfunction that occurs with one partner or in one situation only

Generalized dysfunction
Sexual dysfunction that occurs with all partners, in all contexts and settings

vascular disease) or its treatments may also interfere with physiological or anatomical mechanisms involved in sexual desire, arousal, or orgasm. Burri (2013) further emphasized that "understanding the genetic basis and therefore physiologic key mechanisms of sexual function and dysfunction has the potential for improved treatments (i.e., the development of new medication) and ultimately prevention." However, he noted the "scarcity of genetic epidemiologic research" as related to sexual dysfunction (p. 318).

For both sexes, neurological conditions or diseases—such as stroke, multiple sclerosis (MS), Parkinson's disease (PD), epilepsy, and tumors—may alter the motor and sensory pathways and affect sexual performance. Weight is also related to sexual dysfunction. Erenel and Kilinc (2013) reported that 44% of 203 women who had applied to a diet center in a hospital said that being over-weight affected their sex life.

Although we discussed drugs and sexuality in Chapter 11, here we note that alcohol, marijuana, barbiturates, and amphetamines—as well as numerous medications used to treat various diseases and illnesses—affect sexuality and may cause or contribute to sexual dysfunction. For example, Chiesa and colleagues (2013) emphasized that antipsychotic medications are associated with sexual dysfunctions. Antipsychotic drugs most commonly associated with SD are olanzapine, risperidone, haloperidol, clozapine, and thioridazine. On the other hand, ziprasidone, perphenazine, quetiapine and aripiprazole are associated with relatively low rates of SD. If the goal is to reduce a patient's SD, either dose reduction or switching medication may be indicated.

Age is also a factor in sexual dysfunction. As the body ages, so do the physical underpinnings of sexual functioning. For example, lubrication (the most common sexual dysfunction in women) decreases in menopausal women who report less frequent intimate contact and sexual intercourse (Lo & Kok, 2013). Penile erectile capacity in men also decreases with age.

Finally, sexual dysfunction often results from a combination of biological and psychosocial factors. For example, a woman may experience a lack of sexual desire because she is chronically fatigued (biological factor) from taking care of young children, a husband, and aging parents or a mother-in-law who lives in the house. Compounding her fatigue is resentment (psychosocial factor) toward her husband for not sharing the childcare and/or housework and not helping to care for aging parents.

13.2b Sociocultural Factors

In addition to physical/biological factors, sociocultural factors may cause or contribute to sexual dysfunction. These include restrictive upbringing and religious training. For example, in some families, parents may openly express negative attitudes toward sexuality by teaching their children that "sex is dirty." Some parents punish children and adolescents for engaging in masturbation or other sexual exploration. In many families, sex is never discussed with the children. Children who learn that sex is a taboo subject may come to regard sex as somehow wrong or shameful.

Cultural Diversity

Some religions (Catholicism) teach that sex is only for procreation, or that sexual relations are only appropriate if penile-vaginal and between husband and wife (Islam). Persons who depart from cultural scripts may internalize negative feelings about sexuality, and these feelings may interfere with their ability to experience sexual desire, arousal, and orgasm.

Another sociocultural factor that may contribute to sexual dysfunction is society's traditional gender role socialization. Women may be socialized to be sexually passive and to "please their man" (thus, not giving emphasis to their own sexuality/pleasure); men may be taught to be sexually aggressive and to "be in control" of sexual situations (thus, missing the point of sexual sharing or experiencing a partner who guides the sexual experience). One of our female students noted, "I know a lot of women who love sex, but a lot of my friends engage in sex just to please their boyfriends. It is going to be a shock when their partner finds out otherwise." Women do, indeed, live in a different sociocultural world than men.

Still another sociocultural factor contributing to sexual dysfunction is society's emphasis on intercourse as "the" sexual act and on orgasm as the event necessary for satisfaction. Nongenital sexual expressions and sexual experiences that do not result in orgasm are given little recognition. The result is enormous pressure on couples to engage in "the act" and for orgasm to result.

Finally, as the income of women continues to increase—so that more women earn more money than their husbands—what is the effect, if any, on the sexual relationship? Pierce and colleagues (2013) analyzed data on spouses in Denmark and revealed that men whose wives outearn them are more likely to use erectile dysfunction medication than their male breadwinner counterparts, even when this inequality is small. In addition, breadwinner wives show increased insomnia/anxiety medication usage, with similar effects for men. The results emphasize that cultural factors/social norms play important roles in dictating how individuals respond sexually.

13.2c Psychological Factors

Numerous psychological factors play a role in sexual dysfunction.

1. *Child sexual abuse*   About a quarter of women, worldwide, report that they have been victims of child sexual abuse. Such an experience is associated with anxiety in sexual contexts, a depressed libido, difficulty in getting aroused, and inorgasmia. Victims of child sex abuse also tend to have negative self-concepts, abuse drugs, early sexual debuts, and numerous sexual partners. Zollman and colleagues (2013) noted that the adult female who was sexually abused as a child may also experience daily stress, which may have an effect on her arousal capacity.

2. *Anxiety*   Anxiety may be aroused by thoughts and fears about sexual performance or the ability to please the partner. Other sources of anxiety may result from fear of intimacy, concern about the partner's commitment to the relationship, fear of rejection, and uncertainty about the partner's intentions, or sexual expectations. One specific type of anxiety related to sexual dysfunction is **performance anxiety**, which refers to excessive concern over adequate sexual performance. The woman or man may become so anxious about having an orgasm or erection that the anxiety itself interferes with achieving both goals. Anxiety, in general, may also be problematic. Patrick and colleagues (2013) surveyed 3,800 respondents who had a regular heterosexual partner. Nine percent of the men and 12% of the women reported moderate psychological distress that was associated with low ratings of sexual and relationship satisfaction.

3. *Fear*   Impairment in the desire, arousal, or orgasm phases of sexual response may result from fear of any of the following: unwanted pregnancy or sexually transmitted infections (STIs), intimacy or commitment, physical pain, displeasing a partner, or losing self-control during sexual arousal or

BVT *Lab*

Flashcards are available for this chapter at **www.BVTLab.com**.

Performance anxiety
Excessive concern over adequate sexual performance, which may result in sexual dysfunction

orgasm. Fear of "not measuring up" may also be operative (e.g., "I'm too fat and fear I am not a good lover" [authors' files]).

4. *Guilt* Guilt—which may be related to masturbation, choice of sexual partner (e.g., prostitute), participation in "forbidden" or "sinful" sexual activity, or involvement in an extradyadic sexual relationship—may also interfere with sexual functioning.

> *I thank God I was raised Catholic, so sex will always be dirty.*
> John Waters, comedian, screenwriter

5. *Depression and low self-esteem* Sexual dysfunction may result from depression, which is known to suppress sexual drive. Related to depression is low self-esteem, which may cause an individual to feel unworthy of being loved or experiencing sexual pleasure.

6. *Conflict concerning one's sexual orientation* Because of the social stigma associated with being homosexual, some gay men and lesbians experience internal conflict about their sexual orientation. Some may deny their homosexuality and seek heterosexual relationships, only to find that sexual activity with other-sex individuals doesn't feel right for them and performance is difficult.

7. *Deployment adjustment* Hosain and colleagues (2013) found that 5.5% of 4,755 Iraq/Afghanistan veterans who sought treatment after returning from deployment were identified as having a sexual dysfunction. The researchers noted the total number was likely undercoded for SD.

13.2d Relationship Factors

Sexual dysfunctions do not exist in isolation. Relationship, marriage, and sex therapists always focus on the relationship between the partners before addressing a specific sexual dysfunction, such as lack of orgasm or erectile dysfunction (Nelson & Kenowitz, 2013). Althof and colleagues (2013) reviewed how to take a sexual history and emphasized that a central question was the status of the partner relationship of the patient. When a couple comes to therapy with a sexual problem, the therapist usually asks questions like: "Tell me about your relationship. How do you feel about each other? How much time do you spend together?"

In addition to the importance of relationship satisfaction, Mark and Herbenick (2013) studied 176 women (mean age = 35) in committed relationships and found that women who reported being attracted to their partners, and who were increasing in their level of attraction to their partners, reported higher sexual satisfaction.

Only if the couple has a good relationship is working on the "sexual problem" productive. Anger, lack of trust, lack of intimacy, and/or lack of communication in a relationship contribute to sexual dysfunctions (lack of interest in sex, lack of orgasm, lack of satisfaction, unfulfilled expectations). Sexual dysfunctions may also contribute to relationship problems (spouses who are not fulfilled sexually may be unhappy or angry and seek other sexual partners).

Not only is there a connection between relationship satisfaction and sexual satisfaction, but relationship satisfaction is a good predictor of positive treatment outcome

Having a good out-of-bed relationship is a condition for having a good relationship in bed.
Source: David Knox

for women in sex therapy. Stephenson and colleagues (2013) found that women who reported high relationship satisfaction were the most likely to benefit from cognitive behavioral sex therapy.

The fact that sexual dysfunctions may have multiple causes (biological, psychogenic, interpersonal) raises questions about whether a physician, psychologist, marriage therapist, or sex therapist should be sought for treatment. The Personal Choices section addresses the issue of whom to consult for treatment of a sexual dysfunction.

> *One partner's dysfunction is the other partner's distress.*
>
> William Masters and Virginia Johnson

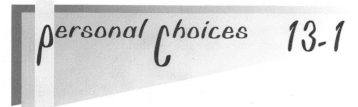

Finding a Sex Therapist

Although second opinions are often required for major surgery, no public policy protects individuals in regard to the treatment they receive for sexual dysfunctions. If you need to consult a professional for a sexual dysfunction, should you consult a physician who is trained to treat the body, a psychologist who focuses on anxiety/phobias, a marriage counselor who emphasizes the relationship with your partner, or a sex therapist who more likely has studied the biological, psychological, relationship and sexual aspects of the dysfunction? Your sex therapist should be credentialed—a certified member of ASSECT (American Association of Sexuality Educators, Counselors, and Therapists), a clinical psychologist (PhD) with specialized training in sexuality, or a licensed marriage therapist with specific training in sexuality. While there are exceptions, most physicians have limited training in sexuality.

13.2e Cognitive Factors

Consider the following examples: A woman in her 50s believes the myth that women her age should not be interested in sex. A man in his 50s believes the myth that men his age are unable to achieve an erection that is satisfactory for intercourse. A heterosexual couple believes that the only appropriate way for the woman to have an orgasm is through sexual intercourse. A person believes that it is wrong to have sexual fantasies during lovemaking.

These are just a few examples of beliefs or myths (cognitions) that may interfere with sexual desire, arousal, or orgasm. Inadequate sex education can also contribute to belief in such myths and to ignorance of sexual anatomy and physiology. For example, a woman who does not know where her clitoris is (or that it even exists) may have difficulty experiencing orgasm. Self-Assessment 13-1 provides a way to assess your knowledge about sexuality.

Self-Assessment 13-1: How Much Do You Know About Sexuality?

Take this true-false test to assess how much you know about sexuality.

1. T   F   Sexual expression is purely natural, not a function of learning.
2. T   F   Foreplay is for the woman; intercourse is for the man.
3. T   F   Once a couple establishes a good sexual relationship, they don't need to set aside time for intimacy together.
4. T   F   If you love each other and communicate, everything will go fine sexually.
5. T   F   Sex and love are two sides of the same coin.
6. T   F   Technique is more important than intimacy in achieving a satisfying sexual relationship.
7. T   F   Casual sex is more exciting than intimate sex.
8. T   F   If you have a good sexual relationship, you will have a fulfilling experience each time you have sex.
9. T   F   After age 25 your sex drive dramatically decreases, and most people stop being sexual by 65.
10. T   F   It is primarily the man's role to initiate sex.
11. T   F   If one or both partners become aroused, intercourse must follow or there will be frustration.
12. T   F   Men are more sexual than women.
13. T   F   Having a "G" spot and multiple orgasms is a sign you are a sexually liberated woman.
14. T   F   Since men don't have spontaneous erections after age 50, they are less able to have intercourse.
15. T   F   When you lose sexual desire, the best remedy is to seek another partner.
16. T   F   The most common female sexual problem is pain during intercourse.
17. T   F   The most common male sexual problem is not having enough sex.
18. T   F   Penis size is crucial for female sexual satisfaction.
19. T   F   Oral/genital sex is an exciting but perverse sexual behavior.
20. T   F   Simultaneous orgasms provide the most erotic pleasure.
21. T   F   Married people do not masturbate.
22. T   F   Using sexual fantasies during intercourse indicates dissatisfaction with your partner.
23. T   F   Clitoral orgasms are far superior to vaginal orgasms.
24. T   F   Male-on-top is the most natural position for intercourse.
25. T   F   People of today are doing much better sexually than the previous generation.

Scoring and Interpretation

Add the number of Ts you checked. This is the number of sex myths you believe. What you took was a sex-myth test—so all the answers are false. Don't be surprised if you believed several of these myths; the average person thinks nine of these statements are true. Even among college students taking a human sexual-behavior course, the average number of myths believed was seven (McCarthy & McCarthy, 1984).

Source: From *Sexual Awareness: Enhancing Sexual Pleasure,* by B. McCarthy and E. McCarthy, 1984, pp. 13–14. Copyright 1984 by Carroll & Graf Publishers, Inc. Reprinted by permission of Avalon Publishers.

13.3 **Interest/Arousal Dysfunctions**

In this section we examine female sexual interest/arousal disorder and male hypoactive sexual desire disorder.

How to rekindle desire or make love all the time or have a passionate marriage is the stuff of big business and unrealistic expectations.

Linda Savage, sex therapist

13.3a Female Sexual Interest/Arousal Disorder

According to the *DSM-5* diagnosis of **female sexual interest/arousal disorder** (previously known as hypoactive sexual desire disorder) involves the lack of, or significantly reduced, sexual interest/arousal as manifested by at least three of the following:

1. Absent/reduced interest in sexual activity
2. Absent or reduced sexual/erotic thoughts or fantasies
3. No initiation of sexual activity and unreceptive to partner's attempts to initiate
4. Absent or reduced sexual excitement during sexual activity in 75% to 100% of the sexual encounters
5. Absent/reduced interest/arousal in response to sexual/erotic cues (e.g., sex texting)
6. Absent/reduced genital and nongenital sensations during sexual activity

At least three of the above must have persisted a minimum of 6 months. Gradations of the dysfunction would be mild, moderate, or severe. Therapists are careful to examine the relationship of the woman with her partner before determining the diagnosis of sexual interest/arousal disorder. For example if the woman has a lower desire for sexual activity than her partner, this condition is not sufficient to label the woman as low interest/arousal disorder. The woman must be distressed by her lack of interest/arousal. If she has always been asexual, and views her lack of interest in sex as no problem, the label of female sexual interest/arousal disorder is not appropriate. The *DSM-5* presented no prevalence data for sexual interest/arousal disorder among females in the United States.

Female sexual interest/arousal disorder
The persistent or recurrent inability to attain or maintain sufficient sexual excitement or a lack of genital lubrication/ swelling or other somatic responses

International **DATA**

Data from France reveals that, in the general female population, prevalence of hypoactive sexual desire disorder ranges from 24% to 43% (Geonet, De Sutter, & Zech, 2013).

Giraldi and colleagues (2013) noted, "Definitions and terminology for female sexual arousal disorder (FSAD) are currently being debated. While some authors have suggested that FSAD is more a subjective response rather than a genital response, others have suggested that desire and arousal disorders should be combined in one entity. Persistent genital arousal disorder (PGAD) is a new entity, suggested to be defined as "Restless Genital Syndrome" (p. 58).

Regardless of the label, female sexual interest/arousal disorder means that the woman has no interest in sex, is not able to become or stay sexually aroused. Associated with no interest/arousal is that the woman lacks genital lubrication and swelling. Like other sexual dysfunctions, female sexual arousal disorder may be lifelong, acquired, situational, or generalized. The diagnosis is not made if the woman is severely depressed or drug addicted, has a serious medical condition

Women in relationships of longer duration are more likely to report engaging in sex, despite no obvious feelings of sexual desire at the outset of a sexual encounter, compared with women in shorter-duration relationships.

DSM-5 (p. 435)

(e.g., diabetes), is in a physically abusive relationship, or has a partner who provides inadequate sexual stimulation. Hence, depression, substance abuse, etc. would become the focus in therapy of the woman's problem, not the sexual side effect. It is not unusual for comorbidity to exist, meaning that the sexual interest/arousal problems occur at the same time as other factors such as depression, thyroid problems, etc,.

Factors that may cause interest/sexual arousal difficulties include relationship dissatisfaction, restrictive upbringing, and exhaustion. Genetics may also be involved. "There appears to be a strong influence of genetic factors on vulnerability to sexual problems in women" (American Psychiatric Association, 2013, p. 435).

Female sexual interest/arousal dysfunction may also result from estrogen deficiency, the most common cause of which is menopause. Other biological factors that may be related to lack of sexual arousal in women include neurogenic disorders (such as multiple sclerosis) and some drugs (such as antihistamines and antihypertensives). Strong emotions—such as depression, fear, anger, and stress—may also interfere with sexual responsiveness.

Treatment for women who have difficulty experiencing sexual arousal often begins with an examination of the relationship with her partner. Not only is a loving, respectful context important for the woman's interest in sex, the kind of stimulation required for arousal by her lover is also paramount. An insensitive, accusatory, selfish partner who does not nurture the love relationship with the partner and provide the time, type, and amount of stimulation his partner needs for arousal becomes the focus of therapeutic intervention. Jiann and colleagues (2013) confirmed in their study of 632 sexually active couples that the sexual functioning of the partner of the female has an effect on the arousal, orgasm, and sexual satisfaction of the female.

Cultural Diversity

Lower rates of sexual desire may be more common among East Asian women compared with European women (*DSM-5*, 2013, 435). One explanation is that Eastern women are more likely taught to be passive and to "serve" their partners than to be focused on their own sexual needs (characteristic of the norm of "individualism" in Europe and in America).

While female sexual interest/arousal disorder may be present in either heterosexual or homosexual relationships, lesbians in long-term relationships sometimes refer to the concept of the **lesbian death bed**. This term refers to a dramatic, sustained drop-off in sexual frequency that is believed to occur in some long-term lesbian couples (Iasenza, 2001). The belief is thought to have its origin in the fact that "there is no man in the relationship to ensure initiation of sexual activity" (p. 59). Although some therapists have observed that lesbian women may not have been socialized to initiate sex, there is also evidence that, compared to heterosexual women, lesbian women may be more sexually arousable, comfortable using erotic or arousing language, and more likely to report a higher level of satisfaction with the quality of their sexual relationship. Indeed, the "lesbian death bed" is a misnomer. In addition, that part of the definition that suggests a drop-off in frequency of sex in long-term relationships is equally true of heterosexual relationships.

Lesbian death bed
Sustained drop-off in sexual frequency of lesbian couples in long-term relationships

Treatment

Treatment for female sexual interest/arousal disorder depends on the underlying causes of the problem. Some of the ways in which lack of sexual desire may be treated include the following:

1. *Improve relationship satisfaction.* As noted earlier, "treating the relationship before treating the sexual problem" is standard therapy with any sexual dysfunction, including lack of interest in sex. A common prerequisite for being interested in sex with a partner—particularly from the viewpoint of a woman—is "psychological intimacy," to be in love and to feel comfortable and secure with her partner. Couple's therapy that emphasizes a mutual loving relationship is the first stage of sex therapy.

2. *Change negative cognitions.* Geonet and colleagues (2013) emphasized the negative role cognitions play in scripting women out of a positive, pleasurable experience. These negative cognitions can be linked to their own self-image (e.g., "I am not beautiful enough"), their partner (e.g., "He disgusts me"), or linked to the marital relationship (e.g., "He is going to leave me," "He doesn't love me anymore"). These negative thoughts trigger emotions like anxiety, shame or guilt. Moreover, these cognitions will have a negative impact on sexual response. Indeed, the more negative thoughts are present, the less subject sexual arousal will be experienced. Consequently, during sexual intercourse, women will focus on these thoughts rather than sexual excitements (p. 9).

3. *Create the conditions for satisfying sex.* Women who report low interest in sex may not have had a partner who created the stimulation, both physiological and psychological, that elicited her sexual feelings or desires. Identifying the conditions of satisfying sex for the woman becomes a goal.

4. *Practice sensate focus.* **Sensate focus** is an exercise whereby the partners focus on pleasuring each other in nongenital ways. Masters and Johnson (1966) developed the sensate focus exercises to treat various sexual dysfunctions. Couples who are not experiencing sexual dysfunction but who want to enhance their sexual relationship may also use sensate focus.

   In practicing the sensate focus exercise, partners (in the privacy of their bedroom) remove their clothing and take turns touching, feeling, caressing, and exploring each other in ways intended to provide sensual pleasure. In the first phase of sensate focus, genital touching is not allowed. The person being touched should indicate whether he or she finds a particular touching behavior unpleasant, and at which point the partner should stop or change what is being done.

   During the second phase of sensate focus, the person being touched is instructed to give positive as well as negative feedback (to indicate what is enjoyable as well as what is unpleasant). During the third phase, genital touching can be included, without the intention of producing orgasm. The goal of progressing through the three phases of sensate focus is to help the partners learn to give and receive pleasure by promoting trust and communication and reducing anxiety related to sexual performance.

5. *View/read erotic materials and invoke sexual fantasy.* Consistent with the principle of modeling, sexual desire can be encouraged by viewing and reading about people having explicit enjoyable sex or reading about a romantic sequence between two appealing people or invoking a fantasy that has been reliably erotic in the past. *Fifty Shades of Grey* is erotic reading popular in 2013.

6. *Replacing hormones.* After the social/relationship conditions for hypoactive sexual desire (including low arousal and low orgasmic capacity) are assessed

Sensate focus
Treatment used in sex therapy developed by Masters and Johnson whereby the partners focus on pleasuring each other in nongenital ways

and treated, hormone assessment may be helpful. A physician may recommend androgen replacement therapy to increase desire, arousal, and satisfaction.

7. *Change medications or dosage (if possible) in cases in which medication interferes with sexual desire.*   Selective serotonin reuptake inhibitors (SSRIs)—such as Prozac or Paxil that are used to treat depression, anxiety, or premenstrual dysphoric disorder—may interfere with interest, arousal, and performance. Careful monitoring of the effects of medication is indicated; it is important for a person taking such medication to work closely with their healthcare provider to plan dosage changes or medication discontinuation.

8. *Masturbate.*   Masturbation may also be recommended on the premise that individuals may "act themselves into a new way of thinking more quickly than they can think themselves into a new way of acting." Rather than trying to think themselves into sexual pleasure, they can masturbate (a vibrator may be helpful) to orgasm which will provide an experiential basis for the development of positive thoughts and feelings about sex.

9. *Rest and relax.*   Other treatments for lack of sexual desire include rest and relaxation. This treatment is indicated when the culprit is chronic fatigue syndrome (CFS), the symptoms of which are overwhelming fatigue, low-grade fever, and sore throat. Women with young children sometimes report that they are exhausted and would rather sleep than have sex.

10. *Learn about alternate models of sexual response.*   Some women have found it helpful to learn that not having "spontaneous" sexual desire can be "normal." Sex therapists also note that desire is not a prerequisite for engaging in sexual behavior. Indeed, one may engage in sexual behavior out of feelings of emotional intimacy and/or to please the partner. The principle of "acting one's self into a new way of feeling" predicts that, once the person engages in sexual behavior with a loving and skilled sexual partner, the outcome may be sexual enjoyment or more.

13.3b Sexual Aversion Disorder

Previous editions of the *DSM* referred to **sexual aversion disorder** (also known as *sexual phobia* and *sexual panic disorder*) which means there is not only low interest in sex but that sex is aversive, also. The person has a persistent or recurrent phobic aversion to and avoidance of sexual contact with a sexual partner. The individual reports anxiety, fear, or disgust when confronted with a sexual opportunity with a partner. Some individuals experience generalized revulsion to all sexual stimuli, including kissing and touching.

Causes and Contributing Factors

The immediate cause of sexual aversion is an intense fear of sex. Such fear may result from negative sexual attitudes acquired in childhood or from sexual trauma, such as rape or incest. Some cases of sexual aversion may be caused by disgust at sexual stimuli, fear of intimacy, intrapsychic conflicts, or hostility toward the other sex. Van Overveld and colleagues (2013) collected data from 762 undergraduates who completed a Sexual Disgust Questionnaire (SDQ) (see Self-Assessment 13-2) and found that high scores on the SDQ for both women and men were associated with low interest in sex. Women with vaginismus (difficulty with penetration) were particularly likely to feel disgusted with vaginal penetration. Murray and colleagues (2013) also investigated the relationship between germ aversion in a sample of 411 respondents and future sexual behavior. For females, germ aversion correlated negatively with short-term mating orientation (wanting to avoid dating or having sex with males).

Sexual aversion disorder
Persistent or recurrent phobic aversion to and avoidance of sexual contact with a sexual partner

SELF-ASSESSMENT 13-2: THE SEXUAL DISGUST QUESTIONNAIRE (SDQ)

To assess the degree to which you experience disgust toward stimuli contaminated with sexual byproducts, read each statement and indicate (by selecting a number) your willingness to engage in each of the identified behaviors.

Certainly not willing		Probably not willing		Maybe willing, maybe not		Probably willing		Certainly willing
0	1	2	3	4	5	6	7	8

To what extent are you willing to do the following?

1. ___ Use a towel after sexual intercourse, for your face, after it has been used to wipe off sperm/vaginal fluids from yourself after sexual intercourse, and smells accordingly.

2. ___ Use a towel for your face after it has been used to wipe off sperm from your partner, after sexual intercourse, and smells accordingly.

3. ___ Lie beneath bedclothes in a hotel, that look unwashed and below which previous guests may have had sexual intercourse.

4. ___ Lie beneath bedclothes, below which you had masturbated the day before, and which show obvious smudge.

5. ___ Use a towel for your face that has been thoroughly cleaned after it has been used, following sexual intercourse to wipe off sperm/vaginal fluids of an unknown person (e.g., a towel in a hotel).

6. ___ Touch a soiled, unwashed towel that had possibly been used to wipe off sperm/vaginal fluid of an unknown person after sexual intercourse (e.g., a towel in a hotel).

Scoring

Add the numbers you wrote down. Zero (certainly not willing) is the response indicating being the least willing to handle sexual contaminants and 8 (certainly willing) is the response indicating being the most willing to handle sexual contaminants. The lower your total score (0 is the lowest possible score), the more difficult it is for you to handle sexual contaminants. A higher total score (48 is the highest possible score) reflects a strong willingness to handle sexual contaminants. A score of 24 places you at the midpoint between not being willing at all and being completely willing to handle sexual contaminants.

Source: Van Overveld, M., de Jong, P. J., Peters, M. L., van Lankveld, J., Melles, R., and ter Kuile, M. M. (2013). The Sexual Disgust Questionnaire; A psychometric study and a first exploration in patients with sexual dysfunctions. *Journal of Sexual Medicine, 10:* 396–407. Used by permission of Van Overveld.

Treatment

Treatment for sexual aversion involves providing insight into the possible ways in which the negative attitudes toward sexual activity developed, increasing the communication skills of the partners, and practicing sensate focus. Understanding the origins of the sexual aversion may enable the individual to view change as possible. Through communication with the partner and sensate focus exercises, the individual may learn to associate more positive feelings with sexual behavior. When there is a history of sexual trauma, therapy for trauma symptoms, or post-traumatic stress disorder may be needed to precede a focus on the sexual aversion.

Systematic desensitization may also be employed in the treatment of sexual aversion. Individuals may be cognitively introduced to progressive stages of sexual touching involvement, while in a relaxed state, so as to remove their anxiety in sexual encounters.

13.3c Male Hypoactive Sexual Desire Disorder

Male hypoactive sexual desire disorder is the male counterpart of female sexual interest/arousal disorder. It is to opposite of **hyperactive sexual desire disorder**. The following are the specific diagnostic criteria from the *DSM-5*:

1. Persistent or recurrent deficient (or absent) sexual/erotic thoughts or fantasies and desire for sexual activity is experienced. It is the clinicians call if the label applies, taking into account the age and context of the male patient.

2. The symptoms in the above criteria have persisted for a minimum of 6 months.

3. The symptoms cause significant distress. (If the male is not concerned about having low sexual interest, the label does not apply).

4. The sexual dysfunction is not better explained by a nonsexual mental disorder such as a severe relationship problem, substance abuse/medication, or another medical condition.

National **DATA**

Approximately 6% of younger men (ages 18–24) and 41% of older men (66–74) report problems with sexual desire. However, persistent (6 months or more) lack of sexual interest in sex among men (ages 16–44) is rare, only 1.8% (American Psychiatric Association, 2013, p. 442).

Male hypoactive sexual desire disorder
Persistent or recurrent deficiency (or absence) of sexual fantasies, thoughts, and/or desire for (or receptivity to) sexual activity, which causes personal distress

Hyperactive sexual desire disorder
Very high (hyperactive) sexual interest, which influences persons to behave as though they are driven to sexual expression and the pursuit of sex, which may have negative effects on the health, relationships, or career of the individual

Satiation
Result of a stimulus losing its value with repeated exposure

Male hypoactive sexual desire disorder is sometimes associated with erectile dysfunction and/or premature ejaculation. The male feels embarrassed/ashamed so avoids sexual encounters/contexts with concomitant loss of interest in sex. As with the woman, the dysfunction can be lifelong, acquired, generalized, or situational and is categorized as mild, moderate, severe. Other terms sometimes used to refer to male hypoactive sexual desire disorder include *inhibited sexual desire, low sexual desire,* and *impaired sexual interest.*

Assessing whether the male has hypoactive sexual desire disorder is problematic. First, there are no clear criteria for determining "abnormal" levels of sexual desire. Two people can vary greatly in the degree to which they experience sexual interest or desire, and each may feel comfortable with his or her level of desire. Hence, if the partner of the male has a higher interest in sex, this fact does not mean that the male should be labeled as having hypoactive sexual desire. Furthermore, sexual desire predictably decreases over time. The principle of **satiation**, a stimulus loses it's value with repeated exposure, ensures that long term lovers will not have sex with each other as frequently as when they were new to each other. It is important not to interpret normal declines in sexual interest and activity as a sexual dysfunction.

Causes and Contributing Factors

Causes and contributing factors for male hypoactive sexual desire disorder include not only satiation but relationship issues (e.g., poor communication/discrepancies in sexual interest), individual issues (poor body image, history of emotional/sexual abuse), cultural factors (e.g., religion), job stress/exhaustion, physical illness, depression, drugs, sexual dysfunctions of partner, and low hormone levels (e.g., testosterone, androgen).

Treatment

The course of treatment depends on the cause, but in general follows the treatment for female sexual interest/arousal disorder: focusing on the relationship, job stress, physical well being, depression, etc. A focus might also be on other sexual dysfunctions, such as erectile dysfunction or premature ejaculation.

13.4 Other Male Sexual Dysfunctions

In addition to low interest in sex, male sexual dysfunctions include premature ejaculation and erectile dysfunction.

13.4a Premature Ejaculation

Premature ejaculation is regarded as the most common sexual dysfunction reported by men (McMahon et al., 2013). Also known as **rapid ejaculation**, **premature ejaculation** (PE) is defined by various diagnostic criteria:

1. Persistent or recurrent pattern of ejaculation that occurs during partnered sexual activity within approximately 1 minute following vaginal penetration, and before the individual wishes.
2. The symptom identified above must have been present at least 6 months and experienced 75% to 100% of the time.
3. The male is distressed about his early ejaculation.
4. The sexual dysfunction is not better explained by a nonsexual mental disorder or as a consequence of severe relationship distress or significant stressors, and is not attributable to the effects of a substance/medication or other medical condition.

While there are differences in how PE is defined (Giami, 2013), the central themes of the definition are that ejaculation is quick, the man can't

> *Remember, if you smoke after sex you're doing it too fast.*
>
> Woody Allen, comedian

Rapid ejaculation
Ejaculation which always or nearly always occurs prior to or within about 1 minute of vaginal penetration, the inability to delay ejaculation on all or nearly all vaginal penetrations, and the presence of negative personal consequences, such as distress, bother, frustration and/or the avoidance of sexual intimacy

Premature ejaculation
See Rapid ejaculation

control it, he feels bad about it (e.g., decreased self-esteem), and there are negative consequences for partner relationships. As with other sexual dysfunctions, PE may be lifelong, acquired, generalized, and situational.

National **DATA**

More than 20%–30% of men, ages 18–70, report concern about how rapidly they ejaculate. When the definition of 1 minute is used, only 1% to 3% of men would be diagnosed with the disorder (American Psychiatric Association, 2013, p. 442).

Causes and Contributing Factors

Historically, attempts to explain the causes of PE have included both biological and psychological theories. Most of these explanations are not evidence-based and are speculative (McMahon, Jannini, Waldinger, & Rowland, 2013). Biological causes suggest that some men are genetically wired to ejaculate quickly—they have a constitutionally hypersensitive sympathetic nervous system that predisposes them to rapid ejaculation. Men with low testosterone levels, with prostate disease, and with hyperthyroidism also have higher incidences of PE (Maggi, Buvat, Corona, Guay, & Torres, 2013). Psychosocial factors associated with premature ejaculation include early learning experiences—such as the adolescent having to ejaculate quickly before being discovered—being anxious about having sex, and feeling as though he must hurry and ejaculate before losing his erection (McMahon, Jannini, Waldinger, & Rowland, 2013).

Treatment

Intervention is educational, interpersonal, and medical. McMahon and colleagues (2013) noted that the male should receive psychosexual education that includes an explanation of possible organic or psychological causes so as to relieve him of feeling responsible or ashamed. While involvement of the partner may be helpful, such involvement is not mandatory. Medical intervention is usually the first line of treatment for lifelong PE and may include "Daily treatment with paroxetine 10–40 mg, clomipramine 12.5–50 mg, sertraline 50–200 mg, fluoxetine 20–40 mg, and citalopram 20–40 mg" which is "usually effective in delaying ejaculation" (p. 9). A specific recommendation used by many physicians is paroxetine, which exerts the strongest ejaculation delay, within 5 to 10 days of starting treatment with the full therapeutic effect in 2 to 3 weeks (p. 9). The article by McMahon and colleagues (2013) details the specifics for medication used in the treatment of PE and should be consulted to increase awareness of doses, side effects, and potential withdrawal effects.

Medical advances have made the use of more traditional techniques for PE (e.g., squeeze technique, pause technique) less viable. However, counseling focused on sex education and communication with the partner, expectations, etc. may still be a valuable adjunct to medical intervention. Some female partners may not be bothered by early, delayed, or no ejaculation. When female pleasure/orgasm is the first priority (e.g., via oral sex, vibrator, digital simulation), when or if the male ejaculates becomes less of an issue. Kempeneers and colleagues (2013) confirmed that men are typically more bothered by PE than their partners

13.4b Erectile Disorder

Erectile disorder
Persistent or recurrent inability to attain, or to maintain until completion of sexual activity, an adequate erection

Erectile disorder is defined having at least one of the three following symptoms that must be experienced in almost all, or 75% to 100%, sexual activity situations:

1. Marked difficulty in obtaining an erection during sexual activity
2. Marked difficulty in maintaining an erection until the completion of sexual activity
3. Marked decrease in erectile rigidity

In effect, the male cannot create or maintain a hard erection. In addition, the condition must have persisted for at least 6 months, cause significant distress to the

To succeed with the opposite sex, tell her you're impotent. She can't wait to disprove it.
Cary Grant, actor

male, cannot be better explained by a nonsexual mental disorder or in reference to severe relationship distress or other significant stressors, and is not attributable to the side effects of a substance/ medication or other medical condition. Erectile problems are common in men diagnosed with depression or posttraumatic stress disorder (American Psychiatric Association, 2013). Occasional isolated episodes of the inability to attain or maintain an erection are not considered dysfunctional; they are regarded as normal occurrences. Erectile dysfunction is most common in men after the age of 40.

- Most cases of erectile dysfunction are caused by a chronic health problem (such as diabetes, hypertension, atherosclerosis, or kidney or liver failure) or physiological condition, including heavy smoking, alcohol or drug abuse, obesity, lack of exercise, blockage in the arteries, and various medications (e.g., for high blood pressure). Prost and colleagues (2013) noted that "changes in sedentary lifestyle with weight loss and optimal treatment of diseases/risk factors (e.g., diabetes, hypertension) can either improve ED or add to the efficacy of ED-specific therapies." Erectile dysfunction is also related to age; the older the man, the more likely he is to report difficulty creating and maintaining an erection.

- Psychiatric, emotional, and psychosocial problems may also interfere with erectile capacity. Examples include depression, fear (of unwanted pregnancy, intimacy, HIV, or other STIs), guilt, and relationship dissatisfaction. For example, the man who is having an extradyadic sexual relationship may feel guilty. This guilt may lead to difficulty in attaining or maintaining an erection in sexual interaction with the primary partner.

- Anxiety may also inhibit the man's ability to create and maintain an erection. One source of anxiety is performance pressure, which may be self-imposed or imposed by a partner. In self-imposed performance anxiety, the man constantly "checks" (mentally or visually) to see that he is erect. Such self-monitoring (also referred to as **spectatoring**) creates anxiety because the man fears that he may not be erect. Partner-imposed performance pressure involves the partner's communicating that the man must get and stay erect to be regarded as a good lover. Such pressure usually increases the man's anxiety, thus ensuring no erection. Whether self or partner imposed, the anxiety associated with performance pressure results in a vicious cycle—anxiety, erectile difficulty, embarrassment, followed by anxiety, erectile difficulty, and so on.

- Performance anxiety may also be related to alcohol use. After consuming more than a few drinks, the man may initiate sex but may become anxious after failing to achieve an erection. (Too much alcohol will interfere with erection—in Shakespeare's words, "Drink—it provokes the desire, but it takes away the performance." [*Macbeth*, act 2, scene 3.]) Although alcohol may be responsible for his initial "failure," his erection difficulties may continue because of his anxiety/fear about not being able to get/keep an erection.

- Men who require of themselves that they satisfy their partner with the use of only their penis are even more vulnerable to erectile failure. Men who are accustomed to satisfying their partner through cuddling, oral sex, use of vibrator and/or digital stimulation feel they have various options for providing their partner pleasure/orgasm. Hence, a flaccid penis is no cause for alarm—they just move to another option.

Treatment

In regard to the treatment of erectile dysfunction, successful oral therapies, namely the phosphodiesterase type 5 inhibitors (Viagra, Cialis, Levitra) are used. Viagra is typically the first option. For those men who aren't helped by Viagra, or for those who are bothered by its side effects (headaches, flushed face, blue tint to vision), two similar drugs, tadalafil (Cialis) and vardenafil (Levitra), are available. Albersen and colleagues (2013) noted that the overall efficacy rates of these phosphodiesterase type 5 inhibitors (PDE5-i) for erectile dysfunction are 60–70%.

Spectatoring
Self-monitoring one's own sexual responses to the point that a sexual dysfunction may occur

Think About It

Alternatives to the medications include penile injections, transurethal suppositories, rod implants, and the vacuum pump. In regard to injection therapy, Caverject™ or Edex™ (Alprostadil) is injected directly into the side of the penis and produces an erection. The medication dilates the arteries of the penis and allows blood to flow in. An erection occurs from 5 to 15 minutes after the injection. The male gives himself the injection just before he wishes to engage in sexual activity (the erection lasts 30 minutes to an hour or up to orgasm).

Transurethral suppositories involve placing a medicated pellet about the size of a grain of rice one inch into the opening at the top of the penis. The only FDA-approved urethral suppository is MUSE (Medicated Urethral System for Erection) that contains the drug alprostadil (also used in the injectable drugs, Caverject and Edex). Within 5 to 10 minutes the medication is absorbed and an erection occurs. The erection may continue after ejaculation; loss of erection usually occurs within an hour.

Penile implants are of two kinds, semirigid or those that inflate, which replace the spongy tissue (corpora cavernosum) inside the penis that fills with blood during erection. Surgery is required. Implants are used when medications (e.g., Viagra) are no longer effective or when the male has a medical condition that affects blood flow, such as diabetes.

In regard to the vacuum pump, it is considered an attractive second-line therapy. In select cases such post-prostatectomy penile rehabilitation, as well as in men who cannot use a PDE5i, the vacuum device is considered first-line treatment (Brison, Seftel, & Sadeghi-Nejad, 2013). Indeed, the most effective treatment of erectile dysfunction encompasses both pharmacology (and alternatives) and psychotherapy in which cognitive aspects of poor sexual performance, including diminished self-esteem, lack of confidence and perceived failures are dealt with (Simopoulos & Trinidad, 2013).

For men who want to delay having problems with erectile dysfunction, the preventative behaviors are regular exercise, no smoking, and maintain age/size appropriate weight (Glina, Sharlip, & Hellstrom, 2013). Since prostate cancer is associated with erectile dysfunction, there is interest in the most efficacious approach. Chung and Brock (2013) reviewed the literature on prostate cancer and male sexual dysfunction. Their conclusion: "while several preventive and treatment strategies for the preservation and recovery of sexual function are available, no specific recommendation or consensus guidelines exist regarding the optimal rehabilitation or treatment protocol."

For men who have had a radical prostatectomy resulting in erectile dysfunction, the patient is taught to give himself a shot in the penis, an alprostadil injection—called IAI for intracavernous alprostadil injection. Yiou and colleagues (2013) studied the sexual satisfaction of 152 women partnered with men who were being treated for ED with IAI. Indexes of female sexual quality of life were low overall, but were highly correlated with the partner's response level to IAI treatment. IAI-related pain, increased age, and poor urinary function of the male partner appeared to negatively impact female sex life.

Cultural Diversity

Cultures differ in the ways they treat sexual dysfunctions. In China, men with erectile dysfunction are sometimes regarded as "suffering from deficiency of Yang elements in the kidney." Their treatment is to drink a solution prepared with water and several chemicals designed to benefit kidney function. They may also be given acupuncture therapy (Shikai, 1990, p. 198).

13.5 Orgasm Dysfunctions

Orgasm dysfunctions include female orgasmic disorder and delayed ejaculation.

> *Sex: the thing that takes up the least amount of time and causes the most amount of trouble.*
>
> John Barrymore, actor

13.5a Female Orgasmic Disorder

Female orgasmic disorder (FOD) is diagnosed under the following conditions (American Psychiatric Association, 2013):

1. A marked delay in, marked infrequency of, or absence of orgasm
2. Markedly reduced intensity of orgasmic features
3. Symptoms have persisted for a minimum of 6 months and cause distress.
4. The sexual dysfunction is not better explained by a nonsexual mental disorder such as severe relationship distress (e.g., partner violence) or other significant stressors, and is not attributable to the effects of substance abuse/medication or another medical condition.

Female orgasmic disorder impairs the woman's ability to participate in a sexual relationship in the way she would like (Laan, Rellini, & Barnes, 2013). Because women vary in their capacity to orgasm, a clinician making this diagnosis takes into consideration the woman's age (younger are more likely to have orgasmic difficulties), previous sexual experiences, current relationship with the partner, and whether the sexual stimulation is adequate. Like other sexual dysfunctions, orgasmic disorder may be lifelong, acquired, situational, or generalized. Female orgasmic disorder may also occur in the presence of other sexual difficulties, such as lack of desire/arousal, no lubrication, and pain.

> **Female orgasmic disorder (FOD)**
> A persistent or recurrent difficulty, delay in, or absence of experiencing orgasm following sufficient stimulation and arousal

National DATA

From 10% to 40% of women report orgasmic problems depending on age, culture, duration, and severity of symptoms. Approximately 10% of women do not experience orgasm throughout their lifetime (American Psychiatric Association, 2013, p. 431).

International DATA

Reported prevalence figures for FOD range from 30–46% in Asia (Laan, Rellini, & Barnes, 2013).

Leeners and colleagues (2013) noted that the pituitary hormone prolactin (PRL) may have an important role in regulating (and thus indexing) sexual satisfaction. The researchers analyzed the correlation of women's post-orgasmic serum PRL surges following sexual intercourse with women's perceived quality of orgasm and resulting sexual satisfaction.

Causes and Contributing Factors

Laan, Rellini, & Barnes (2013) reviewed the literature on the etiology and treatment of female orgasmic disorder and published their findings as "standard operating procedure." Biological factors associated with orgasmic dysfunction can be related to medical issues such as vascular disease, chronic diseases, diabetes, multiple sclerosis, spinal cord injury, and pelvic conditions. Stress, alcohol, and medications—such as selective serotonin reuptake inhibitors (SSRIs), antipsychotics, mood stabilizers, cardiovascular medications, chemotherapy agents, and hypertension drugs—should also be investigated. Over half of the women taking SSRIs reported delay or inhibition of orgasm (Laan, Rellini, & Barnes, 2013).

Psychosocial and cultural factors associated with orgasmic dysfunctions are similar to those related to lack of sexual desire. Causes of orgasm difficulties in women include a restrictive upbringing and learning a passive female sexual role. Guilt, shame, disgust, fear of intimacy, fear of losing control, ambivalence about commitment, and spectatoring may also interfere with the ability to experience orgasm. Other women may not achieve orgasm because of their belief in the myth that women are not supposed to enjoy sex. Experiencing a traumatic event, such as being raped, may interfere with orgasmic capacity as could being involved in a relationship with a partner who does not create a context of love, respect, and security.

For some women, lack of information can result in orgasmic difficulties. (Some women do not know that clitoral stimulation is important for orgasm to occur, for example.) Finally, some women might not achieve orgasm with their partners because they are ashamed and insecure about telling their partners what they want in terms of sexual stimulation.

Medications such as Paxil are associated with suppression or delay of orgasm.
Source: E. Fred Johnson, Jr.

Take a moment to answer the following question. A woman who does not achieve orgasm because of lack of sufficient stimulation is not considered to have a sexual dysfunction. To what degree do you feel women's partners view the woman's not having an orgasm as their not providing the necessary clitoral stimulation?

Treatment

Laan and colleagues (2013) were clear in their recommendation as to how female orgasmic disorder should be treated:

> A PLISSIT approach for treating orgasm disorder is recommended. This approach consists of Providing Permission, Limited Information, followed by Specific Suggestions if the problem is not resolved, followed by Intensive Therapy (PLISSIT) by clinicians/therapists specialized in providing sexological care. (p. 78)

We will detail the PLISSIT approach later in the chapter. For now, it is important to point out that "intensive therapy" identified as part of the PLISSIT method would not only include psychosocial aspects, such as the woman's learning history, but also her current relationship in terms of ensuring that it is a relationship of mutual love, respect, care and security.

Recommending masturbation would also be a part of "intensive therapy." LoPiccolo and Lobitz (1972) developed a nine-step program of masturbation for women with orgasm difficulties. The rationale behind masturbation as a therapeutic technique is that masturbation is the technique that is most likely to produce orgasm. Masturbation gives the woman complete control of the stimulation, provides direct feedback to the woman of the type of stimulation she enjoys, and eliminates the distraction of a partner. The probability of experiencing an orgasm via masturbation is upwards of 95% (compared to 30% through intercourse). In addition, the intense orgasm produced by masturbation leads to increased vascularity in the vagina, labia, and clitoris, which enhances the potential for future orgasms. Vibrators are helpful in providing sufficient stimulation to induce orgasm. A number of different vibrators are available online.

The most effective interventions include a combination of sexuality education, communication on general and sexual issues, attention to relationship, body image, and directed masturbation. A female therapist may be particularly valuable in that she may serve as a model for the client in discussing her own masturbatory experience.

13.5b Delayed Ejaculation

Delayed ejaculation is diagnosed under the following conditions (in order for there to be a diagnosis of delayed ejaculation either of the following symptoms must be experienced with approximately 75%–100% of partnered sexual activity and without the partner desiring delay) (American Psychiatric Association, 2013):

1. Marked delay in ejaculation
2. Marked infrequency or absence of ejaculation
3. Symptoms have persisted for a minimum of 6 months and cause distress.
4. The sexual dysfunction is not better explained by a nonsexual mental disorder, such as severe relationship distress or other significant stressors, and is not attributable to the effects of substance abuse/medication or another medical condition. Like other sexual dysfunctions, delayed ejaculation may be lifelong, acquired, situational, or generalized. Delayed ejaculation is the least understood of the male sexual dysfunctions (Perelman, 2013).

Delayed ejaculation
Absence or delay of ejaculation

National **DATA**

Only 75% of men report always ejaculating during sexual activity. Less than 1% complain of problems with reaching ejaculation that lasted more than 6 months (American Psychiatric Association, 2013, p. 425).

Other terms for delayed ejaculation are **inhibited male orgasm** and **retarded ejaculation**. The clinician making the judgment about delayed ejaculation should take into account the man's age and whether the stimulation has been adequate in focus, intensity, and duration. The man's cultural background is also relevant. Traditional Chinese Taoist philosophy views avoiding ejaculation during intercourse in positive terms because this vital source of energy needs to be preserved (Tang, Lai, Phil, & Chung, 1997).

Causes and Contributing Factors

Several medications may interfere with ejaculation, including some hormone-based medications, tranquilizers, barbiturates, antidepressants, and antihypertensives. Prozac and Paxil are particularly associated with delayed ejaculation. Injury or disease that impairs the neurological system may also interfere with orgasm in the male.

Psychosocial causes of delayed ejaculation include anxiety, fear, spectatoring, and negative attitudes toward sexuality. For example, traumatic experiences or embarrassing ones, such as being discovered by parents while masturbating, can lead to fear, anxiety, and punishment associated with impending orgasm. Thus, the sensation of impending orgasm can become conditioned to produce the response of fear and anxiety, which inhibits orgasm. Some men are obsessed with trying to arouse and please their partners, which they may become anxious and engage in spectatoring, which inhibits the ejaculatory reflex. Fear of pregnancy and guilt may also interfere with a man's ability to achieve orgasm and to ejaculate. Learning negative messages about genitals or sexual activities from one's parents or religious training may also lead to ejaculation difficulties. Perelman (2013) noted that particular attention should be given to psychological issues, including lack of confidence and poor body image. Either a sex therapist or physician should obtain a focused sexual history that includes, but is not limited to, perceived attractiveness of the man's partner, the use of fantasy during sex, anxiety about intercourse, and masturbatory patterns.

Job/career difficulties or the presence of children in the household can also influence sexual performance. Men who have lost their jobs, are depressed about their economic future, or are anxious about children knocking on the door may find that their sexual focus is affected.

Just as with many women, some men are unable to orgasm because of a lack of sufficient stimulation. Some heterosexual men may have developed a pattern of masturbation that involves vigorous stimulation; they then are unable to obtain sufficient stimulation from the vagina during coitus.

Treatment

Treatment for delayed ejaculation may involve changing medications. More frequently, treatment focuses on the psychosocial origins of retarded ejaculation and may consist of exploring the negative attitudes and cognitions that interfere with ejaculation and re-educating to change such negative attitudes.

Inhibited male orgasm
Persistent or recurrent delay in or absence of orgasm following a normal sexual excitement phase

Retarded ejaculation
See Inhibited male orgasm

Treatment may also involve sensate focus exercises, which allow the couple to experience physical intimacy without putting pressure on the man to perform sexually. Eventually, the man's partner helps him ejaculate through oral or manual stimulation. Research on treating delayed ejaculation has focused mainly on men in heterosexual relationships. After the couple is confident that the man can be brought to orgasm orally or manually, the partner stimulates him to a high level of sexual excitement, and at the moment of orgasm inserts his penis into her vagina so that he ejaculates inside her. After several sessions, the woman gradually reduces the amount of time she orally or manually manipulates her partner and increases the amount of time she stimulates him with her vagina (Masters & Johnson, 1970). Alternatively, the goal in treating delayed ejaculation may be to enjoy sexual activities with a partner without the expectation that ejaculation must occur inside the vagina.

13.6 Genito-Pelvic Pain/Penetration Disorder

Persistent genito-pelvic pain/penetration disorder is diagnosed as persistent or recurrent difficulties with one (or more) of the following (American Psychiatric Association, 2013):

1. Vaginal penetration during intercourse
2. Marked vulvovaginal or pelvic pain during vaginal intercourse or penetration attempts
3. Marked fear or anxiety about vulvovaginal or pelvic pain in anticipation of, during, or as a result of vaginal penetration
4. Marked tensing or tightening of the pelvic floor muscles during attempted vaginal penetration
5. The above symptoms have persisted for a minimum duration of approximately 6 months, and the individual is distressed about the symptoms.
6. The sexual dysfunction is not better explained by a nonsexual mental disorder or as a consequence of severe relationship distress (e.g., partner violence) or other significant stressors, and is not attributable to the effects of substance abuse/medication or another medical condition.

   Hence, genito-pelvic pain/penetration disorder is characterized by difficulty having intercourse, genito-pelvic pain, fear of pain or vaginal penetration, and tension of the pelvic floor muscles. The diagnosis applies if there is distress in just one of the four areas. Like other sexual dysfunctions, genito-pelvic pain/penetration disorder may be lifelong, acquired, situational, or generalized. The disorder may also occur in the presence of other sexual difficulties, such as lack of desire/arousal, no lubrication, and pain.

Persistent genito-pelvic pain/ penetration disorder Involves recurrent difficulties accomplishing vaginal penetration during intercourse, pain during vaginal intercourse/ penetration attempts and fear/anxiety surrounding such attempts

National **DATA**

Approximately 15% of women in North America report recurrent pain during intercourse (American Psychiatric Association, 2013, p. 438).

The terms **vaginismus** and **dyspareunia** have been used prior to the term persistent genito-pelvic pain/penetration disorder. These terms help to sort out the two aspects of the disorder. Vaginismus is the tightness or persistent involuntary spasm of the musculature of the outer third of the vagina that makes vaginal penetration difficult. Dyspareunia is pain during sexual intercourse.

13.6a Vaginismus

Cherner and Reissing (2013) compared women with dyspareunia and vaginismus and found that those with the latter reported more sexual desire and less difficulty with lubrication compared to women with dyspareunia. Numerous sexual problems extending beyond vaginal penetration difficulties were confirmed, suggesting a need for broader treatment approaches not limited to the experience of vaginal penetration

Causes and Contributing Factors for Vaginismus

In women who experience dyspareunia (which may be caused by biological or psycho-social factors), vaginismus may be a protective response to prevent pain. In other words, if a woman anticipates coital pain, she may involuntarily constrict her vagina to prevent painful intercourse. A lack of sexual information and a deficit of knowledge of basic anatomy have been suggested as probable causes (American Psychiatric Association, 2013, p. 439).

Vaginismus may also be related to psychosocial factors, such as a restrictive parental and religious upbringing in which the woman learned to view intercourse as dirty and shameful. Other psychosocial factors include rape, incest, and childhood molestation.

Treatment for Vaginismus

Treatment for vaginismus should begin with a gynecological examination to determine if an organic or physical problem is the cause. Treatment often involves teaching the woman to insert a dilator or objects of graduated size (such as her fingers) into her vagina while she is relaxed. After the woman is able to insert one finger into her vagina, she is instructed to introduce two fingers into the vagina, and this exercise is repeated until she feels relaxed enough to contain the penis. Both individual and partner involvement in the exercises have been used. Systematic desensitization, Kegel exercises, and therapy focusing on the woman's cognitions and perceptions about sex and sexuality with her particular partner may precede or accompany the insertion training.

Vaginismus
Recurrent or persistent involuntary spasm of the musculature of the outer third of the vagina that interferes with vaginal penetration

Dyspareunia
The recurrent or persistent genital pain associated with intercourse or attempts at sexual intercourse

13.6b Dyspareunia

The pain may occur as soon as penile entry begins, during penile containment/movement, at ejaculation by the partner, or after intercourse—and may be experienced by either women or men. The symptoms range from mild discomfort to sharp pain. Dyspareunia is a type of genital sexual pain (GSP). There is disagreement about whether it should be regarded as a sexual dysfunction or as a localized genial pain syndrome (Fugl-Meyer, Bohm-Starke, Damsted Petersen, Fugl-Meyer, Parish, & Giraldi, 2013). Nevertheless, dyspareunia is one of the most commonly reported sexual dysfunctions in pre-menopausal women under the age of 40 (Pazmany, Bergeron, Oudenhove, Verhaeghe, & Enzlin, 2013).

Causes and Contributing Factors for Dyspareunia

Dyspareunia in women may be caused by biological factors, such as vaginal or pelvic infections or inflammations, and allergic reactions to deodorants, douches, and contraceptive devices. Chronic discomfort or pain of the vulva, or **vulvodynia**, is a major cause of dyspareunia. Vulvodynia is diagnosed when a woman experiences burning, stinging, irritation, or knife-like pain of the vulva for more than 3 months, without obvious visible lesions. One subtype is vulvar vestibulitis syndrome (VVS), in which a woman has painful patches on the vestibule (the area around the entrance to the vagina).

Dyspareunia may also be caused by a lack of lubrication, a rigid hymen, tender scarring following an episiotomy, or an improperly positioned uterus or ovary. Although there was no common etiology for dyspareunia, trauma is a common theme resulting from operations, vaginal delivery and back injuries.

Psychological factors may also be involved in the etiology of dyspareunia. Pazmany and colleagues (2013) found that a more negative genital self-image was strongly and independently associated with an increased likelihood of reporting dyspareunia.

In men, inflammations of or lesions on the penis (often caused by herpes), **Peyronie's disease** (which causes a curving or bending of the penis during erection), and **urethritis** (inflammation of the urethra) may cause pain. Because dyspareunia is often a symptom of a medical problem, a health-care provider should be consulted.

Dyspareunia may also be caused by psychosocial factors—including guilt, anxiety, or unresolved feelings about a previous trauma, such as rape or childhood molestation. Religious and parental prohibitions against sexual activity and relationship conflicts may also result in dyspareunia.

Treatment for Dyspareunia

Dyspareunia that is caused by biological factors may be treated by evaluating the medical condition that is causing the coital pain. Medical treatments for vulvodynia include the use of tricyclic antidepressants, but there have not been controlled studies of this treatment. Gabapentin (an anticonvulsant medication that is effective in reducing neuropathic pain) has been used successfully. Other treatments include acupuncture, biofeedback, pelvic-floor physiotherapy, lidocaine ointment, interferon, and surgical removal of vestibular tissue. Fortunately, many cases improve over time either with treatment or untreated. However, despite the distress caused by the puzzling problem, there have been few research treatment trials supporting any particular remedy. The National Vulvodynia Association (www.nva.org) has called for federal funding of vulvodynia research.

If medical or surgical procedures cannot resolve the pain, the person with dyspareunia may try different intercourse positions or other sexual activities that provide pleasure with no or minimal pain. When dyspareunia is caused by psychosocial factors, treatment may involve re-education to replace negative attitudes toward sexual activity with positive ones. Individual therapy may help the person resolve feelings of guilt or anxiety associated with sexual activity. Couple's therapy may be indicated to resolve relationship conflicts. Sensate focus exercises may help the individual relax and enjoy sexual contact.

Vulvodynia
Burning, stinging, irritation, or knife-like pain of the vulva for more than 3 months without obvious visible lesions

Peyronie's disease
Disease that causes a painful curving or bending in the penis during erection

Urethritis
Inflammation of the urethra

Hate to sound sleazy, but tease me, I don't want it if it's that easy.

Tupac Shakur, rap artist

13.7 Sex Therapy

Sex therapy is often delivered as part of another service, such as individual or relationship counseling. Most therapists function as physicians, marriage therapists, relationship counselors or psychotherapists. Nevertheless, there are some who specialize in sex therapy.

13.7a Status of the Profession

Sex therapy is, and has been, in flux (Berry, 2013b). There is little agreement among sex therapists about how to treat a specific sexual problem. There have also been changes in treatment strategies across time. In the past, psychology and psychoanalysis dominated the treatment field. More recently, pharmacological treatment has become more prominent. We previously mentioned that sex therapy is becoming increasingly medicalized. In addition, there is a gender power imbalance between professions (most physicians working as sexologists are male, while most psychologists and psychoanalysts are female) (Gogno, Jones, & Ibarlucia, 2013). Female therapists also predominate among marriage and family therapists. These individuals also conduct sex therapy (Bernal, d'Aniello, & Vasquez, 2013).

13.7b Finding a Sex Therapist

"Let the client beware" applies to the person seeking sex therapy. The individual should be careful in choosing a sex therapist. A basic concern is training. With rare exceptions, there are no laws preventing a person from advertising that she or he is a sex therapist. Anyone can legally open an office in most communities and offer sex therapy. Academic degrees, therapy experience under supervision, and exposure to other aspects of formal training in human sexuality are not legally required to market one's self as a sex therapist. California is one of the few states that exercise some legal restraint on sex therapy. To be licensed in California as a physician, psychologist, social worker, or marriage, family, or child counselor, a person must have had training in human sexuality.

To help upgrade the skills of those providing sex therapy, the American Association of Sex Educators, Counselors, and Therapists (AASECT) offers a Certified Sex Therapist certificate to applicants who have a minimum of a master's degree in a clinical field (psychology, social work, nursing, marriage therapy), have conducted sex therapy under supervision for a minimum of 60 hours, and have attended a 2-day workshop on human sexuality (sponsored by AASECT) to sort out their own attitudes and values about human sexuality. AASECT guidelines indicate that the therapist should have a basic understanding of sexual and reproductive anatomy and physiology, sexual development (biological and psychological), interpersonal relationships, gender-related issues, marital and family dynamics, sociocultural factors in sexual values and behavior, medical issues affecting sexuality (including pregnancy, STIs, drugs, illness and disability, contraception, and fertility), sex research, sexual abuse, and personality theories.

The therapists certified by AASECT are expected to conduct their practice in a manner that reflects the organization's Code of Ethics for Sex Therapists. Beyond being knowledgeable about treating sexual dysfunctions, being empathic, and being trained in communication and counseling skills, the certified sex therapist is expected to refrain from engaging in sexual activity with clients. Following are some of the various approaches to sex therapy.

13.7c Cognitive Behavioral Sex Therapy

Cognitive therapy emphasizes that negative thoughts and attitudes about sex interfere with sexual interest, pleasure, and performance. **Cognitive behavioral sex therapy** is recognized as an effective treatment for sexual dysfunctions (Stephenson, Rellini, & Mesto, 2013) and consists of identifying and stopping negative thoughts and replacing them with positive thoughts. Instead of the male thinking "I am anxious and won't be able to get an erection" (which will usually result in erectile failure), he is asked to use the stop-think technique whereby he yells "stop" in his head when he thinks the negative thought and replaces the thought with "It is OK to be a little anxious ... I am going to focus on pleasuring my partner in various ways without my penis." Another example would be to have the individual who thinks masturbation is sinful and selfish to regard it as a means of discovering self-pleasure so as to teach one's partner what one enjoys sexually.

Negative cognitions may also interfere with personal, partner, and relationship functioning. "I'm too fat and not sexually desirable," "My partner is cheating on me," and "We should never have gotten married" are examples of negative thoughts that will affect one's sexual responsiveness. Addressing these cognitions and replacing them with different thoughts ("My partner loves me the way I am," "My partner is faithful to me," and "We are on our eighth year of a great relationship") become the goal of therapy.

Negative attitudes and cognitions about sex often result from sexual trauma, such as rape and incest. One way to change these negative attitudes and cognitions is for the therapist to teach the individual to view himself or herself as a survivor, rather than a victim. In addition, the therapist can suggest that "living well is the best revenge" against the person who perpetrated the trauma.

Unrealistic expectations for one's sex life may also be operative in a couple who report dissatisfaction with their sex life. Media messages suggest a very high bar. Lyrics from the Eagles "Life in the Fast Lane" provide an illustration:

> *They had one thing in common,*
> *They were good in bed,*
> *She said, "Faster, faster,*
> *The lights are turning red ..."*

Cognitive/behavioral sex therapy is based on the premise that sexual thoughts and behaviors are learned. One of the ways to change thoughts and behaviors quickly is to provide a new learning context for the client. Surrogates may be engaged to provide such a context. *The Sessions* movie detailed the work of a sex surrogate with a virgin male. Up Close 13-1 details the therapeutic use of three female relationship surrogates to assist a 29-year-old male virgin whose goal was to feel comfortable talking with, touching, and kissing a female partner.

Cognitive behavioral sex therapy
Treatment method emphasizing that negative thoughts and attitudes about sex interfere with sexual interest, pleasure, and performance

Surrogates in Relationship Therapy: Learning How to Talk, Touch, and Kiss

A surrogate is person who works with clients in therapy as part of a three-way therapeutic team, consisting of the therapist, a surrogate partner and the client. The primary use of surrogates has been as sex surrogates to resolve sexual dysfunctions. Due to the controversy surrounding the use of sex surrogates, this case history reported the use of relationship surrogates. A 29-year-old never married virgin male complained that while he had the goals of love, marriage, and family, and could "talk/joke" with women in casual social contexts, he had been unable to talk "seriously" with a woman, to hold her hand, or to become physically intimate (defined as kissing). A clinical history of the client revealed that he had been reared in virtual isolation (home schooled) from others, was socialized via religion to view physical contact/sex with women negatively (hence, women were an aversive stimulus), and he had had zero previous experience in more than casual encounters with women. Nearing his 30s the client became desperate to overcome his relationship disability.

Role and Socialization of the Three Surrogates

New behaviors are learned most quickly not by "talk therapy" focusing on the past or cognitive rehearsal of the desired behavior but by engaging in the desired behavior. To assist in helping the client to learn how to talk with and to touch a woman without feeling anxious (above a level of 3 on a 10-point scale), two undergraduate females (ages 22 and 23) were recruited to function in the role of "relationship surrogate." Both of these females had taken relationship and sexuality classes under the second author, were socially skilled, and interested in joining the therapeutic team to assist the client in becoming comfortable in talking and touching (including hand holding). The surrogates were paid $25 per hour by the therapist (who obtained the money from the client) after meeting with the client/providing feedback to the therapist and for completing their assignments with the client (e.g., teaching the client how to ask open-ended questions, and how to make reflective statements).

After the client became comfortable in talking with and holding hands with the respective undergraduate surrogates, he was ready to move forward and become comfortable kissing a female. Another surrogate was solicited for this role. She was a married woman in her 40s who received permission from her husband for her to perform in the role of "relationship surrogate." The "rules" for this third surrogate were the same as for the first two surrogates.

Process of Therapy

The client met weekly with the first surrogate to practice asking open-ended questions, making reflective statements, and becoming comfortable touching the hand of the surrogate. Five sessions were held with success (anxiety below a level of 3) achieved gradually over time. The client became very comfortable with the relationship surrogate and felt ecstatic/proud of his success. No violations of the surrogate/client relationship occurred, meaning the client did not text or ask to see the surrogate outside of therapy. The first surrogate reported complete success with her client.

Since habituation to the first surrogate had occurred, a second surrogate was identified and socialized to boost the client's confidence that his initial success was not a fluke. The second surrogate was comfortable with greater degrees of touching (e.g., prolonged hand holding, hand on waist, hand on shoulder/back, etc.). After a meeting, which included the client, therapist and second surrogate, new sessions were set up with the second surrogate. The client met with the second surrogate for four sessions. As with the first surrogate, no violations of the surrogate/client relationship occurred (the client did not text or ask to see the surrogate outside of therapy). The second surrogate reported complete success with her client.

Having developed comfort (anxiety 3 or below) in talking with and touching the two female surrogates, the client wanted to overcome his fear of kissing. To assist the client in achieving his goal, a third relationship surrogate (42-year-old woman) was identified and socialized. She agreed (with the permission of her husband) to assist the client in moving beyond talking and touching to kissing. The client and the third surrogate met for a total of four sessions over a period of 2 months. The early sessions involved only talking and touching (hand holding) with kissing being gradually introduced so as to keep the client's anxiety low. He would move toward the woman while constantly assessing his anxiety level. If he felt above a level of 3, he would move back until his anxiety dropped. Over time, he was able to kiss the surrogate while his anxiety remained at a level of 3 or below. As with relationship surrogates one and two, the third relationship surrogate reported complete success with her client. The client was able to kiss her with ease and was proud of his accomplishment. His self-esteem soared. Transfer of these behavioral skills to "real" women in his social network was slow but occurred within 3 months.

Source: Zenter, M. and Knox, D.. 2013. "Surrogates in relationship therapy: A case study in learning how to talk, touch, and kiss". Psychology Journal (in press).

13.7d Masters and Johnson's Approach

Masters and Johnson's approach to sex therapy was a key influence in the field of sex therapy. When the Masters and Johnson Institute in St. Louis began in the mid-60s, couples went through an intensive 2-week sex therapy program. Treatment began with assessment procedures, including a physical examination and interviews with therapists who took medical and personal histories. On the third day, the therapists met with the couple to discuss their assessment of the nature, extent, and origin of the sexual problem, to recommend treatment procedures, and to answer any questions. All couples receiving treatment at the Masters and Johnson Institute were instructed to engage in sensate focus exercises.

The essential elements of the early Masters and Johnson (1970) approach to resolving sexual dysfunctions are as follows:

1. Both partners in a marital or coupled unit are expected to participate in sex therapy.

2. A male and a female sex therapist provide the treatment for heterosexual couples; in this way, each patient has a same-sex role model.

3. Sexual dysfunctions are conceptualized as having been learned. Hence, much of sex therapy is devoted to sex education and information.

4. Performance anxiety, fear of failure, and excessive need to please the partner are regarded as underlying causes of sexual problems and are addressed in therapy.

5. Communication between the partners is regarded as critical to a good sexual relationship. Hence, enhancing communication between the sexual partners becomes a goal.

6. The specific resolution of a sexual dysfunction involves behavioral change that is accomplished through the assignment of progressive tasks and behavioral prescriptions.

The life, relationship, and therapy of William Masters and Virginia Johnson were the source of "Masters of Sex " on the Showtime television network in the fall of 2013.

13.7e Kaplan's Approach

The approach developed by Helen Kaplan (1974) of Cornell Medical Center does not have a rigid 2-week format, nor does it assume that therapy will continue indefinitely. The goal of this approach is to assist the partners in achieving their sexual goals in as short a time as possible. Sessions are usually held once or twice a week (with an occasional phone call during the week) while the partners continue to live at home. Although participation of both partners is seen as a crucial ingredient for successful sex therapy, Kaplan's approach does not require that sexual partners participate equally in the therapy program. For example, in the case of inhibited female orgasm, the therapist may spend most of the time working with the woman in individual sessions.

Like Masters and Johnson, Kaplan assigned behavioral "homework" tasks that are designed to help the individual, or couple, overcome a sexual dysfunction. However, she suggested that some individuals might not respond to behavioral interventions when the source of the sexual dysfunction is rooted in unconscious intrapsychic conflicts, deep-seated personality traits, or interpersonal dynamics. Thus, an important part of Kaplan's approach to sex therapy is insight therapy, through which the presumed deeper roots of sexual dysfunction are uncovered.

Kaplan also noted that sex therapy clients often resist treatment and that therapists must be aware of such resistance and help clients overcome it. In sex therapy, "resistance" refers to the clients unconscious opposition to or lack of cooperation in treatment. Resistance may involve clients' doing something to interfere with the resolution of their sexual problem. Examples of resistance include "forgetting" therapy appointments, "not finding time" to complete homework assignments, doing homework assignments incorrectly, or antagonizing the partner. For sex therapy to be effective, the sex therapist must diffuse any resistance on the part of the client. The therapist may diffuse resistance by confronting the client directly, exploring unconscious conflicts, or making use of dream material.

13.7f PLISSIT Model Approach

We earlier made reference to the PLISSIT model for treating sexual dysfunctions (Annon, 1976). The **PLISSIT model** outlines four treatment levels: permission, limited information, specific suggestions, and intensive therapy. The permission level of the PLISSIT model involves encouraging clients to discuss their sexual problems. The therapist may also assure clients that (in many cases) their thoughts, feelings, behaviors, and concerns are "normal," common, and understandable. The second level of the PLISSIT model involves giving the client limited information, such as educating the client about sexual response, sexual anatomy, or the effects of medications or alcohol on sexual functioning. This level of intervention also involves dispelling sexual myths. The third level of intervention involves specific suggestions. Examples of specific suggestions include instructing couples on how to do sensate focus exercises, instructing women on masturbation techniques, and instructing men and their partners on how to cope with premature ejaculation (such as using the squeeze technique). The fourth level of treatment involves intensive therapy. This level of intervention is used when the other three have not alleviated the sexual dysfunction or problem. Intensive therapy may consist of any of the other sex therapy approaches described in this chapter (e.g., Masters and Johnson's/Kaplan's approaches).

13.7g LoPiccolo's Approach

Building on the contributions of Masters and Johnson's system of sex therapy, and drawing from cognitive-behavioral therapy and systems theory, Joseph LoPiccolo (1992) offered a three-part theory he dubbed "postmodern." Although his comments focused on erectile failure, the three theoretical elements he described are applicable to understanding other categories of sexual dysfunction as well:

1. *Systems theory* LoPiccolo recommended that in assessing sexual dysfunction, the therapist should carefully examine the effect of the dysfunction on the relationship between the partners. Although sexual problems may cause distress, they may also serve a purpose. Unlike Kaplan's approach, in which resistance is examined when standard therapies haven't worked, in LoPiccolo's framework the therapist begins in the first session to prevent resistance. Clients may be asked to anticipate any possible negative effects on their marital relationship if the husband were to regain erectile functioning. "For example, might a husband feel more powerful and revert to a more authoritarian role with the wife if he became more 'potent' again? Might the wife find his sexual needs burdensome if the husband regained erectile function?" (p. 178).

2. *Integrated (physiological and psychological) planning* Classifying people's dysfunctions as organic or psychogenic is often not useful and may be harmful. As noted, both organic and psychogenic factors are operating. LoPiccolo suggested that even when organic etiology is clearly established, a thorough psychological evaluation is also indicated.

PLISSIT model
Method of sex therapy that involves four treatment levels: permission, limited information, specific suggestions, and intensive therapy

3. *Sexual behavior patterns*   It is important to examine the specific sexual behaviors of the couple. Are the behaviors used to cue sexual desire and arousal adequate? Does the couple need to reconsider the methods, sites, or philosophies of stimulation?

13.7h Feminist Influence

The feminist critique of sex therapy has been articulated by Atwood and Klucinec (2011):

> [... that sex therapy is too genital and goal oriented (basically the male response); that sex therapy relies on sexist sex research, language and theory; that the definition of the sex problem is sexist; that sex therapy neglects gender-related power differentials; that sex therapy sacrifices pleasure for performance; that sex therapy is oblivious to subjective sexual meaning and ignorant of cultural variations; that sex therapy has unintentionally or not reinforced patriarchal interests and sexual double standards; that it has supported heterosexuality; and that sex therapy has historically ignored social causes and solutions of sexual problems.] (p. 107)

An early example of sexist thought in regard to female and male sexual behavior is the belief (held up until the end of the twentieth century) that masochism in women was rare since "psychiatrists saw the desire to be submissive as a normal part of female sexuality" (DeBlock & Adriaens, 2013, p. 280).

13.7i Effectiveness of Sex Therapy

Providing data on the effectiveness of sex therapy is difficult for several reasons. First, the degree to which sex therapy is effective in resolving sexual problems depends on the problem being treated. Some problems are easier to treat than others. In general, acquired problems are easier to treat than lifelong problems, and situational problems are easier to treat than generalized (or global) problems. Vaginismus is likely to respond quickly to therapeutic intervention. Problems of sexual desire may be the most difficult to treat. Erectile dysfunction, inability to achieve orgasm, and hypoactive sexual desire require more time. Second, the presence of restrictive religious beliefs, severe depression, or paraphilias may work against sex therapy progress.

Sex therapy effectiveness rates may also vary because of the methodological problems in determining such rates. For example, who should decide whether treatment has failed or succeeded—the client or the therapist? What criteria should be used in determining success or failure? What if the client is successful in resolving sexual dysfunctions but is not successful in resolving related nonsexual issues, such as marital conflict, negative body image, and low self-esteem? What if the client is successful in resolving these related nonsexual issues but is still sexually dysfunctional? What criteria will be used to measure success and failure? Different answers to these questions will yield different results regarding reported success rates of sex therapy.

BVT *Lab*

Visit **www.BVTLab.com** to explore the student resources available for this chapter.

Chapter Summary

Definitions of Sexual Dysfunctions

A sexual dysfunction is an impairment or difficulty that affects sexual functioning or produces sexual pain. Sexual functions have recently been medicalized with medical etiology and treatment. A **sexual disorder** is diagnosed when a disturbance in sexual desire or the psychophysiological components of one's sexual response cycle cause significant distress and interpersonal difficulty. Sexual dysfunctions may be lifelong, acquired, situational or generalized.

Causes and Contributing Factors in Sexual Dysfunctions

Organic causes of SD (sexual dysfunction) include physical illness, disease, or disability and its treatment (such as surgery, medication, or chemotherapy). A physical condition (such as diabetes, arthritis, pituitary tumors, or vascular disease) or treatment (e.g., medications) may also interfere with physiological or anatomical mechanisms involved in sexual desire, arousal, or orgasm. Age also contributes to SD—the older the individual, the more like he or she is to have a SD.

Other causal factors are sociocultural (e.g., religious teachings that sex is "dirty"), psychological (e.g., history of child sexual abuse), relational (e.g., the couple do not love or respect each other), and cognitive (e.g., accepting the myth that sexual behavior ends with aging).

Interest/Arousal Dysfunctions

Female sexual arousal disorder involves the woman not being able to become or stay sexually aroused, which implies that she lacks genital lubrication and swelling. Like other sexual dysfunctions, female sexual arousal disorder may be lifelong, acquired, situational, or generalized. Treatment involves a detailed sexual history to discover the etiology, which is often followed by the recommendation of masturbation.

Sexual aversion disorder (also known as *sexual phobia* and *sexual panic disorder*) means that not only is there low interest in sex but that, also, sex is aversive. The person has a persistent or recurrent phobic aversion to and avoidance of sexual contact with a sexual partner.

Male hypoactive sexual desire is low interest in sex. The causes of hypoactive sexual desire may be organic, psychological, relational, or cognitive. The cause of sexual aversion is a negative previous learning experience.

Sexual disorder
Diagnosis that a disturbance in sexual desire or the psychophysiological components of one's sexual response cycle cause significant distress and interpersonal difficulty

Other Male Sexual Dysfunctions

Premature ejaculation is regarded as the most common sexual dysfunction reported by men. The first line of treatment is medication; paroxetine exerts the most effective solution beginning within 5 to 10 days of starting treatment, and with full therapeutic effect in 2 to 3 weeks.

Male erectile failure, the inability to create and maintain an erection, may have a psychological or organic etiology. Medications (e.g., Viagra) are the first line of therapy for erectile failure.

Orgasm Dysfunctions

Female orgasmic disorder, the most frequent sexual dysfunction in women, is defined as occurring when there is either a lack of orgasm, markedly diminished intensity of orgasmic sensations, or marked delay in orgasm despite the self-report of high sexual arousal/excitement. Biological, psychological, cultural and relational factor contribute to the cause. The PLISSIT (Permission, Limited Information, Specific Suggestions, Intensive Therapy) approach is the recommended treatment.

Delayed ejaculation results in the man typically being unable to ejaculate. Causes are typically a result of social psychological issues. Some medications may also interfere with ejaculation.

Genito-Pelvic Pain/Penetration Disorder

Genito-pelvic pain/penetration disorder is characterized by difficulty having intercourse, genito-pelvic pain, fear of pain or vaginal penetration, and tension of the pelvic floor muscles. The typical disorders are vaginismus (difficulty inserting an object into the vagina) and dyspareunia (pain during intercourse).

Sex Therapy

Sex therapy is and has been in flux. There is little agreement among sex therapists about how to treat a specific sexual problem. There have also been changes in treatment strategies over time. In the past, psychology and psychoanalysis dominated the treatment field. More recently, pharmacological treatment has become more prominent.

"Let the client beware" applies to the person seeking sex therapy. Having a Certified Sex Therapist certificate from the American Association of Sex Educators, Counselors, and Therapists (AASECT) is one credential to look for. Various modalities of sex therapy include the cognitive behavioral, Masters and Johnson's, and PLISSIT approaches. The feminist influence is instructive in that it reveals the degree to which sex therapy, its conceptions and treatments, are sexist.

Web Links

American Association for Marriage and Family Therapy
http://www.aamft.org/iMIS15/AAMFT/

American Association of Sex Education, Counselors, and Therapists
http://www.aasect.org/

American Psychological Association
http://www.apa.org/

Sexual Health
http://www.sexualhealth.com/

Society for the Advancement of Sexual Health
http://www.sash.net

Society for Sex Therapy and Research
http://www.sstarnet.org/

Key Terms

Acquired dysfunction   359

Cognitive behavioral sex
 therapy   383

Delayed ejaculation   377

Dyspareunia   380

Erectile disorder   372

Female orgasmic disorder (FOD)   375

Female sexual interest/arousal
 disorder   365

Generalized dysfunction   359

Hyperactive sexual desire
 disorder   370

Inhibited male orgasm   378

Lesbian death bed   366

Lifelong dysfunction   359

Male hypoactive sexual desire
 disorder   370

Medicalization of sexual
 dysfunctions   358

Performance anxiety   361

Persistent genito-pelvic pain/
 penetration disorder   379

Peyronie's disease   381

PLISSIT model   386

Premature ejaculation   371

Primary dysfunction   359

Rapid ejaculation   371

Retarded ejaculation   378

Satiation   370

Secondary dysfunction   359

Sensate focus   367

Sexual aversion disorder   368

Sexual disorder   388

Sexual dysfunctions   358

Situational dysfunction   359

Spectatoring   373

Urethritis   381

Vaginismus   380

Vulvodynia   381

Additional study resources are available at www.BVTLab.com

CHAPTER 14

Variant Sexual Behavior

Don't worry, it only seems kinky the first time.

Anonymous

Chapter Outline

Objectives

1. Identify the criteria used to define "normal" sexual behavior.

2. Understand the historical variations in defining "normal" sexual behavior.

3. Review the personal choices associated with paraphilia.

4. Learn the differences between legal and illegal paraphilias.

5. Identify the various types of paraphilias.

6. Discuss the various theories which help to explain the origins of paraphilias.

7. Describe the various treatment options for paraphilias.

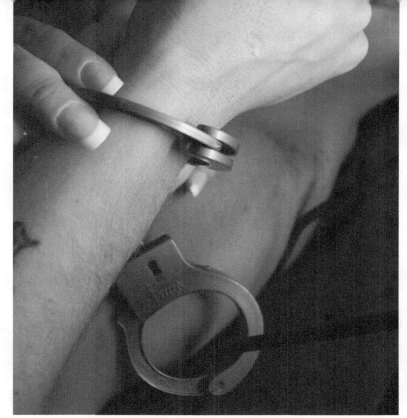

TRUTH OR FICTION?

T/F   Most exhibitionists begin their "flashing behavior" from age 40 on.

T/F   The sexual motivation for cross-dressing increases as the person ages.

T/F   Tattooing and piercing may involve a sexual motive.

T/F   Women are just as likely to have a paraphilia as men.

T/F   It is not unusual for a person who has a sexual dysfunction to be paraphilic.

Answers:
1. F 2. F 3. T 4. F 5. T

The sexting behavior of U.S. Representative for New York, Anthony Weiner and its aftermath (2011–2013) made culturally visible the question, "What is normal sexual behavior?" In this chapter we look at sexual behavior viewed as atypical, or variant, from the norm. We focus on paraphilias and controversies involved in the use of that term. We examine the terminology used for paraphilias identified in the *Diagnostic and Statistical Manual of Mental Disorders DSM-5 ™* and how paraphilias are treated if they become a problem for the individual and/or society (American Psychiatric Association, 2013). We begin by addressing what is considered "normal" sexual behavior while emphasizing the importance of culture in defining what is "normal."

> The type of fig leaf which each culture employs to cover its social taboos offers a twofold description of its morality. It reveals that certain unacknowledged behavior exists and it suggests the form that such behavior takes.
>
> Freda Adler, U.S. educator, author

14.1 What Is "Normal" Sexual Behavior?

One of the most frequent questions students in human sexuality classes ask is "Am I normal?" Because sex is private and secretive, individuals are left to wonder if, indeed, their behavior is "normal."

14.1a Criteria Used to Define "Normal" Sexual Behavior

Various criteria are used to define what is "normal." These criteria include prevalence, moral correctness, naturalness, and adaptiveness/comfort.

Prevalence

We tend to assume that if most people engage in a sexual behavior, it is normal. For example, based on a national survey of U.S. adult women ages 20–24, 80% reported having experienced vaginal intercourse in the past 12 months (Reece, Herbenick, & Fortenberry, 2012). Given this percentage, we tend to think of young females having sexual intercourse as "normal." These same women were asked if they had experienced anal sex in the last 12 months, and 23% reported yes (Reece, Herbenick, & Fortenberry, 2012). Individuals engage in sadistic sexual behavior even less frequently so we tend to think the lower the prevalence, the higher the "abnormality" or deviance.

> *There is no such thing as a value-free concept of deviance; to say homosexuals are deviant because they are a statistical minority is, in practice, to stigmatize them. Nuns are rarely classed as deviants for the same reason, although if they obey their vows they clearly differ very significantly from the great majority of people.*
>
> Dennis Altman, Australian sociologist

Another way to conceptualize prevalence is via the *statistical model of normality*, better known as the *normal curve*. This statistical presentation of the prevalence of a phenomenon reveals the distribution in a large population. Havelock Ellis was one of the first to view sexual interests as being normally distributed with "most of the population located near the mean (the sexually "normal" people) and only a handful of individuals located at either extreme (the sexually "abnormal" people)" (DeBlock & Adriaens, 2013, p. 284).

Moral Correctness

Sexual behaviors are also considered normal if they are viewed as morally correct. According to many religions (e.g., Islam), penile-vaginal intercourse between husband and wife is the only morally correct form of sexual behavior. Other forms of sexual expression, including oral sex, masturbation, anal sex, sex between persons not married, and sex between persons of the same sex, are considered abnormal because they are viewed as immoral. One of the reasons some homosexuals seek the approval of the church is that religion is such a powerful gatekeeper of definitions of sexual morality and normality.

Naturalness

Sexual behaviors also are viewed as natural or unnatural, depending on whether they result in procreation. Because masturbation, anal sex, and bestiality do not result in conception, they are sometimes viewed as unnatural—and by implication, abnormal/perverted/deviant (DeBlock & Adriaens, 2013). Sometimes people judge a behavior as natural if it occurs in the natural world (in the animal kingdom) or is biologically determined. People often ask if "homosexual" behavior occurs in animals, implying that if so, the behaviors of gays and lesbians are more "natural" and acceptable.

Some individuals have a fetish for red, high heel shoes.
Source: David Knox

Adaptiveness/Comfort

Sexual behaviors are usually considered "normal" if they are adaptive, comfortable, and have positive outcomes for the participants. Sexual behavior that causes physical or emotional harm or suffering or that interferes with one's functioning may be considered abnormal. An example of sexual behavior considered abnormal is adults engaging in sexual acts with children, which is typically associated with negative outcomes for both adult and child.

Think About It

Take a moment to answer the following questions. Which of the four criteria used to define what is "normal" sexual behavior carries the most weight in your own personal view? What sexual behavior, if any, do you or have you engaged in that might be labeled as abnormal or deviant?

Social Construction of Deviance

Michel Foucault, a French historian and philosopher in the late 1960s, emphasized that what is normal is socially defined and constructed: "what is accepted as normal and healthy sexuality is not determined by nature but changes with the values and norms of a particular society at a particular place and time" (DeBlock & Adriaens, 2013, p. 277).

Nothing is either good or bad but thinking makes it so.

Shakespeare

14.1b Historical Variations in Definitions of "Normal" Sexual Behavior

Within the same culture, sexual behaviors may be labeled as normal at one historical time and abnormal at another. For example, although kissing in public is acceptable normal behavior today (be aware of this PDA phenomenon on your campus), in the American colonial era, kissing in public was considered unacceptable and punishable by being "lodged in the stocks" in public. During this era, unmarried persons who were discovered to have engaged in intercourse were viewed as individuals who had succumbed to the temptations of the flesh. After they were discovered, they had to make a public confession and were also subject to fines and a public lashing. Public kissing in Taiwan and in Mainland China today is not illegal, but it is frowned upon—there is social disapproval for kissing one's beloved in public.

Another example of a behavior that seems to be regarded differently in American contemporary culture compared to past decades is the concept of "voyeurism." Metzl (2004) noted that from the 1950s through the 1970s, voyeurism received a great deal of attention in psychiatric discussion of "sexual deviation." However, beginning in the mid-1980s psychiatric notions of voyeurism became more narrow, whereas popular concepts of the term have expanded. Today, there are television programs—such as HBO's *Cathouse*—which allow the viewer (voyeur?) to enter the Bunny Ranch brothel and observe the bedroom behavior of the hookers and their Johns.

14.2 Variant Sexual Behavior: Definitions and Overview

What are determined to be acceptable sexual interests vary over time and across cultures. Scientific views of what is acceptable have changed drastically over time. Prior to 1850, the definition of sexual deviance was moral and theological. The Old Testament prohibited same-sex, masturbation, and anal sexual behavior. With the replacement of "the clergy as authorities in the sexual domain," early psychiatrists conceptualized insanity as "diseases of the will and emotion." Krafft-Ebing and his *Psychopathia Sexualis* viewed sexual deviance as caused by "hereditary taintedness" in the family tree which led to an imbalance of sexual instinct and inhibition. Hence, the exhibitionist inherited a basic predisposition to behave in nonnormative ways which the exhibitionist felt powerless to control (DeBlock & Adriaens, 2013).

Freud influence (sexuality was fixation on early love objects and denial of a traumatizing sexual experience, such as with the Oedipal complex) overlapped with Germany's Magnus Hirschfeld who founded the Institute for Sexual Science in Berlin. Hirschfeld, along with Havelock Ellis, viewed "deviations from the sexual norm as neither pathological nor dangerous to society" (p. 283). Indeed they fostered the idea that there is a range of human sexual interests and behaviors, and these should not be considered pathological (including homosexuality and masturbation). The exception was when the behavior harmed someone else.

The only unnatural sex act is that which you cannot perform.

Alfred C. Kinsey, biologist/sexologist

With the publication of the *DSM-III*, the word "paraphilia" was used which reaffirmed the idea that these were "unusual or bizarre imagery, or acts necessary for sexual excitement," involving "sexual objects or situations that are not part of normative arousal-activity patterns and that in varying degrees may interfere with the capacity for reciprocal affectionate sexual activity." Hence the downside of a paraphilia was that the individual might not be able to make a love connection.

The term *paraphilia* is derived from the words *para*, meaning "deviation," and *philia*, meaning "attracted." Hence, the *paraphiliac* is attracted to a stimulus that is regarded by the society as deviant. It is not unusual for a person to express more than one paraphilia.

The *DSM-5* defines **paraphilia** as being aroused by certain objects or situations that are not typical and that may interfere with the capacity for reciprocal, affectionate sexual activity with a partner. For example, a person who has a high heel fetish may be unable to become aroused unless the partner wears 3-inch, red high heels. Although the partner may not mind wearing heels, feeling required to do so for the partner to become aroused may be problematic.

Paraphilia
Overdependence on a culturally unacceptable or unusual stimulus for sexual arousal and satisfaction

Personal REFLECTION

Take a moment to express your thoughts about the following question. Sex-offending paraphilic behavior may go unnoticed for years. What paraphilic sexual behaviors have you encountered that escaped legal detection?

The essential elements of a paraphilia are recurrent, intense, sexually arousing fantasies, sexual urges, or behaviors generally involving the following:

1.   Nonhuman objects (e.g., high heel fetish)
2.   The suffering or humiliation of one's self or one's partner (not just simulated; e.g., sadism, masochism)
3.   Children or other nonconsenting persons (pedophilia, exhibitionism, voyeurism, frotteurism)

All three of these criteria need not necessarily be involved for the label of paraphilia to apply. For example, the pedophile focuses on human subjects (which leaves out the first criterion), and the cross-dresser focuses on clothing, not people (which leaves out the third criterion). What all paraphilias have in common is that the object being focused on becomes imbued with erotic value, and there is an intense yearning to experience the object. In some cases, the paraphilia is experienced as a compulsion that interferes with work and relationships. Using our example of the high heel fetish, the person may spend hours and a great deal of money collecting high heels, and require the partner to strut around in them for show.

There is disagreement about whether paraphilias constitute a mental disorder. DeBlock and Adriaens (2013) noted that "nonnormative sexuality need not necessarily be a mental disorder" (p. 293). This conclusion is based on the observation that there is a difference between paraphilias (defined as atypical sexual behavior) and paraphilic disorders. The latter exists when the satisfaction of a paraphilia for a person involves causing harm, or risk of harm, to self or others. Such an outcome is not always the case since an individual may have urges or fantasies or desires or wishes. Moran (2013) noted that "a paraphilia by itself does not automatically justify or require clinical intervention" and that "to warrant the diagnosis of paraphilic disorder the sexual behavior must cause distress, impairment in function or involve nonconsenting individuals."

Paraphilias vary in severity from disturbing fantasies (sometimes accompanied by masturbation) to sexual victimization, which may include murder (e.g., erotophonophilia—lust murder, in which the partner is killed as a means of atoning for sex with the individual, as in

A fetish can involve a certain material, such as leather.
Source: Chelsea Curry

a serial killer who murders prostitutes after having sex with them). Although there are few classic profile characteristics (sexual orientation, ethnicity, socioeconomic background), paraphilias most often occur in men and are very rarely diagnosed in women. Among individuals seen clinically for the treatment of paraphilias, approximately half are married.

Some people with a paraphilia may become so preoccupied with the object that they feel out of control. They experience uncontrollable urges, feel unable to stop themselves from pursuing the activity, and increase the frequency and intensity of their involvement. In other cases, the person may feel in control of the paraphilic impulses and does not feel driven to engage in the behavior.

The relationships of the person with a paraphilia may suffer if the partner becomes aware of the paraphilia. For example, wives are sometimes shocked by the discovery of their husbands dressing in women's clothes. In some cases the spouse may be asked to participate in the paraphilia—for example, the partner is asked to be the recipient of the sexual sadist's paraphilia or to dress the partner in wet diapers (autonepiophilia).

Take a moment to answer the following question. Some couples practice some sexually variant behaviors (e.g., sadism/masochism) with the goal of enhancing physical excitement. These behaviors may be a part of mature sexual expression when they are mutually agreed to and pleasurable for both parties. However, intervention may be needed if the behavior becomes compulsive and distressing to the individual, or coercive. To what degree do you think sexual behaviors that result in pain should be of concern to the law?

14.2a Legal Versus Illegal Paraphilias

The definitions of paraphilias presented in this chapter, which are based on the *DSM-5* developed by mental health professionals, do not necessarily meet legal or other nonmedical criteria for what constitutes mental disability. Paraphilias are legal or illegal depending on the degree to which the rights of others are affected. Formicophilia (ants or other insects crawling on the body) and klismaphilia (arousal from having enemas) do not infringe on the rights of others and are of little concern to the law. Voyeurism, exhibitionism, and pedophilia are examples of paraphilias that interfere with the rights of others and carry legal penalties. Voyeurism and exhibitionism are clinical terms; in the legal system, these criminal acts may be referred to as "secret peeping" and "indecent exposure." They are usually regarded as misdemeanors and are punishable by a fine. (Repeat offenses may involve mandatory outpatient treatment at a mental health facility.) Pedophilic acts are punishable by imprisonment. Legal charges may range from taking indecent liberties with a minor to sodomy or rape. When people with paraphilias break the law, they are referred to as *sex offenders*. The majority of apprehended sex offenders are arrested for acts of exhibitionism, pedophilia, and voyeurism (American Psychiatric Association, 2013).

Laws regulating sexual behavior vary from state to state. Some states regard exhibitionism as a misdemeanor; others classify it as a felony. The penalty ranges from a fine to a prison term. If the exhibitionist is drunk or has a mental disability, police officers tend to regard this self-exposure differently from those who compulsively expose themselves and are repeatedly picked up for exhibitionism.

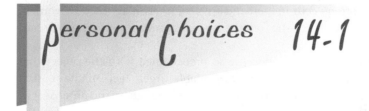

Whose Business Is a Paraphilia?

Some paraphilias are illegal, and the person does not seek treatment unless forced to do so. An example is the pedophilic that agrees to treatment in exchange for a reduced prison term. Other paraphilias may be legal but harmful to the person with the paraphilia.

Autoerotic asphyxiation involves the individual cutting off his or her air supply while masturbating. An example is a person who would "place pillows over his face, strangle himself with different cords, and lean over chairs to restrict his breathing during mastur-bation" (Faccini & Saide, 2013, p. 100). Sometimes the person restricts too much air and dies. Sometimes another person is involved, such as with asphyxiophilia, (choking a partner during sex).

Some paraphilias seem unusual but do not hurt anyone. Examples include acrotomo-philia (amputee partner), autonepiophilia (wet diapers), and zoophilia (arousal via sexual contact with animals). Individuals with these paraphilias that are not harmful to them-selves or others might choose to disregard society's negative label of their behavior. Such a choice, in combination with a positive view of themselves, may have positive consequences for them with no negative consequences for society. For example, cross-dressing is a para-philia that may be enjoyable for the individual and of limited consequence to the partner (assuming the partner's knowledge and acceptance).

14.3 Types of Paraphilic Disorders

In this section, we discuss the major types of paraphilias identified in the *DSM-5* and listed in Table 14-1, and briefly identify a variety of others (American Psychiatric Association, 2013). The emphasis in diagnosis of a paraphilia is that it involves intense urges and fantasies with action on the urges secondary and needing not necessarily to occur, and whether the behavior occurs is irrelevant.

TABLE **14-1** | Major Paraphilias Identified by *DSM-5*

Paraphilia	Description
Voyeuristic Disorder	Spying on others engaged in private (e.g., nude) behavior
Exhibitionistic Disorder	Exposing one's genitals to strangers
Frotteuristic Disorder	Touching or rubbing against an unsuspecting/nonconsenting person
Sexual Masochism Disorder	Becoming sexually aroused/enjoying being humiliated and/or hurt via being tied up, whipped, beaten, etc.
Sexual Sadism Disorder	Becoming sexually aroused/enjoying humiliating or causing physical pain in a partner
Pedophilic Disorder	Being sexually aroused by children
Fetishistic Disorder	Being sexually aroused by nonliving objects
Transvestic Disorder	Being sexually aroused by cross-dressing

14.3a Voyeuristic Disorder

Voyeuristic disorder (also called **scopophilia**) is defined as recurrent and intense sexual arousal (over a period of at least 6 months) from observing an unsuspecting naked person; the individual is at least age 18 and has acted on these urges, which caused significant distress (American Psychiatric Association, 2013).

Voyeuristic disorder
Paraphilia that involves recurrent, intense urges to look at unsuspecting people who are naked, undressing, or engaging in sexual behavior (See also Scopophilia.)

Scopophilia
Also called Voyeuristic disorder.

Voyeurs (sometimes referred to as "Peeping Toms") spend a lot of time planning to peep and will risk a great deal to do so. They regard climbing over fences, hiding in bushes, and shivering in the cold as worth the trouble. Peeping is the stimulus for sexual excitement, which most often results in ejaculation through masturbation either during the peeping or later. The target of the voyeur is usually a female stranger. Although some voyeurs are married, they may not derive excitement from watching their wives or any familiar woman undress. Persons who report they do not experience distress or shame for spying on others are regarded as having voyeuristic sexual interest, but should not be diagnosed with voyeuristic disorder.

Elder and colleagues (2012) suggested that voyeurism for men may be dysfunctional in that they may not learn how to relate to women as individuals but only as sexual body parts. They reviewed *The Centerfold Syndrome*, developed by Gary Brooks (1995), who noted that male socialization encourages voyeurism—looking at naked females (e.g., centerfolds in magazines and pornography on the internet)—which encourages objectification of the female devoid of establishing emotionally intimate sexually gratifying relationships with them. One of the men interviewed by Elder and colleagues (2012) commented on how unrealistic pornography can be:

> In pornography, typically, you don't see women expressing pain. So when she [his sexual partner] does say, "It hurts" or "Not anymore," you know, when there are things that in the "ideal world of sex," are not expressed, I think subconsciously, "Why can't it be like in porn, where everything's just perfect? (p. 170)

14.3b Exhibitionistic Disorder

U.S. representative for New York, Anthony Weiner gave visibility to the phenomenon of exhibitionism when he was discovered to have sent sexually explicit photos (sexting) of his penis to various women in 2011. After he resigned from office, it was revealed that he continued sexting (highlighting the compulsive nature of this fetish). **Exhibitionistic disorder** is defined as recurrent and intense sexual arousal from the exposure of one's genitals to an unsuspecting person as manifested in fantasies, urges or behaviors (for a period of at least 6 months). The individual has acted on these urges with an unsuspecting person, or the sexual urges or fantasies cause significant distress (American Psychiatric Association, 2013). The exhibitionism referred to here is unlike mediated exhibitionism whereby a person sends a nude photo via email or text message (Jones, 2013).

Exhibitionistic disorder
Paraphilia that involves an intense, recurrent (over a period of at least 6 months) sexual urge, often accompanied by sexually arousing fantasies, to expose one's genitals to a stranger

National **DATA**

Prevalence of exhibitionistic disorder in the general population is unknown. Based on exhibitionistic sexual acts in non-clinical samples, the highest possible prevalence for exhibitionistic disorder in the male population is 2%–4%. The percentage for females is even more uncertain but believed to be much lower than in males (American Psychiatric Association, 2013, p. 690).

Swindell and colleagues (2011) identified the conditions under which a male learned exhibitionist behaviors: sharing a bathtub with a female who was allowed to look at his genitals which served the function for the male of his exhibitionism being both pleasurable and sexually arousing. In addition, the male was allowed to be nude in his mother's presence, which provided the experience of the mother's approval for his engaging in exhibitionism.

Exhibitionists expose themselves to people they do not know for several reasons. Sexual excitement is a primary one. Hearing a victim yell and watching his or her horrified face is sexually stimulating for some individuals. Once sexually excited, the exhibitionist individual may masturbate to orgasm.

A male exhibitionist may expose himself to shock women. Exhibiting himself may be a way of directing anger and hostility toward women. Although the woman he exposes himself to has not injured him, other women may have belittled him (or he has perceived it that way); or he has recently been unable to have and maintain an erection, blames his lack of erection on women, and exposes himself as a way of getting back at them.

Some individuals expose themselves as a way of relieving stress. When the stress reaches a peak, individuals exhibit themselves, masturbate, and relieve the stress. Still others expose themselves with a sexually arousing fantasy in which the person observing them will become sexually aroused (American Psychiatric Association, 2013).

Some people have referred to exhibitionism, public masturbation, and voyeurism as "victimless crimes"; however, these behaviors *can* cause harm because victims may be distressed. An example is a student who was looking for a book in the library and pulled a book from a lower shelf. She discovered a penis when she pulled out the book as a male was on the other side "exhibiting." She was shocked, horrified, and distressed.

Ideally, if confronted by exhibitionism, try to make no response but quietly remove yourself from the situation and call the police. Law enforcement agencies may benefit from obtaining reports of "minor" offenses of exhibitionism and voyeurism because a person who engages in one offense may engage again in the same offense or different types of offenses as well.

14.3c Frotteuristic Disorder

A crowded bar, concert, or subway is the ideal environment for the frotteur. According to the *DSM-5*, **frotteuristic disorder** is the recurrent and intense sexual arousal (for at least 6 months) from touching or rubbing against an unsuspecting person as manifested in fantasies, urges or behaviors. The individual has acted on these urges with an unsuspecting person, or the sexual urges or fantasies cause significant distress (American Psychiatric Association, 2013).

Frotteuristic disorder
Paraphilia that involves recurring, intense, sexual urges (for at least 6 months), accompanied by fantasies, of touching or rubbing—often with the genitals—against a nonconsenting person

National **DATA**

It is estimated that 30% of adult males in the general population have engaged in frotteuristic behavior. About 10%–14% of adult males are seen in outpatient clinics for paraphilic disorders that meet the criteria for frotteuristic disorder (American Psychiatric Association, 2013, p. 693).

Toucheurism involves actively using one's hands on the victim. Although the person may be distressed about the overwhelming urge to touch or rub against another, he also may act on those fantasies. The person usually chooses a crowded place for the activity. He presses against the sexually desired person while saying, "Excuse me," and then moves to another part of the crowd and presses against someone else. This behavior, known as *frottage*, usually goes unnoticed; however, the feelings aroused by pressing against another may be used in a masturbatory fantasy later.

14.3d Sexual Masochism Disorder

Sexual masochism disorder is diagnosed when there is recurrent and intense sexual arousal (over a period of at least 6 months) from the act of being humiliated, beaten, bound, or otherwise made to suffer as manifested in fantasies, urges or behaviors. The fantasies, sexual urges, or behaviors cause significant distress (American Psychiatric Association, 2013, p. 694).

International **DATA**

In Australia, it is estimated that 2.2% of males and 1.3% of females have been involved in bondage and discipline, sadomasochism, and dominance and submission in the past 12 months (American Psychiatric Association, 2013, p. 694).

Toucheurism
Related to frotteurism, paraphilia, that involves actively using one's hands on the victim

Sexual masochism disorder
Paraphilia characterized by recurrent, intense, sexual urges and sexually arousing fantasies of at least 6 months' duration, in which sexual arousal or gratification is obtained through enacting scripts that involve suffering and pain

The masochist enjoys and is sexually aroused by either or both physical pain and psychological humiliation. While the person may actually experience pain, the diagnosis only requires intense, recurrent urges and fantasies for at least six months. The person may have these fantasies while masturbating or while having sexual relations. "Up Close 14-1: My Entry/Enjoyment into the World of Dominance and Submission" describes the roles of dominance and submission of an undergraduate (author's files).

The individuals in this relationship report that engaging in S and M takes them to a new level of intimacy due to the need to trust each other.
Source: Mikey Howell

My Entry/Enjoyment into the World of Dominance and Submission

The terms "dominant" and "submissive" never really meant much to me before I met Conrad. "Sadomasochism" was just this weird concept that conjured up images of gay men dressed in leather, spanking and beating each other: a caricature of abnormal sexual activities. I had no interest in that alternate lifestyle. I wasn't like that; I had "normal" sex. Unfortunately, this sex usually left me unsatisfied, but I didn't understand this dissatisfaction until I met Conrad my sophomore year of college. By introducing me to the world of domination and submission, he made me reconsider my previous notions of normality when it came to sex. What he showed me were not the stereotypes I had associated with this lifestyle, but rather a side of me I had never explored. What I had once thought was weird and abnormal had now become a part of my sexual identity: became a submissive.

I met Conrad in one of my classes, and we quickly became friends. There was something about his demeanor, his ability to focus on me and listen to what I had to say, that attracted me. We shared common interests in literature, music, politics, film, etc. I admired his intelligence, and his respect for me as a woman. I was not used to this respect; most boys treated me with a condescending attitude, as if my gender were a flaw. He was a soft-spoken Southern gentleman, and I was instantly attracted to him. If someone had told me that Conrad enjoyed dominating women with whips and paddles, while they were tied to his bed, I would have laughed and said no way, not Conrad. He's not like that.

When we began having sex, nothing out of the ordinary happened. He didn't bring me into a dungeon and chain me to a wall; it was the same sex I had been having before: "normal sex." But I did notice something different; I noticed a sexual connection between us. There was this sense of attentiveness that I had never experienced from a man before. Conrad seemed to be able to read my body: what it needed and what it wanted, and by doing this, I think he also witnessed the trust I quickly developed and invested in him.

Once this level of comfort was established, Conrad began to slowly introduce me to the world of domination and submission, or "D/S." His gradual introduction was perfect for me because I was hesitant at first. I trusted Conrad, but I didn't know how I would respond to the activities he had in mind. We began with spankings and bondage scenarios, which usually involved me being cuffed to the bed, spread-eagle. Shortly, we began using more toys rather than his hand: riding crops, paddles, whips, ball-gags, etc. After I had grown comfortable with this, Conrad applied power roles while we enacted sexual scenarios: he was the dominant, and I was the submissive, his slave. I had to say "please" and "thank you" after every sentence; I had to ask permission to orgasm. If at any point I was not enjoying myself, I used our safe word, "red," and Conrad stopped immediately to make sure I was all right.

The first time he placed a collar around my neck and told me to lick his boots, I realized this is what had been missing in my previous sexual activities. This loss of control, abandonment of power, was so erotic, so arousing, that it almost scared me. I was putting myself in a powerless position I never thought I would enjoy. All my life, I had been an out-spoken leader, a feminist, an independent woman, someone who did not enjoy answering to authority. But here I was getting sexual pleasure out of being dominated; being treated like a slave, being beaten. It was difficult to balance my everyday sense of autonomy with this newfound loss of power, until I realized how to separate the two emotions. I am a different person in the bedroom; I don't need to bring my day into my night. At times I receive more respect from Conrad while he's dominating me, than I do from people I encounter in my everyday life. For me, domination and submission is about love and respect.

People always ask me if we still have "normal sex," or if we engage in a D/S relationship 24 hours a day. First, I ask them to define normal for me, and then I respond with "no," we do not always engage in D/S when having sex. We have an even balance between "vanilla" sex (normal/ordinary sex) and D/S situations because we don't depend on D/S for sexual satisfaction; a dependency would diminish the eroticism for me. I don't *need* to be a submissive, but I enjoy being one for Conrad. The act of submission has allowed me to embrace my sexuality and has provided me with a kind of identity I never thought I could comfortably possess, until now.

14.3e Sexual Sadism Disorder

Sexual sadism disorder is diagnosed when there is recurrent and intense sexual arousal (for a period of 6 months) from the physical or psychological suffering of another person as manifested in fantasies, urges or behaviors. The individual has acted on these sexual urges with an nonconsenting person, or the sexual urges or fantasies cause significant distress.

National **DATA**

Prevalence figures in the general population are unknown. Among civilly committed sex offenders in the United States, less than 10% have sexual sadism (American Psychiatric Association, 2013, p. 696).

When the sadist and masochist get together, it is the sadist who enjoys inflicting the pain on the masochist. Such infliction of pain and social scripting ("Have you been a bad boy? Mommy must give you a good spanking" by the sadist and "Oh! Thank you, mistress. May I have some more, please, and harder?" by the masochist) normally occurs in the context of an explicit (and sometimes written) agreement between the parties as to the limits of what is acceptable (handcuffs, hot wax, whipping) and a "safe" word which alerts the sadist that the masochist wants to stop whatever is going on (and the sadist agrees to stop when the masochist says this word). Hence sado/masochistic sexual behavior, by partners who choose this pattern of sexual expression, is consensual.

The term *sadism* can be traced back to the Marquis de Sade (1740–1814)—French author, philosopher, and sadomasochist, who described literally the experiences of people who enjoyed hurting and dominating their sexual partners. The cries and suffering of the sexual partner were the source of sadistic sexual excitement. Such suffering may be by consenting masochistic partners or by those who are forced to participate. Sadistic acts or fantasies may involve several venues: dominance (forcing the victim to crawl), restraint or bondage (tying the victim to a chair), spanking, whipping, beating, burning, shocking (with electricity), cutting, strangling, mutilating, and/or killing.

Sometimes it is difficult to understand how loving/intimate partners can hurt each other. Below is an example of a boyfriend revealing his feelings when his new girlfriend told him that she was a masochist (hence, she needed him to be her sadistic partner).

> I never could figure out how hurting someone could come from love, now I realize it is one of the most intimate acts out there. To trust someone or be trusted that much is incredible; the amount of trust needed to know that those things can happen but it will never be abused, used outside of the right contexts and will never cause problems takes the relationship to a level I never could have imagined. (authors' files)

14.3f Pedophilic Disorder

Pedophilic disorder is diagnosed when there is recurrent and intense (for a period of at least 6 months) sexually arousing fantasies, sexual urges, or behaviors involving sexual activity with a prepubescent child or children (generally age 13 or younger). The individual has acted on these sexual urges or the sexual urges or fantasies cause significant distress. The individual is at least age 16 and at least 5 years older than the child or children.

Sexual sadism disorder
Paraphilia characterized by recurrent, intense, sexual urges and sexually arousing fantasies, of at least 6 months' duration, involving acts that hurt or humiliate the sexual partner

Pedophilic disorder
Sexual arousal in reference to a child

National **DATA**

Population prevalence for pedophiles is unknown. The highest possible prevalence for pedophilic disorder in the male population is approximately 3% to 5%; for females the percentage is even more uncertain, but likely a small fraction of the prevalence in males (American Psychiatric Association, 2013, p. 698).

Alanko and colleagues (2013) investigated the degree to which a sexual interest in children has an inherited component. The researchers analyzed data on male twins and their male siblings from a Finnish sample ages 21–43 years (N = 3,967). Results revealed that the incidence of sexual interest in children under the age of 16 was 3%, with twin correlations being higher for monozygotic than for dizygotic twins. Hence, the study provides the first indication that genetic influences may play a role in shaping sexual interest toward children and adolescents among adult men. However, the contribution of any genetic factors seems comparatively weak.

Pedophiles are often in denial. Nunes and Jung (2013) noted that child sex offenders often distort reality to avoid their own culpability. For example, pedophiles may say that children often make up stories about adults having sex with them as a way of getting attention and deny they (the sex offender) would ever sexually aggress against children.

14.3g Fetishistic Disorder

Fetishistic disorder (**fetishism** is the generic term for various fetishes) is diagnosed when there is recurrent and intense sexual arousal (for at least 6 months) from either the use of nonliving objects or a highly specific focus on nongenital body parts(s) as manifested in fantasies, urges or behaviors. The fantasies, sexual urges, or behaviors cause significant distress (American Psychiatric Association, 2013, p. 700). When a fetish begins at the slight preference level, it may progress in its intensity from being a preference, to being a necessity, to being a symbolic substitute for a sexual partner.

> *I like feet. I definitely have a fetish. I love to see a man's bare foot, but its got to be taken care of. If they're not well manicured, you've got to wonder what the rest of him is like. I don't want to get in bed with somebody and feel his gnarly feet.*
>
> Brooke Burke

Fetishes may be divided into two types: substance and form. A substance fetish means the substance itself is the fetish object. Leather is an example. Whatever forms the leather comes in—belt, shoe, clothes—it is imbued with an erotic connotation. A form fetish refers to a particular object, regardless of its makeup. For example, a person with a shoe fetish responds to shoes as an erotic stimulus no matter whether the shoes are made of plastic, leather, or cloth. The most common form of fetish objects are clothing items, including panties, stockings, lingerie, high-heeled shoes, and boots. Common substance fetishes include leather, satin, and latex. Fetishes may also include sounds (a particular song, the clicking of a train on the tracks) and scents (perfume, incense). The Salience of Fetishism Scale in Self-Assessment 14-1 is a way researchers assess the degree to which an individual has a foot fetish. However, you can substitute most any word you choose (e.g., leather or shoe) to assess the degree to which you have an alternative fetish.

Fetishism
Paraphilia that involves a pattern, of at least 6 months' duration, of deriving sexual arousal or sexual gratification from actual or fantasized inanimate objects or nongenital body parts

SELF-ASSESSMENT 14-1: SALIENCE OF FETISHISM SCALE

This scale assesses the degree to which an individual has a foot fetish. The data were collected by researchers on a nonclinical sample; the researchers felt that the data they gathered voluntary may have wider applicability to other fetishists besides their sample. You may be interested in reviewing the questions to determine the degree to which the fetish was central to the respondent's sex life.

1. Is foot play necessary for your sexual arousal?
2. Is foot fantasy necessary for your sexual arousal?
3. Is foot fantasy usually the main focus of your self-masturbation?
4. What was the frequency of masturbatory fantasies about feet during adolescence?
5. Are feet usually the main focus of your sexual activity with others?
6. How often do you self-masturbate without fantasizing about feet?
7. How often do you self-masturbate while fantasizing about feet?
8. Do you think you could stop fantasizing about feet if you wanted to?
9. Have you ever made a serious attempt to stop your interest in feet?
10. How often do you engage in sexual activity with another without foot play?
11. How often do you engage in sexual activity with another involving foot play?

Scoring and Interpretation

Since the variables used in the scales had different possible ranges, the researchers standardized the scores and made each variable range from 0 to 1. Then they summed the scores for each respondent. The results revealed that while there was a range of salience among the respondents, most clustered at the high end of the scale; 22% had the highest possible score on most of the variables. The salience of fetishism in the men's sex lives was not highly correlated to a measure of self-reported psychological problems. This showed that a man could report that fetishism was very important in his sex life but still have little in the way of psychological problems.

Source: Used with the permission of *The Journal of Sex Research* from "If the shoe fits ... ": Exploring male homosexual foot fetishism," by M. S. Weinberg, C. J. Williams, and C. Calhan, *Vol. 32,* 17–27, (1995). Scale from page 25. Permission conveyed through Copyright Clearance Center, Inc.

Transvestic disorder
Sexual arousal by dressing in the gender of the other sex

Transvestic fetishism
Paraphilia that involves recurrent, intense, sexual urges and sexually arousing fantasies, of at least 6 months' duration, that involve cross-dressing (e.g., a man dressing in a woman's clothes)

14.3h Transvestic Disorder

Transvestic disorder (also known as **transvestic fetishism**) is diagnosed when there is recurrent and intense sexual arousal (for at least 6 months) from cross-dressing as manifested by fantasies, sexual urges or behaviors. The fantasies, sexual urges, or behaviors cause significant distress. Cross-dressing typically involves a man dressing in a woman's clothes. Although women regularly cross-dress in terms of wearing pants and a bow tie, there is little to no cultural disapproval for doing so. However, men who cross-dress are the subject of considerable disapproval.

National **DATA**

Prevalence figures in the general population are unknown. Fewer than 3% of males report having ever been sexually aroused by dressing in women's attire (American Psychiatric Association, 2013, p. 703).

Cross-dressing may range from occasional solitary episodes to immersion into a cross-dressing subculture. Most cross-dressers are heterosexual men. At first they may masturbate while dressed as the other gender. Over time, the sexual arousal motive for their cross-dressing diminishes and is replaced by the payoff of reducing anxiety, coping with depression, or creating a feeling of peace and calm.

Many men who cross-dress do not report motives of sexual excitement. When asked why he dressed up in women's clothes, one of the speakers for our human sexuality class said, "I feel more relaxed … like this is who I am. When I dress like a male, I feel anxious and "not right." Unless you are a cross-dresser, you won't understand."

If the partner of the cross-dresser discovers the cross-dressing, she may ask him to stop. Some men resort to **purging**—throwing away their female attire in a desperate attempt to rid one's self of the urge to cross-dress. But the urge does not vanish with the clothes; new purchases occur and the cross-dressing behavior resumes. Some wives adjust to the fetish of their husbands. "He's a good provider, family man, and faithful," said one wife. "Everyone comes with a catch, and I can put up with a dress as long as he only dresses up at home, not too often, and mostly when I am out of the house shopping." (authors' files).

Think About It

Take a moment to answer the following question. Individuals may cross-dress for various reasons: They want to make a fashion statement, they want to express their androgyny, cross-dressing makes them feel congruent with their self-identity, they want to entertain, and they want to experience sexual arousal. To what degree do you think the motivation people attach to cross-dressing influences their evaluation of the cross-dresser?

Whereas the term *cross-dresser* typically refers to a heterosexual male who dresses in the clothes of a woman, currently the term **transvestite** more often refers to a homosexual man (the exception is Lady Gaga who sometimes dresses as a male) who dresses as a woman to attract men as sex partners or to perform before an audience as a "drag queen" for a drag show. Such a show typically involves dressing as a famous person (e.g., Mariah Carey) and lip-synching songs.

14.3i Other Paraphilias

Although we have discussed the major paraphilias presented in the *DSM-5*, there are many others (American Psychiatric Association, 2013). Examples of other varieties are presented in Table 14-2.

Cross-dressing
Dressing in the clothes of the other gender, typically a man dressing in a woman's clothes

Purging
Act of throwing away or burning one's clothes as a desperate means of ending one's cross-dressing

Transvestite
Broad term for an individual who may dress or present himself or herself in the gender of the other sex; a more pejorative term than *cross-dresser*

TABLE **14-2**	Other Paraphilias
Paraphilia	Description
Acrotomophilia	Deriving sexual arousal or gratification from engaging in sex with an amputee
Apotomnophilia	Becoming sexually aroused by the thought of becoming an amputee
Asphyxiophilia	Cutting off one's air supply to enhance orgasm
Autonepiophilia	Deriving sexual arousal or gratification from wearing wet diapers
Avoniepiphilia	Deriving sexual arousal by wearing diapers
Coprophilia	Using feces for sexual arousal either by watching another defecate or by defecating on someone
Ephebophilia	Engaging in sexual behavior with an adolescent or having a recurrent urge to do so
Erotophonophilia	Committing lust murder in which the partner is killed as a means of atoning for sex with the individual
Formicophilia	Becoming sexually aroused by ants, bugs, or other small, crawling creatures
Gerontophilia	Becoming sexually aroused by elderly individuals
Klismaphilia	Becoming sexually aroused by receiving an enema
Mysophilia	Deriving sexual excitement from filthy or soiled objects
Narratophilia	Listening to "dirty talk" as a means of becoming sexually aroused (Phone sex companies depend on people with this paraphilia for their income.)
Necrophilia	Deriving sexual arousal or gratification from sexual activity with a dead person (or a person acting the role of a corpse)
Nepiophilia	Becoming sexually aroused by babies
Olfactophilia	Becoming sexually aroused by certain scents
Partialism	Deriving sexual arousal or gratification from a specific nongenital body part (such as the foot)
Pictophilia	Becoming sexually aroused in reference to sexy photographs
Raptophilia	Becoming sexually aroused by surprise attack and violent assault
Scatalogia	Becoming sexually aroused by calling a stranger on the phone and either talking about sex or making sexual sounds (breathing heavily; also called telephonicophilia)
Somnophilia	Fondling a person, often a stranger, who is sleeping so as to become sexually aroused.
Urophilia	Using urine for sexual arousal either by watching someone urinate or by urinating on someone
Zoophilia	Becoming aroused by sexual contact with animals (commonly known as bestiality)

In addition to the acts listed in the table, other variant activities that may be engaged in for erotic motives include tattooing, piercing, and scarification. Most of these activities are controversial and illegal, in some jurisdictions, even when engaged in by consenting persons. However, learning about them can help explain part of the mystery and complexity of human sexual expression.

Personal ~~REFLECTION~~

Take a moment to express your thoughts about the following questions. Have you experienced a preference for a sexual stimulus that you feel borders on a compulsion? To what degree does such a proclivity affect you or your relationships? Are there any potential legal consequences for the transition of this preference into a compulsion?

14.3j Pathologizing Kink?

While this chapter has referred to the *DSM-5* regarding various forms of sexual expression, it is important to emphasize that these definitions pathologize what others may consider normal. Dr. Julie Fennell (2013) noted:

> In much the same way that gays and lesbians feel that their sexual desires were unfairly pathologized by the medical establishment prior to the removal of homosexuality as a mental disorder from the *DSM*, people who participate in BDSM (Bondage & Discipline/Dominance & Submission/Sadism & Masochism) feel that they have been unfairly pathologized for their sexual desires. People who engage in BDSM apply principles of consent to their practices—meaning that there are no victims or abusers, only "tops" and "bottoms." As explained by the National Coalition for Sexual Freedom, when BDSM is practiced correctly, only people who want to get hurt get hurt. People who have medical disorders associated with sadism and masochism are not engaging in consensual behaviors, and most people in the BDSM community view the diagnoses of "fetishism" and "transvestism" as obsolete and heteronormative, respectively.

14.3k Sexual Addiction?

Although the *DSM-5* does not recognize the concept of "sex addiction or **sexual addiction**" the behavior associated with the term is lack of control. Just as the alcoholic cannot consistently avoid alcohol, the "sex addicted" person feels compelled to seek sexual opportunities regardless of the consequences. In effect, the person has a very high (hyperactive) sexual interest, behaves as though he or she is driven to sexual expression, and will pursue sex in spite of negative effects on the following: their health (e.g., sexually transmitted infections); relationships (e.g., affair leading to divorce); or career (e.g., sex with co-workers/supervisors). Having repetitive extradyadic affairs, frequenting massage parlors, and hiring prostitutes are all associated with hyperactive sexual desire. Just as the person cannot control his or her sexual behavior, lack of control of money (e.g., gambling), Internet use (e.g., pornography) and substances (e.g., alcohol or other drugs) are common. The authors have had self-described "sex addicts" speak to their sexuality classes who have recounted that their "addiction" was one of several—gambling, etc. (see Up Close 14-2 on sex addiction).

Sexual addiction
Sometimes described as an intimacy disorder manifested by a compulsive cycle of preoccupation and ritualization of sexual behavior and despair

"Hello, My Name Is KJ, and I'm a Sex Addict."*

While I understand that there is disagreement about the validity of the term "sexual addiction," I would like to assert that I am a sex addict and define the term as my inability to control my sexual behavior. While I am now in recovery (and have been for seven years), I am constantly on alert to exercise control over my life by practicing recovery. Sex is only one of my addictions: I am also a gambler by compulsive stock trading, an alcoholic, and I am addicted to pornography. My life has been ruined by all of these as I am now on my fifth marriage and have had very estranged relationships with my children.

Part of my recovery is to help others who feel helpless with control over their sexual behavior. I am a member of our local Sex Addicts Anonymous organization, which uses the 12-step program of recovery, similar to recovering from alcoholism. I have authored a recovery workbook (The Circle of Life: The Process of Sexual Recovery Workbook) on sexual addiction which is available in electronic format as well as my own recovery story (Dying to Live: Boulevard of Broken Dreams) from Amazon.com.

*Provided by a speaker in Knox's human sexuality class who asks to remain anonymous.

14.4 The Origins of Paraphilias: Theoretical Perspectives

Various theoretical perspectives offer explanations for why a particular individual develops paraphilias.

14.4a Psychoanalytic Theory

From a psychoanalytic perspective, paraphilias may be viewed as symptoms of unresolved subconscious conflicts. For example, an exhibitionistic man may frighten unsuspecting women by exposing himself to them as a way of rebelling against them. Such rebellion may stem from having a domineering mother or an unresolved Oedipal complex, which has left the person unable to engage in heterosexual intercourse. The urge to exhibit may be a subconscious symbolic substitute that compensates for the inability to have sexual relations with women.

14.4b Feminist Perspective

Paraphilias such as pedophilia and sexual sadism are, from a feminist perspective, expressions of aggression more than sexuality. The pedophile, sadist, and rapist express control and dominance through their paraphilic fantasies and behaviors.

The feminist perspective explains why there are many more men with paraphilias than women with paraphilias: Our culture has perpetuated traditional gender roles that emphasize male dominance, sexual aggression, and control. Men act out these fantasies and may become dependent on them for sexual arousal.

14.4c Learning Theory

Learning theorists emphasize that paraphilias are learned by means of both classical and operant conditioning. In 1966, Rachman demonstrated how a fetish could be learned through classical conditioning. Using an experimental design, Rachman paired women's boots with erotic slides of nude women. As a result, the participants began to experience erotic arousal at the sight of the boots alone.

Scarf, panty, and high-heeled shoe fetishes may be a result of classical conditioning. The person may have experienced sexual pleasure when in the presence of these objects, learned to associate these objects with the pleasure, and developed a preference for these objects during sex.

Operant conditioning (behaviors followed by a reinforcer will increase in frequency) may also account for the development of some paraphilias. For example, the exhibitionist may be reinforced by the startled response of a woman and seek conditions under which she will exhibit a startled response (exposing his penis). By exposing his penis, the exhibitionist causes her to yell, is reinforced, and wants to repeat the behavior with another new stranger. If the masochist has an orgasm while being tied up, the act of being bound is reinforced operantly.

Similarly, paraphilias may result from negative reinforcement. *Negative reinforcement* is defined as the strengthening of a behavior associated with the removal of something aversive. A paraphilia may be learned because the associated behaviors remove feelings of anxiety, sadness, loneliness, and anger. Hence, when the exhibitionist exhibits to a victim, he feels a temporary reprieve from feelings of anxiety, which are replaced by feelings of excitement.

14.4d Biological Theory

The degree to which biological variables are responsible for the development of paraphilias is controversial. Just as heterosexuality, homosexuality, and bisexuality may be based on biological predispositions, so may paraphilic tendencies. Some people may be biologically "wired" to respond erotically to atypical stimuli.

Dunsieth and colleagues (2004) studied the backgrounds of individuals with a paraphilia and found that these correlated with the presence of a mood disorder, major depression, bipolar disorder, anxiety disorder, impulse control disorder, and avoidant personality disorder. All of these may have their root in and be influenced by biological factors.

14.4e Paraphilia as a Vandalized Lovemap

John Money's (1986, 1988) term **lovemap** has been used to describe a mental representation or template that develops early in the individual's life. It establishes, or at least influences, the type of sexual partner and activities that will arouse a person. Given the standard developmental hormones introduced into the developing fetus at the appropriate time and the traditional heterosexual socialization, people tend to be emotionally and sexually attracted to the other sex.

The critical years in the development of the lovemap are between ages 5 and 8 (Carnes, 2001). "Major erotosexual traumas during this period may disrupt the consolidation of the lovemap that would otherwise be taking place" (Money, 1986, p. 19). Money provided examples of the social experiences that "vandalize" or disrupt traditional sexual-erotic development socialization and showed how these disruptions may contribute to the development of pedophilia.

For example, a pedophile may have been involved in a relationship with an older man and learned to repeat the age-discrepant sexual experience with a younger boy. Often, the experience itself will not be enough to trigger a pedophiliac lovemap; but in combination with a traumatic experience, such as grief over a loved one's death, the man may become particularly vulnerable. Hence, the feeling of having lost a significant other and the enjoyment of sexual pleasure in an age-discrepant context may bond one to that context for reasons related to emotional insecurity and physical pleasure.

Operant conditioning
Learning theory which states that behavior is learned in reference to its consequences. A behavior that is punished will decrease in frequency a behavior that is reinforced will increase in frequency

Lovemap
Mental representation or template of one's idealized lover that develops early in the individual's life

14.4f Paraphilia as a Courtship Disorder

The disorder in this case is a distortion of "normal" courtship, which is assumed to consist of a series of phases in which progressively more intimate expressions of sexual behavior occur. An example is that courtship includes flirting and seducing the partner. This pattern may be twisted (and hence, a **courtship disorder**) so that the person flirts with the goal of seducing out of power and conquest, not intimacy. The person is "hooked on falling in love and winning the attention of the other" (p. 61). Similarly, "the rapist short circuits all stages and immediately attempts intercourse" (Langevin & Lang, 1987, p. 203). Hence, the disorder is the fact that the individual does not progress along a sequence of relationship stages from initial attraction, flirting, spending time together, love … but only enjoys the interaction in which controlling, manipulating, dominating, and conquering occur. The interaction isn't satisfying unless the individual is succeeding with conquering.

14.5 Treatment of Paraphilias

The behavioral expression of some of the paraphilias we have discussed (such as exhibitionism and pedophilia) interferes with the rights of others. When people engaging in such behaviors come to the attention of the law, they are often required to enter a treatment program. Indeed, the U.S. Supreme Court has upheld the civil commitment of sexually violent predators for treatment as constitutional. In effect, these individuals may be legally kept in psychiatric hospitals or special facilities for the treatment of their sexual deviation prior to release. Whereas most people with paraphilias must be forced to address them, some individuals seek treatment voluntarily.

After the existence of the paraphilia has become socially visible, treatment of the sex offender begins with a thorough assessment. This assessment involves collecting information regarding the offense of record, as well as a sexual, social, and psychiatric history.

The therapist usually gathers the law enforcement report, victim statement, presentence investigation, and summaries of previous placements and treatment. Interviews with the client and relevant other people are conducted, and psychological testing may be done. The Multiphasic Sex Inventory obtains reports of deviant behaviors, as well as indications of sexual knowledge and cognitive distortions. Its scales measuring child molestation and rape are the most well-developed, although it does address other paraphilias. The polygraph is sometimes used to corroborate self-reports obtained in clinical interviews. Measurements of penile tumescence (changes in the volume and circumference of the penis) are also used to assess physiological arousal. The penile plethysmograph employs a sensor or transducer that measures and records changes in penis size in response to sexual stimuli (audiotapes or slides).

Models for treatment of paraphilias, particularly pedophilia, view sex as a biological drive that can be disturbed in both intensity and direction. After a thorough evaluation, treatment begins and is usually focused on decreasing deviant sexual arousal, increasing nondeviant sexual arousal, teaching social skills, changing faulty cognitions, resolving sexual dysfunctions, managing substance/alcohol abuse, or a combination of these tasks.

14.5a Decreasing Deviant Sexual Arousal

Effective treatment of a paraphilia involves decreasing the deviant sexual arousal response, or the response to that which society regards as nonsexual stimuli. The therapeutic goal is for the person to no longer require the paraphilic target stimulus as a preferred or necessary condition of sexual arousal. Treatment that focuses on

Courtship disorder
Distortion of the standard sequence of interpersonal events in courtship that lead to the development of an intimate relationship; used as a theory to explain rape, the rapist short-circuits the courtship stages and progresses immediately to intercourse

decreasing deviant sexual arousal may involve medications, aversive conditioning, and covert sensitization. In regard to the use of medications to control paraphilias, there is considerable social debate. This controversy is discussed in the Social Choices 14-1 feature.

Social Choices 14-1

Treating Paraphilic Sex Offenders with Hormones

The use of hormones to quell the sexual lust of paraphiliac sex offenders involves a consideration of the rights of society to be protected from harm versus the rights of an offender to avoid being given medication that may have unwanted side effects. The rights of society have been established by the Supreme Court, which views the protection of children from pedophiles as paramount. California, Georgia, Montana, and Florida offer chemical castration as a condition of parole for repeat sex offenders.

Because sex is seen as a biological drive, hormones and neurotransmitters are used to mediate the intensity and direction of that drive. Antiandrogen drugs, such as Depo-Provera (medroxyprogesterone acetate, or MPA), may be used to lower the blood level of testosterone and seem to have a direct pharmacologic effect on brain pathways that mediate sexual behavior. Alternatively, cyproterone acetate may be used. Either may have the effect of removing the paraphilic preoccupation but still allowing the person to act on his sexual interest in his partner without dysfunction. In other cases, Depo-Provera may result in a complete shutdown of eroticism. Although these treatments are controversial, Depo-Provera and cyproterone acetate may be used to treat pedophiles, exhibitionists, voyeurs, and rapists.

More recently, selective serotonin reuptake inhibitors (SSRIs), such as fluoxetine (trade name Prozac), have been used to treat paraphilias and to reduce an individual's sexually deviant fantasies, urges, masturbation, and sexual behavior. For severe cases, luteinizing hormone-releasing hormone agonists (LHRH agonists), which have the effect of pharmacological castration, may be used. These hormone and serotonin reuptake inhibitors, "[w]hen combined with cognitive behavioral treatment," may provide some reduction in the urge to express paraphilic behaviors. However, there are also negative effects, such as loss of capacity to orgasm.

In addition, LHRH agonist leuprolide acetate (leuprolide) is a chemical compound that has been used in the treatment of paraphilias to successfully reduce sexually aggressive behavior, as well as to reduce penile erection, ejaculation, masturbation, sexually deviant impulsiveness, and fantasies.

Turner and colleagues (2013) observed the effect of testosterone-lowering medications (TLM) on sex offenders in Germany. Data were collected from the directors of 69 German forensic-psychiatric hospitals/outpatient clinics who oversaw the treatment of sex offenders (sex with children or sexual assault-rape). Almost all of the sex offenders were being treated psychotherapeutically, and 37% were receiving an additional pharmacological treatment. Of all the sex offenders, 15.7% were treated with TLM, 10.6% were treated with a gonadotropin-releasing hormone agonist, and 5.1% were treated with cyproterone acetate. Of these, 26%–75% showed improvements in such outcomes as reduction of frequency and/or intensity of sexual thoughts.

A rarely used alternative to chemical castration is surgical castration, whereby repeat child molesters in Canada may agree to the surgery in exchange for reduced jail time. The procedure results in reducing the man's interest in sex, sexual arousal, and activity in that it helps to control sexually deviant compulsions.

14.5b Aversive Conditioning

Deviant sexual arousal may also be decreased through **aversive conditioning**. Such conditioning involves pairing an aversive or unpleasant stimulus with the paraphilic stimulus to decrease the deviant sexual arousal and reduce the probability of engaging in the paraphilic behavior. One example of an aversive stimulus is an unpleasant smell. For the heterosexual male pedophile, during this type of aversion therapy, the patient listens to audio depictions of sexual activities with children or with adult women. After the taped narrative of sexual activity with the child is played, the therapist administers a noxious odor so that the patient associates this with the stimulus of the child. After removing the odor, the therapist changes the tape narrative to that of sexual activity with an adult woman. In this way, the patient associates relief from the noxious stimuli (and, consequently, a more pleasant feeling) with the stimulus of the adult woman.

The therapist might also use emetic drugs (which induce vomiting or nausea). Because it is believed that a fetish results from learning to associate a particular object with sexual pleasure, the stimulus object may be reconditioned by associating an unpleasant experience with it. For example, the person might be given emetic drugs to induce vomiting when in the presence of the fetish object. These procedures are still being researched.

14.5c Covert Sensitization

Covert sensitization involves using negative thoughts as a way of developing negative feelings associated with a deviant sexual stimulus. For example, a therapist may induce negative thoughts by saying the following to the patient:

> I want you to imagine going into the bedroom of your 7-year-old niece when her parents are in another part of the house. As you open the door, you see her asleep in her bed. But as you approach the bed, you begin to feel very nauseous and feel that you are going to throw up. You vomit and feel the particles in your mouth and the stench in your nostrils. You also think that if you act on your urges and are discovered, you will be shamed out of the family.

This scenario is designed to associate negative feelings and thoughts with acting on a sexual urge to touch a child so as to reduce the probability that the patient will engage in this behavior. Covert sensitization may be used to apply negative imagined consequences for offending and positive consequences for imagining alternatives to offending.

14.5d Increasing Nondeviant Sexual Arousal

In treating individuals with paraphilias, it is important not only to decrease deviant sexual arousal but also to increase nondeviant sexual arousal. Thus, treatment of paraphilias also involves increasing the level of sexual arousal the individual has in reference to culturally appropriate sexual stimuli. For example, the therapist would try to increase the sexual urges of a pedophile to the stimulus of a consenting adult partner. The mechanisms for increasing nondeviant sexual arousal include masturbatory conditioning, exposure, and systematic desensitization.

Masturbatory conditioning involves associating the pleasure of orgasm with a nondeviant stimulus. In this way, the previously nonarousing, nondeviant stimulus becomes a stimulus for arousal. The therapist instructs the client to fantasize about the paraphilic urge or behavior while masturbating. Gradually, the client replaces the first fantasy of the deviant stimulus with the nondeviant stimulus.

Aversive conditioning
Type of behavior therapy that involves pairing an aversive or unpleasant stimulus with a previously reinforcing stimulus; used in sex offender treatment to decrease deviant sexual arousal and reduce the probability of engaging in paraphilic behavior

Covert sensitization
Therapeutic technique that involves instructing the client to use negative thoughts as a way of developing negative feelings associated with a deviant sexual stimulus

Exposure involves introducing the individual to the nondeviant stimulus for increasingly longer periods of time, during which the individual has an opportunity to develop positive associations. For example, if the exhibitionist feels uncomfortable in the presence of adult women, the therapist might assign the patient to attend social functions with a male friend and to stand increasingly closer to women in social contexts. Such exposure may help to reduce the fear and anxiety associated with women and facilitate a greater willingness to engage in social interaction with women.

Systematic desensitization is another procedure to promote behaviors that are incompatible with offending behaviors. Where the client feels extreme anxiety in the presence of the nondeviant stimulus, systematic desensitization may be employed to reduce such anxiety. In systematic desensitization, the client imagines a series of scenes that involve the nondeviant sexual stimulus (such as an adult female) and then ranks these scenes according to the level of anxiety or discomfort they produce. Then, while the client is relaxed (the therapist will have taught the person how to relax using a progressive relaxation procedure), the therapist will present the various scenes from lowest to highest anxiety to the client. The client's feeling relaxed while fantasizing about the various encounters with women reduces the fear and anxiety associated with women. To ensure generalization, the therapist will ask the person to increase the level of real-life exposure to adult women using the exposure technique described in the preceding paragraph.

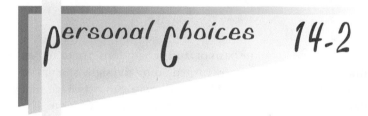

personal choices 14-2

Can People Control Their Paraphilias?

Therapists disagree about the degree to which persons with paraphilias can control the behavioral expression of their paraphilia. Whereas some feel that those with pedophilia, exhibitionism, and voyeurism are uncontrollably and compulsively driven to express their paraphilia (and will not be able to change their reaction to sexual cues), others suggest that these persons can exercise conscious control over their paraphilic behavior.

Pedophilia, exhibitionism, and voyeurism may be conceptualized as requiring a series of choices leading to the expression of the paraphilic behavior. For example, a pedophile who fondles a young boy in the park on a summer afternoon is engaging in a behavior that was preceded by a number of choices leading to that behavior. These choices may have included taking off from work, looking at child pornography, drinking alcohol, going to the playground, buying candy, sitting on the bench where a young boy was also sitting, talking to the boy, offering the boy some candy, and so on. At any of these choice points, the pedophile may have chosen to engage in a behavior that was incompatible with child molestation. Each of these behaviors, when taken alone, is a relatively easier choice: The person might choose to stay at work, look at alternative magazines, and so forth.

Similarly, the exhibitionist who exposes himself in the library to a stranger may alternatively have chosen to masturbate at home, to avoid alcohol, and to go with a friend to a movie. Finally, the voyeur might choose to schedule time with others when he is particularly vulnerable to "peeping," to avoid walking on another person's property (where peeping often occurs), and to select alternative behaviors, such as going to a movie during prime "peeping time."

In addition to making deliberate choices that are incompatible with the expression of paraphilic behaviors, the person who is concerned about his sexual interest may choose to seek therapy to address such issues as self-esteem, guilt, anxiety, sexual dysfunctions, and lack of social skills. By confronting these issues and ensuring that they do not contribute to unwanted behavior, the person is taking deliberate control of his sexual expression.

14.5e Learning Social Skills

Earlier we discussed courtship disorder as an underlying problem in the development of some paraphilias. People with paraphilias typically have low self-esteem, anxiety in social situations, and no skills in initiating and maintaining an intimate interpersonal relationship. Treatment of paraphilias often involves teaching the person how to initiate a conversation, empathize, listen, and keep a conversation going so that the person will be better able to develop a close emotional bond with an adult partner. Social skill training often takes place in a group therapy setting where group members may practice basic communication and interaction skills with each other.

Therapists seeing a client who lacks social skills can also devise an individual treatment plan to assist the client in learning these skills. Recall the Up Close 13-1 feature in the last chapter where a therapist used relationship surrogates to assist a virgin male in his 30s in how to talk with, touch, and kiss a female.

14.5f Changing Faulty Cognitions

Some paraphilic behaviors are continued on the basis of faulty cognitions. For example, the exhibitionist may think that "women are really turned on by the sight of a naked penis and would enjoy someone exposing himself." The pedophile may believe that children profit from sexual experiences with adults as a form of sex education. The rapist may think that women really mean 'yes' when they say 'no' and enjoy having forced sex.

Correcting these cognitive distortions often occurs in the context of group therapy. Group members challenge the irrational beliefs of each other and acknowledge their own irrational beliefs. Irrational beliefs are replaced with new beliefs: Women are disgusted by exhibitionists, children are harmed by adult sexual exploitation, and women abhor being raped.

14.5g Resolving Sexual Dysfunctions

Some paraphilias continue because of sexual dysfunctions that prevent the individual with a paraphilia from engaging in sexual behavior with a partner. For example, the exhibitionist and voyeur may feel unable to engage in sex with a partner due to erectile dysfunction. They may also suffer rapid ejaculation or retarded ejaculation and want to avoid exposure of these dysfunctions in a relationship. Unless these sexual dysfunctions are treated, the individual with a paraphilia may continue to feel sexually inadequate and perceive no alternative for sexual gratification other than engaging in paraphilic behavior.

Chapter Summary

Most people have some preference for how, when, and with whom they experience sexual expression. Although a paraphilia involves a preference, it is usually experienced as a drive and the preference is typically unusual.

What Is "Normal" Sexual Behavior?

A sexual behavior is defined as "normal" in regard to its prevalence (the higher the incidence, the more "normal"); moral correctness (religion supports penile-vaginal intercourse between spouses); naturalness (procreation); and adaptiveness/comfort (the more comfortable, the more normal).

Within the same culture, sexual behaviors may be labeled as normal in one historical time and abnormal in another. Kissing in public, prohibited during the Colonial era, is now commonplace.

Variant Sexual Behavior: Definition and Overview

Paraphilias are an overdependence on a culturally unacceptable or unusual stimulus for sexual arousal and satisfaction. The most common paraphilias are exhibitionism and frotteurism. Most individuals who have a paraphilia have an average of three to four different types. Paraphilias may become the major sexual activities in a person's life and may interfere with the person's capacity for reciprocal, affectionate sexual interactions. Although there are few classic profile characteristics (sexual orientation, ethnicity, socioeconomic background), paraphilias most often occur in men and are very rarely diagnosed in women. Paraphilias are legal or illegal depending on the degree to which the rights of others are affected. The majority of apprehended sex offenders are arrested for acts of exhibitionism, pedophilia, and voyeurism.

Types of Paraphilias

The major paraphilias considered in this chapter are exhibitionism, frotteurism, voyeurism, fetishism, transvestic fetishism, sexual sadism, and sexual masochism. People who engage in exhibitionism, frotteurism, and voyeurism are usually not violent; yet such acts should be reported to law enforcement officials.

The Origins of Paraphilias: Theoretical Perspectives

Theoretical explanations for paraphilias include psychoanalytic (unconscious processes), feminist (control, power, aggression), learning (classical/operant paradigms), biological (innate), and lovemap (biological predisposition plus unusual learning experiences) perspectives. Paraphilias may also be conceptualized as a courtship disorder whereby the individual does not enact the culturally acceptable social skills for emotional and sexual engagement.

Treatment of Paraphilias

Treatment of paraphilias involves decreasing deviant sexual arousal, increasing nondeviant sexual arousal, developing interpersonal social skills, changing faulty cognitions, and resolving sexual dysfunctions.

Web Links

AtHealth

http://www.athealth.com/Consumer/disorders/Paraphilias.html

Fetish

www.fetlife.com

Sexaholics Anonymous

http://www.sa.org/

Sex Addicts Anonymous

http://saa-recovery.org/

Key Terms

Aversive conditioning 414

Courtship disorder 412

Covert sensitization 414

Cross-dressing 407

Exhibitionistic disorder 400

Fetishism 405

Frotteuristic disorder 401

Lovemap 411

Operant conditioning 411

Paraphilia 396

Pedophilic disorder 404

Purging 407

Scopophilia 399

Sexual addiction 409

Sexual masochism disorder 402

Sexual sadism disorder 404

Toucheurism 402

Transvestic disorder 406

Transvestic fetishism 406

Transvestite 407

Voyeuristic disorder 399

Additional study resources are available at www.BVTLab.com

CHAPTER 15

Sexually Transmitted Infections

While abstinence is a public health message that we can all support, it cannot be the only message. Public health officials are obligated to dwell in the real world and support an approach … that reflects how Americans really live.

Theresa Raphael, Executive Director of the National Coalition of STI Directors

Chapter Outline

Objectives

1. Identify the current data on STIs in the U.S. and worldwide.

2. Understand how ignorance promotes the spread of STIs.

3. Review the risks and consequences associated with STIs.

4. Distinguish the different types of STIs.

5. Explain how STIs represent a major individual and public health concern.

6. Know how to actively protect oneself from STIs.

7. Review the various treatment options for STIs.

8. Learn how to access sexual health services.

AIDS (HIV) INFORMATION & TREATMENT

See Also Clinics; Crisis Intervention Service; Hospitals; Human Services Organizations; Laboratories-Medical; Laboratories-Testing; Social Service Organizations; Social Service Organizations

National AIDS Hotline Toll Free .... 800 CDC-IN

Pitt County AIDS Service Organization-Picaso
609 Country Club Dr Greenville......................... 830-

Source: Chelsea Curry

TRUTH OR FICTION?

T/F   Many STIs are asymptomatic, which means they don't produce any symptoms or signs.

T/F   Candidiasis, also known as monilia and yeast infection, cannot be spread to a partner.

T/F   Most cervical cancer is caused by the human papillomavirus.

T/F   The most common bacterial sexually transmitted infection in the U.S. is gonorrhea.

T/F   Rates of STIs are higher among economically disadvantaged populations.

Answers: 1.T 2.F 3.T 4.F 5.T

Michael Douglas gave national visibility to sexually transmitted infections when he suggested that his throat cancer was caused by HPV contracted through oral sex. The 68-year-old actor, married to Catherine Zeta Jones since 2000, said that his years of drinking and smoking did not cause his throat cancer but that "without wanting to get too specific, this particular cancer is caused by HPV [human papillomavirus]; it actually comes about from cunnilingus" (Douglas, 2013).

Every semester, we ask a health educator from the university where we teach to talk with our classes about sexually transmitted infections. Every semester, the health educator leads off the discussion with the same phrase—"One-in-four undergraduate students in colleges/universities throughout the U.S. is estimated to contract a sexually transmitted infection during their college career" (Purkett, 2013). The message is clear. Human sexual interactions are not just about fun, pleasure, and relationships; they may have profound implications for health and one's well-being.

This chapter presents information about these life-impacting, sexually transmitted infections (STIs). How widespread are these infections? Who is at risk? What behaviors are associated with contracting STIs? What are the health, economic, and psychological consequences of STIs? What choices can you make to reduce your risk of acquiring an STI? What can society do to control and prevent the spread of STIs?

15.1 Sexually Transmitted Infections: An Overview

Sexually transmitted infections (STIs) are infections spread primarily through person-to-person sexual contact. There are more than 30 different sexually-transmissible bacteria, viruses, and parasites (World Health Organization, 2013). Person-to-person sexual contact is the main mode of infection, with vaginal and anal intercourse providing the most efficient transmission; the infections can also be transmitted orally.

Last time I had sex I was so good I got a standing ovation. Well, actually, I just got the clap."

Jarod Kintz

Discovering that one has a STI is an emotionally charged experience, often including feelings of fear, shame, and embarrassment. One's relationship may also be jeopardized. One of our students noted, "When my partner finds out she has HPV, she'll know it was me; and I'll be cooked. Everything has changed."

Researchers estimate that only the common cold infects more people than STIs. However, it should not be surprising that infections spread through sexual contact are so common. Kissing, oral sex, sexual intercourse, and anal sex are all body-to-body contacts that provide a conduit for STIs to be transmitted.

Sexually transmitted infections (STIs)
Infections transmitted primarily through sexual activity; a more recent term sometimes used to avoid the negative connotations sometimes associated with STD

Take a moment to answer the following questions. What's in a name? STDs used to be referred to as venereal diseases, or VD (a term derived from the name for the Roman goddess of love, Venus). As that term became stigmatized, it was replaced with STD (sexually transmitted disease). Currently, many public health organizations and educators are using the term sexually transmitted infection (STI). Some feel the use of "STI" is less stigmatizing and reduces some of the negative emotional reaction some people now associate with "STD." In this text we typically use the term STI because it is the terminology currently used by SIECUS and the U.S. Centers for Disease Control and Prevention. Would you have a different reaction to learning you had acquired a sexually transmitted infection in contrast to a sexually transmitted disease?

15.1a Current Status of STIs in the United States

National & International DATA

Each year, approximately 20 million new sexually transmitted infections occur in the U.S. Worldwide, STIs cause over 1 million deaths per year (Stanberry & Rosenthal, 2013).

The Center for Disease Control estimates that there are more than 110 million total STI cases among Americans at any given time. Table 15-1 identifies the incidence annually. While representing only 25% of the sexually active population, young Americans ages 15 to 24 account for over 50% of all new STI cases (Satterwhite, et al., 2013).

TABLE **15-1**	Incidence Rates of the Most Common STIs in the United States
STI	Annual Estimated Incidence
Human papillomavirus (HPV)	14.1 million
Chlamydia	2.86 million
Trichomoniasis	1.09 million
Gonorrhea	820,000
Herpes (HSV-2)	776,000
Syphilis	55,000
Hepatitis B	19,000

Source: Centers for Disease Control and Prevention. (2013). Incidence, prevalence, and cost of sexually transmitted infections in the United States. Fact Sheet. Centers for Disease Control and Prevention http://www.cdc.gov/std/stats/STI-Estimates-Fact-Sheet-Feb-2013.pdf.

The most well-publicized among the STIs is HIV/AIDS. The CDC estimates that there are more than 1.1 million Americans living with HIV, including 18% who are unaware of their infection (Centers for Disease Control, 2012d).

Cultural Diversity

The threat of STIs to developing countries is even greater. The World Health Organization (WHO) estimates that as of 2011, there are 34 million people living with HIV with 2.5 million newly infected and 1.7 million deaths each year (World Health Organization, 2013).

15.1b Ignorance Promotes Infection

Despite the fact that much information has been learned about STIs, many people around the world remain largely ignorant of these infections. The vulnerability of young people to infection is compounded by their lack of knowledge. Individuals in developing world countries are often unaware that STIs exist or that they are vulnerable. Throughout the world, most young adults have not been tested for HIV and other STIs. Many people are infected and do not even know it.

My son has died of AIDS.
Nelson Mandella, former leader of South Africa

Many STIs are **asymptomatic** (do not produce symptoms or signs) or yield symptoms so mild that medical care is not sought. People may be asymptomatic yet pass on the disease to others. For example, up to 85% of women and 50% of men who are infected with chlamydia have no symptoms. They may not be aware of the infection until years later when a significant health problem develops. The CDC estimates that at least 24,000 U.S. women become infertile because of undiagnosed STIs (Healthy People 2020, 2012).

Asymptomatic
Producing no symptoms or signs, or as in some STIs, yielding symptoms so mild that medical care is not sought

15.1c Risk Factors for Sexually Transmitted Infections

The risk of acquiring a STI depends on a variety of factors:

1. Exposure (the rate of sexual contact between uninfected persons and infected individuals)
2. Transmission (the probability of an exposed person acquiring the infection)
3. Duration (the length of time an infected person is contagious and able to spread the disease)

The following behaviors and characteristics can affect rates of disease exposure, transmission and duration:

Number of Sex Partners

The more sexual partners an individual has, the higher the risk of being exposed to a sexually transmitted infection. The good news is that from 1991 to 2001, the percentage of high school students who reported having four or more lifetime sex partners declined significantly among black students (from 43% to 25%) and remained relatively stable among white (15% to 13%) and Hispanic students (17% to 15%), according to Centers for Disease Control and Prevention (2012f).

Age

In general, the younger the person, the greater the probability there is of infection. It is estimated that 1 in 15 sexually active females ages 14–19 years has chlamydia (Centers for Disease Control and Prevention, 2011a). STI rates are highest among this age group because they are least likely to use protection. Youth assume they will be "lucky," are not skilled in negotiating condom use, or feel uncomfortable "planning ahead" (if they plan ahead, they are "guilty"; if they are "swept away" in the heat of passion, they are not). Teens are also reluctant to seek medical services for STIs and may encounter difficulties in accessing services (Healthy People 2020, 2012).

However, young people are not the only age group experiencing serious STI consequences. For example, while the U.S. HIV rate has leveled off, the percentage of older adults with HIV grew by 77% between 2001 and 2005 (Centers for Disease Control and Prevention, 2012a). This increase is due not only to the fact that more seniors are acquiring HIV but also to the fact that people who acquired HIV in their younger years are living past age 50 due to the success of antiretroviral therapy. Older women may be especially vulnerable to STIs in terms of biologic risk due to the bodily changes of menopause, less use of barrier contraceptive methods, and marital status change through widowhood or divorce that reimmerses them in dating and courtship roles with lacking knowledge about HIV protections.

Sex

The transmission of an STI (likelihood of acquiring the infection once exposed) is influenced by one's sex. Women are biologically more susceptible than men to becoming infected if exposed to STIs. This is due to the larger mucosal surface area exposed to the virus in women, the greater amount of virus present in semen as compared with vaginal secretions, and the shortness and location of the female urethra (shorter distance for infectious organisms to travel). See Table 15-2, which reviews the different effects of STIs on women and men.

TABLE **15-2**	Ways STIs Affect Women Differently from Men

1. A woman's anatomy can place her at a unique risk for STIs compared to a man.
2. Women are less likely to have symptoms of common STIs, such as chlamydia and gonorrhea, compared to men.
3. Women are more likely to confuse symptoms of an STI for something else.
4. Women may not see symptoms as easily as men.
5. STIs can lead to serious health complications and affect a woman's future reproductive plans.
6. Women who are pregnant can pass STIs on to their babies.
7. Human Papillomavirus (HPV) is the most common STI in women and is the main cause of cervical cancer.

Source: Centers for Disease Control and Prevention (2011b). Fact sheet: 10 ways STDs affect women differently from men. Retrieved from http://www.cdc.gov/nchhstp/newsroom/docs/STDs-Women-042011.pdf

Although lesbians are not immune to HIV and other STIs, women who have sexual relations only with women (and whose partners do likewise) have a substantially lower risk of acquiring STIs than heterosexual women. The risk associated with the most common female-to-female sexual practices (oral sex and manual stimulation) is less than with heterosexual sexual intercourse. Hence, the main source of HIV infection among lesbians is related to injection drug use and sex with HIV-infected men.

Alcohol/substance abuse are associated with *not* using condoms.
Source: Chelsea Curry

Alcohol/Substance Use

Drinking alcohol or using drugs is associated with an increased risk of acquiring HIV and other STIs. At the community level, the introduction of new drugs can have a drastic influence on sexual behavior in high-risk sexual networks. Substance use increases the risk of STI transmission when it is associated with the exchange of sex for drugs, a greater number of anonymous sex partners, or decreases in use of barrier protection (e.g., condoms) and seeking medical care. For example, in the late 1980s the nationwide syphilis epidemic was fueled by increases in the use of crack cocaine (Healthy People 2020, 2012). At the individual level, substance use is associated with impaired judgment regarding sexual decisions.

Sexual Abuse

A history of sexual abuse increases the likelihood of a young woman beginning voluntary intercourse at an earlier age, an STI risk. Individuals who have been raped or sexually assaulted are also at risk for acquiring an STI because sexual coercion decreases the possibility of self-protection. Forced sexual activity is also more likely to result in vaginal or anal abrasions, thereby increasing susceptibility to HIV and other STIs. Women who are physically abused (even if not through sexual violence) may engage in risky sexual behaviors out of fear and may be unable to negotiate use of condoms.

Racial and Ethnic Disparities

Race and ethnicity in the U.S. are correlated with other determinants of health status—such as poverty, limited access to healthcare and health education, fewer attempts to get medical treatment, and living in communities with high rates of STDs. Accordingly, certain racial and ethnic groups have high rates of STDs compared with rates for whites (Centers for Disease Control and Prevention, 2012a; Healthy People 2020, 2012). For example, despite the fact that African Americans make up only 13% of the U.S. population, of the 197,090 diagnosed cases of HIV infection from 2008–2010, blacks accounted for the following:

- 47% of the total
- 64% of women diagnosed
- 66% of infections attributed to heterosexual contact
- 67% of cases in children under 13
  (Centers for Disease Control and Prevention, 2012b)

In 2011, the rate of chlamydia among blacks was more than 7 times higher than among whites and the rate among Hispanics was more than 2.4 higher than the rate among whites (Center for Disease Control and Prevention, 2011a).

One of the reasons STIs remain "hidden" is that they disproportionately impact disenfranchised persons and vulnerable groups (e.g., sex workers, youth, persons in detention, migrant workers, and the poor in developing countries) whose needs may not be apparent to more affluent society (Healthy People 2020, 2012). People who live in poverty or on the margins of society are more likely to be part of social networks encouraging risky sexual behavior and less likely to seek or have access to healthcare.

Sex Worker

Many of the aforementioned risk factors converge in those who engage in sex work. Compounding their educational and economic disadvantages with unsafe sexual behaviors and the use of alcohol and other drugs, often in a context of coercion and violence, increases their risk for HIV/AIDS. Sex workers are also more likely to have histories of sexual partners at higher HIV risk (men who have sex with men, inject drugs, or are known to be HIV positive).

High Risk Sexual Behavior

The term **high risk group** implies that certain traits determine who will become infected with an STI; however, it is not the group that one belongs to but rather the behaviors that one practices that puts one at risk for contracting an STI. Anyone who engages in risky sexual behavior is susceptible to acquiring STIs (see Table 15-3). With some exceptions (such as sexual victimization and mother-child transmission), STIs result from people choosing to engage in behaviors that place them at risk. These choices most influence STI transmission, rather than a person's group affiliations. However, as previously noted, group membership may be associated with risk-taking patterns. These high risk sexual patterns include having multiple partners, having sex with persons who have multiple partners, males having sex with males, and alcohol/drug use.

High risk group
Certain behaviors help to identify who will become infected with an STI

TABLE **15-3** | Risky Sexual Behaviors

Extremely High Risk	Moderate Risk
Unprotected anal and vaginal intercourse	Unprotected oral sex on a man or woman
Sharing needles (for drug use and body piercing)	Unprotected oral-anal contact (rimming)
Sharing devices that draw blood (such as whips)	Unprotected fisting or intercourse using one or more fingers
Allowing body fluids to come in contact with broken skin and mucous membranes	
Low Risk	**No Risk**
Deep (French) kissing	Dry kissing
Anal and vaginal intercourse with a condom used correctly	Hugging and nongenital touching/massage
Fisting or intercourse using one or more fingers protected by a finger cot* or latex glove	Using vibrators or sex toys (not shared)
Oral-anal contact (rimming) with a dental dam**	Masturbation (alone or with partner)
Oral sex on a man or woman using a condom or dental dam	

* A finger cot *is a mini-condom worn on the fingers for finger intercourse.*
**A dental dam *is a latex square used to cover the anus or vagina during oral sex. Household plastic wrap or a condom cut lengthwise can be used as a substitute for a dental dam.*
Source: U.S. Department of Health and Human Services (2012). Sexual risk factors. AIDS.gov. Retrieved from http://aids.gov/hiv-aids-basics/prevention/reduce-your-risk/sexual-risk-factors/

Although worldwide most cases of HIV and AIDS are found among the heterosexual population, in the United States HIV rates are highest among men who have sex with men (MSM). In the U.S., 77% of the diagnosed HIV infections from 2008 through 2011 were in males. Of these, according to Centers for Disease Control and Prevention (2012c):

- 76% were in MSM.
- 21% were among those ages 18–24—and of these, 90% were attributed to MSM contact.

In 2006, MSM constituted 57% of all new HIV infections in the United States (Centers for Disease Control and Prevention, 2012c). Their risky behaviors included unprotected anal intercourse, seeking sex partners on the Internet, substance use, and failing to maintain prevention practices. Risk behaviors among the MSM may have increased due to optimism about the success of highly active antiretroviral therapy (HAART), the challenge of maintaining safer sex behaviors over time, and the younger MSM not having seen the toll of AIDS firsthand.

15.1d STI Testing

The CDC recommends regular STI testing for all sexually active individuals, especially young people. Many people do not get tested for STIs because they believe they are not infected. Many STIs are asymptomatic; that is, they often do not produce symptoms. Thus, individuals may have an STI and not know it. Other individuals believe that if they are not in a "high-risk category," testing is not needed. Some individuals do not get tested because they fear the results may indicate they *are* infected. For this same reason, some individuals get tested but never follow up to get the results.

Personal REFLECTION

Take a moment to express your thoughts about the following question. We have just reviewed data showing that many individuals who engage in high risk behavior for acquiring HIV and other STIs are nevertheless unlikely to seek testing for STIs. If you are sexually active, have you ever reasoned any of the following: "I could tell if someone is infected." "It would be too embarrassing to be tested." "I wouldn't want my partner to think I didn't trust him/her."

With many STIs, what you don't know *can* hurt you. The longer an STI goes undiagnosed and untreated, the more likely that it will produce serious health consequences, including infertility, cancer, and even death. The sooner an infected individual is tested and diagnosed, the sooner that individual can begin treatment for the disease and begin to alter high risk behaviors.

Early detection of HIV is especially important because it enables the infected individual to begin interventions that slow the growth of HIV and prevent opportunistic diseases. Early detection of other STIs can prevent or minimize the negative health effects they might otherwise produce. Because of the ulcerations caused by genital herpes, syphilis, and chancroid, and the inflammation caused by gonorrhea, chlamydia, and trichomoniasis, these infections facilitate transmission of HIV. Therefore, rapid diagnosis and treatment of these STIs may help prevent sexual transmission of HIV.

STI testing is available at most local public health centers, STI clinics, family planning clinics, private health-care providers, hospitals, and university health centers. One can also get tested for HIV in the privacy of the home. Getting tested for STIs requires an investment of time, effort and, potentially, money. Getting tested also requires individuals to overcome any embarrassment and fear associated with discussing their sexual behaviors with healthcare providers, having their genitals examined, and coping with the possibility of being told they have an STI.

Some STI testing involves getting a sample of the person's blood or urine and testing it for the presence of a particular STI. Testing for chlamydia can be done through non-invasive methods such as self-administered vaginal swabs or a urine test. Many young people mistakenly assume they are being screened for chlamydia when they see a healthcare provider, but in 2009 only 43% of eligible females enrolled in commercial healthcare plans and 57% of the eligible Medicaid population were screened (Center for Disease Control and Prevention, 2011a).

15.1e Consequences of Sexually Transmitted Infections

In the United States, most teenagers and adults today are aware that HIV and AIDS can cause serious health consequences. However, in addition to health consequences, HIV and other STIs can cause psychological distress and can also place an economic burden on individuals and society.

Health Consequences

Untreated STIs can result in severe health consequences. Recent CDC analysis reveals that while the annual number of new STI infections is roughly equal among young women and young men (51% vs. 49%, respectively), young women are more likely than men to suffer serious health consequences from untreated STIs. Also, because women are less likely to produce symptoms, they are less likely to be diagnosed until severe problems develop (Centers for Disease Control and Prevention, 2011b).

Untreated sexually transmitted infections may cause infections of the cervix, uterus, and fallopian tubes, and life-threatening ectopic (tubal) pregnancy or **pelvic inflammatory disease (PID)**. PID is a major health problem in women of reproductive age, often requiring hospitalization and surgery. It is associated with complications such as infertility, ectopic pregnancy, and chronic abdominal pain. Chlamydia and gonorrhea are important causes of PID in women.

STIs are also associated with health problems for pregnant women and infants. Various STIs may be transmitted to the fetus, newborn, or infant through the placenta (congenital infection), during passage through the birth canal (perinatal infection), or after birth through breast-feeding or close contact. Health consequences include spontaneous abortion, stillbirth, and premature delivery.

HPV causes almost all cervical cancers. The health consequences of HIV and AIDS have caused great alarm; AIDS causes more deaths than any other STI. Untreated syphilis can cause serious damage to the cardiovascular and nervous systems, and may also cause blindness and death.

Economic Consequences

The economic costs of STIs place a burden on individuals and their families and drain the tax dollars that support public health insurance (e.g., Medicaid) and public healthcare facilities. The CDC conservatively estimates that the lifetime cost of treating the eight most common STIs contracted in just one year is over $15.6 billion (Centers for Disease Control and Prevention, 2012a). Some STIs—such as HPV, herpes, and HIV—require lifetime treatment and consequently are the most costly. However, even the cost of curable STIs is considerable, estimated to be over $742 million annually.

The cost of treating HPV-related cancers is particularly costly. In addition, individuals with AIDS (and their families) are particularly hard-hit by the financial costs associated with this disease. Medicines alone can cost more than $1,000 per month, and some individuals must choose between food and their medicine. Drug therapies would be out of reach of most of those suffering the most from HIV if it weren't for programs from the World Health Organization and others, which through 2012 had provided antiretroviral drugs to almost 10 million people living with HIV/AIDS (World Health Organization, 2013).

Psychological Consequences

Individuals who learn they are infected with a sexually transmitted infection often experience psychological consequences similar to those experienced with other life crises. These psychological reactions include shock, withdrawal from social interaction, anger (especially at the person who gave them the infection), fear, shame, and depression (see Up Close 15-1 from one of our students). Telling one's partner (or a potential partner) that one has an STI can be very stressful. Individuals infected with an STI often encounter rejection.

Pelvic inflammatory disease (PID)
Inflammation of the pelvic organs often requiring hospitalization and surgery (PID is associated with complications such as infertility, ectopic pregnancy, and chronic abdominal pain.)

Close 15-1

"I Have HPV"

I was 19 years old and a sophomore in college when I was first diagnosed with HPV. I have what's called high-risk HPV, which has no visible signs except for abnormal pap smears. I never thought in a million years I would have to deal with something so serious in my life. I thought I did everything right—I waited 19 years to lose my virginity to my first true love

I found out I had HPV after a routine doctor visit and pap smear on campus. The doctor called me to let me know they found abnormal cells and that I needed to go see a gynecologist to get another pap and possibly more tests. I freaked out! I was so angry wondering how did this happen to me? I immediately picked up the phone and called my now ex-boyfriend and demanded to know why he didn't tell me he had this. He told me he had been recently tested and everything came back normal. The problem was although he may have been tested for some STIs, HPV is not routinely tested for. Also, high-risk HPV is asymptomatic, so he had no symptoms or signs that either one of us could visibly see.

After the initial shock I spent a lot of time researching the virus. One of the hardest parts of this was calling my mom and letting her know what was going on and that I needed to come home to see a gynecologist. That phone call was very difficult because I felt like I had let my mother down and disappointed her.

Three weeks later I was in the doctor's office waiting for my exam. I felt very scared and felt that at this point I had very little control over what was going on in my body, and I felt very deceived. My first doctor's appointment was horrid. The doctor spoke harshly and very demeaning to me, leaving me feeling dirty. The result of that visit was that I learned that I have precancerous cells. The only treatment for my diagnosis was continuous screening of my cervix and to keep as much stress out of my life as possible. Since I have an advanced case, I have to return home from school every few months just to go to the doctor. Sometimes it is hard to believe how I can have something that could [be] detrimental to my health yet I cannot see the damage.

I have chosen to be honest with anyone that I have become involved with regarding my having HPV. My ex-boyfriend, who infected me, has gone on to a new relationship but has not disclosed to his new girlfriend that he has HPV and claims he has no intention of doing so. I know he is not the only one not telling. I am in a sorority on my campus and several of the girls have HPV, and they claim that they never tell the guys they [have] sex with that they have an STI. It makes me so angry because I wish someone had told me.

There are parts of the future that are scary for me to deal with. One day I will have to tell my future husband that I will most likely have cervical cancer early in life, I may be sterile, and that he may get HPV as well.

As of writing this I am a junior in college and have found comfort in learning all I can about HPV. I wish I had known the facts earlier in life since this is not something that antibiotics can cure, and I must live with this the rest of my life. Looking back on my "true love," I know now it was not so true and was not worth the rest of my healthy life. At this point I feel my part is to always be honest from the beginning with anyone I am sexually active with; unfortunately I do not believe that most people are.

15.2 Sexually Transmitted Infections: A Pandemic

Sexually transmitted infections represent a major individual and public health concern. An overview of U.S. and global statistics on STIs reveals how widespread sexually transmitted infections are. The consequences on an STI on one's physical health, economic well-being, and psychological well-being convey the seriousness of the STI pandemic.

15.2a The Scope of the Problem in the U.S.

On any given day in the United States there are more than 110 million cases of STIs. (Satterwhite, et al., 2013).

15.2b Global STI Statistics

At the end of 2009, the World Health Organization reported that there were 33.3 million people worldwide living with HIV infection. Globally there are an estimated 2.6 million new HIV infections each year. While the incidence has decreased in many sub-Saharan African countries, it has increased by more than 25% in the last decade in countries in Central Asia, Bangladesh, and the Philippines (Stanberry & Rosenthal, 2013).

Sexually transmitted infections and their consequences represent major public health problems, especially for developing countries that lack resources for preventing and treating STIs. Africa has suffered the highest incidence of AIDS cases; in Sub-Saharan Africa HIV/AIDS is the leading cause of death.

15.3 Types of STIs

STIs can be classified based on the type of microorganism that causes the infection and by the type of infection produced. Some remain located at the site of infection, but others progress and affect body systems. Some are curable, and some are only treatable. The main agents responsible for STIs are parasites, bacteria, protozoa, and viruses.

> *AIDS destroys families, decimates communities, and, particularly in the poorest areas of the world, threatens to destabilize the social, cultural, and economic fabric of entire nations ...*
>
> Rabbi David Saperstein, Director of the Religious Action Center of Reform Judaism

15.3a Ectoparasitic Infections

An ectoparasite is a parasite that lives on or in the skin, but not within the body of the host. Pubic lice and scabies are common, sexually-transmissible ectoparasites and are found throughout the world.

Pubic Lice

Pubic lice (*pediculosis pubis*), also called "crabs," are parasitic insects. They attach themselves to the base of coarse pubic hair but may also be found on other coarse hair of the body, such as hair on the legs, armpits, mustache, beard, eyebrows, or eyelashes. (Lice found on the head are head lice, not pubic lice.) They bite the skin, causing severe itching, to feed on blood. Crawling lice may be observed although it is hard to see them because they move quickly from light. Nits (lice eggs) may be visible. An infected person transmits pubic lice most often through sexual contact. Clothing, towels, and bedding may harbor the creatures, but infestation is rarely spread this way. Sitting on a toilet seat does not spread lice, as they are unable to hold onto smooth surfaces. An infestation is most effectively treated with a pediculicide (lice-killing agent), usually a cream that is applied to the affected area and then washed off after 10 minutes. The CDC reports that pediculicide resistance is widespread and increasing. If the recommended treatment is ineffective, others should be tried. An infected person should notify sexual partners and should not have sexual contact until treatment is complete. Those with pubic lice should be screened for other STIs (Centers for Disease Control and Prevention, 2010c).

Scabies

Scabies results from a microscopic mite, *Sarcoptes scabiei*, that penetrates the skin and lays eggs. The larvae of these eggs burrow tunnels under the skin and cause intense itching. They may cause skin rash, burrows, or pimple-like irritations between the fingers and in skin folds of the wrist, elbow, knee, penis, breast, or shoulder blades. Because the itching is intense, especially at night, scabies sufferers tend to scratch the affected area, which may result in sores on the body that may become infected. Scabies

Pubic lice
Parasitic insects found in coarse body hair of humans, causing itching; also known as "crabs"

Scabies
Infestation of the skin by microscopic mites that causes intense itching

is spread by direct, prolonged skin-to-skin contact with an infested person (not a quick handshake or hug). In addition, it is easily spread to sexual partners and household members through clothing, towels, and bedding. Institutions such as nursing homes, extended-care facilities, and prisons are often sites of scabies outbreaks since it can spread rapidly under crowed conditions where skin-to-skin contact is frequent. Several prescription lotions are available to treat scabies, but no "over-the-counter" products have been proven to be effective. Household members and/or sexual partners should also be treated to prevent reinfestation. Machine-washing in hot water and drying on the hottest temperature of all bedding, clothing, and towels is advised (Centers for Disease Control and Prevention, 2010b).

15.3b Bacterial Infections

STIs caused by bacteria and protozoa can generally be cured through treatment with antibiotics.

Gonorrhea

Also known as "the clap," "the whites," "morning drop," and "the drip," **gonorrhea** is a bacterial infection. In 2011, 321,849 cases of gonorrhea were reported. However, the CDC estimates that less than half of the actual cases are detected and reported. In the U.S., the highest reported rates of infection are among sexually active teenagers, young adults, and African Americans (Centers for Disease Control and Prevention, 2012e). Individuals most often contract gonorrhea through sexual contact with the penis, vagina, mouth, or anus of an infected partner. Gonococci cannot live long outside the human body. Even though these bacteria can be cultured from a toilet seat, there are no documented cases of gonorrhea being transmitted in any way other than intimate physical contact or perinatally from mother to baby during childbirth. These bacteria thrive in warm, moist cavities, including the urinary tract, cervix, rectum, mouth, and throat.

Although some infected men show no signs, about two-thirds of men exhibit symptoms between 1 and 14 days after infection. They produce a thick, white, yellow or green discharge from the penis and start to feel pain or discomfort during urination. They may also have swollen lymph glands in the groin and complain of testicular or scrotal pain. Most women with gonorrhea have no symptoms; when they do, however, the symptoms may include a discharge from the vagina, along with a burning sensation and sometimes bleeding between periods. Symptoms of rectal infection in both men and women can include anal itching, discharge, soreness, and bleeding or painful bowel movements. Usually, gonorrhea infections in the throat cause no symptoms (Centers for Disease Control and Prevention, 2012e).

Untreated gonorrhea can cause serious complications in both men and women. Often, a woman becomes aware of gonorrhea only after she feels extreme discomfort, which is usually a result of the untreated infection traveling up into her uterus and Fallopian tubes, resulting in pelvic inflammatory disease (PID). PID can lead to internal abscesses, chronic pelvic pain, infertility, and ectopic pregnancy. The major complication for men is epididymitis, which may be signaled by severe scrotal pain. This could result in abdominal pain, infertility, and erectile problems. Untreated gonorrhea can eventually spread to the blood causing disseminated gonococcal infection (DGI). DGI results in bone and joint disease and can be life-threatening. Untreated gonorrhea also increases a person's risk of acquiring or transmitting HIV (Centers for Disease Control and Prevention, 2012a).

Gonorrhea is treated with antibiotics. It is important to take medication as prescribed and to finish all medication. In 2013, the news media reported that a new

Gonorrhea
Bacterial infection that is sexually transmitted; also known as "the clap," "the drip," "the whites," and "morning drop"

super strain—H041—had been reported in Japan and would eventually threaten Americans. The CDC quickly denied these claims, reporting that no cases of this superbug were ever reported in the U.S. and that the Japan case was an isolated incident. However, the CDC warns that gonorrhea has progressively developed resistance to the antibiotics typically used to treat it, recommends continuous evaluation of gonococcal antibiotic resistance, and encourages research and development of new treatment regimens for gonorrhea (Centers for Disease Control and Prevention, 2013b).

Syphilis

Syphilis is a sexually transmitted infection caused by bacteria. From 1990–2000 the rate of syphilis declined 89.7%, with the 2000 rate being the lowest reported since reporting began in 1941. However, the rate increased annually from 2000–2009, before decreasing in 2010. Overall increases in rates occurred only among men, particularly among men who have sex with men (MSM). After an 18% increase in the rate of congenital syphilis (2006–2008), the rate has decreased in all the years since (Centers for Disease Control and Prevention, 2013a).

Syphilis is transmitted through kissing or having genital contact with an infected individual. The spirochete bacteria enter the body through mucous membranes that line various body openings, such as the inside of the cheek, the vagina, and the urethra of the penis. Syphilis can also be transmitted from an infected pregnant woman to her unborn baby (congenital syphilis).

Syphilis progresses through identifiable stages. Each of these stages—primary, secondary, latent, and tertiary—involves different symptoms. In stage one (primary stage syphilis), a small sore or chancre appears at the site of infection between 10–90 days after exposure. The chancre, which appears on the man's penis, in the labia or cervix of the woman, or in either partner's mouth or rectum, neither hurts nor itches— and if left untreated will disappear in 3 to 5 weeks. This is one of the tricky aspects of syphilis because the disappearance leads infected people to believe that they are cured. In reality, the disease is still present and doing great harm, even though there are no visible symptoms. Because the chancre is painless and often occurs internally in women, it is far more likely to remain undetected in women than in men.

During the second stage (secondary stage syphilis), beginning from 2 to 12 weeks after the chancre has disappeared, other signs of syphilis may become evident, including a rash over the entire body or on the hands or feet. Syphilis has been called "the great imitator" because it mimics so many other diseases (mononucleosis, cancer, and psoriasis, for example). Welts and swelling of the lymph nodes can also occur, as well as fever, headaches, sore throat, and hair loss. Whatever the symptoms, they too will disappear without treatment, perhaps causing the person to again believe that nothing is wrong.

Following the secondary stage is the latency stage, during which there are no symptoms and the person is not infectious. However, the spirochetes are still in the body and can attack any organ at any time.

Tertiary syphilis is quite uncommon today, but this third stage can cause serious disability or even death. Heart disease, blindness, brain damage, loss of bowel and bladder control, difficulty walking, and erectile dysfunction can result. Complications may not begin until 15 to 30 years after initial infection.

It is important to identify and treat syphilis; if left untreated, it can cause significant health complications and facilitate the transmission of HIV infection (Centers for Disease Control and Prevention, 2012a). Treatment for syphilis is similar to that for gonorrhea. Penicillin or other antibiotics are effective. Infected persons treated in the early stages can be completely cured with no ill effects. If the syphilis has progressed into the tertiary stage, however, damage that has been done cannot be repaired.

Syphilis
Sexually transmitted (or congenital) infection caused by a spirochete (Treponema pallidum) that if untreated, can progress to a systemic infection through three stages and be fatal

Chlamydia

Chlamydia (clah-MID-ee-uh), is a common STI caused by infection with the *Chlamydia trachomatis* bacterium. Since 1994, it has been the most frequently reported STI in the United States with an estimated 2.86 million new infections occurring, annually (Centers for Disease Control and Prevention, 2012a).

Chlamydia is easily transmitted directly from person to person through sexual contact with the penis, vagina, mouth, or anus of an infected partner. The microorganisms are found most often in the urethra of men; the cervix, uterus, and Fallopian tubes of women; and in the rectum of both women and men. Genital-to-eye transmission of the bacteria can also occur. If a person with a genital chlamydia infection rubs his or her eye (or touches the eye of a partner) after touching his or her infected genitals, the bacteria can be transferred to the eye (and vice versa). In addition, an infant can get chlamydia while passing through the cervix of its infected mother during delivery.

While any sexually active person can contract chlamydia, those most at risk are adolescents and young adults ages 14–24, men who have sex with men, and non-Hispanic blacks. Among sexually active females aged 14–19 years, chlamydia prevalence is 6.8% overall (Center for Disease Control and Prevention, 2011a).

Chlamydia rarely shows obvious symptoms, which accounts for it being known as "the silent disease." When men have symptoms, they usually have urethritis (inflammation of the urethra), discharge, painful urination, and testicular pain and swelling. In women, early symptoms may include abnormal vaginal discharge, frequent urge to urinate, and a burning sensation when urinating. Left untreated, chlamydia can spread to the fallopian tubes and can lead to pelvic inflammatory disease, sterility, arthritis, blindness, miscarriage, and premature birth. Worldwide, 10–15% of women with untreated chlamydial infection develop symptomatic pelvic inflammatory disease (PID), and about 10–15% of clinical PID cases lead to infertility. Over 40% of ectopic (tubal) pregnancies are caused by chlamydia (Center for Disease Control and Prevention, 2011a).

Chlamydia can be effectively treated with antibiotics, especially with early and uncomplicated infections.

Nongonococcal Urethritis

Nongonococcal urethritis (NGU) is an infection of the urethra—the tube that carries urine from the bladder. Organisms that cause nongonococcal urethritis are transmitted through sexual contact and from mother to newborn. Several different sexually transmitted organisms cause NGU. The most common and most serious organism that causes NGU is chlamydia.

Because individuals with NGU are often asymptomatic, they unknowingly transmit infection to their partners. In men, symptoms of NGU include penile discharge, burning during urination, and burning or itching around the opening of the penis. Some men experience no symptoms or have symptoms so mild that they go unnoticed. In women, symptoms of NGU may include vaginal discharge, burning during urination, abdominal pain, bleeding between periods, and fever. Many infected women show no symptoms.

Once identified, NGU is treated with tetracycline or other antibiotics. Even when symptoms are mild or nonexistent, untreated NGU can cause damage to the reproductive organs and lead to infertility; result in miscarriages; and cause eye, ear, and lung infections in newborns.

Chlamydia
Common sexually transmitted infection caused by the microorganism chlamydia trachomatis, often asymptomatic, and therefore known as "the silent disease"

Nongonococcal urethritis
Infection of the urethra—the tube that carries urine from the bladder

Vaginitis

Three types of **vaginitis**, or vaginal infection, include trichomoniasis, Gardnerella, and candidiasis. Most women get vaginitis at some time in their lives, and many do not develop it from sexual contact. It can be caused by anything that upsets the balance of vaginal microflora, including illness, antibiotics, or overgrowth of one organism. It may be the result of bacteria from the rectum being transferred to the vagina. This can result from improper hygiene, anal intercourse, manipulation combined with vaginal intercourse, or manipulation. Vaginal infection may also result from foreign objects, such as tampons and diaphragms, being left in the vagina too long.

Although some infected women show no symptoms, trichomoniasis is usually characterized by a foul-smelling, thin, frothy discharge that may be green, yellow, gray, or white and causes an irritating rash in the vulva and painful intercourse if left untreated. Antibiotics, such as metronidazole (Flagyl), are usually effective in treating trichomoniasis. When taking Flagyl, patients need to be aware of its nausea-inducing effect when combined with alcohol. Because the partner may harbor trichomoniasis organisms without symptoms, both the woman and her sexual partner should be treated.

Gardnerella may not cause symptoms or may result in a profuse discharge and a "fishy" odor. This organism (bacterium) is quite common. Estimates of prevalence of bacterial vaginosis range from 5% in college students up to 60% in STI clinics. It may also be treated with Flagyl, and partners should be treated.

The most common cause of vulvitis (irritation of the vulva) is **candidiasis**, also known as "monilia" and "yeast infection." Candidiasis tends to occur in women during pregnancy, when they are on oral contraceptives, or when they have poor resistance to disease. Symptoms of candidiasis include vaginal irritation, itching, thick cottage-cheese-like discharge, and pain during intercourse. Treatment involves inserting anti-fungal suppositories or creams into the vagina. Antibiotics are not effective because candida is a genus of yeasts, not bacteria. This type of infection can spread to a partner, so it is important for both the identified patient and the sexual partner to be treated.

Chancroid

Also known as "soft chancre," chancroid is most common in tropical countries. In the United States, chancroid is predominantly seen among immigrants or U.S. citizens who travel to developing countries. This STI is more common among men. Chancroid is transmitted through either sexual contact with the chancroid ulcer or discharge from infected local lymph glands. Two to five days after exposure, a small papule forms at the site of contact. This lesion develops into an ulcer that exudes pus, bleeds easily, and is very painful.

15.3c Viral Infections

Treatment for viral STIs is palliative (may relieve symptoms or slow down the disease progression, but does not cure the disease). The course of viral infections may include latent periods (times with no outward symptoms), but the symptoms may reappear.

Herpes

The term *herpes* refers to more than 50 related viruses (including the viruses that cause infectious mononucleosis, chickenpox, and shingles). One type of herpes virus is **herpes simplex virus type 2 (HSV-2)**, also known as **genital herpes**. Another type of herpes, known as **herpes simplex virus type 1 (HSV-1)**, is usually associated with fever blisters around the mouth (oral-facial lesions). **Oral herpes** is very commonplace and is usually a benign infection. Although researchers estimate that

Vaginitis
Infection of the vagina

Candidiasis
Vaginal yeast infection that tends to occur in women during pregnancy, when they are on oral contraceptives, or when they have poor resistance to infection

Herpes simplex virus type 2 (HSV-2)
See Genital herpes

Genital herpes
Viral infection that may cause blistering, typically of the genitals, and may also infect the lips, mouth, and eyes

Herpes simplex virus type 1 (HSV-1)
Viral infection that may cause blistering, typically of the lips and mouth, and may also infect the genitals

Oral herpes
Sores of the lip and mouth, often caused by herpes simplex virus type I, but can also be caused by herpes simplex virus type II

66% of people over the age of 12 are infected with HSV-1, only about one-third of those have had flare-ups with visible cold sores. Although the two types of HSV have sites of preference, HSV-1 also can infect the genitals, and HSV-2 can result in facial cold sores. In fact, HSV-1 is becoming an increasingly common cause of genital infections, especially in adolescents. In young women, HSV-1 infections occur three times more often as genital rather than oral infections (Bernstein, et al., 2012).

The herpes virus is spread by direct skin-to-skin contact, such as kissing and oral, vaginal, or anal sex with an infected individual. Pregnant women can transmit the herpes virus to their newborn infants, most often during delivery. Fortunately, this type of transmission is rare in the U.S. Herpes may also be spread from one part of the body to another by touching the infected area and then touching another area of the body. For example, touching a herpes infection can allow the virus to spread to a finger that has a cut or abrasion. This most often occurs during an initial outbreak. Although this type of transmission is not common, it is a good idea to avoid touching HSV lesions and avoid biting your nails if you have oral-facial herpes.

Some people believe that herpes can be spread only when there are obvious signs or symptoms of the infection. However, herpes may be active without causing signs or symptoms. Herpes is often transmitted by people who are unaware that they are infected and by people who do not realize that their herpes infection is in its active phase.

When a person is first infected with herpes, symptoms usually appear within 2 weeks after exposure. The initial symptoms of oral herpes infection often include small pimples or blisters ("cold sores" or "fever blisters") on the mouth or face. Herpes may produce sores in the genital areas of women and men, and skin lesions may appear on the thigh or buttocks. These sores, resembling blisters or pimples, eventually crust over and scab. In the 2 to 4 weeks herpes sores need to heal, some people experience a second outbreak of lesions, and some will have flu-like symptoms including fever, aches, and swollen glands. Primary infections may be treated with acyclovir.

After the symptoms of genital herpes subside (the sores dry up, scab over, and disappear, and the infected person feels well again), the virus settles in the nerve cells in the spinal column. HSV-2 causes repeated outbreaks in about one-third of those who are infected. Stress, menstruation, sunburn, fatigue, and the presence of other infections seem to be related.

While researchers are making progress toward developing vaccines to prevent herpes infection, because of the HSV's complicated lifecycle and unique way of spreading from cell to cell, an effective vaccine remains elusive (Coleman & Shukla, 2013). Pregnant women with herpes outbreaks at the time of delivery can have cesarean deliveries to prevent exposure of newborns to the herpes virus.

Human Papillomavirus (HPV)

All warts on any part of the body are caused by one of the 120 strains of the **human papillomavirus (HPV)**. More than a dozen of the HPV types can cause warts in the skin around the vulva, cervix, penis, or anus (**genital warts**), or more subtle signs of infection in the genital tract. HPV can be transmitted through vaginal or anal intercourse and through fellatio and cunnilingus. It is also possible for HPV to be transmitted from an infected pregnant woman to her infant.

HPV can remain inactive for months or years before any obvious signs of infection appear. Many strains of HPV infection are asymptomatic. Some strains (primarily 6 and 11) cause small to large warts or bump-like growths to appear within 3 to 6 months after exposure. Warts may be pink or red and may appear in clusters or alone. In women, genital warts most commonly develop on the vulva, in the vagina, or on the cervix. They can also appear on or near the anus. In men, the warts appear most often on the penis, but can appear on the scrotum, the anus, or within the rectum. Although rare,

Human papillomavirus (HPV)
Sexually transmitted viral infection that may produce genital warts

Genital warts
See Human papillomavirus

HPV also can produce warts around the mouths of both sexes. Genital warts pose no health threat to you or your partner but can be treated by several methods, depending on the number of warts and their location, the availability of equipment, the training of healthcare providers, and the preferences of the patient. Treatment options for removing warts include cryotherapy (freezing), surgical removal, laser surgery, cauterization (burning), and topical application of chemicals such as podophyllin.

High-risk types of HPV can cause normal cells in the body to turn abnormal, which can lead to cancer. In recent years, HPV has also been recognized as one of the primary causes of a subset of head and neck cancers among nonsmokers and nondrinkers (Berthet, Bertolus, Gessain, & Goudot, 2012; Bertolus, Goudot, Gessain, & Berthet, 2012; Chen, Yn, Chang, Fu, Nieh, & Lin, 2012).

While in 90% of cases the body's immune system clears HPV within 2 years, there is no way to determine which people who contract HPV will eventually develop health problems from it. Consequently, vaccines play an important role in reducing the rate, but serious health complications can develop the rate of HPV infection.

In June 2006, the U.S. Food and Drug Administration (FDA) approved a vaccine for females ages 9–26 years that prevents the types of human papillomavirus (HPV) infections that cause most cases of cervical cancer (Markowitz, Dunne, Saraiva, Lawson, Chesson, & Unger, 2007). There has been widespread marketing of the HPV vaccine warning young women that HPV causes cancer. However, a recent study found that it is the threat of contracting genital warts, and not the threat of cancer, that motivates young women to get the vaccine (Krieger & Sarge, 2013). Further, young females' decisions to become vaccinated largely depend on the extent to which their parents support HPV vaccination (Dempsey, Abraham, Dalton, & Ruffin, 2009). Unfortunately, the United States lags behind many other industrialized countries regarding the number of females who receive the vaccine. In 2008, fewer than 20% of adolescent females were vaccinated against HPV, as compared to countries such as Australia and the United Kingdom where 75–80% of 12- to 13-year-old girls have been vaccinated. Because of the risk of penile, anal, and oral cancers posed by HPV in men, the CDC now recommends the HPV vaccine for males between the ages of 11 and 21 (Centers for Disease Control and Prevention, 2011c).

Hepatitis B

Hepatitis B (HBV) is an inflammatory disease of the liver caused by a virus. Other forms of hepatitis viruses include types A, C, D, and E. HBV is most often transmitted through vaginal, oral, or anal sexual contact with an infected individual. Infection may also occur from transfusions of contaminated blood or from sharing contaminated personal items, such as razors or needles (used for steroid injections, drug use, body piercing, or tattoos). Pregnant women may also transmit hepatitis B to their newborns.

The symptoms of HBV infection, which take 2 to 6 months to appear, include skin rash, muscle and joint pain, fatigue, loss of appetite, nausea and vomiting, headache, fever, dark urine, jaundice, and liver enlargement and tenderness. There is no treatment to cure hepatitis B; people usually recover naturally and develop immunity to future infection. While the disease is running its course, healthcare professionals recommend rest, a high-protein diet with lots of fluids, and the avoidance of alcohol and drugs that may stress the liver. As many as 10% of those infected with hepatitis B become carriers of the virus for several years or even over their lifetime. Some hepatitis B infections lead to cirrhosis of the liver or liver cancer.

Until the recent availability of a new HPV vaccine to prevent cervical cancer, the only effective vaccine for prevention of an STI was the hepatitis B vaccine. The CDC recommends that all adolescents and young adults receive a hepatitis B vaccination. The vaccine is given in the arm in three separate doses.

Hepatitis B
Inflammatory disease of the liver caused by a virus

15.4 HIV and AIDS

Although HIV/AIDS is a viral infection, a separate section is devoted to HIV/AIDS because of its serious global impact.

The global HIV/AIDS epidemic is an unprecedented crisis that requires an unprecedented response. In particular it requires solidarity—between the healthy and the sick, between rich and poor, and above all, between richer and poorer nations. We have 30 million orphans already. How many more do we have to get, to wake up?

Kofi Annan, former UN Secretary General

15.4a Definitions of HIV and AIDS

Human immunodeficiency virus (HIV) attacks the white blood cells (T-lymphocytes) in human blood and causes **acquired immunodeficiency syndrome (AIDS)**. AIDS is characterized by a breakdown of the body's immune system that makes individuals vulnerable to a variety of opportunistic diseases. Before 1993, a diagnosis of AIDS was made only when an HIV-infected individual developed one of more than 20 serious illnesses—such as pneumocystis carinii pneumonia, pulmonary tuberculosis, cervical cancer, or Kaposi's sarcoma (a form of cancer)—as delineated by the Centers for Disease Control and Prevention (CDC). Since 1993, the definition of AIDS has been expanded to include anyone with HIV whose immune system is severely impaired, as indicated by a T-cell (or CD4 cell) count of less than 200 cells per cubic millimeter of blood. T-cell counts in healthy people not infected with HIV range from 800 to 1,200 per cubic millimeter of blood.

15.4b Transmission

The human immunodeficiency virus can be transmitted in various ways including:

1. *Sexual contact*   HIV is found in several body fluids of infected individuals, including blood, semen, and possibly vaginal secretions. During sexual contact (anal, vaginal, or oral) with an infected individual, the virus may enter a person's bloodstream through broken skin or mucous membranes (wet, thin body tissue, as in the mouth, eyes, nose, vagina, rectum, and opening of the penis). Globally, 85% of all HIV infections are acquired through heterosexual contact (Stanberry & Rosenthal, 2013).

2. *Intravenous drug use*   Drug users who are infected with HIV can transmit the virus to other drug users with whom they share needles, syringes, and other drug-related implements. This transmission method accounts for an increasing proportion of new HIV infections in Eastern Europe, South America and Asia.

3. *Blood transfusion*   HIV can be transmitted through HIV-infected blood or blood products. Currently, all blood donors are screened, and blood is not accepted from high-risk individuals. The U.S. blood supply is considered among the world's safest supplies. Blood that is accepted from donors is tested (began in 1985) for the presence of HIV.

4. *Mother-child transmission of HIV*   A pregnant woman infected with HIV can infect her unborn child in utero, during labor, and via breastfeeding. However, this risk is profoundly decreased if the mother receives anti-HIV treatment during pregnancy. Although HIV can be transmitted through breast-feeding, formula feeding reduces this risk. However, this solution can be problematic in developing countries in which there are problems obtaining adequate supplies of formula and clean water.

5. *Organ or tissue transplants and donor semen*   Receiving transplant organs and tissues, as well as receiving semen for artificial insemination, could involve risk of contracting HIV if the donors have not been tested for HIV. Such testing

Human immunodeficiency virus (HIV)
Virus that attacks the immune system and may lead to AIDS

Acquired immunodeficiency syndrome (AIDS)
Last stage of HIV infection in which the immune system of a person's body is so weakened that it becomes vulnerable to infection and disease (opportunistic infections)

is essential, and recipients should insist on knowing the HIV status of the organ, tissue, or semen donor.

6. *Occupational transmission of HIV*   Certain occupational workers regularly come into contact with human blood and are, therefore, susceptible to occupational transmission of HIV. Health-care workers (such as nurses and physicians), laboratory technicians, morgue technicians, rescue workers, dentists, police officers, prison guards, and other individuals who are likely to come into contact with bleeding individuals should use protection, such as latex gloves, before making physical contact with an injured or bleeding individual. Laypersons also should use latex gloves when coming into contact with another person's blood, and these gloves should be part of every first-aid kit.

HIV cannot be transmitted from casual contact (shaking hands, hugging, casual kissing) or from contact with objects in homes or in public settings (toilet seats, water fountains, door knobs, dishes, drinking glasses, or food). Pets, animal bites, or insect bites do not transmit HIV. There has been no documented HIV transmission during sports participation.

> *When a friend tells you he or she has AIDS, the appropriate first reaction is an embrace, not a shudder.*
>
> Mary Catherine Bateson, Richard Goldsby

15.4c Symptoms

HIV/AIDS is known as a "spectrum illness" in that, although everyone infected with HIV is exposed to the same virus, he or she may have different symptoms at different stages. Some HIV-infected individuals display no symptoms at all for many years after exposure. Unless they are tested for HIV, many HIV-infected individuals don't know they are infected. When symptoms do appear, they may include rapid loss of weight, dry cough, recurrent fever or heavy night sweats, profound and unexplained fatigue, swollen lymph glands (in the armpits, groin, or neck), oral thrush (a white coating or spotting in the tongue, mouth, or throat), skin blotches (red, brown, pink, or purple), depression, memory problems, or other neurological dysfunctions.

If full-blown AIDS develops, severe immune system breakdown can lead to the onset of illnesses such as pneumocystis carinii pneumonia, pulmonary tuberculosis, cervical cancer, and Kaposi's sarcoma. A diagnosis of AIDS is made by a healthcare professional based on specific criteria established by the Centers for Disease Control and Prevention.

No person should assume that if he or she has some of these symptoms he or she is infected with HIV, as other illnesses cause them as well. The only way to know if one is infected with HIV is to be specifically tested for it. The standard screening test for detecting HIV is the antibody screening test, which tests for the antibodies that your body makes against HIV. It is usually performed in a clinical setting on blood drawn from a vein. The newest tests can find HIV as soon as 3 weeks after exposure to the virus. Rapid tests and ones using oral fluid (not saliva) can also be performed; however, the rapid tests may give false-negative results, and the oral fluid tests take longer to provide results. Any test that is positive needs a follow-up test to confirm results. Home testing kits may be purchased at pharmacies and on the Internet. Similar to other forms of testing, a positive result is confirmed with a follow-up test. Some rapid screening tests are available that offer results in 20–60 minutes; however, up to 1 in 12 people may test false-negative with these tests (Centers for Disease Control and Prevention, 2010a).

15.4d Treatment

Presently, there is no cure for HIV/AIDS. However, the advent of the potent combination antiretroviral therapy (ART), which uses a "cocktail" of three or more antiretroviral drugs, has changed the course of the HIV epidemic. While these drugs do not cure HIV, they do slow the progression of the disease and increase survival rates in patients. Also, early initiation of ART can reduce the risk of an infected partner transmitting HIV to an uninfected, heterosexual partner by 96% (Cohen, et al., 2011).

There are currently five different "classes" of HIV drugs. Each class of drug attacks the virus at different points in its life cycle, preventing it from replicating in the body. Patients are typically prescribed three drugs from two different classes:

- Nucleoside/nucleotide reverse transcriptase inhibitors (NRTIs) and Non-nucleoside reverse transcriptase inhibitors (NNRTIs), which both use different mechanisms to prevent HIV from making copies of its own DNA

- Protease inhibitors (PIs), which block the enzymes that HIV needs to cut long strands of genetic material into smaller functional pieces needed to replicate its DNA

- Entry/fusion inhibitors which block HIV from entering cells in the first place

- Integrase inhibitors which block enzymes from allowing HIV to integrate its genetic material into the genetic material of a person's cells

This combination approach of physicians prescribing three drugs from two classes is referred to as "cocktail" therapy, or a regimen known as **highly active antiretroviral therapy (HAART)**. This type of therapy has extended the life of an HIV-infected person by substantially restoring immune function. The downside of HAART therapy is that it may be so successful that HIV/AIDS may no longer be so feared as to induce safe sex behavior.

Due to the serious health consequences of AIDS, STI prevention and control efforts in recent years have largely focused on preventing transmission of HIV. However, given the potentially serious health consequences of other STIs—including the increased susceptibility to HIV infection—prevention and control of all STIs are warranted.

The risk of HIV transmission via semen is increased by concurrent infection with a sexually transmitted infection. Ulcerations, lesions, or sores caused by many sexually transmitted infections provide a site for HIV to enter the bloodstream. Because STIs facilitate transmission of HIV, efforts to prevent, detect, and treat STIs may help reduce HIV transmission.

Treatment for HIV and AIDS also includes adopting lifestyle habits that promote well-being: a balanced diet, ample rest, regular exercise, and relaxation. It is also important for persons with HIV/AIDS to avoid stressors on the immune system, such as tobacco, recreational drugs, and other STIs. Establishing a supportive network of family and friends is also essential in managing the stress of having HIV/AIDS.

Highly active antiretroviral therapy (HAART)
Combination of drugs an HIV-infected person takes to treat the virus; also known as "cocktail therapy"

15.4e Prevention and Control

It is no exaggeration to say that prevention of HIV promotes sexual health, saves lives, and averts devastating social and economic costs to people and countries. Currently, there is no vaccine to prevent HIV infection. Education is paramount.

History will judge us on how we respond to the AIDS emergency in Africa—whether we stood around with watering cans and watched while a whole continent burst into flames, or not.

Bono, AIDS activist and musician

Efforts to prevent and control STIs involve modifying high-risk behaviors, delivering public and private sexual healthcare, reducing the sharing of potentially infected needles, using computer technology, providing educational interventions, and initiating community development. In addition, significant political and financial commitment will be required. Political commitment is needed, to reduce barriers to implement preventive efforts and to reduce stigma so that people will seek counseling, testing, and treatment.

15.5 Protecting Yourself from STIs

According to the CDC (Centers for Disease Control and Prevention, 2012e), the most effective STI prevention strategies are as follows:

- Abstaining from sex
- Reducing the number of sexual partners and mutual monogamy
- Using condoms, consistently and correctly
- Getting available vaccines
- Screening for STIs, and treating promptly if infected

15.5a Abstaining from Sex

Abstinence from sexual intercourse (including oral sex) does provide protection from most STIs. However, certain diseases, such as herpes and HPV, can be transmitted from any sexual contact. A bigger problem with abstinence as a STI protection strategy is that it's just not a popular practice. Over half of U.S. college students are sexually active, and 65% of college students in the annual National College Health Assessment (ACHA, 2013) report that they have engaged in vaginal intercourse.

Abstinent couples can achieve physical intimacy and pleasure by practicing **outercourse**—activities that do not involve exposing a partner to blood, semen, or vaginal secretions. Outercourse includes hugging, cuddling, masturbating, fantasizing, massaging, and rubbing body to body while clothed.

15.5b Reducing the Number of Sexual Partners and Mutual Monogamy

Individuals (including virgins) who engage in outercourse may reduce their risks of acquiring an STI by having sexual contact only with one partner who is not infected, who is also monogamous, and who does not inject drugs. A commitment to **mutual monogamy** is key to reducing STI risk. Mutual monogamy means that both partners agree to be sexually active only with each other. Rather than rushing into sexual relationships, allow time to build trusting, caring, and honest relationships in which you can share your sexual histories. Also, carefully inspect your partner's genitals, as well as your own, before sexual contact. Although some STIs produce no visible signs, it is possible to see herpes blisters, chancres, genital warts, and rashes. If you notice anything unusual about your partner's genitals (or your own), abstain from sexual contact and seek a medical examination. Also, be aware that even "monogamous" partners cheat. Vail-Smith and colleagues (2010) found that 27.2% of the males and 19.8% of the females out of 1,341 undergraduates reported having oral, vaginal, or anal sex outside of a relationship that their partner considered monogamous.

Outercourse
Sexual activities that do not involve exposing a partner to blood, semen, or vaginal secretions

Mutual monogamy
A relationship in which both partners agree to be sexually faithful to each other

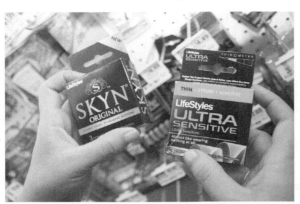

Females are now taking responsibility for their own safety.
Source: Chelsea Curry

15.5c Using Condoms Consistently and Effectively

Studies have shown that consistent, correct condom use reduces the overall risk of acquiring and transmitting HIV and other STIs. Laboratory studies have conclusively demonstrated that latex condoms provide an essentially impermeable barrier to STI pathogens (Centers for Disease Control and Prevention, 2013a). However, even when a condom is used, it does not offer a 100% guarantee against the transmission of STIs for a variety of reasons. First, condoms are not always used consistently and correctly. Using a condom "most of the time" or "almost always" does not provide the same protection as using one every time a person engages in vaginal or anal intercourse or fellatio. It is also important to use a condom correctly (see Table 15-4 on correct condom use). Even when a condom is used correctly, breakage and slippage may still occur.

TABLE **15-4**	Correct Condom Use
1. Use only condoms that are made in the United States or Japan. Condoms that are made in other countries may not have been tested for effectiveness.
2. Check the expiration date of the condom. Do not use condoms that have passed the expiration date.
3. Store condoms in a cool, dry place. Do not keep condoms in a wallet or car, where they can become hot. Do not keep them in the refrigerator.
4. Use only latex or polyurethane condoms for fellatio and vaginal or anal intercourse. A natural, lambskin condom is an ineffective barrier against HIV.
5. Use condoms with a reservoir tip, or pinch 1/2 inch at the tip of the condom to collect the semen.
6. Unroll the condom slowly and carefully onto the erect penis before the first contact of penis to vagina, anus, or mouth.
7. If the penis has a foreskin, put the condom on with the foreskin pushed back. When the shaft is covered, push the foreskin toward the top of the penis to allow the foreskin to move without breaking the condom.
8. Make sure there is no air trapped inside the condom. (If there is, it could cause breakage.) Have a spare condom available in case you find a tear or a hole in the one you are using.
9. Use only water-based lubricants, such as K-Y Jelly or other personal lubricants. Products containing oil—such as Vaseline, baby oil, and lotions—can destroy latex products.
10. Remove the penis from the partner immediately after ejaculation, before the penis loses its erection. Hold the condom securely on the base of the penis while withdrawing it from the partner, and be careful not to spill the contents.
11. Never reuse a condom.

Source: Planned Parenthood (2013). How do I use condoms? Retrieved from http://www.plannedparenthood.org/health-topics/birth-control/condom-10187.htm

Finally, condoms do not protect against all STIs because some STI infections, such as HPV and herpes, can occur on the testicles and vulva, around the anus, and in other areas that are not protected by a condom. While not providing full protection, condom use may reduce the risk for HPV and HPV-associated diseases such as genital warts and cervical cancer (Centers for Disease Control and Prevention, 2013a).

Research on condom use has identified a number of factors that influence whether an individual uses condoms. These factors include the following:

- Perceived susceptibility (the degree to which an individual feels he or she is at risk of being infected with an STI)
- Perceived seriousness of STIs (the degree to which an individual views STIs as having severe or serious consequences)
- Belief that using condoms will reduce the risk of STIs
- Belief that the benefits of using condoms will outweigh any of the costs (inconvenience, decreased pleasure, expense, and so on)
- Sense of *self-efficacy* regarding condom use; that is, the person's belief that he or she has the skills and abilities necessary to use condoms in a variety of circumstances in the face of various obstacles, such as a reluctant or unwilling partner
- A person's intention to use condoms
- A person's perception of the degree to which social norms expect condom use

Self-Assessment 15-1 to follow provides a way for you to assess your attitudes toward condoms.

SELF-ASSESSMENT 15-1: THE UCLA MULTIDIMENSIONAL CONDOM ATTITUDES SCALE

Directions:

Indicate your level of agreement with each of the following items by writing a number from 1 to 7 next to each item, based on the following answer key.

1	2	3	4	5	6	7
Very strongly Disagree	Strongly disagree	Disagree slightly	Neither agree nor disagree	Agree slightly	Strongly agree	Very strongly agree

Reliability and Effectiveness

1. ___ Condoms are an effective method of birth control.
2. ___ Condoms are an effective method of preventing the spread of AIDS and other sexually transmitted infections.
3. ___ I think condoms are an excellent means of contraception.
4.* ___ Condoms are unreliable.
5. ___ Condoms do not offer reliable protection.

Pleasure

6. ___ The use of condoms can make sex more stimulating.
7.* ___ Condoms ruin the sex act.
8.* ___ Condoms are uncomfortable for both partners.
9. ___ Condoms are a lot of fun.
10.* ___ Use of a condom is an interruption of foreplay.

Identity Stigma

11.* ___ Men who suggest using a condom are really boring.
12.* ___ If a couple is about to have sex and the man suggests using a condom, it is less likely that they will have sex.
13.* ___ Women think men who use condoms are jerks.
14.* ___ A woman who suggests using a condom does not trust her partner.

Embarrassment about Negotiation and Use

15.* ___ When I suggest using a condom, I am almost always embarrassed.
16.* ___ It is really hard to bring up the issue of using condoms with my partner.
17. ___ It is easy to suggest to my partner that we use a condom.
18. ___ I'm comfortable talking about condoms with my partner.
19.* ___ I never know what to say when my partner and I need to talk about condoms or other protection.

Embarrassment about Purchase

20.* ___ It is very embarrassing to buy condoms.
21.* ___ When I need condoms I often dread having to get them.
22. ___ I don't think that buying condoms is awkward.
23.* ___ It would be embarrassing to be seen buying condoms in a store.
24.* ___ I always feel really comfortable when I buy condoms.

Scoring

*Reverse-score the following items: 4, 7, 8, 10, 11, 12, 13, 14, 15, 16, 19, 20, 21, 23, and 24. To reverse-score, make the following changes in your answers: 1 = 7; 2 = 6; 3 = 5; 4 = 4 (no change); 5 = 3; 6 = 2; 7 = 1.

After reversing the scores of the items indicated, compute a mean (average) score for each of the scale's subsections. The higher the score, the more positive your attitudes toward condoms are. You might pencil your mean scores in the spaces provided and compare them with those obtained in a study of 239 students ages 15 to 35 (mean age = 19) (Helweg-Larsen & Collins, 1994).

Subsection	Mean Score	Men	Women
1. Reliability and Effectiveness (measures attitudes toward the reliability and effectiveness of condoms)		5.4	5.3
2. Pleasure (measures the pleasure associated with condom use)		4.1	4.3
3. Identity Stigma (measures the stigma attached to being a condom user)		5.6	6.2
4. Embarrassment about Negotiation and Use (measures the embarrassment associated with the negotiation and use of condoms)		4.8	4.8
5. Embarrassment about Purchase (measures the embarrassment associated with the purchase of condoms)		4.3	3.5*
*p is less than 0.05			

Discussion

After analyzing the scores of 239 students on the Multidimensional Condom Attitudes Scale, researchers found that overall, men were less embarrassed about purchasing condoms than women, whereas women were more positive about issues related to identity stigma (Helweg-Larsen & Collins, 1994).

Source: From "The UCLA Multidimensional Condom Attitudes Scale: Documenting the Complex Determinants of Condom Use in College Students," by M. Helweg-Larsen & B. E. Collins, 1994, *Health Psychology, 13*(3): 224–237. Copyright 1994 by the American Psychological Association. Reprinted by permission of the author.

One of the more controversial STI prevention strategies involves making condoms available to high school students. The Social Choices 15-1 section looks at this controversy.

Social Choices 15-1

Condom Availability in High Schools

Unprotected teenage sexual activity contributes to teenage pregnancy and the high rate of STIs among adolescents, who constitute 25% of the 12 million new STI cases each year. The average age that both women and men have their first sexual intercourse experience is 17 (Gardner, Martin, & Grooks-Gunn, 2012). Despite the proven effectiveness of condoms in preventing STIs and pregnancy, 40% of adolescents report that they engage in unprotected intercourse (Centers for Disease Control and Prevention, 2010e).

School programs that provide condoms are designed to reduce teenage pregnancy and the spread of STIs by increasing condom use; they do so by reducing teenagers' embarrassment when buying condoms, eliminating the cost, and improving access. These programs are reaching less than 40% of the students since only 39% of American high school students are taught how to correctly use a condom in their health classes (Centers for Disease Control and Prevention, 2010d).

Most schools in the U.S. do not make condoms available to students. Indeed, most schools do not provide comprehensive sex education: 37 states require that information on abstinence be provided, 18 states require instruction on the importance of engaging in sexual activity only within marriage, and only 13 states require that sex and HIV education programs are medically accurate. In addition, only 9 states require that programs provide instruction that is not biased against any race, sex, or ethnicity (Guttmacher Institute, 2012).

Why aren't responsible sex education programs widely implemented? Despite evidence to the contrary, some parents are afraid that increased condom availability will encourage students to be more sexually active. Parental opposition to school condom availability programs is in contrast to the recommendation of such organizations as The American School Health Association, the American College of Obstetricians and Gynecologists, the National Medical Association, and the National Institute of Medicine—that all support condoms being made available to adolescents as part of comprehensive school health and STI prevention programs.

At present, it is uncertain whether the public will demand, or even allow, public schools to implement this recommendation throughout the United States. Giving teenagers condoms contradicts moral values that are against nonmarital sexual relations. Evangelical religious groups disapprove of making condoms available and feel that an unwanted pregnancy or sexually transmitted infection is the "natural punishment" for engaging in this "sinful" behavior outside of marriage. In some states, there are legal restrictions against condom availability programs. Segments of the population, as well as powerful conservative groups such as the Family Research Council and Focus on the Family, strongly oppose school condom availability on the premise that giving young people condoms might seem to condone their sexual activities or encourage promiscuity.

Think About It

Take a moment to answer the following questions. Suppose you are responsible for deciding whether condoms should be available in the public school system your children are attending. What would you recommend and why? How would you respond to disagreements with your recommendation?

15.5d Getting Available Vaccines

Currently, there are effective vaccines available for only two STIs: Hepatitis B (HBV) and HPV. Research continues to discover vaccines for herpes and HIV, to date there have been no breakthroughs that are considered broadly useful (Cohen, 2010). The three-dose HBV vaccine is recommended for all children at birth and for all children and adolescents under age 19 who have not received it. The recommended age for the HPV vaccine for both males and females is 11–12 years, although it can be administered to children as young as age 9. What is important is that the vaccine be administered before exposure to the virus (Centers for Disease Control and Prevention, 2011c). At-risk adults should also be vaccinated.

I would like to see it that if you don't have your HPV vaccine, you can't start high school.
Juan Carlos speaking of high schools in Spain

15.5e Seeking STI Screening and Prompt Treatment

As mentioned previously, screening and prompt diagnoses and treatment of STIs are also major prevention strategies. A screening test, or a test used for screening purposes, is one that is applied to someone with no symptoms or signs of the disease being assessed. If the person has either symptoms or signs of a particular STI, the test is not a screening test but rather a diagnostic test. The CDC recommends annual chlamydia screening for sexually active women age 25 and under. Sexually active gay and bisexual men should be tested, at least annually, for HIV, syphilis, chlamydia, and gonorrhea. All Americans should be screened at least once for HIV (Centers for Disease Control and Prevention, 2010a).

Although symptoms may vary depending on the pathogen, the following are common to many STIs:

- urethral discharge
- genital ulcers
- inguinal (groin) swelling
- scrotal swelling
- vaginal discharge
- lower abdominal pain

It must be remembered that some STIs are asymptomatic and are, consequently, less likely to be diagnosed and potentially more likely to lead to long-term consequences. The Personal Choices 15-1 section is focused on whether you should be screened for STIs.

personal **choices**   *15-1*

Should You Be Screened for STIs?

The CDC offers the following guidelines for STI screening. Based on these guidelines, do you think you should be screened?

- All adults and adolescents should be tested at least once for HIV.
- Annual chlamydia screening for all sexually active women age 25 and under, as well as older women with risk factors such as new or multiple sex partners
- Yearly gonorrhea screening for at-risk, sexually active women (e.g., those with new or multiple sex partners, and women who live in communities with a high burden of disease)
- Syphilis, HIV, chlamydia, and hepatitis B screening for all pregnant women, and gonorrhea screening for at-risk pregnant women at the first prenatal visit, to protect the health of mothers and their infants
- Trichomoniasis screening should be conducted at least annually for all HIV-infected women.
- Screening should be done at least once a year for syphilis, chlamydia, gonorrhea, and HIV for all sexually active gay men, bisexual men, and other men who have sex with men (MSM). MSM who have multiple or anonymous partners should be screened more frequently for STIs (e.g., at 3 to 6 month intervals). In addition, MSM who participate in illicit drug use or whose sex partners participate in these activities should be screened more frequently.

Source: CDC (2013). Fact Sheet: Incidence, prevalence and cost of sexually transmitted infections in the United States. http://www.cdc.gov/std/stats/STI-Estimates-Fact-Sheet-Feb-2013.pdf

15.6 Accessing Sexual Health Services

Public clinics, agencies, health centers, and private healthcare providers provide sexual health services. In addition to screening, diagnostic testing, and STI treatment, sexual health services may perform the following functions:

- Identify persons who are unaware, misinformed, or in denial of their risks for HIV and other STIs and facilitate an accurate self-perception of risks.
- Teach clients how to reduce their risks of acquiring or transmitting an STI.
- Refer clients to resources that provide psychosocial support to facilitate desired behavior changes.
- Provide referrals to drug treatment services for clients whose substance abuse problems increase their STI risks.

This couple is in a relationship and want to be sure that they are "safe" for each other. They are at a clinic to be tested.
Source: Lizzie Scarboro

- Provide family planning information and referrals to women of childbearing ages, who are infected or at high risk for contracting HIV or other STIs.
- Provide referrals for any necessary medical and psychosocial services.
- Communicate to clients the responsibility to notify sex and needle-sharing partners.

Most public health departments, university and community health centers, and other agencies (such as Planned Parenthood) also provide condoms free of charge or at very low cost. Primary healthcare providers (pediatricians, family physicians, nurse practitioners, and physician assistants), in both public and private settings, can play an important role in preventing STI transmission.

Cost is one barrier to STI services; in addition, many individuals do not have easy access to sexual health services. To improve accessibility, more STI prevention and control programs need to be delivered through alternative approaches, such as school health programs, peer teen outreach, and mobile clinics. Stigma is also operative so norms need to change so that buying condoms, getting the HPV vaccine, and getting STI tested are normative and socially approved.

Chapter Summary

As more individuals have more sex with more partners, the risk of contracting a sexually transmitted infection increases. The physical, psychological, and economic effects of STIs can be dramatic; thus, individual and social efforts to prevent and treat STIs are warranted.

Sexually Transmitted Infections: An Overview

Sexually transmitted infections (STIs) are infections spread primarily through person-to-person sexual contact. There are more than 30 different sexually-transmissible bacteria, viruses, and parasites. Person-to-person sexual contact is the main mode of infection, with vaginal and anal intercourse providing the most efficient transmission; the infections can also be transmitted orally. Each year, approximately 20 million new sexually transmitted infections occur in the U.S. Researchers estimate that only the common cold infects more people than STIs. Persons most at risk for an STI have a high number of sexual partners or have sex with those who have had a high number of sexual partners, are adolescents and/or young adults, are female, use drugs, have been sexually abused, and are of minority status. Individuals also likely to become infected engage in s sexual behavior, such as unprotected anal and vaginal intercourse and sharing needles.

Sexually Transmitted Infections: A Pandemic

There are nearly 20 million new STI case diagnosed annually in the U.S., with HPV, trichomoniasis, and chlamydia accounting for 91% of these. Worldwide there are 33.3 million people living with HIV, with 2.6 million new infections each year.

Types of STIs

The main agents responsible for STIs are bacteria, protozoa, and viruses. STIs caused by bacteria and protozoa can generally be cured through treatment with antibiotics. Many STIs are asymptomatic, so regular screening is key to diagnosis and treatment. Treatment for viral STIs is palliative (may relieve symptoms or slow down the disease progression, but does not cure the disease).

HIV and AIDS

STIs are transmitted through sexual contact, intravenous drug use, blood transfusion, mother-child transmission of HIV, organ or tissue transplants, donor semen, and occupational transmission of HIV. Treatment for HIV and AIDS includes taking drugs as well as adopting lifestyle habits that promote well-being, such as eating a balanced diet and getting ample rest, regular exercise, and relaxation.

Protecting Yourself from STIs

Due to the serious fatal consequences of AIDS, STI prevention efforts in recent years have emphasized preventing transmission of HIV. However, given the potentially serious health consequences of other STIs—including the increased susceptibility to HIV infection—prevention and control of all STIs are warranted. The most reliable ways to avoid getting sexually transmitted infections are to reduce risky sexual contact and to avoid injecting illicit drugs.

Individuals (including virgins) who engage in outercourse may reduce their risks of acquiring an STI by abstaining from sex, reducing the number of sexual partners, consistently and correctly using condoms, getting available vaccines, and seeking STI screening and prompt treatment.

Accessing Sexual Health Services

Sexual health services—including screening, diagnostic testing, and STI treatment—are provided by public clinics, agencies, health centers, and private healthcare providers.

Web Links

American Social Health Association

http://www.ashastd.org

Centers for Disease Control and Prevention (CDC) (Sexually Transmitted Diseases)

http://www.cdc.gov/STD/

World Health Organization—Sexually Transmitted Infections

http://www.who.int/topics/sexually_transmitted_infections/en/

HIV/AIDS

American Foundation for AIDS Research (amfAR)

http://www.amfar.org

Joint United Nations Programme on HIV/AIDS

http://www.unaids.org

Medline on STDs

http://www.nlm.nih.gov/medlineplus/sexuallytransmitteddiseases.html

Key Terms

Acquired immunodeficiency syndrome (AIDS) 438

Asymptomatic 423

Candidiasis 435

Chlamydia 434

Genital herpes 435

Genital warts 436

Gonorrhea 432

Hepatitis B 437

Herpes simplex virus type 1 (HSV-1) 435

Herpes simplex virus type 2 (HSV-2) 435

Highly active antiretroviral therapy (HAART) 440

High risk group 426

Human immunodeficiency virus (HIV) 438

Human papillomavirus (HPV) 436

Mutual monogamy 441

Nongonococcal urethritis 434

Oral herpes 435

Outercourse 441

Pelvic inflammatory disease (PID) 429

Pubic lice 431

Scabies 431

Sexually transmitted infections (STIs) 422

Syphilis 433

Vaginitis 435

Additional study resources are available at www.BVTLab.com

> *There have been a number of press articles referring to San Diego Mayor Bob Filner
> and suggesting that he asked a woman to work without her panties.*
>
> Attorney Gloria Allred, representing Irene McCormack Jackson

Chapter Outline

Objectives

1. Know the definitions and prevalence of rape/
   sexual assault.
2. Explain the various theories of rape.
3. Review the consequences of rape and the
   treatment for rape survivors.
4. Describe the various strategies for the
   prevention of rape.
5. Discuss intrafamilial and extrafamilial child
   sexual abuse.
6. Know the consequences, treatment and
   prevention of child sexual abuse.
7. Review the definition, theories, and
   consequences of sexual harassment.

Source: Chelsea Curry

TRUTH OR FICTION

T/F   Of rapes, 75% to 95% are not reported.

T/F   In parts of India, men can rape, beat, and kill a woman with impunity.

T/F   In the U.S., about one in four women will experience rape.

T/F   Brother-sister incest is more damaging than father-daughter incest.

T/F   Some children can't remember sex abuse that happened.

Answers: 1. T 2. T 3. T 4. F 5. T

Gina Dejesus (age 14), Amanda Berry (age 16), and Michelle Knight (age 21) were kidnapped and repeatedly raped in the home of Ariel Castro in Cleveland, Ohio, for almost a decade. They were rescued in May 2013. A 6-year-old daughter of Berry was also held against her will in the home. Castro pleaded guilty to 937 criminal counts of rape, kidnapping, and aggravated murder and was sentenced to life in prison without chance of parole, plus 1,000 years (he committed suicide in prison in September 2013).

Jaycee Lee Dugard, at age 11, was kidnapped in 1991 and repeatedly raped in the home of Phillip Garrison for 18 years. During this time, Dugard bore two daughters who were ages 11 and 15 at the time of her reappearance. Garrison was sentenced to 431 years imprisonment. *A Stolen Life: A Memoir by Jaycee Dugard* (Dugard, 2011) recounts her experience.

> *I spent 11 years in hell. Now your hell is just beginning.*
>
> Michelle Knight, kidnapping victim, to Ariel Castro, who had held her captive and had just been sentenced to life in prison.

I was only nine years of age when I was raped by my 19-year-old cousin. He was the first of three family members to sexually molest me.

Oprah Winfrey, media giant and philanthropist

Although we tend to think of sexual involvement as a series of voluntary, gentle, and intimate encounters, the data reveal that an alarming percentage of people are forced to have sex against their will (not only by strangers, but also by intimates). In this chapter we discuss the various forms of sexual coercion, its victims, and the perpetrators. At the outset we emphasize that forced sex occurs in dating, living together, and marriage contexts in both heterosexual and homosexual relationships.

16.1 Sexual Coercion: Rape and Sexual Assault

Sexual coercion involves using force (actual or threatened) to engage a person in sexual acts against that person's will. Although sexual coercion has existed for centuries, only in the past couple of decades have individuals, social scientists, medical and mental health professionals, and politicians been confronted with the pervasiveness of sexually coercive acts. Examples of what television and print media have revealed about sex abuse include the sex abuse scandal of the Catholic Church, sexual harassment in the military, and the Castro pedophile horror story referred to at the beginning of the chapter.

16.1a Definitions of Rape

One of the difficulties in studying rape and sexual assault is that these terms are variously defined in legal codes and research literature. Criminal law distinguishes between forcible rape and statutory rape. **Forcible rape** includes three elements: penetration of the vagina, mouth, or anus; force or threat of force; and no consent of the victim. Statutory rape involves sexual intercourse without use of force with a person below the legal age of consent. The age of consent for sex between a male and a female varies by state in the United States from age 14 for the male in Iowa to age 18 for the female in 14 states. In most states, the legal age for sex between men and women is 16. **Marital rape**, now recognized in all states, is forcible rape by one's spouse. In no state is a husband legally entitled to force his wife to have sex.

Because legal definitions of rape are varied and restrictive, the term **forced sex** is more descriptive. In this section, we use the terms *forced sex* and **rape** interchangeably to refer to acts of sex (or attempted sex) in which one party is nonconsenting, regardless of the age and sex of the offender and victim—whether or not the act meets criteria for what legally constitutes rape. The Personal Experience reveals the horror of an undergraduate female who was raped on a date.

Sexual coercion
Use of force (actual or threatened) to engage a person in sexual acts against that person's will

Forcible rape
Sexual force involving three elements: vaginal, oral, or anal penetration; the use of force or threat of force; and non-consent of the victim

Marital rape
Forcible rape by one's spouse; now illegal in all states

Forced sex
Acts of sex (or attempted sex) in which one party is nonconsenting, regardless of the age and sex of the offender and victim—whether or not the act meets criteria for what legally constitutes rape (also called Rape.)

Rape
Act of sex (or attempted sex) in which one party is nonconsenting, regardless of the age and sex of the offender and victim—whether or not the act meets criteria for what legally constitutes rape (also called Forced sex.)

PERSONAL Experience 16-1

"I Was Raped by My Boyfriend."

Last spring, I met this guy on campus and a relationship started which was great. One year later, he raped me. The term was almost over and we would not be able to spend much time together during the summer. Therefore, we planned to go out to eat and spend some time together.

After dinner we drove to a park. I did not mind or suspect anything for we had done this many times. Then he asked me into the back seat. I got into the back seat with him because I trusted him and he said he wanted to be close to me as we talked. He began talking. He told me that he was tired of always pleasing me and not getting a reward. Therefore, he was going to "make love to me" whether I wanted to or not. I thought he was joking, so I asked him to stop playing. He told me he was serious, and after looking at him closely, I knew he was serious. I began to plead with him not to have sex with me. He did not listen. He began to tear my clothes off and confine me so that I could not move. All this time I was fighting him. At one time, I managed to open the door, but he threw me back into the seat, hit me, then he got on me and raped me. After he was satisfied, he stopped, told me to get dressed and stop crying. He said he was sorry it had to happen that way.

He brought me back to the dorm and expected me to kiss him good night. He didn't think he had done anything wrong. Before this happened, I loved this man very much, but afterward I felt great hatred for him.

My life has not been the same since that night. I do not trust men as I once did, nor do I feel completely comfortable when I'm with my present boyfriend. He wants to know why I back off when he tries to be intimate with me. However, right now I can't tell him, as he knows the guy who raped me. (authors' files)

16.1b Prevalence of Rape

National **DATA**

Approximately one in five females will be a victim of rape. Regardless of the official rape reports, it is estimated that from 75% to 95% of female rapes are not reported (Fisher & Pina, 2013).

A sequence of events sometimes lead up to a rape—flirting, alcohol, physical intimacy in the form of kissing, isolation from the female's support network/girlfriends, and movement to an isolated place (e.g., her apartment or his). Alcohol and drugs are a major contextual factor in rape. McCauley and colleagues (2013) assessed the substance use of 104 women who received post rape medical care. One-third (33%) of the women reported consuming alcohol or drugs at the time of their rape incident. Nearly one in four (24.7%) endorsed drug (marijuana, illicit, non-medical use of prescription drugs, or club drug) use; and 8.4% of the women reported at least monthly binge drinking in the past year. Messman-Moore and colleagues (2013) emphasized alcohol as a key variable associated with rape. In their study of 353 college women, they categorized 15.6% of the rapes as "alcohol involved rape." Heavy episodic drinking was particularly associated with being raped.

16.1c Characteristics of Men Who Rape Women

Most rapists are men who believe in **rape myths**. Also referred to as **rape-supportive beliefs**, rape myths are attitudes and beliefs that are generally false but are widely and persistently held, and that serve to deny and/or justify male sexual aggression against women. Such rape myths include that women have a secret desire to be controlled/raped, that when a woman says "no" she really means "yes," that only strangers commit rape, and that women who dress provocatively are really asking for sex. Mouilso and Calhoun (2013) confirmed that the acceptance of rape myths is associated with psychopathy in

Rape myths
Generally false but widely held attitudes and beliefs that serve to justify male sexual aggression against women (also called Rape-supportive beliefs.)

Rape-supportive beliefs
See Rape myths

both incarcerated and nonincarcerated individuals. In a sample of 308 college males, those who believed that females were responsible for their own rapes (e.g., they dress provocatively, they drink too much) also had the traits of being "callous and manipulative." In addition, those who thought, "rape is trivial" also reported being both impulsive and antisocial.

In addition to believing in rape myths, men who rape may share several characteristics. They ignore personal space (e.g., hands all over you), abuse alcohol or other drugs (reduced judgment), sexualize conversations, are dominant/aggressive, have rigid gender roles, use threats in displays of anger, have a quick temper, are sadistic/narcissistic, and are impersonal/aloof emotionally.

Men who rape may be an acquaintance/boyfriend, husband, or stranger. The rape may be perpetrated by one individual or by a group of individuals. An example of the latter is a female who said she awakened upstairs in the fraternity house to discover that eight of the brothers had already had sex with her.

College women may also buy into rape myths. Deming and colleagues (2013) noted, in a sample of first- and fourth-year college women, that college women are ambivalent about the definition of when rape has occurred when there are other "contributing" factors: alcohol consumption (e.g., Should the woman not have had so much to drink? Should she have been more in control?); varying degrees of consent (e.g., the female consented to the man coming back to her apartment, to being unclothed); and the woman knowing the perpetrator (e.g., the boyfriend versus just a hookup).

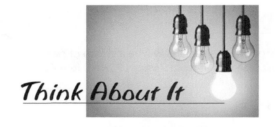

Take a moment to answer the following question. Because men with whom the women were acquainted or romantically involved perpetrate most rapes of adult women, rape is one of the most underreported violent crimes in the United States. What social changes do you feel can be made to increase the reporting of rape?

Acquaintance rape
Nonconsensual sex between people who are dating or on a date (also called Date rape.)

Date rape
Nonconsensual sex between people who are dating or on a date (also called Acquaintance rape.)

Rohypnol
Drug used in date rape scenarios which causes profound and prolonged sedation, a feeling of well-being, and short-term memory loss; also known as dulcitas, the "forget me drug"

GHB (Gamma hydroxybutyrate)
also known as "liquid ecstasy" because like X, it inspires a tendency to be touchy-feely and relaxed. It is a more powerful drug that may cause deep sedation.

Acquaintances

Most rapists know the person they rape. One form of **acquaintance rape** is sometimes referred to as **date rape**. Date rape refers to nonconsensual sex between people who are dating, on a date (the concept includes individuals who are sexually active that previously dated), or hooking up. Thirty percent of 3,468 undergraduate females and 19% of 1,101 undergraduate males reported that they had been pressured to have sex by a person they were dating (Hall & Knox, 2013).

Acquaintance rapes most often occur in the context of alcohol or drugs. Indeed, alcohol is the drug men used to reduce the inhibitions/alter the judgment of their target female. The word target is used deliberately. Some men spend time with/drink with women for the express purpose of getting them loaded and having sex with them.

Two illegal drugs that have been associated with date rape cases are Rohypnol and gamma hydroxybutyrate (GHB). **Rohypnol** (also known as dulcitas, the "forget me drug") causes profound and prolonged sedation and short-term memory loss. It has 10 times the potency of Valium by weight and lasts for about 8 hours. **GHB**, which is potentially fatal, acts faster than Rohypnol to induce confusion, intense sleepiness, unconsciousness, and memory loss. Although most symptoms last 3 to 6 hours, the drowsiness may last for 3 days. Police in Los Angeles County routinely test date rape victims for both Rohypnol and GHB.

Although both of these drugs may be used to incapacitate a woman, alcohol is more typical. It is legal, available and normative—the woman sees her friends drinking so its use is not questioned.

Husbands

Marital rape may occur as part of a larger pattern of verbal and emotional abuse. Historically, husbands could not be prosecuted for rape because the wife was the husband's property and "taking her sexually" was his right. Today, every state recognizes marital rape as a crime. Most wives are reluctant to press charges, but those who do are usually successful in seeing their husbands convicted. One reason for such a high conviction rate is that such rapes are often particularly brutal or deviant.

Strangers

Rape by a stranger is known as **predatory rape** or **classic rape**, and may involve a weapon (a gun or knife). The courts take rapes by strangers more seriously, and prosecuted rapists who do not know their victims are more often convicted. Whenever there is a discussion of a rape, it is assumed that the male is the perpetrator and that the target is a female. Of the undergraduate females referred to above, 20% reported that they have been pressured to have sex by a stranger (Hall & Knox, 2013).

However, the rape target may be a male. Of the undergraduate males referred to above, 13% reported that they have been pressured to have sex by a stranger (Hall & Knox, 2013). Lundrigan and Mueller-Johnson analyzed 209 cases of stranger rape involving male offenders and male victims with the aim of developing an interpersonal model of offender-victim interaction. Multivariate analysis of the male stranger rape cases revealed three themes of offender-victim interaction. The first was "hostility" which was characterized by demeaning the victim, threatening the victim, and hurting the victim—forceful anal penetration by the hand or object. A second theme was "involvement intimacy" whereby the male attempted to create a pseudo-intimate relationship by revealing personal information and asking for the same. There are "attempts to prolong the encounter between offender and victim" via drug administration, imprisonment, and blocking the entry/exit points. Almost half (49%) of the offenses were classified as including involvement intimacy. A third theme was involvement exploitative whereby the offender had a weapon (gun or knife) and required the victim to perform sexual acts on the offender. The request was verbal, and the individual was urged to comply. In 92% of the cases, violence was not used.

Gang Rapes

Some rapes involve more than one perpetrator, and they may be either strangers or acquaintances. Gang rape by strangers involves a group of men targeting a woman they do not know and raping her. The example is a woman who was jogging in the park where three male friends were "hanging out" and decided to rape her. Gang rape by acquaintances involves a group of men the woman knows. For example, she may be at a fraternity party, know several of the "brothers," and be gang raped one night while she is drunk (she may also be a willing participant).

Gang rape also exists in war, where men enter a context where there are females whom they can control/rape, and they do so in a group. Paul (2013) saw men as responsible for war rape not only as individuals, but also as "collective bystanders, facilitators and beneficiaries."

There are a couple of social-psychological factors that help explain why group members who individually would not commit rape would do so in a group context. First, the group context allows members to diffuse responsibility for the gang rape

Predatory rape
Rape by a stranger which may involve a weapon (also called Classic rape.)

Classic rape
Rape by a stranger which may involve a weapon (also called Predatory rape.)

by blaming others in the group (e.g., "'they were just all having sex with her so I went along"). Second, in a group setting, modeling of aggression occurs. Not only does watching while group members rape a woman convey to other group members that this behavior is considered appropriate and fun, it also demonstrates techniques of how to force someone to have sex.

Cultural Diversity

The rape and murder of a 23-year-old female physiotherapy student from Delhi (six men were arrested for the attack) took place on December 16, 2012, and gave national visibility to the plight of women in India "where men can rape, beat, and kill a woman with impunity" (*Lancet*, 2013).

16.1d Women Who Rape Men

Data on both the rape of females and the rape of males in the United Kingdom in 2002 revealed 852 recorded rapes of men compared to 11,441 reported rapes of women. While most of these male rapes were by other men, there are women who rape men (Fisher & Pina, 2013).

Research on rape of men by women is problematic since rape is defined in reference to penetration by a penis. Hence, no legal definition exists for a female who rapes a male. Even though women report sexual assault/abuse of males, the legal definition of rape remains gender biased in the United Kingdom.

Women who rape men have no problem being physically aggressive toward males.
Source: Chelsea Curry

Think About It

The absence of a legal definition for a female raping a male in the U.K. has important legal outcomes. Since a woman can be charged with sexual assault, not rape (by definition), the penalty for assault is much lower (max of 10 years in prison) than the penalty for rape (life imprisonment).

U.S. law allows for rape to be the penetration of any orifice, so a penis is not required. Thus, a woman could be considered a rapist if she used a penis shaped vibrator and penetrated a male anally or aroused him and inserted his penis into her vagina. Of those who have been "forced into sexual activity" by a female, 21% were men; of those who were threatened or suffered physical abuse by a female who forced them to engage in sexual activity, 24% were men. These reports (Fisher & Pina, 2013) are problematic since the definition of a forced sexual activity could be kissing. In one study of 248 women who sexually assaulted men, they (the female perpetrators) talked of using physical aggression, taking advantage of the man who was altered (e.g., alcohol), or using verbal aggression.

Just as there are female rape myths, there are male rape myths. Three such myths are that men are stronger than women and can't be raped, that men not women instigate rape so male rape does not exit, and that men who are raped by women lose their masculinity. Acceptance of the male rape myths results in considerable underreporting—"males can't really be raped" and the male fears he will be held responsible for whatever happened.

Regardless of definitions or frequencies, the negative consequences of a male being sexually assaulted/raped by a female are the same as when a male rapes a female. There are long-term psychological (e.g., depression, substance abuse), relationship (e.g., insecurity, instability), and physical (e.g., insomnia, anxiety) problems. Sexual dysfunction is particularly problematic after a heterosexual assault against a male by a female because it affects current and future relationships with women. One fear is that if the male is sexual with a woman, she will begin another assault (this is the reverse of the fear of women who are raped by men).

In addition to men raping women and women assaulting/raping men, it is important to also keep in mind that assaults on lesbians, gay men, and bisexuals also occur at rates similar to or higher than their heterosexual counterparts. These assaults are less often reported since the person does not want to be "outed."

16.2 Theories of Rape

Various theories have been suggested in an attempt to explain why rape occurs.

16.2a Evolutionary and Biological Theories of Rape

Evolutionary and biological theories explain rape on the basis of anatomy, biologically-based drives, and natural selection for reproductive success. In addition to men being physically stronger than women, some biological theories of rape emphasize that rape results from a strong biological sex drive in men. The high level of androgens and other sex hormones to which the male brain is exposed explains, in part, this strong sex drive.

Evolutionary (or sociobiological) theory suggests that males have a strong sex drive because natural selection favors males who copulate with numerous females. Males achieve reproductive success through copulating with as many females as possible; females achieve reproductive success through limiting their copulation behavior to males who are committed to help care for the female and her offspring.

Evolutionary/biological theories of rape have been criticized on the basis that societies differ in their rape rates (suggesting that such rates are due to social not biological influences), that insemination from rapes might yield a low pregnancy rate (so having many offspring would not result), that some women are very strong and can defend themselves, that the expression of testosterone is heavily influenced by social norms which dictate appropriate interpersonal sexual behavior, and that being genetically programmed to rape is nonsense. Indeed, evolutionary/biological theories suggest

BVT *Lab*

Flashcards are available for this chapter at **www.BVTLab.com**.

that men are hormonally predisposed to rape; critics argue this is an exaggeration of biological influences. We will later argue that rape is due more to differences in social power between women and men than to biological differences.

Another evolutionary view of rape suggests that this act evolved to enable men of low mate value to circumvent female choice. This hypothesis has been questioned on the grounds that during human evolution, parents controlled the mate choices of women. Apostolou (2013) used anthropological and historical evidence to reconstruct the evolutionary context in which a forced-sex mating strategy emerged and argued that forced sex is the outcome of an innate conditional strategy which enabled men "to circumvent parental and female choice when they experience a competitive disadvantage, or when the costs of doing so are low."

16.2b Psychopathological Theory of Rape

According to the psychopathological theory of rape, rapists are viewed as having a mental disorder. Most people in the general population agree with this theory and think of rapists as being "crazy." These individuals do not have the proper social controls to inhibit their sexual impulses.

The psychopathological theory of rape may be criticized on the basis that the subject populations used for studies on rapists have been made up of incarcerated rapists. Also, not all rapists display the same symptomology or show marked deviation on standard psychological tests.

16.2c Feminist Theory of Rape

The feminist theory of rape emphasizes the unequal distribution of power between men and women in society. Proponents of this theory believe that men dominate women in the political and economic sphere, and that rape is an extension of the dominance, power, and control men exert over women. Hence, rape is viewed as an act of power and dominance, not an act of sex.

Feminist scholarship and activism have ... led to a paradigmatic shift away from the notion of women as temptress of innocent man and toward the insistence on male responsibility for his actions in the perpetration of violence against women.

Patricia Rozee and Mary Koss, research professors

Support for the view that rape is essentially a male response associated with the social inequality between the sexes is provided by data suggesting that the incidence and prevalence of rape in different societies vary by the degree of inequality between the women and men in those societies. In one study of 95 societies (Sanday, 1981), rape was either absent or rare in almost half (47%) of the cases. In these societies (the Ashanti of West Africa, for example), women tend to have equal status with men. "In 'rape free' societies women are treated with considerable respect, and prestige is attached to female reproductive and productive roles" (p. 16). Similarly, Lottes and Weinberg (1996) found lower rates of sexual coercion among Swedish students when compared to U.S. students. The researchers pointed out that women in Sweden have more institutional power and social benefits than women in the United States, which means there is greater equality between the sexes in Sweden.

Societies in which women are viewed as inferior to men tend to be more rape prone. Women in rape-prone societies are also viewed as property, implying that men may take them by violent means. However, critics of the feminist theory of rape assert that the theory misses the reality that men are driven by hormones, not by ideology.

16.2d Social Learning Theory of Rape

The social learning theory of rape views rape as "behavior that males learn through the acquisition of social attitudes favorable to rape, and through the imitation of depictions of sexuality interlinked with aggression" (Ellis, 1989, p. 16). According to Ellis (1989), men learn aggressive behavior toward women, including rape behavior, through the following four interrelated processes (also see Self-Assessment 16-1):

1. *The sex-violence linkage effect*   This process refers to the association of sexuality and violence. For example, many slasher and horror films, some pornography, and even some music videos depict sex and violence together, thus causing the viewer to form a link or association between sex and violence.

2. *The modeling effect*   This process involves imitating rape scenes and other acts of violence toward women that are seen in real life and in the mass media.

3. *The desensitization effect*   This process involves becoming desensitized to the pain, fear, and humiliation of sexual aggression through repeated exposure to sexual aggression. Since it is common to see men sexually aggressing against women in movies/pornography, men slowly adapt to believing that such sexually aggressive behavior is normative.

4. *The rape myth effect*   In this process, men learn to view women as "really wanting it" and to deny that their force constitutes rape.

16.3 Consequences of Rape and Treatment for Rape Survivors

In this section we note that most rapes are not reported. The consequences are catastrophic, and the treatment is variable and time consuming.

SELF-ASSESSMENT 16-1: RAPE SUPPORTIVE ATTITUDE SCALE

Directions

Indicate whether you *strongly disagree* (1), *disagree* (2), *are undecided or have no opinion* (3), *agree* (4), or *strongly agree* (5). The scale takes about 10 minutes to complete.

Strongly disagree	Disagree	Undecided	Agree	Strongly agree
(1)	(2)	(3)	(4)	(5)

1. ___ Being roughed up is sexually stimulating to many women.
2. ___ A man has some justification in forcing a female to have sex with him when she led him to believe she would go to bed with him.
3. ___ The degree of a woman's resistance should be the major factor in determining if a rape has occurred.
4. ___ The reason most rapists commit rape is for sex.
5. ___ If a girl engages in necking or petting and she lets things get out of hand, it is her fault if her partner forces sex on her.
6. ___ Many women falsely report that they have been raped because they are pregnant and want to protect their reputation.
7. ___ A man has some justification in forcing a woman to have sex with him if she allowed herself to be picked up.

8. ___ Sometimes the only way a man can get a cold woman turned on is to use force.
9. ___ A charge of rape 2 days after the act has occurred is probably not rape.
10. ___ A raped woman is a less desirable woman.
11. ___ A man is somewhat justified in forcing a woman to have sex with him if he has had sex with her in the past.
12. ___ In order to protect the male, it should be difficult to prove that a rape has occurred.
13. ___ Many times a woman will pretend she doesn't want to have intercourse because she doesn't want to seem loose, but she's really hoping the man will force her.
14. ___ A woman who is stuck-up and thinks she is too good to talk to guys deserves to be taught a lesson.
15. ___ One reason that women falsely report rape is that they frequently have a need to call attention to themselves.
16. ___ In a majority of rapes the victim is promiscuous or had a bad reputation.
17. ___ Many women have an unconscious wish to be raped, and may then unconsciously set up a situation in which they are likely to be attacked.
18. ___ Rape is the expression of an uncontrollable desire for sex.
19. ___ A man is somewhat justified in forcing a woman to have sex with him if they have dated for a long time.
20. ___ Rape of a woman by a man she knows can be defined as a "woman who changed her mind afterwards."

Scoring and Interpretation

All of the items are scored in the same direction. To determine your score for the scale, add the responses (coded 1 through 5) to the 20 items (possible range 20–100). The higher the score, the more rape supportive or victim-callous attitudes are supported. This scale measures seven beliefs that have been found to promote rape, and also interfere with the recovery of rape survivors. The beliefs include: "(a) women enjoy sexual violence, (b) women are responsible for rape prevention, (c) sex rather than power is the primary motivation for rape, (d) rape happens only to certain kinds of women, (e) a woman is less desirable after she has been raped, (f) women falsely report many rape claims, and (g) rape is justified in some situations" (Lottes, 1998).

The Rape Supportive Attitude Scale was administered to college students, mostly single and in the 19- to 22-year-old age range, at schools in the northeastern United States (Lottes, 1991). In both studies the students took the scale in regularly scheduled classes. The scale items were randomly distributed within a 70-item questionnaire. The first sample included 98 men and 148 women from education, health, and sociology classes at two universities. Students from three universities comprised the second sample, which included 195 men and 195 women enrolled in business, engineering, English, education, history, mathematics, physics, political science, and sociology classes. Men scored significantly higher on the scale than women.

The Rape Supportive Attitude Scale was one of the measures used in a university study in the United Kingdom that investigated sexually aggressive attitudes and behaviors among 298 male students who participated in contact sports and non-contact sports, as well as non-athletes (Smith & Stewart, 2003). This study's findings were consistent with prior research that men who held rape-supportive beliefs and were hostile to women were more likely than other men to have committed rape. However, the study did not find that being an athlete was correlated with being sexually aggressive toward women; rather it was the characteristics of being very win-oriented and strongly desiring to dominate one's opponent.

Reliability and Validity

The Cronbach alpha value for the first sample of students was 0.91, and 0.91 for the second sample as well, showing high internal reliability (Lottes, 1991). A single, dominant factor emerged from a principal components analysis of the data, which accounted for 37% of the variance. Men's scores on the Rape Supportive Attitude Scale were correlated with scores on the Hypermasculinity Inventory. For men and women scores on the Rape Supportive Attitude Scale were significantly correlated with measures of nonegalitarian gender role beliefs, traditional attitudes toward female sexuality, adversarial sexual beliefs, arousal to sexual violence, and non-acceptance of homosexuality.

Source: From "Rape Supportive Attitudes Scale" by Ilsa L. Lottes in *Handbook of Sexuality-Related Measures.* Edited by C. M. Davis, W. L. Yarber, R. Bauserman, G. Schreer, and S. L. Davis. (1998). p. 504. Reprinted by permission of Dr. Lottes.

International DATA

About 11% of rapes in England are reported to the police (Lundrigan & Mueller-Johnson, 2013).

16.3a Reporting a Rape

A person who has been raped will often tell a close friend. Paul and colleagues (2013) found that 40% of 2,000 female college students reported that they had received a rape disclosure, but the police were usually not contacted. Cohn and colleagues (2013) studied 44 women who were raped but who did not report the rape to the police. Their reasons for not reporting the rape included not wanting others to know, not acknowledging the rape (e.g., feeling that they were drunk and led the person on), and criminal justice concerns (e.g., fear they may get in trouble for drinking too much/being incapacitated). Of course, it is the woman's decision to involve the police. It is important to note that becoming involved in therapy may also facilitate recovery from rape.

Unfortunately, individuals who seek help from legal and medical personnel sometimes experience **secondary victimization** whereby they (the sexually assaulted) feel that they become the victim and are blamed for the rape (e.g., "You didn't lead him on did you?" "You weren't dressed provocatively, were you?" "How much did you have to drink?").

Cultural Diversity

The ultimate example of secondary victimization occurs when a woman is murdered via an **honor killing**. In some parts of the Arab world (e.g., Jordan), a woman who is raped (or who has unmarried sexual intercourse) brings shame to her parents and siblings. By killing her, the family retains their honor and moves beyond the shame brought on by the daughter. Honor killings have a long tradition, so until recently, the murder of the daughter who was raped could occur with no consequence. The "laws" that were in place would either be ignored, not enforced, or result in symbolic punishment. For example, a brother who killed his sister who had been raped because she brought shame on the family was be "sentenced" to 6 weeks in jail—but he was released after a month. Attempts are being made to provide severe penalties for honor killings, but change will be slow because the legislative bodies are controlled mostly by men who value tradition.

Secondary victimization
Experience in which a person has been raped and seeks help, but despite being the victim is blamed for the rape by those from whom she or he seeks help

Honor killing
Killing of a woman in the Arab world (e.g., Jordan) who is raped or who has intercourse before marriage, which brings great shame to her parents/family (She may be killed to absolve the family of the shame.)

16.3b Consequences of Rape

An individual who has been raped has been traumatized. Initial reactions to rape include an acute period of disorganization, helplessness, vulnerability, and anger. The person may also blame himself or herself for the incident. The most devastating aspect of rape is not the genital contact but the sense of cognitive and emotional violation. The woman who felt that her environment was safe and predictable, that other people were trustworthy, and that she was competent and autonomous may become someone who is fearful of her surroundings, suspicious of other people, and unsure of her ability to control her life.

Burgess and Holstrom (1974) described **rape trauma syndrome**, following their study of women who sought post-rape assistance through a hospital emergency department. This syndrome refers to the acute and long-term reorganization process that occurs as a result of forcible rape or attempted rape. The acute phase involves fear, anxiety, crying, and restlessness. Long-term reorganization may involve moving to another community and changing one's phone number. Nightmares, sexual dysfunctions, and phobias associated with the rape may also occur. Examples of the latter include fear of being alone, being in the dark, or touching a man's penis.

More contemporary descriptions for rape after-effects are acute stress disorder and **post-traumatic stress disorder** (PTSD) which include a particular set of reactions to traumatic events—including military combat, natural disasters, or other events—that invoke terror, helplessness, and fear of loss of life. These are also the reactions experienced by some rape victims. Acute stress disorder is diagnosed within a month after a trauma and is highly predictive of subsequent PTSD. PTSD is diagnosed when a pattern of symptoms persists longer than a month post-trauma. The rape survivor may have persistent episodes of re-experiencing the event, such as flashbacks, hallucinations, or nightmares. The survivor may attempt to avoid any stimuli associated with the trauma. This may involve efforts to avoid thoughts, feelings, or activities associated with the trauma; a restricted range of affect (such as the inability to have love feelings); feelings of detachment or estrangement from others; and the inability to recall aspects of the trauma. The person may also report symptoms of increased arousal, such as difficulty sleeping, increased irritability, and outbursts of anger.

In a longitudinal study of 1,399 youth (women and men)—both college students and noncollege youth—having been raped was associated with anger, social isolation, depressed mood, and lower self-esteem. The more violent the coercion was, the more difficult the adjustment (Zweig, Barber, & Eccles, 1997).

In addition to the psychological and interpersonal consequences of rape, there is also the physical consequence of STI and HIV infection. Stockman and Lucea (2013) reviewed 21 studies on coerced/forced sexual initiation and sexual intimate partner violence (sexual IPV) and found a significant contribution to a woman's risk for STI and HIV infection.

Rape trauma syndrome
Acute and long-term reorganization process that occurs as a result of forcible rape or attempted rape

Post-traumatic stress disorder
Mental health diagnostic category that characterizes a particular set of symptoms following traumatic events (including military combat, natural disasters, or other events that invoke terror, helplessness, and fear of loss of life), experienced by many rape victims

Think About It

It sometimes happens that one's partner (girlfriend or spouse), relative, or friend is raped. How might one be of help to someone who has just been sexually assaulted? Creating a safe context whereby the person no longer feels under threat is paramount. This means staying with the person and maintaining close physical contact. Accepting the person's range and flood of emotions is also important; these emotions may vary from rage to passivity to sadness to guilt. Other issues include helping the person assess the degree to which she should or is willing to go to the hospital to rule out any medical concerns and/or to assess her willingness to contact a rape counselor and report the rape to the police.

16.3c Treatment for Rape Survivors

Crisis counseling may last from a few days to 2 or 3 months after the assault. The primary goals of crisis counseling include establishing a therapeutic relationship, encouraging emotional expression, and providing information about reporting rape to the police and symptoms the victim may experience. The therapist may also promote adjustment of immediate role responsibilities, which may take the form of encouraging the person to take time off from work or eliciting the support of others to provide a period for processing the rape experience.

Crisis counselors also discuss with the victim the importance of seeing a physician to take care of medical needs (care for physical injuries, testing for STIs and pregnancy) as well as to document the rape if the victim decides to take legal action. The latter is often a difficult choice for most rape victims because it makes their rape experience public and exposes them to questioning and interrogation by strangers.

Long-term therapy for rape may include a number of behavioral techniques, sexual therapy, exposure, and cognitive therapy. Exposure techniques may involve survivors retelling the traumatic event or writing a narrative to be used in treatment to reduce rape-related fears. Jaycee Dugard wrote *A Stolen Life* (2011) as part of her therapy.

Cognitive therapy emphasizes reframing the rape experience from one of great horror to one in which the person has benefited—by learning to be more cautious, by recognizing one's vulnerability, and by appreciating the safety of one's close relationships. Cognitive therapy also encourages the person to increase the frequency of positive self-statements so as to enhance self-esteem. For example, persons who have been raped are encouraged to view themselves as survivors rather than as victims.

Feminist therapy helps survivors recognize that rape is a social problem, not solely an individual problem. Women are encouraged to empower themselves to become a survivor, not a victim. Feminist approaches are often combined with cognitive therapy techniques.

Medication is also used in treatment for sexual assault survivors. Medications include sedatives, tranquilizers, and antidepressants following the assault. Some survivors obtain their prescriptions without disclosing the assault to their healthcare provider, which shows how reluctant some survivors are to disclose.

16.4 Prevention of Rape

Effective rape prevention includes addressing issues in both women and men.

16.4a Teaching Women to Avoid Rape

Women must acknowledge that rape is a real possibility, particularly acquaintance rape, and that they must monitor their alcohol/drug consumption to keep their wits about them. They must also identify the signs of an impending rape. The male who sexualizes the conversation, who encourages the woman to drink, who is "all hands," who seeks to isolate her from her friends, and who does not take "no" for an answer— all should be identified as dangerous; and the woman should extricate herself or escape from such a person ASAP. Being assertive early in the chain is important.

Senn (2013) found that a rape prevention program taken by 88 university females and 59 high school students resulted in these students being more aware that young women were at personal risk of acquaintance rape and that they could defend themselves effectively if necessary.

How much resistance to show in a gang rape context was studied by Woodhams and Cooke (2013) who examined the police files of 90 multiple-perpetrator rapes against female victims. They found that the greater the resistance, the greater the aggression of the rapists, and that older victims were targets of greater aggression.

As noted earlier, war rape is a hidden aspect of rape. Grey and Shepherd (2013) emphasized that war is a context that permits sexual violence, which damages both perpetrators and victims. Despite the formulation of United Nations Action Against Sexual Violence in Conflict and the appointment of a United Nations Special Representative of the Secretary-General to lead policy and practice in the area of war rape, survivors/victims remain a marginal concern. Attention must be given to this low visibility but accepted violence by acknowledging the factors of gender and masculinity at play so as to avoid war rape and its devastating effects.

16.4b Teaching Men Not to Rape

Teaching men not to rape involves alerting them that U.S. society provides the context for them to be socialized to dominate women and to believe in rape myths (e.g., "no" means "yes"). Correction of the tendency to believe in rape myths must begin early. Reyes and Foshee (2013) studied a sample of 459 male adolescents across grades 8 through 12 and emphasized the negative effects of early rape myth acceptance. They found that early physical aggression towards peers and dates and sexual aggression onset were stronger for teens reporting higher levels of rape myth acceptance. The researcher highlighted the importance of rape myth acceptance as a construct that should be addressed early by violence prevention programs.

Rejecting sexual myths and respecting the dignity and privacy of women must be followed by not sexualizing conversations, not getting her drunk, and including her friends. Men must also remember that a woman being in an altered state (alcohol/drugs) and passive does not imply consent to have sex. Having sex with a woman who is cognitively altered is against the law.

16.5 Child Sexual Abuse

Child sexual abuse may be both physical and emotional. Physical sexual abuse includes sexual intercourse or penetration, genital or anal fondling or touching, oral sex, kissing, and/or forced performing of fellatio and cunnilingus of a minor by an adult or to an adult. Emotional sexual abuse of a child can include behaviors such as forcing a minor to watch sexual acts, encouraging the child to undress in front of others, and/or making lewd comments about a minor. In either case of child sexual abuse, the child experiences a breakdown of trust, destruction of boundaries and a sense of violation (Blumer, Papaj, & Erolin, 2013).

An alarming percentage of adults report having been sexually abused as children. Researchers have noted that one in four women in the general population report being sexually abused as a child. In the female clinical population, seven in ten females report childhood sexual encounters (Blumer, Papaj, & Erolin, 2013).

International & National DATA

In a study of 1,928 Canadian children ages 4 through 14 years, 22% of the females and 8% of the males reported having been sexually abused (MacMillan, Tanaka, Duku, Vaillancourt, & Boyle, 2013).

Factors associated with these children being sexually abused were living in poverty, growing up in an urban area, parental adversity, and child physical abuse. Siblings of the sexually abused were also at increased risk for sexual abuse themselves (MacMillan, Tanaka, Duku, Vaillancourt, & Boyle, 2013).

International rates sometimes vary by the source of the data. Ji and colleagues (2013) compared child sexual abuse data in English/International and Chinese peer-reviewed journals. For example, data from international journals reported that 15% of females in China reported penetrative child sex abuse compared to 1% data revealed through Chinese journals. The discrepancy was explained in terms of the need for China to "use well validated instruments, avoid face-to-face interview formats, and be careful to maintain methodological standards when sampling large populations over multiple sites."

16.5a Intrafamilial Child Sexual Abuse

Perpetrators of child sexual abuse are often categorized based on whether they are members of the child's family (intrafamilial child sex abuse) or external to the family (extrafamilial child sex abuse).

Also known as incestuous child abuse, **intrafamilial child sexual abuse** refers to exploitative sexual contact or attempted or forced sex that occurs between relatives when the victim is under the age of 18. Sexual contact or attempted sexual contact includes intercourse, fondling of the breasts and genitals, and oral sex. "Relatives" in this instance include biologically-related individuals, stepparents, and stepsiblings. Child sexual abuse occurs in any family regardless of income, race, ethnicity, religion, education, occupation, political affiliation, or social class.

Fathers as Perpetrators

Father-daughter incest is the type of incest that has received the most attention in society. Such incest is a blatant abuse of power and authority. Stroebel and colleagues (2013) identified 19 adult women who reported father-daughter incest. These women represented 1.2% of the anonymous 1,521 adult women who took a computer-assisted self-interview. When compared to those who had experienced no child sexual abuse, the victims of father-daughter incest were more likely to endorse feeling like damaged goods, to think that they had suffered psychological injury, and to have undergone psychological treatment for childhood sexual abuse. When compared to victims of brother-sister incest, the victims of father-daughter incest were more likely to endorse feeling like damaged goods, to think that they had suffered psychological injury, and to have undergone psychological treatment for childhood sexual abuse. The experience of a woman who, as a child, was forced to have sexual relations with her biological father is described as follows:

> I was around 6 years old when I was sexually abused by my father. He was not drinking at the time; therefore, he had a clear mind as to what he was doing. On looking back, it seemed so well planned. For some reason, my father

Intrafamilial child sexual abuse
Exploitative sexual contact or attempted or forced sex that occurs between related individuals when the victim is under the age 18 (Also known as incestuous child abuse.)

wanted me to go with him to the woods behind our house to help him saw wood for the night. I went without any question. Once we got there, he looked around for a place to sit and wanted me to sit down with him. In doing so, he said, "Susan, I want you to do something for daddy." I said, "What's that, daddy?" He went on to explain that "I want you to lie down, and we are going to play mamma and daddy." Being a child, I said "okay," thinking it was going to be fun. I don't know what happened next because I can't remember if there was pain or whatever. I was threatened not to tell, and remembering how he beat my mother, I didn't want the same treatment. It happened approximately two other times. I remember not liking this at all. Since I couldn't tell mama, I came to the conclusion it was wrong and I was not going to let it happen again.

But what could I do? Until age 18, I was constantly on the run, hiding from him when I had to stay home alone with him, staying out of his way so he wouldn't touch me by hiding in the corn fields all day long, under the house, in the barns, and so on, until my mother got home, then getting punished by her for not doing the chores she had assigned to me that day. It was a miserable life growing up in that environment. (authors' files)

Factors contributing to father-daughter incest include extreme paternal dominance (the daughter learns to be obedient to her father), maternal disability (the mother ceases to function as an emotional and sexual partner for the husband), and imposition of the mothering role on the oldest daughter (she becomes responsible for housework and child care). An added consequence of the oldest daughter taking over the role of the mother is her belief that she is responsible for keeping the family together. This implies not only doing what the father wants but also keeping it a secret because she or her father will be expelled from the family for disclosure.

Although some fathers may force themselves on their daughters (as in the example of the 6-year-old girl described above), incest may begin by affectionate cuddling between father and daughter. The father's motives may be sexual; his daughter's are typically nonsexual. Indeed, the daughter is often unaware of any sexual connotations of her behavior; her motive is to feel acceptance and love from her father. Ambivalent feelings often result:

My daddy never touched me unless he wanted to have me play with his genitals. I didn't like touching him there, but he was affectionate to me and told me how pretty I was. I was really mixed up about the whole thing. (authors' files)

Because of her ambivalence, the daughter may continue to participate in sexual activity with her father. She not only derives attention and affection from the relationship but may also develop a sense of power over her father. As she grows older, she may even demand gifts in exchange for her silence.

Uncles may also be perpetrators. One of our students reported the following:

Our family was having a family gathering with all the relatives for Thanksgiving. It was held in the backyard of my aunt's. I had to go inside the house to get something, and while I was inside one of my uncles came in. At that time we were pretty close, and so, at first, I didn't think anything of the following events.

My uncle came into the kitchen where I was alone and hugged and kissed me. I kissed him back. Then he kissed me again; and because we were close, I didn't think anything about the second kiss. I then moved into the walk-in pantry, and my uncle followed me and wanted to hug and kiss me again.

I then realized this was no longer a "friendly kiss." I tried to move from the pantry and he blocked me. I tried not to act scared, even though I was. Trying to dodge him, he moved quickly and knocked a glass jar off the shelf. He told me to get paper towels to clean up the mess. Then my cousin came in the kitchen, so I asked her to help with the broken jar and made an excuse to get outside. That was all that happened. To this day, I get chills when I have to be around my uncle, but I'm always careful not to be alone in his presence.

I never told anyone of this event. He is my mother's favorite and closest brother and at the time I decided not to hurt her. (author's files)

Brothers as Perpetrators

Stroebel and colleagues (2013) identified 40 adult women who reported brother-sister incest. These women represented 2.6% of the anonymous 1,521 adult women who took a computer assisted self-interview. When compared with controls (those who had experienced no incest), the female victims of brother-sister incest were more likely to endorse feeling like damaged goods, to endorse thinking that they had suffered psychological injury, and to have undergone psychological treatment for childhood sexual abuse. However, the victims of father-daughter incest were worse off than the victims of brother-sister incest (e.g., depression, substance abuse, sexual dysfunction).

Cultural Diversity

Although brother-sister incest taboos are nearly universal across cultures, there are exceptions. Siblings in royal families in ancient Egypt, Hawaii, and the Incas of Peru were permitted to have sex to keep power invested in a small group. Also there is the psychological factor that the king can do regularly what the average person should not even think about doing. It makes the ruler more godlike and separate from ordinary beings. The rulers of Egypt, Hawaii, and the Incas were treated as divine beings descended from the gods. The Egyptians believed (or were told to believe) that the sun god Re had impregnated the mother of the ruler (sound familiar?). This idea also facilitated the change of dynasties in the New Kingdom period (Bunger, 2013).

Women as Perpetrators

Incest between mothers and sons (or daughters) is thought to occur less frequently than between fathers and daughters. Mother-son incest rarely includes intercourse but is usually confined to various stimulating behaviors. The mother may continue to bathe her son long after he is capable of caring for himself, during which time she stimulates him sexually. Later, she may stimulate her son to ejaculation. The mother may also sleep with her son. Although no specific sexual contact may occur, she may sleep in the nude; this behavior is provocative as well as stimulating.

Although the data suggest that women are much less likely to sexually abuse their children than men, mothers "have historically been charged as co-offenders of the abuse ... for their alleged failure to protect" (Bolen, 2001, p. 193). Indeed, some treatment models for incest require that mothers apologize to their child for their not protecting the child.

16.5b Extrafamilial Child Sexual Abuse

Another pattern of child sexual abuse is extrafamilial child sexual abuse, which includes sexual abuse by adults in day-care contexts, caretakers in institutional settings, same- or opposite-sex peers, and strangers. Technically, **extrafamilial child sexual abuse** is defined as attempted or completed forced sex with a child, before the child reaches the age of 14, by a person who is unrelated to the child by blood or marriage. The nature of the sexual behavior may range from touching breasts and genitals to rape. The sex abuse scandal of the Catholic Church is the most recognized example of extrafamilial child sex abuse involving over 3,000 priests and an estimated payout, as of 2012, of $3 billion.

Whether sex between children and adults is considered acceptable varies across societies and historical time periods. Bullough (1990) observed that "what appears obvious from a historical overview is that adult/child and adult/adolescent sexual behavior has had different meanings at different historical times" (p. 70) For example, during the eighteenth and nineteenth centuries in England, a child of 12 could consent to sexual behavior with a middle-aged adult. Even children under 12 "could be seduced with near impunity in privacy" (p. 74).

16.5c Recovered Memories of Abuse

Before we leave this discussion on childhood sexual abuse, it is important to comment on the issue of *recovered memories of abuse* (also known as *delayed*, *recovered*, and *discontinuous memory*). A number of factors may be involved to account for the fact that traumatic memories may be "forgotten." They include failure to encode (no memory was created at the time of the event), repression (active prevention of retrieval of memory), and long-term depression (cellular changes that suppress transmission of data from other cells to others) (Roth & Friedman, 1997).

Along with discussions of how memory is affected, there is debate among professionals, as well as the general public, as to whether some sexual molestation charges are the product of a therapist's suggestion or the client's imagination. One can indeed imagine events that never happened, thus creating a false memory. Laboratory research on memory has shown that children can be persuaded to "remember" a traumatic event that did not actually happen to them, such as being separated from a parent on a shopping trip (Loftus, 1993).

McWilliams and colleagues (2013) conducted an experiment whereby participants mentally took the part of a sexual abuse victim as they read an account of the sexual assault of a 7-year-old. After reading the narrative, participants were randomly assigned to one of four experimental conditions: They (1) rehearsed the story truthfully (truth group); (2) left out the abuse details of the story (omission group); (3) lied about the abuse details to indicate that no abuse had occurred (commission group); or (4) did not recall the story during Session 1 (no-rehearsal group). One week later, participants returned for Session 2 and were asked to truthfully recall the narrative. The results indicated that, relative to truthful recall, untruthful recall or no rehearsal at Session 1 adversely affected memory performance at Session 2. However, untruthful recall resulted in better memory than did no rehearsal. Moreover, gender, PTSD symptoms, depression, adult attachment, and sexual abuse history significantly predicted memory for the childhood sexual abuse scenario. This experiment shows the precarious nature of memory as related to a sexual assault simulated scenario.

In an effort to provide a balanced report on the scientific knowledge base of the reality of repressed memories of childhood trauma, the International Society for Traumatic Stress Studies summarized the research on traumatic memory and its

Extrafamilial child sexual abuse
Attempted or completed forced sex, before a child reaches the age of 14, by a person who is unrelated to the child by blood or marriage

implications for clinical and forensic practice (Roth & Friedman, 1997). They reviewed a number of research studies that show a significant proportion (20–60%) of adult women and men with documented cases of childhood sexual abuse did not seem to recall the abuse when they were interviewed as young adults. The younger the person at the time of the trauma, the more likely he or she was to have forgotten and to report recovered memories.

Cognitive psychologists and neurobiologists studying human memory processes explain that memory does not perfectly represent an event (like a photograph). Instead, the memory processes prioritize information based on what is thought to be the most important when the event occurred. Memory storage has been compared to a "spider web in which specific memories are represented by the pattern of connections among fibers in the entire network. Memory is not a process of locating intact bits of information but rather involves partially recreating a pattern of associated threads of information across an entire network" (Roth & Friedman, 1997, p. 11). In addition, there may be differences in how traumatic and nontraumatic memories are encoded, consolidated, and retrieved. Professional societies in North America, Europe, Australia, and New Zealand have produced position papers that agree on three points:

1. Traumatic events are usually remembered in part or in whole.
2. Traumatic memories may be forgotten, then remembered at some later time.
3. Illusory memories can also occur. (Roth & Friedman, 1997, p. 15)

Traumatic memories are related to a number of post-traumatic symptoms. Specific trauma memories may be an important focus of treatment because they are likely to be distressing and affect assumptions about one's self. Talking in detail about one's experience can be an important part of cognitive and emotional processing. However, it is important for therapists to keep in mind that memory is fallible. They should adhere to recognized principles of therapy and be cautious not to use therapeutic approaches that create or reinforce false beliefs of trauma. They should not assume that the presence of specific symptoms or symptom groups substantiate a history of trauma or abuse. Therapists can help clients explore their past and come to their own conclusions about the best course of action to take. "Whether or not there is traumatic material under discussion, improving current functioning is ultimately the major goal of treatment. While childhood traumatic experiences may always remain an important part of a survivor's identity, after successful treatment survivors are likely to be facing forward rather than looking back" (Roth & Friedman, 1997, p. 17). Hence, practitioners have moved away from aggressively pursuing the recovery of abuse memories to discussing the best way to interview child victims and providing therapy for survivors.

16.6 Consequences and Treatment of Child Sexual Abuse

In this section, we look at the impact of—and the treatment alternatives for—child sexual abuse.

16.6a Impact of Child Sexual Abuse

Child sexual abuse is associated with numerous negative outcomes: depression, anxiety, PTSD, alcohol/substance abuse, sexual dysfunction, distrust in relationships, difficulties with intimacy, lower self-esteem, and eating disorders (Blumer, Papaj, & Erolin, 2013).

Fergusson and colleagues (2013) analyzed data from over 900 members in the New Zealand birth records to identify associations with child sexual abuse at age 30. In addition to the negative outcomes listed above, the findings included suicidal ideation, suicide attempt, decreased life satisfaction, decreased age of onset of sexual activity, increased number of sexual partners and increased medical contacts for physical health problems. The researchers concluded that CSA is a traumatic childhood life event in which the negative consequences increase with increasing severity of the sexual abuse.

In addition, a team of researchers studied the histories of 60 individuals who had experienced physical/sexual abuse and observed a lower capacity to invest in relationships in an emotionally and mutually engaging manner. This deficit contributed to higher levels of posttraumatic stress disorder symptomatology. The individuals also tended to view the world as threatening and painful in regard to interactions with others (Bedi, Muller, & Thornback, 2013).

Tripodi and colleagues (2013) interviewed a random sample of 125 women prisoners and found that those who had been sexually abused as children were more likely to have been hospitalized as an adult for a psychological problem, to have a substance abuse disorder, and to have attempted suicide.

Suicide is also related to child sexual abuse, particularly for males. Easton and colleagues (2013) analyzed survey data on 487 men (ages 19 to 84) who were sexually abused during childhood to assess any relationship to recent suicide attempts. Results revealed that five variables—duration of the sexual abuse, use of force during the sexual abuse, high conformity to masculine norms, level of depressive symptoms, and suicidal ideation—increased the odds of a suicide attempt in the past 12 months. The researchers emphasized the need for mental health practitioners to be alert to sexual abuse severity in assessing one's current mental health.

16.6b Treatment of Sexually Abused Children and Adults Sexually Abused as Children

The following is the sequence of events after a girl tells a school nurse or counselor that she is being sexually molested by her stepfather. First, the counselor calls the designated child protection agency to report the suspected abuse. Next the child protection agency will probably involve the local law enforcement agency, and an officer may be sent to obtain an initial statement from the girl. If the community has an interdisciplinary, child abuse investigation team, this reduces the number of times the child must be interviewed. Then, if the investigation suggests sufficient evidence exists to warrant an arrest and referral to the district attorney for prosecution, the stepfather is arrested and placed in jail or released on his own recognizance. Ideally, he is not allowed to make contact with the stepdaughter or to return to the home until legal disposition of the case is completed and progress in therapy has been made.

Incest is viewed as a family problem in terms of assessment and intervention. Counseling begins immediately; the individuals are first seen alone and then as a family. The focus of the counseling is to open channels of communication between all family members and to develop or re-establish trust between the husband and the wife. Another aspect of the program involves the confrontation between the stepfather and the stepdaughter, in which the stepfather apologizes and takes full responsibility for the sexual abuse. The ideal outcome of therapy is for the stepfather to take complete responsibility for the sex abuse, for the mother to take responsibility for not having been more vigilant, and for the child to feel completely absolved of any guilt for having participated in the sex abuse.

> *Pedophilia can't be cured any more than alcoholism can be cured, but that doesn't mean either one of those can't be successfully treated.*
>
> Fred Berlin, psychiatrist

It is not surprising that quality of family relationships is related to the adjustment of a child who has been sexually abused. Beaudoin and colleagues (2013) analyzed data from parents of 116 children who disclosed that they had been sexually abused. Parents revealed their own psychological stress and provided their observations of the behavioral and psychological problems of the children. Almost three-fourths of the children had experienced "very severe sexual abuse," and yet over half reported "secure attachment." Results revealed that the quality of the parent-child relationship and the attachment to the parents are important factors in a child's response/coping/adjustment to sex abuse. Clinicians are advised to attend not only to the sex abuse events of the child but also to the quality of the relationship with the parents.

Coren and colleagues (2013) examined the effects of eight intervention projects across England and Wales on a sample of 42 children who had been sexually abused. The average age was almost 13 (range = 4 to 18), 69% female, and 63% had been sexually abused by someone in the family. The various types of therapy included counseling, play therapy, and cognitive behavioral therapy (CBT)—all of which are consistent with what has been previously reported in the literature on child sexual abuse interventions. Both qualitative and quantitative data were collected from the children's parents, from the therapists, and from the children themselves. Results revealed a significant reduction in the number of children/young people who showed violent/aggressive behavior, improved sleep (sleeping through the night, fewer nightmares), fewer emotional problems, and decreased hyperactivity. While these interventions occurred in England and Wales, help for sex abuse victims in the U.S. is available nationwide through Childhelp USA (1-800-422-4453).

Blumer and colleagues (2013) emphasized that in working with females who were sexually abused as children, the focus is on "empowering the survivor to take control over her own life ... which involves challenging the survivor to redefine many aspects of herself and her external relationships." For example, the woman will be encouraged to redefine her sense of guilt, shame, and self-blame. A beginning is to stop using the term *victim*, "which implies a power differential where the client is vulnerable, helpless, and hopeless," and begin to use the term *survivor* which "inspires hope and helps the client take back the power stolen from her as a child."

Some individuals who have experienced child sexual abuse prefer to avoid mainstream therapy and seek self-help groups. Rham and colleagues (2013) studied 87 women who had been sexually abused and who participated in self-help groups. Results revealed that these women were in poor mental health and more than half were at risk for developing PTSD.

personal choices   16-1

Children Testifying in Cases of Alleged Child Sexual Abuse

In a study by Burgess and colleagues (1990), parents whose children testified in trials against defendants charged with committing sexual abuse in day-care centers were compared with parents whose children were also alleged to have been sexually abused but who decided not to encourage their children to testify. The parents' motivation for encouraging their children to testify was "to create safety for their child as well as other children. Safety was defined in terms of the child feeling safe to know the perpetrator was 'locked up' and that the child would be believed and protected during testifying" (Burgess, Hartman, Kelley, Grant, & Gray, 1990, p. 402). When parents who encouraged their children to testify were asked whether they had made the right decision, 70% said "yes."

However, the cost to the parents for their children testifying was high. Parents of children who testified presented higher symptoms of psychological distress than parents whose children did not testify. Such distress involved decreased income (legal expenses, time in court), job changes, alcohol or drug abuse, and separation or divorce. Some children also felt tricked. They were told that it would be good for them to testify, but they found the court experience harrowing. In some cases their father was sent to prison, so the children wondered whether they had done the right thing (Burgess, Hartman, Kelley, Grant, & Gray, 1990).

Peters and colleagues (1989) emphasized the importance of prosecuting alleged child sexual abuse perpetrated by family members. Although the argument for not prosecuting is to "keep the family together," there are at least two reasons to pursue prosecution vigorously:

1. Criminal prosecution clearly establishes that children are innocent victims and that the perpetrators are solely responsible for their wrongful behavior.
2. Successful prosecutions educate the public and provide community visibility for the unacceptability of child sex abuse.

16.7 Prevention of Child Sexual Abuse

16.7a Strategies to Reduce Child Sexual Abuse

Strategies to reduce child sexual abuse include regendering cultural roles, providing specific information to children on sex abuse, improving the safety of neighborhoods, providing healthy sexuality information for both teachers and children in public schools at regular intervals, promoting public awareness campaigns, and improving the economic well-being of children.

Specific child sex abuse prevention programs should be implemented in the public school system for young children. An empirically evaluated program worthy of duplication was executed in Turkey (Cecen-Frogul & Kaf Hasirci, 2013). The subjects were 36 fourth grade students—18 randomly assigned to the experimental and 18 randomly to the control group. For the experimental group, a "preventing child sexual abuse psycho-educational training program" as an independent variable included topics about personal rights, ("my body belongs to me"), good touch–bad touch discrimination, breaking a promise, body safety rules, say "No", bad secrets, talking with a grown-up who believes the child, and the theme that sexual abuse is never a child's fault. One-hour sessions, with a 10-minute break, were carried out on 4 consecutive days. During this period, the control group did not receive any treatment. ANCOVA analysis showed that the students who attended the sexual abuse prevention program scored significantly higher than the control group (p 0.05). As a result, the prevention child sexual abuse program was effective on fourth-grade students, and this effect was continuing at 8-week follow-up.

> *Before I worked in sex crimes, I would see kids getting off the school bus and imagine those kids running into the house greeted by a hug and anxious to talk about their day. After sex crimes, I worried that every single one of those kids dreaded going in that house because they knew they were going to be molested by someone in their house before mom got home from work.*
>
> Prosecutor in Sex Crimes Unit

Helping to ensure that children live in safe neighborhoods where it is known if neighbors are former convicted child molesters is the basis of Megan's Law (see Social Choices 16-1).

Social Choices 16-1

Megan's Law and the Jessica Lunsford Act

In 1994, Jesse Timmendequas lured 7-year-old Megan Kanka into his Hamilton Township house in New Jersey to see a puppy. He then raped and strangled her and left her body in a nearby park. Prior to his rape of Megan, Timmendequas had two prior convictions for sexually assaulting girls. Megan's mother, Maureen Kanka, argued that she would have kept her daughter away from her neighbor if she had known about his past sex offenses. She campaigned for a law, known as **Megan's Law**, requiring that communities be notified of a neighbor's previous sex convictions. Every state has enacted similar laws. President Clinton signed a federal version in 1996.

The law requires that convicted sexual offenders register with local police in the communities in which they live. It also requires the police to go out and notify residents and certain institutions (such as schools) that a dangerous sex offender has moved into the area. It is this provision of the law that has been challenged on the belief that individuals should not be punished forever for past deeds. Critics of the law argue that convicted child molesters who have been in prison have paid for their crime. To stigmatize them in communities as sex offenders may further alienate them from mainstream society and increase their vulnerability for repeat offenses.

In many states, Megan's Law is not operative because it is on appeal. Although parents ask, "Would you want a convicted sex offender, even one who has completed his prison sentence, living next door to your 8-year-old daughter?" the reality is that little notification is afforded parents in most states. Because of appeals, the issue is tied up in court and will likely remain so until the Supreme Court decides. A group of concerned parents (Parents for Megan's Law) is trying to implement Megan's Law nationwide. The group's website is http://www.parentsformeganslaw.org/.

In March 2005, 9-year-old Jessica Lunsford of Florida was raped and killed by a registered sex offender. Less than a month later, 13-year-old Sarah Lunde met a similar fate at the hands of another registered sex offender. Within weeks, Governor Jeb Bush signed into law the **Jessica Lunsford Act**, which established a mandatory sentence of 25 years to life behind bars for people convicted of sex crimes against children—and lifetime tracking by global positioning satellite when the offender is released from prison.

Megan's Law
Federal law that requires that convicted sex offenders register with local police when they move into a community

Jessica Lunsford Act
Florida law that establishes a mandatory sentence of 25 years in prison for a person convicted of a sex crime against a child, and on release, the person must wear a global positioning device

What effect has the passage of sex offender registration and notification laws had on the rate of forcible rape? Maurelli and Ronan (2013) analyzed archival crime data of forcible rapes for all 50 of the United States dating from 1960 to 2008, looking at the rates before and after passage of sex offender legislation. The results were mixed, with 17 states demonstrating a significant drop in rates of forcible rape and 32 states demonstrating no discernible change. Potential explanations included the effect of differences in notification practices, registration practices, and the availability of sex offender treatment.

Think About It

Take a moment to answer the following questions. Assume that you have a young child. A convicted child molester has been released from prison and now lives in your neighborhood. What do you feel your rights are as a parent in terms of knowing about the presence of this person? What about this person's right to privacy?

16.8 Treatment of Rape and Child Sexual Abuse Perpetrators

Of 92,490 rapes reported, less than 5% actually resulted in a conviction (Langan & Dawson, 1988). The U.S. Justice Department reported that convicted sex offenders are much more likely to recommit sex offenses than any other type of felon.

Sex offenders rarely seek treatment on their own volition prior to any involvement with legal authorities. Most sex offenders in treatment are required to be there by legal authorities, and many therapists in outpatient programs refuse to take voluntary clients. The timing of therapy is important. Unless therapy occurs when the offender is facing a court sentencing or as a condition of probation, the perpetrator usually denies the existence of a problem and has little motivation for treatment. Experienced clinicians typically request a court order before beginning treatment or recommending a period of inpatient treatment. This approach has proved to be important in keeping offenders in treatment, due to their denial and minimization of their offenses. It also helps reduce the '2-week cure"—"Thank you, doc. That was great. I learned a lot. No, I don't think I need therapy any more. Well, I'll never do that again. So long." (Salter, 1988, p. 87)

Therapeutic alternatives used in the treatment of sex offenders include the use of testosterone-lowering medications (TLM). Turner and colleagues (2013) identified the use of TLM in the treatment of sex offenders in Germany. The heads of all 69 German forensic-psychiatric hospitals and outpatient clinics completed a question-naire assessing treatments used for sex offenders. Thirty-two participating institutions reported on 3,963 patients, 611 of them being sex offenders (15.4%). Most sex offenders had been convicted for child sexual abuse (39.8%) or a sexual assault/rape (37.6%). Almost all sex offenders were treated psychotherapeutically, and 37% were receiving an additional pharmacological treatment. Of all the sex offenders, 15.7% were treated with TLM; 10.6% were treated with a gonadotropin-releasing hormone agonist; and 5.1% were treated with cyproterone acetate. Of these, 26.0%–75.4% showed improvements in such outcomes as reduction of frequency and/or intensity of sexual thoughts. The remaining 21.3% of sex offenders who received a pharmacological agent were treated with selective serotonin reuptake inhibitors (11.5%) or antipsychotic medications

(9.8%). The researchers concluded that TLM are frequently used in addition to psychotherapy in the treatment of sex offenders with some positive outcomes. However, the lack of controlled clinical trials requires caution in interpreting the results.

Other treatments used for sex offenders include group therapy, learning relaxation techniques and stress management, communication skills training, impulse control, increasing arousal to appropriate stimuli, and dealing with the offender's own past sexual or physical abuse. Some treatment programs involve after-care treatment designed to assist the client when he is released from treatment. After-care treatment may include assisting the client in gaining further education or in securing employment.

Is it possible to predict which sex offenders have the highest chance of *not* reoffending after treatment? Somewhat. In a study by Kingston and Bradford (2013), they emphasized the value of hypersexuality (defined in terms of high frequency, intensity, and time devoted to sexual activity) being predictive of sex offender recidivism. A relatively high proportion of sexual offenders report hypersexual behavior, and this construct seems to be associated with re-offending in these men. In a study of 586 adult male sexual offenders with follow-up data up to 20 years, approximately 12% of men met the clinical criterion for hypersexuality; and the presence of this construct was significantly associated with long-term sexual and violent recidivism.

In another study, Wakeling and colleagues (2013) examined the relationship between psychometric changes in treatment and recidivism in a sample of 3,773 sex offenders. All had completed treatment in a prison between 1996 and 2006. Clinically significant changes were calculated for the psychometrics, and for the overarching psychological problems as represented by the four domains: (1) sexual interests, (2) pro-offending attitudes, (3) socio-affective problems, and (4) self-regulation problems. Analyses indicated that those offenders whose scores were in the 'normal range' before and after treatment were reconvicted at a significantly lower rate than those whose scores were not in the 'normal range' after treatment on selected psychometric scales. Additionally, participants who were deemed 'changed' overall on three of the four risk domains were reconvicted at a lower rate than those who were deemed not to have changed on these domains. The overall treatment change status was also computed; however, this did not add significantly to the predictive validity of who would reoffend. The results of the study indicate the potential role and limitations of clinical methodologies in ascertaining whether treatment has worked.

What is the outcome of treating sex offenders? Does it work, or do they reoffend? Craissati and Blundell (2013) provided data on the recidivism of mentally disordered sex offenders who were treated and released in London. Fifty-four had completed a community treatment and followed up for an average of 40 months. Eleven percent were reconvicted for sexual crimes.

16.9 Sexual Harassment

Like rape or child sexual abuse, sexual harassment is another form of sexual coercion. Sexual harassment is a form of sex discrimination that violates Title VII of the Civil Rights Act of 1964.

16.9a Definition and Incidence of Sexual Harassment

According to the Equal Employment Opportunity Commission (EEOC), **sexual harassment** is defined as unwelcome sexual advances, requests for sexual favors, and other verbal or physical conduct of a sexual nature that unreasonably interferes with an individual's work performance or creates an intimidating, hostile, or offensive work

Sexual harassment Unwelcome sexual advances, requests for sexual favors, and other verbal or physical conduct of a sexual nature when submission to or rejection of this conduct explicitly or implicitly affects an individual's employment; unreasonably interferes with an individual's work performance; or creates an intimidating, hostile, or offensive work environment

environment. Both the victim and the harasser can be either male or female, and the victim and harasser can also be of the same sex (Equal Employment Opportunity Commission, 2013).

Sexual harassment often occurs in contexts where a higher status male takes physical liberties with a female who works under him.
Source: Chelsea Curry

Although definitions vary across studies, there is agreement on two elements of the definition: Sexual harassment occurs when sexual behavior is (a) inappropriate for the context and (b) unwanted by a participant or observer. As noted above, sexual harassment may involve men harassing women, women harassing men, men harassing men, and women harassing women.

Two types of sexual harassment have been identified. **Hostile environment sexual harassment** refers to deliberate or repeated unwanted sexual comments or behaviors that affect one's performance at work or school. **Quid pro quo sexual harassment** (*quid pro quo* means *this for that*) sets up workplace consequences contingent upon sexual favors (such as requiring sexual favors to obtain a raise or promotion, or to prevent being fired or demoted). Some common sexual harassment behaviors include unwanted touching, asking sexual questions, asking to be alone with the person, making sexual comments about one's dress or appearance, and sexual graffiti—placing sexual notes or material on a target's desk. The victim does not have to be the person harassed but could be anyone affected by the offensive conduct (e.g., someone else in the office is the target of direct sexual harassment but observing this behavior makes the person uncomfortable).

16.9b Theories of Sexual Harassment

Five theories have been advanced to explain sexual harassment (Sbraga & O'Donohue, 2000). Some of them are the same theories used to explain other types of sexual coercion:

1. The *natural/biological model* implies that sexual harassment is a natural consequence of men's sex drive. The sociobiological model fits here with the assumption that men engage in sexual harassment to increase their probability of gaining sexual access to more women.

2. The *sociocultural model* considers the social and political context of male dominance in the society. Male and female workers often act on gender roles and stereotypes at work. Luo (2013) emphasized that sexual harassment is patriarchal oppression of women.

3. The *organizational model* considers the power hierarchies, norms, and situations within an organization that may be conducive to sexual harassment. For example, there may be personal appearance demands for women, requirements for travel, or working behind closed doors.

4. The *sex-role spillover model* hypothesizes that workers bring gender-biased behavior expectancies into the workplace, even if these beliefs are not appropriate for work. When the sex-role stereotypes are discrepant from the work demands, conflicts arise. Therefore, women in work roles that do not involve nurturing or being an object of sexual attention are more likely to be harassed.

5. The fifth theory, the *four-factor model* offered by O'Hare and O'Donohue (1998), offers a more comprehensive model. It states that for sexual

Hostile environment sexual harassment
Environment whereby deliberate or repeated unwanted sexual comments or behaviors affect one's performance at work or school

Quid pro quo sexual harassment
Type of sexual harassment whereby the individual is provided benefits (promotions, salary raises) in exchange for sexual favors

harassment to occur, four factors must be present: (a) motivation to harass, (b) overcoming internal inhibitions that might suppress harassment, (c) overcoming external inhibitions, and (d) overcoming victim resistance. This model takes into consideration the complexity of a combination of factors (human predispositions, social values and norms, organizational policy, and sex-role beliefs).

16.9c Sexual Harassment in the Workplace

The person most likely to be sexually harassed is the adult female who is financially insecure. Professions that reflect the context of men in high status roles working with women in low status roles are medicine, military service, office work and nursing. Although sexual harassment of men does occur, it is less common because men have greater power in society. Indeed, sexual harassment is often directed toward young, unmarried women in traditionally all-male organizations.

Due to increased visibility of sexual harassment suits in our society, various policies have been instituted for dealing with such harassment. These policies are the topic of the Social Choices 16-2 feature.

Sexual Harassment Policy in the Workplace

The Equal Employment Opportunity Commission (EEOC) of the federal government, major companies, and academic institutions have developed sexual harassment policies. The formal goals of these policies are to go on record as being against sexual harassment, to discourage employees from engaging in sexually harassing behavior, and to provide a mechanism through which harassment victims can inform management. The informal goals are to provide the organization with guidelines for reacting to allegations of harassment and to protect the organization from being taken to court and being forced to pay punitive damages. Organizations and schools also offer educational programs about sexual harassment by developing and distributing brochures and conducting training workshops. Increasingly, policies emphasize the rights of the harassed and the responsibility of the organization to prevent harassment and provide mechanisms for dealing with it when it occurs.

Persons who file sexual harassment suits may encounter empathy for their experiences, or they may discover that the full weight of the organization is being used against them. Both the institution and the alleged harasser may be willing and have the resources to launch a full-scale attack on the professional, personal, and sexual life of the complainant.

16.9d Sexual Harassment in the Military

In 2012, according to the Department of Defense, there were 26,000 sexual assaults in the military, yet only about 14% filed a complaint. Fear of reporting sexual harassment is a primary reason for not reporting such sexual harassment (Lawrence & Penaloza, 2013). The problem is not unique to the U.S. military. Gill and Febbraro (2013) interviewed

BVT *Lab*

Visit **www.BVTLab.com** to explore the student resources available for this chapter.

women in the Canadian military who noted that they feared they might lose their jobs or be derogated by colleagues if they reported sexual harassment.

> It is essentially the woman who is on trial, and the trial can be worse than the rape.
>
> Colonel Elspeth Ritchie, army psychiatrist

Even when a complaint is filed, the "good ole boy" system has ensured that complaints were mostly ignored or denigrated. *The Invisible War* is a 2012 documentary, which details sexual assault in the military. The documentary features women who have been raped and felt that their complaints were ignored and their careers were ruined.

In 2013, Secretary of Defense Chuck Hagel issued statements that the military would not tolerate sexual harassment. Congressional hearings were held on Capitol Hill, and new policies were to be forthcoming. Among these was to remove prosecution from within the military to outside the military. Previously, an assaulted military person could only complain within the military system.

> We are going to work together—all of us to stop these crimes of sexual assault and uphold the honor and integrity that defines the finest military on Earth.
>
> Barack Obama

16.9e Consequences of Sexual Harassment

Although fraudulent charges of sexual harassment can wreck a career, sexual harassment may be devastating for its victims. Direct experiences with harassment can lead to a shattering of victims' core assumptions about the world and themselves—which, in turn, can result in considerable psychological distress. Victims complain of depression, anxiety, anger, fear, guilt, helplessness, sexual dysfunction, isolation from family/friends, and substance abuse. A former student recalled how her boss was giving favors to several of the female workers in the office and paying their rent bills, letting them come in late/leave early, etc. When she was asked to "have a drink" (translate as "become sexual") and she refused, she reported that her boss "turned her life into a living hell" by complaining about her work, dumping unreasonable amounts of work on her, refusing to let her leave early, etc.

Take a moment to answer the following questions. Suppose Mark, a restaurant manager, likes Maria, a waitress at the restaurant. Mark wants to pursue a relationship with Maria but is afraid that any suggestive comments he might make may be construed as harassment. How could Mark "flirt" with Maria without risking an accusation of harassment? How could Maria communicate to Mark that his behavior makes her uncomfortable and that she wants him to stop? Or, how could she communicate to him that she wants a relationship with him and for him to stop being worried about "sexual harassment"?

16.9f Responses to Sexual Harassment

Victims' most frequent response to sexual harassment is to ignore it. Unfortunately, ignoring harassment does not make it go away. Many victims try to avoid the harasser by dropping a class, changing a position, or quitting a job. These indirect strategies are not very effective and do nothing to deter the harasser from violating others. However, victims may not be more direct about voicing their complaints out of fear of retaliation if they do complain.

personal Choices 16-2

Confronting Someone Who Sexually Harasses You

Aside from ignoring or avoiding the sexual harasser, a victim has at least three choices: verbal, written, or institutional/legal action. The verbal choice consists of telling the harasser what behavior he or she is engaging in that creates discomfort and then asking the person to stop. The victim could soften the accusation by saying something like, "You may not be aware that some of the things you say and do make me uncomfortable. … " Some harassers might respond with denial, such as "What are you talking about? I was just joking." Others might apologize and stop the behavior.

If direct communication is not successful in terminating the harassment, a written statement of the concerns is the next level of intervention. Such a letter should detail the sexual harassment behaviors (with dates of occurrence) and include a description of the consequences (personal distress, depression, sleeplessness). The letter should end with a statement of what the victim would like to happen in the future. For example, "I ask that our future interaction be formal and professional."

The letter should be sent immediately after it becomes clear that the offender did not take the verbal requests for change seriously. If the desired behavior is not forthcoming, the letter can be used as evidence of an attempt to alert the offender of the sexual harassment problem. Use of this evidence may be internal (inside the organization) or external (a formal complaint filed with the Equal Employment Opportunity Commission). Information for filing a complaint with the EEOC can be found at its website.

Unfortunately, women who take the direct approach to confront the harasser are at greater risk for experiencing adverse psychological and somatic symptoms than those who attempt to solve the problem indirectly. Although the direct approach is assertive, harassment victims who speak up often encounter reprisals, counter-allegations, forced time off from work, and slander. "My boss had a team of lawyers waiting on any female who did not play along," recalled a former student.

Chapter **Summary**

Sexual coercion involves depriving a person of free choice and using force (actual or threatened) to engage that person in sexual acts against that person's will. This chapter discussed rape and child sexual abuse.

Sexual Coercion: Rape and Sexual Assault

Approximately one in five females will be victim of a rape. Regardless of the official rape reports, it is estimated that from 75% to 95% of female rapes are not reported. Sexual coercion involves using force (actual or threatened) to engage a person in sexual acts against that person's will.

Theories of Rape

Theories of rape include evolutionary/biological theory (men are predisposed to rape women to plant their seed and reproduce); psychopathological theory (rapists have a mental disorder); feminist theory (rape is due to unequal status between men and women in society); and social learning theory (men are socialized that it is okay to rape women).

Consequences of Rape and Treatment for Rape Survivors

Rape is a traumatic experience, and the effects of successful treatment is slow. Initial reactions to rape include an acute period of disorganization, helplessness, vulnerability, and anger. The person may also blame himself or herself for the incident. The most devastating aspect of rape may not be the genital contact, but rather the sense of cognitive and emotional violation. Post-traumatic stress disorder may follow if the assault invoked terror, helplessness, or fear of loss of life. The rape survivor may have persistent episodes of re-experiencing the event, such as flashbacks, hallucinations, or nightmares. Anger, social isolation, depressed mood, and lower self-esteem are other consequences.

Prevention of Rape

Women must acknowledge that rape is a real possibility, particularly acquaintance rape, and that they must monitor their alcohol/drug consumption to keep their wits about them. They must also identify the signs of an impending rape. A male who sexualizes the conversation, who encourages the woman to drink, who is "all hands," who seeks to isolate her from her friends, and/or who does not take "no" for an answer should be identified as dangerous; the woman should extricate herself or escape from him ASAP.

Rape prevention also involves teaching men *not* to rape. This includes alerting men that U.S. society provides the context for them to be socialized to dominate women and to believe in rape myths (e.g., "no" means "yes"). Correction of the tendency to believe in rape myths must begin early. Rejection of sexual myths and respect for the dignity and privacy women must be followed by not sexualizing conversations, not getting her drunk, and including her friends. Men must also remember that a woman in an altered state (alcohol/drugs) who is passive does not imply consent to have sex. Having sex with a woman who is cognitively altered is against the law.

Child Sexual Abuse

Child sexual abuse may be both physical and emotional. Physical sexual abuse includes sexual intercourse or penetration, genital or anal fondling or touching, oral sex, kissing, and/or forced performing of fellatio and cunnilingus of a minor by an adult or to an adult. Emotional sexual abuse of a child can include behaviors such as forcing a minor to watch sexual acts, encouraging the child to undress in front of others, and/or making lewd comments about a minor. In either case of child sexual abuse, the child experiences a breakdown of trust, destruction of boundaries and a sense of violation.

Consequences and Treatment of Child Sexual Abuse

Child sexual abuse is associated with numerous negative outcomes: depression, anxiety, PTSD, alcohol/substance abuse, sexual dysfunction, distrust in relationships, difficulties with intimacy, lower self-esteem and eating disorders. The various types of therapy include counseling, play therapy, and cognitive behavioral therapy (CBT)—all of which are consistent with what has been previously reported in the literature on child sexual abuse interventions.

Prevention of Child Sexual Abuse

Strategies to reduce child sexual abuse include regendering cultural roles, providing specific information to children on sex abuse, improving the safety of neighborhoods, providing healthy sexuality information for both teachers and children in public schools at regular intervals, and promoting public awareness campaigns. Megan's Law is an effort to make communities safe. Some advocates of Megan's Law have sought incarceration of sex offenders in treatment facilities after they are released from prison. There is debate about whether this violates the civil liberties of a person who has paid the debt for his crime. The Jessica Lunsford Act established (in Florida) a mandatory sentence of 25 years to life behind bars for people convicted of sex crimes against children, followed by lifetime tracking by global positioning satellite when released from prison.

Treatment of Rape and Child Sexual Abuse Perpetrators

Reporting an incident of rape or sexual abuse to legal authorities may help to leverage treatment for the offender. Therapeutic interventions include techniques to reduce deviant arousal and to increase arousal to appropriate stimuli. Training to improve communication skills and impulse control may be used, as well as treatment to deal with an offender's own past sexual or physical abuse.

Sexual Harassment

Sexual harassment is defined as unwelcome sexual advances, requests for sexual favors, and other verbal or physical conduct of a sexual nature when submission to or rejection of this conduct explicitly or implicitly affects an individual's employment. Men and women, of both heterosexual or homosexual orientation, report having been sexually harassed.

Web Links

Campaign to Prevent Child Abuse

    http://www.stopitnow.com/

Equal Employment Opportunity Comission

    http://www.eeoc.gov/facts/fs-sex.html

Rape, Abuse, and Incest National Network

    http://www.rainn.org

SAFE: Sexual Assault Facts & Education

    http://rivervision.com/safe/index.html

Stop Rape Now

    www.stoprapenow.org

Key Terms

Acquaintance rape   456

Classic rape   457

Date rape   456

Extrafamilial child sexual abuse   470

Forced sex   454

Forcible rape   454

GHB- Gamma hydroxybutyrate   456

Honor killing   463

Hostile environment sexual harassment   478

Intrafamilial child sexual abuse   467

Jessica Lunsford Act   475

Marital rape   454

Megan's Law   475

Post-traumatic stress disorder   464

Predatory rape   457

Quid pro quo sexual harassment   478

Rape   454

Rape myths   455

Rape-supportive beliefs   455

Rape trauma syndrome   464

Rohypnol   456

Secondary victimization   463

Sexual coercion   454

Sexual harassment   477

Additional study resources are available at www.BVTLab.com

CHAPTER 17

Commercialization of Sex

I believe that sex is one of the most beautiful, natural, wholesome things that money can buy.

Steve Martin, comedian and actor

Chapter Outline

Objectives

1. Explain the impact of sex in advertising.
2. Understand the various expressions of sexuality on the Internet, including the benefits.
3. Discuss sex and the law.
4. Describe the four types of sexuality businesses.
5. Review the data on the effects of exposure to pornography.
6. Know the different types of prostitution and the demographics of "Johns."
7. Learn about sex trafficking.
8. Discuss sex trafficking.

Source: Shutterstock

Truth *OR* Fiction?

T/F   Of 1,550 men reporting anal sex during their last encounter, half had not used a condom.

T/F   The *DSM-5* recognizes the concept of Internet addiction.

T/F   Pornography use is associated with extramarital sex for both men and women.

T/F   Pimping has been regarded as the "second oldest profession."

T/F   Vaginal sex is the most frequent sexual behavior men have with streetwalker prostitutes.

Answers:
1.T 2.F 3.T 4.T 5.F

George Flint is Senior Lobbyist for the Nevada Brothel Owners Association. He says that "Other than the urge to survive, the urge for sex in a normal man is the strongest urge he has to deal with. I have come to the conclusion that legal and regulated prostitution is better than the alternative since it eliminates pimps and eliminates crimes on the client and on the woman" (Procon. org, 2013). Earlier in his career Flint insisted that a trip to the Mustang Ranch (a brothel) could be as important as driving to Mount Rushmore and that brothels are part of Nevada's history. While Mr. Flint has a unique approach to commercializing sex,

> *Advertising doesn't mirror how people are acting but how people are dreaming.*
>
> Jerry Goodis, advertising executive

more common examples include phone sex, erotic massage, stripping, pornography, and prostitution—all examined in this chapter. While the morality of these commercial uses of sex is often the focus of heated debate, there are other ways that people make money in reference to sex that is not questioned. For example, sex therapists make money on sex, yet this is an "acceptable" example of the commercialization of sex that occurs with passive recognition.

17.1 Sex in Advertising

The use of sex in advertising continues to increase (Cheung, Chan, Han, Sze, & Fan, 2013). A television advertisement shows an affectionate couple dressed with minimal clothes in a context where sex could occur. "Be ready for the moment" is the phrase of the announcer; Levitra, the new quick-start Viagra, is the product for sale. The advertiser uses sex to get the attention of the viewer and punches in the product. In this chapter, sex is the product.

> *If we define pornography as any message from any communication medium that is intended to arouse sexual excitement, then it is clear that most advertisements are covertly pornographic.*
>
> Philip Slater, sociologist

17.2 Sexuality and the Internet

Internet sex searches range from finding educational sexual material (e.g., Siecus. org) to finding a sex therapist; shopping for, purchasing, or selling sexuality related items (books, DVDs, sex toys) for entertainment/masturbation use offline; engaging in mutual erotic dialogue; and having **cybersex**—engaging in self-stimulation while online. The Internet is also used to find a sex partner. Rosenbaum and colleagues (2013) examined how people advertise themselves on Craigslist and revealed that both heterosexuals and homosexuals seek and offer sex.

> *The Internet is a virtual store open 24 hours a day ... with millions of users on-line. ... Someone who knows how to navigate the World Wide Web can, at any moment, find a kindred spirit with a similar sexual interest or desire.*
>
> Al Cooper, Sylvain Boies, Marlene Maheu, David Greenfield, researchers and authors

National DATA

There are 4.2 million pornographic websites, which represent 12% of the total number of websites. There are 68 million search engine requests each day for pornography, 25% of all requests. Of Internet users, 43% watch pornography (Internet Pornography Statistics, 2013).

17.2a Sexuality on the Internet

Cybersex
Engaging in self-stimulation while online to include "looking at pictures, engaging in sexual chat, exchanging explicit sexual emails, and sharing mutual sexual fantasies while masturbating"

Sexual content of the Internet is extensive. The Internet features erotic photos and webcams whereby some females strip/dance (via SKYPE) for their long distance partners. Other webcam strippers generate income from nude dancing. Some suggest that the government should intervene and control the sexual content on the Internet (see Social Choices 17-1).

> *It is the policy of the United States to promote a global Internet free from government control and to preserve and advance the successful multistakeholder model that governs the Internet.*
>
> Bill submitted to U.S. House of Representatives, April 2013

Government Control of Sexual Content on the Internet

Should the government censor sexual content on the Internet? This question is the focus of an ongoing public debate that concerns protecting children from sexually explicit content on the Internet. One side of the issue is reflected in the Communications Decency Act, passed by Congress in 1996, which prohibited sending "indecent" messages over the Internet to people under age 18. The Supreme Court rejected the law in 1997, however, citing that the law was too broadly worded and violated free-speech rights in that it restricted too much material that adults might want to access. A similar ruling in 2002 has hampered government crackdown on pornography, including virtual child pornography. In support of not limiting sexual content on the Internet, the American Civil Liberties Union emphasized that governmental restrictions threaten material protected by the First Amendment, including sexually explicit poetry and material educating disabled persons on how to experience sexual pleasure.

Congress passed another law (Child Online Protection Act or COPA) in 1998, which made it a crime to knowingly make available to people under age 17 any web materials that, based on "contemporary community standards," were designed to pander to prurient interests. The law required commercial operators to verify that a user was an adult through credit card information and adult access codes. Businesses that broke the law would be subject to a $50,000 fine and 6 months in jail. An inadvertent effect of the act has been to require public libraries to install Internet filters to block access to objectionable sites. However, a U.S. appeals court and panel of federal judges have struck down this law on the basis that it violates free speech guaranteed by the First Amendment.

Other than child pornography, there are virtually no restrictions on sexual content on the Internet in the U.S. However, some other countries have restrictive Internet policies. China has the world's largest Internet population. The Chinese government has customized blocking strategies for what it considers to be important websites (Feng & Guo, 2013). In Singapore, the government requires Internet service providers to block access to certain websites that contain pornography or inflame political, religious, or racial sensitivities. China's largest service provider blocks at least 100 sites, including *Playboy*.

In the United States, parents—not the government—are expected to be responsible for regulating children's use of the Internet. Software products such as Net Nanny, CYBERsitter, and CyberPatrol are marketed to help parents control what their children view on the Internet. These software programs allow parents to block unapproved websites and categories (such as pornography), block transmission of personal data (such as address and telephone numbers), scan pages for sexual material before they are viewed, and track Internet usage. NQ Family Guardian provides a smartphone for children that has a "web filter" (parents can block inappropriate website); "app filter" (to ensure child-friendly apps); "contact filter" (parents can choose what numbers to block); "monitors" (allows parents to know where their children are, their texts, photos, and browsing history); and scheduling (allows parents to set up times their children can use the phone, including blocking its use for school and bedtime).

Parents can also use the Internet with their children, both to monitor what their children are viewing and to teach their children values about what they believe is right and wrong on the Internet. Some parents believe that children must learn how to safely surf the Internet. One parent reported that the Internet is like a busy street—just as you must teach your children how to safely cross in traffic, you must teach them how to avoid giving information to strangers on the Internet.

17.2b Benefits of Sexuality on the Internet

Sex on the Internet has both positive and negative consequences and poses many ethical dilemmas. The advantages are educational, social, emotional, cognitive, and sexual (e.g., sexual health).

Get Sex Information/Education

Smith (2013) confirmed the value of the Internet in regard to sex education. He conducted 51 interviews with young adults who revealed their motivations for using the Internet which included curiosity about sex, curiosity about sexually explicit material, sex with romantic partners/in groups, or for individual sexual pleasure. Many participants described incorporating ideas gleaned from sexually explicit material into their sexual experiences.

> *Internet dating: the odds are good, but sometimes the goods are odd.*
>
> Anonymous

> *Finding a partner on the Internet for a committed relationship is a full time job. It takes hours to find the right photo of yourself to post, complete your own profile, go through the profiles of hundreds of guys online, and respond to emails … but I found my man!*
>
> Anonymous

McCarthy and colleagues (2012) conducted focus groups and one-on-one interviews with 67 young people ages 16–22 in London to find out what sexuality information they wanted on a website. The participants specified that they wanted "straightforward information" on sexual pleasure, sexually transmitted infections and pregnancy, how to communicate with partners, how to develop skills in giving pleasure, and emotions involved in sex and relationships.

Go Ask Alice is an online question-and-answer sex information resource sponsored by Columbia University (http://www.goaskalice.columbia.edu/). Alice fields questions on sex, relationships, drugs, and other topics. No question is taboo. Other sex education sites are www.sexetc.org (a website by teens for teens), http://www.plannedparenthood.org/info-for-teens/ (a sexuality teen site sponsored by Planned Parenthood), and http://www.iwannaknow.org (a teen sexual health and STI information site sponsored by the American Social Health Association).

BVT *Lab*

Flashcards are available for this chapter at **www.BVTLab.com**.

Go Ask Alice is a website dedicated to answering sexual questions.
Source: E. Fred Johnson, Jr.

Anonymous STI Testing

For persons unwilling to go to a health clinic for an STI check, the Internet provides a quick, anonymous alternative. Private Med Labs is an online resource that allows one to be tested (http://www.privatemdlabs.com/lp/OnlineSTDTesting.php).

Find a Mate

Using the Internet to find a mate is losing its stigma. No longer do members of a couple lie about how they met—they simply say "we met on Match" (and laugh). A person can log on to one of the hundreds of dating services (e.g., Match.com and eHarmony.com) (or meet through Facebook), sift through page after page of individual profiles to identify those with basic desired characteristics (e.g., race, age, education, religion, smoking preference, sexual orientation, presence/absence of children), and select those he or she wants to pursue.

One caveat is to be aware that persons who meet on the Internet often disclose a great deal through emails/text exchanges with the result that they "fall in love" quickly. Relationship development cannot be short-circuited. The Internet couple needs time to meet, spend time together, meet each others' family, etc., and in general, know each other for about 2 years before a wedding. Personal Experience 17-1 reflects the experience of a divorced woman who met a new partner (and future husband) online.

PERSONAL Experience 17-1

I Met My Husband on the Internet

I was 28, recently divorced from an 8-year marriage, and alone. I didn't want to complicate my life by getting involved with anyone at work, and I didn't like the loud smoky bar routine. Alone one night, I turned on my computer, logged onto one of the commercial services, and went to one of the bulletin boards where a lot of people "hang out." I posted a note entitled, "Make me laugh." I thought this was innocuous enough as I did not want to appear desperate.

To my surprise, I received over 50 responses. Most (85%) were from guys seeking cybersex, a few shared jokes, and still fewer just wanted to talk. Soon I was regularly sending emails to men in five different states. After several weeks I fell in love with one of them, arranged to meet him, and fell deeper in love. But he was recently divorced and didn't want to tie himself to one partner. I was heartbroken and alone again ... but turned my computer back on.

A man from Arizona began to pique my interest. Suddenly we began to email each other nightly and share our histories, interests, values, and goals. Within a short time, I knew I had discovered my soul mate and fell even more deeply in love with this man than the previous cyber man. After a photo exchange, hours of phone conversations, and enormous phone bills (I mean $400 monthly phone bills), we met and discovered that we had found the love of our lives.

Quickly we planned to meet each other's family and were married in 6 weeks. Although this sounds very impulsive, we discussed every imaginable issue and just felt that this was "right." Although we met six states away from each other via computer, we now live in our home and are rearing our twins born last month. Meeting "on-line" certainly worked for us. (authors' files)

Find a Sex Partner

While heterosexual and LGBT individuals use the Internet to find lifetime partners, they also use the Internet to find hook-up partners. Some of the profiles on Match.com reveal the person's sexual motives: "Looking for someone to be physically intimate without strings attached." Hooking up is becoming normative. Fielder and colleagues (2013) surveyed 483 first-year female college students (mean age, 18.1 years; range, 18–21 years; 64% white) monthly over the first year of college about the frequency of sexual behavior in the context of hookups. Forty percent reported hooking up during the first year. While most of these hookups were doubtless on campus, the data show an openness to hooking up with a new person who can also be met online.

Take a moment to answer the following questions. Internet infidelity is also an issue about which some partners disagree. Does developing an online emotional relationship involving the exchange of sexual fantasies constitute being unfaithful to one's partner? Does such interaction degrade the value of faithfulness an individual has toward one's partner and relationship? What amount of time emailing others is appropriate?

Maintain a Long-Distance Relationship

The Internet/email/SKYPE help to bridge the distance and maintain long-distance relationships. Couples separated due to career (job in another town), education (college in another town), family responsibilities (caring for a parent in another town), or war (deployed) can connect with each other daily. Such frequent contact helps to nurture the relationship and reduces the negative effect of being separated.

Experience Sexual Fantasies/Cybersex

Individuals with similar sexual interests and fetishes may exchange photos and play out their sexual fantasies online. Safe sex (as long as it is limited to cybersex) is a benefit of Internet sex in that individuals can share sexual fantasies online with no risk of contracting sexually transmissible infections.

In addition, sexual fantasy may be used to reignite one's sexual arousal. Boncinelli and colleagues (2013) emphasized the role of sexual fantasy in the therapy of hypoactive sexual desire in women. The researchers analyzed 52 cases of women with little interest in sex and noted that, for some, sexual fantasy can be used to bring back the eroticism in the partner and in the relationship. The Internet can be used to find visuals and erotic reading material to enhance one's sexual interest.

Connect Disenfranchised or Marginalized Groups

Persons who have unique demographic features or backgrounds may find others who share their background. Persons who have been raped; have sexually transmitted infections (herpes, HPV, AIDS); or are paraplegic/disabled, a cross-dresser, or a transsexual may find others on the Internet who share these experiences and communicate with them. Doing so reduces the feeling of isolation and increases feeling "normal" (since others share the same phenomenon).

Try Out a New Identity

The Internet provides a way to gain information about a set of practices or an identity concept and to try out a new identity online. A person who experiences feelings of being attracted to same-sex individuals may interact with homosexuals online to experience how such interaction feels without the attendant anxiety of doing so in person. Cross-dressers, transsexuals, etc., may also try out new identities.

17.2c Disadvantages of Sexuality on the Internet

Sexual uses of the Internet may also involve negative consequences.

Spread of STIs/HIV

National DATA

In a national sample of 2,865 men who have sex with men, 62% met their partner through the Internet. Among those reporting anal sex during their last encounter (*n* = 1,550), half had not used a condom (Groy, Hirshfield, Remien, Humberstone, & Chiasson, 2013).

Cybersex Crime

Examples of cybersex crimes include obscene emails, unsolicited porn, spam, and the posting of false personal ads advertising the victims' availability for sex. These behaviors are also an example of online sexual harassment.

Deception

Lincoln and Coyle (2013) studied sex predators on the Internet and emphasized that they use deception to lure unsuspecting youth to participate in sexual behavior. Indeed, since one only sees words on a computer screen, the pedophile is advantaged.

Finding a partner on the Internet also involves deception with the partners presenting inaccurate information—about their marital status, their weight, their height, their income, their bad habits (e.g., alcoholism) etc. Because deception is rampant on the Internet, adults who are connecting with other adults might set up a time to meet at Starbucks or some other public place to provide a reality check on who is behind the computer screen.

Internet Addiction (IA)

Griffiths (2012) reviewed the literature on "internet sex addiction" and provided a summary:

> "The advent of the Internet has added another medium in which people can engage in sexual behavior. This ranges from the passive consumption of online pornography to the interactive exchange of sexual content in cybersex chat rooms. It is believed that access, affordability, and anonymity are critical factors that make the Internet viable for the acquisition, development, and maintenance of online sexuality. For some, sexual behaviors online are used as a complement to their offline sexuality, whereas for others, they serve as a substitute, potentially resulting in Internet sex addiction, which can be conceptualized as the intersection between Internet addiction and sex addiction. The current literature suggests that there does not appear to be

a clear dividing line between these psychopathologies. ... Based on the five qualitative and nine quantitative studies conducted in Western countries, it was concluded that engaging in sexual behaviors on the Internet can go awry and result in Internet sex addiction, as it can lead to a wide variety of negative consequences for the individuals affected" (p. 111).

Among these consequences is an example of a man who lost his job (since he spent 12 hours a day on the Internet looking at porn) and almost lost his marriage. His wife knew nothing about his online Internet behavior.

One of the potential negative consequences of Internet "addiction" for individuals is that their partners may feel betrayed and replaced. Because social, emotional, and sexual connections can be made quickly on the computer, people sometimes abandon face-to-face relationships in reality. Indeed, they may become so socially isolated with their computer relationships that they neglect the development of their live interpersonal skills and relationships. One woman complained that "he's always in there on the computer and would rather be in chat rooms than in the room talking with me" (authors' files).

Whether Internet addiction exists is controversial. Those who support the concept regard excessive and uncontrollable use of the Internet as proof of its existence. Those who feel the term "addition" is inaccurate point out that the *DSM-5* does not recognize the term (Starcevic, 2013).

In spite of the controversy, Dalbudak and colleagues (2013) investigated the relationship of Internet addiction with alexithymia (emotional aloofness). A total of 319 students from two conservative universities in Ankara, Turkey, took the Internet Addiction Scale and the Toronto Alexithymia Scale. Of those students, 12% were characterized in the moderate/high IA group and 26% in the mild IA group. Twenty percent of the men in contrast to 9% of women were classified into the moderate/high group. Findings revealed that the severity of IA was positively correlated with alexithymia.

Pedophiles on the Internet

The Internet is used by pedophiles to lure victims into forced sex. Wolak and Finkelhor (2013) analyzed national data on 2,653 arrests of Internet related sex crimes against minors. The charges included statutory rape (i.e., nonforcible illegal sexual activity with underage youth) or noncontact offenses, such as child pornography production.

Through the Internet, dissemination of child pornography has become pervasive because pedophiles can connect with each other and share pictures. Youth can be used in pornography without contact between the child and the perpetrator because images of a child can be digitally transformed into pornography and distributed without the knowledge of the victim. Pornographic images can be a source of repeated, long-term victimization that can last for years.

Our society is on hypersensitive alert for child pornography. Wal-Mart refuses to develop any photos containing nudity in any context, adult or child. Pornography fueled by the Internet can be complex to investigate; and criminal activity can transcend jurisdictional boundaries and may involve victims from various communities, states, and countries. Perpetrators will travel great distances to engage in sexual acts with children they contacted through the Internet.

Although the Internet has become one of the most valuable information and educational tools of our society, it can be lethal if children are not properly supervised in its use. Pedophiles, posing as friends, may enter chat rooms with unsuspecting prepubescents, interact with them as though they are peers, arrange to meet them at the mall, and abduct them. Awareness of the presence of pedophiles on the Internet has become a concern for parents who want their children to become computer literate. Pedophiles have no shortage of sites.

One strategy to reduce the exposure of children to pedophiles on the Internet is to not allow children to have a computer in their bedroom where they can spend long hours in isolation on the computer without the content being monitored. Rather, the computer should be placed in the living room, family room, or other open space where constant monitoring of content can occur. Websites such as GetNetWise (http://kids.getnetwise.org/) address safe Internet use by children. Personal Choices 17-1 presents a recommended agreement between parents and children. Still another Internet site designed to help children remain safe on the Internet is Kidshield (http://www.kidshield.com/).

Sexting—Both Positive and Negative

Sexting has become fairly common across all types of romantic relationships (committed, casually sexual, and cheating) with text messaging the primary medium used to send sex pictures and videos (Drouin, Vogel, Surbey, & Stills, 2013). Sexting may be positive as a relationship enhancer, or a ticket to becoming a felon if the photos are of underage individuals. Sexting may also put one's career in jeopardy (e.g., Congressman Anthony Weiner).

personal Choices 17-1

Online Safety—An Agreement Between Children and Parents

1. I will ALWAYS tell a parent or another adult, immediately, if something is confusing or seems scary or threatening.
2. I will NEVER give out my full name, real address, telephone number, school name or location, schedule, password, or other identifying information when I'm online. I will check with an adult for any exceptions.
3. I will NEVER have a face-to-face meeting with someone I've met online. In rare cases, my parents may decide it's OK; but if I do decide to meet a cyber pal, I will make sure we meet in a public place and that a parent or guardian is with me.
4. I will NEVER respond online to any messages that use bad words or words that are scary, threatening, or just feel weird. If I get that kind of message, I'll print it out and tell an adult immediately. The adult can then contact the online service or appropriate agency. If I'm uncomfortable in a live chat room, I will use the "ignore" button.
5. I will NEVER go into a new online area that is going to cost additional money without first asking permission from my parent or teacher.
6. I will NEVER send a picture over the Internet or via regular mail to anyone without my parent's permission.
7. I will NOT give out a credit card number online without a parent present.

Young Person_____ Date_____
Parent/Guardian_____ Date_____

Source: Reprinted by permission of Internet Education Foundation. http://www.getnetwise.org/

17.3 Sex and the Law

An unending debate in U.S. society exists around the issue of private rights versus social morality. For example, should consenting adults be permitted to engage in any sexual behaviors they choose, or should the law define morally acceptable parameters?

John Stuart Mill (1859/1985) emphasized the rights of the individual by arguing that the only purpose of government should be to protect its citizens from harm by others. He also advocated that:

> The liberty of the individual must be thus far limited; he must not make himself a nuisance to other people. But if he refrains from molesting others in what concerns them, and merely acts according to his own inclination and judgment in things which concern himself, … he should be allowed, without molestation, to carry his opinions into practice at his own cost (pp. 119–120).

In contrast, the Meese Commission Report on pornography reflected a version of legislating morality (*Attorney General's Commission on Pornography*, U.S. Department of Justice, 1986). The commission took the position that the protection of society's moral environment was a legitimate purpose of government and recommended more restrictive laws on pornography. The George W. Bush administration launched a new "war on pornography."

One of the ways that society has achieved compromise and balance between the radically opposing views of private versus public morality has been to view certain sexual behaviors on a continuum of offensiveness and to assign relative penalties for engaging in them. For example, child sexual abuse and rape are regarded as severely offensive and are subject to strong social sanctions. However, frottage may go unrecognized in criminal statistics because such behavior is likely to be prosecuted under a more generalized category, such as assault.

The following are five categories of sexual acts according to criminal classification:

- *Category I*—Criminal acts that require enforcement to protect society (Rape and child molestation are examples.)
- *Category II*—Sexual acts with potential victimization (Exhibitionism and voyeurism are examples. Although these behaviors themselves may not be regarded as morally severe, they may create harm to the victims, who deserve protection.)
- *Category III*—Sexual acts midway between those considered morally reprehensible and those creating victims (Prostitution and adultery are examples. Both are said to reflect immorality; and both have the potential to produce victims, the prostitutes in the case of prostitution and the spouse or children of the adulterer.)
- *Category IV*—Sex acts between consenting adults, including homosexual behavior and behaviors within marriage
- *Category V*—Behaviors that do not involve sexual contact, but are either criminalized or considered to be sex crimes (abortion, in countries where it is illegal, and the sale and distribution of child pornography are examples.)

17.4 Sexual Businesses

A number of businesses exist to sell sex. Their products are sexual fantasy (phone sex), nudity (stripping), and orgasm (erotic massage parlors), etc.

17.4a Phone Sex

Phone sex (sometimes referred to as "guided masturbation") is a telephone conversation between a caller and a sex worker (also referred to as "phone-actress," "fantasy artist," or "adult phone entertainer") who verbally arouses, stimulates, and moves the caller toward orgasm in exchange for money. Phone sex advertisements (usually provocative photos with toll-free numbers) are in men's magazines, on websites, and on late-night cable TV. The individual (usually heterosexual) calls the 800 or 900 number, tells the sex worker the kind of sex fantasy or "dirty talk" desired, and masturbates to the words of the sex worker. Phone sex is not prostitution because there is no live, face-to-face, body-to-body exchange of sexual service for money. Popular in the 80s/90s, phone sex has largely been replaced by web cam sex in which a person connects online with a female and "directs" her to do as he asks. Nevertheless, the phone sex section to follow provides an insight into the perception of the sex worker.

> *When a man talks dirty to a woman, it's sexual harassment. When a woman talks dirty to a man, it's $3.95 a minute.*
>
> Anonymous

Inside the Phone Sex Industry

Amy Flowers (1998) was a participant observer in the phone sex industry. She noted one of her first discoveries as a "fantasy artist":

> *What callers are really buying is a few minutes of human contact within a society where personal contact is fraught with ambiguity.*
>
> Amy Flowers, *The Fantasy Factory*

> [P]hone sex requires real skill and creativity. Imagine, for example, talking for ten minutes or longer to someone with a foot fetish. Removing high-heeled shoes and stockings and then describing the color of nail polish and the shape of my toes took a scant two minutes. As soon as I began to slow down or stammer for lack of material, the caller would hang up. (p. 19)

Amy Flowers (1998) spoke with an estimated 3,200 callers during her 4 months as a phone sex actress. She also interviewed 21 phone sex actresses about their experience in the industry. Entry into the role was driven by economics and lack of alternatives. As one informant revealed,

> [Y]ou really have no choice but to work there. Any of the skills I have, they can pay [an immigrant] $3.00 an hour. So that was the only thing available to me, and it was fun at first. I sit there, put my feet up. I read a book, I've got my drink, I light a cigarette at my ash tray at my own desk. The phone rings, I talk to some weirdo, say a bunch of stuff, and I get paid 10 bucks an hour—this is great. (p. 29)

The actual place from which the calls were made was a small cubicle in corporate America with 8:00 p.m. to 4:00 a.m. being a typical shift.

> The phone room had six rows of six cubicles for a total of thirty-six stations. … Each station had two single-line telephones. … A nearby operator offered me some rubbing alcohol to disinfect my phones. She also explained that I should first ask the caller's age and when he graduated from high school in order to screen underage callers. (p. 18)

Pretending was part of the role of the phone sex operator. There was a straight man who took calls as a heterosexual woman, black women who presented themselves as white, and fat girls who said they were thin with hourglass figures. Lying about love feelings was also part of the job.

> I'd feel sorry for them. They'd say they love me, and I'd say, "Oh, no you don't really love me. You love what you think is me." "And my supervisor is going [makes cut-throat gesture]." "Don't give him therapy. Just say, 'I love you, too. Now what else do you want to do with me?' " (p. 50)

Phone sex
Telephone conversation between a caller and a sex worker who verbally arouses, stimulates, and moves the caller toward orgasm in exchange for money

17.4b Camming

The Internet has allowed the customer to not only talk with a sex worker, but see her. **Camming** is the use of a webcam to facilitate the customer seeing/directing/interacting with the female performer. Camming allows the illusion that he is sitting in the room with her—he can talk and see her—except the script is sexual, he tells her what he wants her to do (e.g., masturbate). Livejasmin.com, Myfreecams.com and ImLive.com are examples of the over 800 web cam sites on the Internet.

> *The customers think they are going to get laid, but all they get is screwed out of their money.*
>
> A stripper

17.4c Strip Clubs

Modern day strip clubs (euphemistically called "adult entertainment") owe their heritage to the art of striptease, which flourished in the 1940s and 1950s. Gypsy Rose Lee is the most famous of the striptease performers. She took her time, toyed with the men she performed for, and took off relatively little. See the Personal Experience 17-2 insert for the revelations of a modern day stripper.

What It's Like to Be a Stripper

While some people refer to what I do as "stripping," to me, I am a dancer. I have always loved to dance. I was a cheerleader in high school and on the dance team—I have always been a dancing performer and I love it.

I got into dancing on a lark. One night my girlfriends and I were out and decided to go to amateur night at a local club. Three of us got up and danced. I found that I liked it, did not mind taking my clothes off, and when the music stopped I was hooked.

I've been dancing for five months and I'm on the two year plan. I'll make enough money to take care of getting me through dental hygiene school. The lowest I have made in a night was $10, the highest $700.

Both my parents know I dance, and they are OK with it. My mom came to the club and was impressed that it was "upscale." Both parents asked that I not tell their parents (my grandparents) since they would not understand.

I don't have a boyfriend. I'm happy without one for now. Guys can't handle their lady being a dancer, so I am going to avoid the drama. I have close relationships with my family and girlfriends.

I have been offered money for sex three times in five months. The highest offer was a guy offered me $5,000 to do him and his wife. I am not for sale, so it was easy to say no.

I think the hardest part of my job is that some people look down on me. I work hard for my money, am not promiscuous, am good to people ... so I'm sorry they don't understand.

Camming
The use of a webcam to facilitate the customer seeing/directing/ interacting with the female performer

Although some strip clubs feature male strippers for gay men and female strippers for gay women, the overwhelming majority of strip clubs exists for the heterosexual man and that will be the focus of this section.

Due to Internet pornography/web cams, men have access to seeing whatever they want. So the pressure on strippers is to do less "tease" and just take off their clothes.

The dancer knows the script, so she strips quickly, picks up the money, and returns to her dressing room or to the floor to solicit a private **table dance** whereby she dances and/or disrobes on the customer's table or in front of the seated customer. Although the dancer may put her hands on the shoulders of the customer, typically he is not to touch her; and there must be a one-foot distance between the dancer and the customer. Some strip clubs offer a **lap dance**, also known as "friction dance" or "straddle dance," which allows for varying amounts of physical contact and can result in sexual release on the part of the customer. Still other strip clubs offer manual manipulation, oral sex, and sexual intercourse. Déjà vu Inc. operates 67 "adult-oriented businesses" in 16 states and has private rooms with small, cushioned sofas. No hand jobs, oral sex, or sexual intercourse are allowed.

Whereas some strip clubs pay the "girls" an hourly fee and let them keep their tips, others charge the girls "stage fees" ($50) for the "privilege" to dance and a $200 "commission" for each 6-hour shift. In effect, the stripper may feel pressure to offer more explicit sex. Morrow (2012) pointed out that strippers must present two social images. One is at work, which is that of a sex kitten to put forth a profitable image to keep the dollars flowing from clients. Outside of work, they engage in additional role-playing so as to avoid stigmatization or the endurance of social maltreatment. Price-Glynn (2010) provides an intimate look inside the Lion's Den strip club following her 14 months spent working in the club as a cocktail waitress. The author emphasizes the ways in which strippers experience both economic autonomy and dependence, gaining little respect despite relatively high earnings.

Profile of a Strip Club Customer

Katherine Frank (2002, 2003) was a nude entertainer who worked in five strip clubs in a large southern city over a period of 14 months. Also a graduate student in the Department of Cultural Anthropology at Duke University, she talked informally with hundreds of men in the various clubs and conducted 30 formal interviews lasting 2 to 4 hours outside the strip club at the office of the customer or at a coffee shop. The age range of the customer was 28–57, with most customers being middle aged/older, white, educated, and middle class. Among the motivations the men identified for coming to the strip club were to relax, to experience a different context from both home and work, to look at naked women, to talk with a friendly/sexy/young woman who is the aggressor, to have a beer with a friend and be "masculine," to be able to leave when they wanted without any game playing/commitment, to have no fear of being accused of sexual harassment for telling a woman she looks pretty, and to have a "relationship of convenience." In regard to the latter, some men said they worked so much they did not have time to meet or date women but that coming to the strip club allowed for quick interaction with a woman without having to go through all the stages of courtship:

Stripping can be a springboard to something better or an abyss of drugs, alcohol, abuse and prostitution.

Trixie, Palomino Club in Las Vegas

> [W]hat is often being sold is a gendered combination of leisure, entertainment, and service ... visiting the clubs means that male customers will be attended to by women who are young, accepting, usually attractive, hopefully friendly, and whose services (in the form of conversation or dancing) can be purchased for an agreed upon price ... (Frank, 2002, p. 88) [I]t [the strip club] provided a safe place in which to be both married (or committed) and sexually aroused (or at least interact with other women in a sexualized setting). (p. 106)

Table dance
Type of dance in which the woman dances or disrobes on the customer's table or in front of the seated customer

Lap dance
Type of dance also known as "friction dance" or "straddle dance" that involves varying amounts of physical contact and can result in sexual release on the part of the customer

17.4d Erotic Massage Parlors

Erotic massage parlors are places that provide sexual services (manual manipulation, oral sex, and sometimes sexual intercourse) in exchange for money. Homeowners who live near these massage parlors consider them undesirable and object to their presence. Not only is there a moral concern, but also they may depress property values. Erotic massage is to be differentiated from **therapeutic massage**, which requires academic training at one of the more than 400 accredited programs, a supervised internship, and a license. The more than 45,000 therapeutic massage therapists often struggle for professional status and credibility because of the traditional association of massage with eroticism and sex work. The professional associations of therapeutic massage specify that sex is not only "never appropriate in massage—it's illegal." Professional organizations of persons offering therapeutic massage are ABMP (The Associated Bodywork and Massage Professionals) and AMTA (The American Massage Therapy Association). NCBTMB is the National Certification Board of Therapeutic Massage & Bodywork, the only national certifying group of massage therapists in the United States. This organization provides the test that professional massage therapists take in the United States, even if their states don't offer licensure, in an effort to demonstrate their knowledge. More than 25 states currently use it as a requirement for their state license as well.

Men visiting strip clubs is more about sexuality and gender than about sex.

Katherine Frank, *G-Strings and Sympathy*

Get 'em in, get 'em up, get 'em off, and get 'em out.

Motto of sex worker in erotic massage parlor

Erotic massage parlors make little pretense of providing anything other than sexual release. "Want a happy ending?" is a typical question erotic massage parlor workers may ask their customers. Handlovsky and colleagues (2012) noted that condom use must be negotiated with the customer.

17.4e Community Attitudes Toward Adult Businesses

Former New York mayor Rudolph W. Giuliani pursued an 8-year crusade to eliminate adult businesses in the Times Square area of Manhattan. Strip bars, peep shows, and adult toyshops were everywhere. New zoning regulations prohibited these establishments from operating within 500 feet of each other—and of schools, residences, and places of worship. While the ordinance was effective in removing the sex business from Times Square—the businesses simply moved to the west side of Manhattan, past the last exit for New Jersey.

Erotic massage parlors
Places that provide sexual services (manual manipulation, oral sex, and sometimes sexual intercourse) in exchange for money

Therapeutic massage
Non-erotic massage by a person who has received academic training at one of the more than 400 accredited programs, completed a supervised internship, and has a therapeutic massage license

Residents of a community usually do not want adult businesses near where they live. Communities attempt to control adult business by restricting where they can locate. West Virginia has 57 strip clubs, which were subjected to a new ordinance that prohibited exotic entertainment businesses from opening within 2,000 feet of a school, religious building, public park, hotel, or home. Although most people do not want to live near an adult business, the increased crime rate thought to be associated with such places may be a stereotype. A decade ago, Linz and colleagues (2004) studied the effect of 20 topless nightclubs on the surrounding areas (500 and 1,000 foot radii) in terms of reported crime, and then matched these with similar sites with no adult businesses. They found smaller numbers of reported crimes in the areas surrounding adult businesses.

17.5 Pornography

What turns me on is erotic. What turns you on is pornographic.

R. Shea

17.5a Defining Pornography and Erotica

The term **pornography**—derived from the words *porne* ("prostitute") and *graphein* ("to write")—originally meant "stories of prostitutes." There is debate over what is pornography and what is **erotica**. One viewpoint suggests that the perception of what is "pornographic" or what is "erotic" is subjective.

Not all sexually explicit material is pornographic. Although consistent proof of a causal link between sexually explicit material and "harm" is lacking, attacks against such material continue. In fact, some sex researchers have found neutral to positive effects from exposure to sexually explicit material. In one study, more than 7,000 adults who had been exposed to sexually explicit materials in sex education seminars or workshops were asked about the effects of such exposure. Almost all the research participants reported experiencing these media as not harmful, and most reported positive responses to the explicit visual material (Rosser, et al., 1995). This conclusion is not surprising, however, given that all the participants had volunteered to view the films.

> *The pornography industry has been tremendously successful in using the tools of modern communication to respond to the alienation of modern man, and the impoverishment of modern women, by manufacturing intimacy in industrial quantities.*
>
> Amy Flowers, *The Fantasy Factory*

There are different types of pornography. **Degrading pornography** is sexually explicit material that degrades, debases, and dehumanizes people, generally women. **Violent pornography** is sexually explicit and endorses the utility and normativeness of sexual violence usually directed by men toward women. Pornography has become more brazen and extreme. Kirk and Boyer (2002) used the acronym CURBFHP to emphasize the type of pornography that is becoming the target of federal prosecution: Children, Urination, Rape, Bestiality, Fisting, Homicide, and Pain.

Obscenity has been legally defined by meeting three criteria. First, the dominant theme of the material must appeal to a prurient interest in sex. Such interest implies that the material is sexually arousing in a lewd way. Second, the material must be patently offensive to the community. In general, a community can dictate what its standards are regarding the sale, display, and distribution of sexual materials. Third, the sexual material must have no redeeming social value. If the material can be viewed as entertaining or educational (if it helps with the sexual communication of couples, for example), a case can be made for its social value.

Pornography
Sexually explicit pictures, writing, or other images, usually pairing sex with power and violence

Erotica
Sexually explicit material that is neither a degrading nor violent portrayal of consensual sexual activity

Degrading pornography
Sexually explicit material that degrades, debases, and dehumanizes people, typically women

Violent pornography
Sexually explicit visual images of sexual violence usually directed by men toward women

Obscenity
Label for sexual material that meets three criteria: (a) The dominant theme of the material must appeal to a prurient interest in sex; (b) the material must be patently offensive to the community; and (c) the sexual material must have no redeeming social value

17.5b Prevalence of Pornography

National DATA

In regard to U.S. males, Wright (2013) analyzed national data on pornography exposure over a 27-year period. There has been a slight increase with 36% of all U.S. males reporting exposure at least once a year. Being younger rather than older, non-white rather than white, and non-religious rather than religious—all are associated with higher levels of pornography consumption.

National **DATA**

In regard to women, Wright and colleagues (2013) assessed pornography consumption, predictors, and correlates using nationally representative data gathered from U.S. women between 1973 and 2010 (N = 18,225). Of women ages 18–30, 34% said they viewed a pornographic movie in the prior year in the 2000s. Women who were younger, less religious, and non-white were more likely to consume pornography.

Chen and colleagues (2013) provided data on exposure of Taiwanese adolescents to Internet pornography (IP) and found results not unlike the exposure of U.S. adolescents—71% of respondents had been exposed to IP. Of this group, 41.3% reported only unintentional exposure (UE), and 58.7% reported intentional exposure (IE). Compared with the female respondents, male respondents tended to report more intentional IP exposure, longer terms of IP exposure history, and greater identification with a positive value of IP.

Gonzalez-Oretega and Orgaz-Baz (2013) analyzed data from an online survey of 494 students of the University of Salamanca. Results showed that 63% of the males and 30% of the females had been exposed to online pornography during adolescence. Males were more likely to have ever been exposed for more than 30 minutes and were more likely to report deliberate consumption and sexual excitement seeking. In contrast, females were more likely to report involuntary exposure. Both genders remember viewing a variety of images, including contents of bondage, child pornography, and rape. One in six of exposed participants remembered strong reactions. While more males reported sexual excitement and masturbation, more females reported avoidance, disgust, or concern.

Self-Assessment 17-1 allows you to identify the degree to which you are interested and/or aroused by erotic visual stimuli.

SELF-ASSESSMENT 17-1: INTEREST IN VISUAL SEXUAL STIMULI

After reading each item, write the number that indicates your disagreement-agreement using the following continuum:

1 = strongly disagree
2 = mildly disagree
3 = disagree
4 = neither disagree nor agree
5 = agree
6 = mildly agree
7 = strongly agree

1.*   ___ Seeing attractive people nude doesn't sexually arouse me.
2.   ___ It would be exciting to watch two people have sex.
3.   ___ Seeing attractive people (of my preferred sex) in skimpy clothing, such as lingerie or tight briefs, is very sexually exciting to me.
4.   ___ I find photographs of attractive naked bodies (of my preferred sex) sexually exciting.
5.*   ___ Being around a group of attractive naked people (of my preferred sex) does not sound very sexually arousing to me.

6. ___ When I meet someone I find attractive, I fantasize about what they would look like without clothes on.
7. ___ Seeing the genitals of an attractive person (of my preferred sex) would be extremely sexually arousing.
8. ___ Seeing my sexual partner undress is a real turn-on.
9. ___ Whether or not I approve of them, I find films of attractive people having sex to be very sexually exciting.
10. ___ When I see someone especially physically attractive, I may follow them briefly to get another look.
11. ___ When I fantasize about having sex with someone, I try to picture very vividly in my mind what his or her body would look like.
12.* ___ If I had to choose, I'd rather have a long conversation with someone I'm attracted to than see them naked.

Scoring

*Reverse score items 1, 5, and 12 (For example, if you selected 7 for item 1, replace 7 with a 1.) Add the 12 numbers. The higher the score, the greater the sexual arousal in response to visual stimuli (84 is the highest possible score); the lower the score, the lower the sexual arousal in response to visual stimuli (12 is the lowest possible score).

Discussion

Bailey (2003) noted significant differences between men and women in regard to being sexually aroused by visual stimuli and stated, "This is one of the largest sex differences in human mating psychology" (p. 93). He also noted that consumers of pornography are disproportionately male and that gay men respond to porn very much as straight men do, and both very differently from how women do. "The motivation to seek erotic stimuli, such as strippers or pornography, and the tendency to be sexually aroused by erotica depicting one sex or the other (but not both) are characteristic of male sexuality. In these senses, gay men are masculine" (p. 96). Furthermore, "Even visual erotica that is targeted at straight women is disproportionately consumed by men—gay men. *Playgirl* magazine, which was intended to let women share in the objectification of the nude body, probably has as many gay men as women readers" (p. 96).

Source: Bailey, J. M. (2003). *The man who would be queen: The science of gender-bending and transsexualism* Washington, DC: Joseph Henry Press.

17.5c Pornography and the Law

The Supreme Court has made a number of decisions regarding obscenity and child pornography. In 1973, the court decided in *Miller v. California* that a work is obscene if taken as a whole it appeals to the prurient interest; portrays sexual conduct in a patently offensive way measured by community standards; and lacks serious social value (literary, artistic etc.). Shortly thereafter in *New York v. Ferber* the court decided that the "states have a compelling interest in protecting children; that child pornography is inextricably intertwined with child exploitation and abuse … and that child pornography has very little social, scientific, political, literary or artistic value" (Ferraro & Casey, 2005, p. 16). In effect, the court distinguished child pornography from obscenity—material need not be obscene to be illegal child pornography. Furthermore, in *Osborne v. Ohio* the court found that the mere possession of child pornography was illegal.

Pornography involving children may result in devastating consequences to child participants. **Child pornography** is defined as an image that depicts a clearly prepubescent human being in a sexually explicit manner. Also referred to as **kiddie porn** and **chicken porn**, a strong cultural value views the use of children in sex films as immoral and abusive. These children do not have the option of free choice and are manipulated or forced into participation.

Child pornography
Image that depicts a clearly prepubescent human being in a sexually explicit manner (also called Kiddie porn and Chicken porn)

Kiddie porn
See Child pornography

Chicken porn
See Child pornography

The Communications Decency Act of 1996 (which made it a crime—punishable by a $250,000 fine or up to 2 years in prison—for anyone to make "indecent" material available to children on the Internet) was designed to protect children from pornography. Although this act was found to be constitutionally too broad, subsequent federal initiatives have included the 1998 Child Online Protection Act, which mandates that commercial pornographers require potential users of adult pornographic websites to verify that they are over age 18. The 2000 Children's Internet Protection Act denies federal funds to libraries unless they have installed software preventing minors from accessing harmful material (United Family Services, 2004).

Possession of child porn carries a 5-year prison sentence. Greater involvement involves stronger penalties. Owner Thomas Reedy of Landslide Operation was convicted on federal charges related to possessing and distributing child pornography and received 1,335 years in prison (Johnson, 2001).

The courts are still trying to figure out how to protect children without censoring the content available to adults (Mauro, 1997). The U.S. Customs Service is the country's front line of defense to combat the illegal importation and proliferation of child pornography. See the "Weblinks" section for the Internet address to Victims of Pornography and Regulation of Pornography on the Internet (two anti-pornography organizations).

17.5d Effects of Pornography

The effects of pornography have been studied extensively. In 1967, the U.S. Commission on Obscenity and Pornography found no evidence that explicit sexual material played a significant role in causing individual or social harm. Rather, such material seemed to be sought for entertainment and educational purposes and seemed to enhance sexual communication. Further, the commission recommended that all federal, state, and local legislation prohibiting the sale, exhibition, and distribution of sexual material to adults be repealed. The U.S. Senate and President Nixon rejected the committee's recommendations.

To update the commission's findings, President Reagan established the Meese Commission on Pornography in 1985. This 11-person commission concluded that pornography is harmful to both individuals and society and called for more stringent law enforcement regulation. Linz and colleagues (1987) examined the same data as the commission and concluded, "we can find no consistent evidence for these specific conclusions" (p. 951). Critics of the Meese Commission argued that it was biased against pornography. Of the 11 members, 6 had gone on record prior to the conference as opposed to pornography because they believed it had harmful effects. For example, one of these was Dr. James Dobson, the then president of Focus on the Family, a conservative organization.

In the summer of 1986, the Surgeon General's workshop on Pornography and Public Health was convened in Arlington, Virginia, with 19 specialists in the area of pornography. Conclusions about the workshop's presentations and discussions (Koop, 1987) follow:

1. Prolonged exposure to pornography results in people believing that less common sexual practices are more common than they are.

2. Pornography depicting sexual aggression as pleasurable to the victim increases the acceptance of the use of coercion in sexual relations.

3. Acceptance of aggression may increase the chance of engaging in sexual aggression.

4. In laboratory studies measuring short-term effects, exposure to violent pornography increases punitive behavior toward women.

   In regard to this latter conclusion, Linz and colleagues (1987) noted, "what is conspicuously absent from the Surgeon General's summary is an endorsement of the view that exposure to sexually violent material leads to aggressive or assaultive behavior outside the confines of the laboratory" (p. 950). Fisher and Grenier (1994) failed to find consistent negative effects of violent pornography on men's fantasies, attitudes, and behaviors toward women. Like much sex research, the data are inconclusive.

5. Children who participate in the production of pornography experience adverse and enduring effects.

Wright (2013) examined national data on pornography exposure of U.S. males over a 27-year period and found that exposure to pornography (for males) was associated with having more positive attitudes toward teenage sex, adult premarital sex, and extramarital sex. Pornography consumption was also positively related to actually engaging in extramarital sex. Other associations included having more sexual partners and engaging in paid sex behavior. As was found true with males, Wright and colleagues (2013) found that U.S. women exposed to pornography had more positive attitudes toward extramarital sex, adult premarital sex, and teenage sex. Women who consumed pornography also had more sexual partners in the prior year and prior 5 years, and were more likely to have engaged in extramarital sex and paid sex.

What effect does viewing pornography have on individuals and couples? Staley and Prause (2013) studied 44 monogamous, heterosexual couples that viewed erotic, exciting (non-erotic films), and nature films both alone and together. They rated their feelings of general arousal and relationship satisfaction, as well as perceptions of self and partner sexual behaviors and attractiveness. Participants viewing both the erotic and exciting films reported equivalent increases in excitement; however, the erotic film was rated as slightly more generally arousing and increased participant's desire to be close to their partner. Viewing the erotic films also induced greater reports of negative affect, guilt, and anxiety.

> *Prostitution exists today because women are objectified sexually, and because it is considered more permissible for men than for women to have purely sexual experiences.*
>
> Ruth Mazo Karras, *Common Women*

17.6 Prostitution

When people hear the term "sex for sale," they think of prostitution. Prostitutes (also called whores, call girls, escorts, courtesans, fallen women, harlots, hookers, hustlers, sluts, streetwalkers, strumpets, tramps, and sex workers) are the focus of this section.

17.6a Definition of Prostitution as Sex Work

Prostitution is defined as providing sexual behavior through the use of one's body (typically manual stimulation, oral sex, sexual intercourse, anal sex) in exchange for money, drugs, or other goods. Prostitution is one type of **sex work**, which is earning one's living by providing sexual services. Other types of sex work include posing/acting for pornographic photographs/DVDs, being a phone sex actress, stripping, lap dancing, providing an erotic massage, and being a professional dominant. Although prostitutes are typically thought of as adult women, men are also prostitutes (gigolos) as are children.

> *I have chosen to recognize one of society's most unappreciated and misunderstood classes: women who, generally through no fault of their own, sold their own bodies and risked their lives simply in order to survive.*
>
> Jan MacKell, *Brothels, Bordellos, & Bad Girls*

Prostitution
Act of providing sexual behavior (typically manual stimulation, oral sex, sexual intercourse, anal sex) through the use of one's body in exchange for money, drugs, or other goods

Sex work
Way in which one earns a living by providing sexual services, such as acting in a pornographic video, being a stripper, or being a phone sex worker

"Red-light" districts are known as the places where prostitutes work. In America the term *red-light* has its origin "from the days when railroad men left their red signal lanterns outside the brothels while paying a visit to a lady of the evening—so they could be found in an emergency" (MacKell, 2004, p. 1).

17.6b Types of Prostitutes

There is a status hierarchy among prostitutes in terms of working conditions, clients, and income. As noted above, prostitutes may be female or male.

Streetwalker

Prostitutes who are referred to as "streetwalkers" get this name because they proposition individuals waiting at a street corner, walk alongside them/proposition them, or nego-

Streetwalker prostitute is the lowest status prostitute. She is vulnerable to STIs/HIV, violence, and murder.
Source: Chelsea Curry

tiate with a potential customer in a car who stops at the street corner. The sex act takes place in a rented room, street alley, or in the customer's car. Streetwalkers are the least respected and lowest level of prostitutes who turn tricks (have sex) in exchange for money to buy food, drugs, or shelter.

Streetwalkers live a particularly difficult life. Prior and Birch (2013) estimated a sex worker population of 10,000 in New South Wales, Australia and noted higher victimization among streetwalkers.

Oselin and Blasyak (2013) emphasized that streetwalker prostitutes live in a context of violence, both physical and sexual. They interviewed 17 street prostitutes who revealed the horror and danger of working on the streets.

I thought I was going to die in the life … that I would die using or be killed by a trick because I didn't see any way out no matter how much I wanted it to end. I wasn't expecting my life to be too much longer out there because things were getting worse on the streets day by day. I've seen about 5 girls I knew who were working the streets along with me end up dead in garbage cans. One girl that used to live with me they found her rolled up in a carpet in back of this restaurant in the area we used to prostitute together. When I found out about her death [she shakes her head] … I knew her … I knew her children and her husband.

Another said:

I knew I was going to get killed out there soon—out on the street—because I was what they called a renegade. I didn't have a pimp. I was on my own and pimps hated that. They wanted me dead. They really wanted me dead. They don't like girls that take away their business. So it could have happened really easily.

Finally, a 47-year-old street walker reported:

I did have a few close to death situations at the hands of male customers. And I even had officers that would call me and I would take care of them [sexually]. They told me that whenever I came across a man that assaulted me I should call them … so there were times that I did. One guy took a knife out after I did it and wanted his money back and I said no problem here you go. I got out of the car and wrote down his license plate number. I called the officers I knew and they caught him. I had three incidents like that. Another time, I was in front of a church when a white man pulled out a machete after I had already done my job ... I had my $20 and I had my hand on the door to open it and he started forcing me back to do more. I said, I don't play that game, and I opened the door and I ran. I ran to the park across the street. I'm yelling and he's chasing me with a machete. I started yelling so loud that the lights starting coming on from surrounding apartments and people were looking. So he went back to his car and he came back up to try to hit me with the car. I went into the middle of the street and these people stopped and I said take me to the police station. The guy took off. I reported the incident to the police.

Apartment Prostitute

In some European cities such as Amsterdam (the red-light district "De Wallen"), prostitutes may legally rent one-room apartments in red-light districts and solicit customers from behind windows. Patrons walk by and are enticed to come inside. The prostitute identifies what the customer wants, negotiates the price, and the service begins.

Erotic Massage Parlor Worker

Although therapeutic massage is a legitimate service provided by educated, trained, and licensed masseuses, some "massage parlors" are fronts for prostitution, offering "hand jobs," oral sex, and intercourse. These sex workers typically have no training in traditional massage (which the clients are not there for anyway).

House Prostitute

Some prostitutes work out of an established house or **brothel** (also known as a "whorehouse," "cathouse," or "bordello"). In the past a **madam**, who took care of the business and the girls, ran a brothel. **Mama san** is the term for an Asian female madam.

Modern-day brothels have all the efficiency of a fast-food establishment where the customer comes in, orders from a menu, consumes, and leaves satisfied. The Moonlite Bunny Ranch in Las Vegas, Nevada, is a legal brothel that features around 15 prostitutes (HBO is now in its fifth season with episodes of life at the ranch). Men come in; select from a "lineup"; have a drink; go to the girl's room; negotiate a price; pay the money to the girl, who then leaves the room and takes it to the madam; and the "party" begins on her return. The party is over after the time is up. If the customer wants another "party" (e.g., more time, two women, etc.), the negotiation starts over. The prostitute pays the owner a cut of what the customer pays. The house prostitute is relatively safe from violence because a video camera may be in every room and a bouncer on the premises. The "girls" have weekly STI/HIV checks and require their customers to use condoms. Prices at brothels may range from $500 to $10,000, depending on what the customer wants in terms of time (20 minutes to all night hours), activities, and number of participants.

Call Girl

The **call girl** is a sex worker who is called on the phone and asked to come to the customer's room to provide a sexual service. Call girls are the top hierarchy of prostitutes and personified by Heidi Fleiss (the Hollywood Madam) and Sydney Biddle Barrows (also known as the Mayflower Madam). Both Fleiss and Barrows began as high-priced call girls who—because of their youth, beauty, intelligence, and social skills—were able to command considerable fees. Later, these women attracted other girls with similar credentials and became madams of large-scale call girl rings. Both Fleiss and Barrows were eventually caught and prosecuted.

Brothel
Place, typically a house or rented space, where prostitutes service their customers

Madam
Woman who runs a house of prostitution

Mama san
Asian woman who runs a house of prostitution

Call girl
Sex worker who is called on the phone and asked to come to the customer's room to provide sexual service

Escort is another term for call girl; this term implies a wider range of behavior, such as being a social companion for an evening that typically ends in sexual intimacy. The escort may entertain the patron in her own residence, that of the patron, or a hotel room. Although some escort services offer nonsexual services, most are fronts for prostitution.

Courtesan

Courtesan refers to women in Renaissance Europe who provided social and sexual companionship for money or support by upper-middle/upper class men. These women were educated, socially skilled mistresses. The term *prostitute* did not seem appropriate in that courtesans held a socially recognized (and accepted) position even though they were paid for their services. Indeed, some courtesans were thought of as upper class women because they often held simultaneous careers as performers or artists.

Male Prostitute

Although the term *prostitute* is most often used in reference to women, male prostitutes (also referred to as "escorts," "hustlers," or "rent boys") are not uncommon. Male prostitutes may service men (escorts), women (gigolos), or both (taxi boys).

In addition to these various types of prostitutes, another way of categorizing prostitutes is whether they work for themselves, work for a pimp, or are forced into prostitution—bought and sold as sex slaves. Some call girls are independent workers who set up their own clients on their cell phones. Other call girls work for escort agencies that have a central office where prospective clients call and identify what they want (blue-eyed blond, providing bondage and discipline, etc.), and the call is "routed" to the girl who has the characteristics or meets the requests of the caller.

Other prostitutes (more often streetwalkers) have a pimp who "controls" them and takes a percentage of their earnings. They are not free to leave the business but are free to walk about when they are not turning tricks. Slave trade girls are bought and sold as children by owners who put them in brothels to service men daily. These girls are not free to leave, are beaten into submission, and live horrible lives. Some illegal immigrants are, in effect, sexual slaves in that they are forced into prostitution to pay for their travel and expenses—which are never paid off. We will discuss sex trafficking later in the chapter.

17.6c Becoming a Prostitute

Studies on recruitment into prostitution have focused on the characteristics associated with women who end up as prostitutes. Early first sexual experiences, childhood physical/sexual abuse, estrangement from parents, and low economic status are background characteristics of most prostitutes. Some parents sell their children into prostitutions as a means of providing income for the family (e.g., in India).

A common theme among recruitment into sex work is the need for money. Girls quickly learn that selling sex is one of the fastest ways to earn a lot of cash (and the alternative of working at Wal-Mart 40 hours a week may be less attractive). An erotic dancer in one of the authors' classes noted that she can make up to $1,500 a week, and this money is not taxed.

Some girls report peer influence and stumbling into the connection between sex and money. Another student in the authors' classes noted the following:

It was amateur night at the local titty bar. I went with my friends to see another of our friends who was dancing. We got liquored up and dared each other to

Escort
Another term for call girl which implies a wider range of behavior, such as being a social companion for an evening that typically ends in sexual intimacy

Courtesan
Woman in Renaissance Europe who provided social and sexual companionship for money or support by upper-middle/upper class men

get on stage and do a dance. I got a lot of tips and loved the attention. It wasn't long before I was a regular. Then the strip bar closed but the owner wanted five of us to work for him at new club. The men there were older and had more money. I got used to the money and was hooked. It wasn't long before I was turning tricks. (authors' files)

Some females are seduced by a "loverboy" or "pimp" into the role of prostitute. Van San and Bovenkerk (2013) revealed how some women are manipulated into prostitution by "loverboys." As background, "pimping" is considered "the second oldest profession." A typical scenario occurred at the end of the 19th century in the Netherlands at the Central Train station in Amsterdam where girls just arrived to find a job. Young men would seduce them, get them pregnant, which would ensure a bad reputation so they could not return home as unwed mothers, thus making it easy for their "loverboy" to pressure them into prostitution.

More recently, the researchers interviewed, for 2 to 3 hours, 13 "loverboys" (then in prison) about their experiences of seducing young females into the role of prostitute. The "loverboys" were ages 21 to 24, none had completed high school, and none had a job. All had been involved in crime (street robberies, drug trafficking) from a young age. "In the criminal hierarchy, pimps occupy a much lower position than drug dealers or bank robbers."

The respondents claimed that the females initiated the idea of their earning money (by doing sex work) if the boyfriend (loverboy) would not break up with them. Hence, the loverboys presented the prostitution as the idea of the girl and that the role of the guy was only as protector—they denied violent force (which was a lie according to police reports).

The "loverboys" pointed out that they knew how to spot a vulnerable girl. She was "on the stupid" side and could be easily manipulated.

Listen, these are mostly problem girls. They have problems with their parents or they have debts; a long-term relationship has recently ended, or they just broke up with their boyfriend. They're at an all-time low, and then a loverboy comes along. Someone with a lot of money, who takes her out to all the right places, pays for everything, spoils her or what have you. Eventually, there comes a time when the girl who gets everything from her man is expected to do something for him in return, but they often don't know how. Sooner or later these girls are simply going to be manipulated. (Van San & Bovenkerk, 2013)

The set of steps included making the girl fall in love by spending money on them and making promises (e.g. "we will open a club together"), isolating the girl from her friends/family (so that the loverboy is the only person in her life), and telling her the pimp is broke/needs money so the girl turns tricks to come up with the money. Some of the loverboys gave the girls drugs (got them hooked), so that they would do sex work for drugs. Progression through the various steps takes months or years and often includes the loverboy spinning up several women at once so that he eventually gets them competing against each other for the pimp's favor.

17.6d Life as a Prostitute

Most prostitutes are poor, have limited education, and little opportunity of getting the job skills to increase their job prospects. Some are drug addicts; others have children to support. The sex trade offers them the most money with the greatest flexibility. They are vulnerable to HIV infection and being beaten up or murdered. Maintaining a relationship with someone outside the business is difficult (see Personal Experience 17-3).

Impact of Sex Work on One's Personal Intimate Relationship

Syvertsen and colleagues (2013) interviewed 44 couples where one partner was involved in sex work and emphasized the emotional toll of the sex work on both partners. "Couples employed multiple strategies to cope with sex work, including psychologically disconnecting from their situation, telling "little lies," avoiding the topic, and to a lesser extent, superficially discussing their risks."

In most cases, the economic reality necessitated the need for the partner to cope with the situation:

He got used to it. I mean, what else can he do?   Jazmine, 46

Yes, yes there are problems sometimes because of [sex work] but, well he has to put up with it because where else are we going to get money from? If it's not because of me, from where? Adrianna, 28

The partners' also felt inadequate that they did not earn enough so that sex work wouldn't be necessary:

I feel responsible because I can't give her more, you know? If I had it, I would give it to her so she wouldn't have to do that.   Ronaldo, 44

I get very jealous, and it makes me feel bad, do you know what I mean? I feel bad because I know that I can't satisfy her [economic] needs, and that's why she needs to work, do you know what I mean? I wish I was able to sustain her, and give her everything she needs so that she wouldn't have to work.   Marco, 27

The researchers noted, "While such strategies served to protect both partners' emotional health by upholding illusions of fidelity and avoiding potential conflict, nondisclosure of risk behaviors may exacerbate the potential for HIV/STI acquisition." Hence, the partners circumnavigated the fact that one partner was a sex worker by withholding information or minimizing the information that was available.

Source: Syvertsen, J. L., Robertson, A. M., Rolon, M. L., Palinkas, L. A., Martinez, G., Rangel, M. G., and Strathdee, S. A. 2013. "Eyes that don't see, heart that doesn't feel": Coping with sex work in intimate relationships and its implications for HIV/STI prevention. *Social Science and Medicine. 87:* 1–8.

Not all prostitutes are destitute or regard their profession as particularly dangerous. Some, especially call girls (at the top of the prostitution hierarchy) who are more likely to work in a relatively safe environment with regular clients and may run a lucrative business, feel that they are unfairly harassed for earning a living the way they choose. They argue that they are abused by the courts and the police who harass them. These women note that prostitutes are more often women than men, and are more often arrested than the men they serve.

17.6e Clients of Prostitutes

National **DATA**

Kinsey and colleagues (1948) found that two-thirds of their male sample (68%) had paid for sex at least once in their life, and 15% to 20% were regular clients. Men who seek and pay prostitutes for their services can be of any marital and socioeconomic status, ethnicity, and age (Serughetti, 2013).

Teela Sanders (2008) identified five types of males who seek prostitutes:

1. Explorers are men that seek prostitutes because of their desire for sexual experimentation, curiosity, and fantasy.

2. Yo-yoers are men in their 30s who stop seeing sex workers when in a relationship, and then start again when the relationship with their primary partner becomes unsatisfactory.

3. Compulsives are men who seek/have sex with prostitutes as a compulsive behavior/fetish.

4. Bookends are men who have initial sexual experiences with sex workers and go back to buying sex in later life as the ultimate chance to satisfy their sexual desires.

5. Permanent purchasers are men who seek paid sex sporadically throughout their lifetime.

Sabbah (2013) analyzed data on 1,342 men arrested for soliciting street prostitutes to create a profile to determine the behavior the prostitutes were most likely to engage in—fellatio or vaginal intercourse. The men revealed that fellatio was more likely to occur regardless of age, sexual desire, interest, and marital status of the customer. The results for vaginal sex were conflicting. Finally, frequency of condom use was a significant predictor of vaginal sex but not fellatio.

Cultural Diversity

Serughetti (2013) identified a global trend "towards the criminalization of clients, represented as responsible for the perpetuation and proliferation of the sex market and for its oppressive and victimizing effects on sex workers." Sweden was the first country to propose and approve consequences for both sex worker and client, over-throwing the traditional model that punished those who sold sexual services rather than those who purchased them. Countries such as Norway, Iceland, England, and Northern Ireland have proposed similar legislation. Indeed, law enforcement in some large U.S. cities (e.g., New York, San Francisco) have targeted "Johns" who seek prostitutes.

17.6f Prostitution and the Law

The Trafficking Victims Protection Act, passed by the U.S. Congress in 2000, criminalizes the forced or deceptive movement of people into exploitative conditions of labor and provides services to victims. The law makes a symbolic distinction (although it holds no legal meaning) between "sex" and "non-sex" trafficking, (i.e., movement into forced prostitution and movement into other forced labor sectors), thereby marking "sex trafficking" as a special category (Peters, 2013).

Earlier (in 1910), the Mann Act, also known as the White Slave Traffic Act, was enacted to prohibit transporting women across state lines for the purpose of prostitution. The act, which was strengthened in 1986, "prohibits coercion or enticement and transportation of minors (under 18) for prostitution or criminal sexual activity" (Stetson, 2004, p. 255).

While prostitutes are often stigmatized and blamed for their choice to be involved in sex work, Shdaimah and Wiechelt (2013) emphasized that prostitutes occupy a unique position of being both victim and criminal. They are a victim in that prostitutes, particularly streetwalkers, "suffer from a variety of problems including past and current trauma and abuse, substance abuse, mental and physical health disorders, and housing instability" (p. 23). The researchers interviewed and conducted focus groups, with 17 women currently or formerly engaged in prostitution, which revealed that both survival needs and coercion were factors in their becoming involved in prostitution. In response, the States Attorney's Office of the City of Baltimore began an initiative to create an alternative for people who are charged with prostitution (a crime in Maryland). Rather than treat the prostitutes as criminals, they were viewed as individuals who are victims of economics, structure, and socialization who could benefit from compassion and help toward an alternative job. The Social Choices 17-2 section addresses the controversy of whether or not prostitution should be legalized.

Should Prostitution Be Legalized?

Prostitution is a controversial topic, with some individuals viewing it as a form of sexual abuse and exploitation and others viewing it as a legitimate way of earning a living, in which adults have the right to engage. Proponents of the prostitution-as-abuse perspective argue that prostitutes are physically, morally, and economically exploited. Dangers of prostitution include murder, rape, beatings, robbery, psychological abuse, and emotional pain. We have detailed the horror and danger reported by streetwalkers. Vulnerability to diseases—particularly AIDS—is also a substantial risk.

However, there is another view of prostitution. COYOTE, acronym for Call Off Your Old Tired Ethics, was formed in San Francisco in 1973 by an ex-prostitute, Margo St. James. COYOTE has promoted the idea of a prostitutes' union to change the public image of prostitutes and to fight the moral and legal discrimination to which they are subjected. COYOTE supports programs to assist sex workers in their choice to change their occupation, works to prevent the scapegoating of sex workers, and aims to educate sex workers and their clients to use safe sex practices. COYOTE's affiliates identify three main claims: (1) Not all prostitution is forced but often is voluntarily chosen, (2) prostitution is a type of service work and should be destigmatized, and (3) not allowing a woman to work as a prostitute (under conditions of her choice) is a violation of her civil rights.

Sex researchers, enforcement officials, politicians, and prostitutes continue to debate the issue of whether prostitution should be legalized or decriminalized in the United States. Arguments for the legalization of prostitution include that it would permit the taxation of the billions of currently untaxed dollars spent on prostitution, help control and regulate the criminal activity associated with prostitution, help prevent teenage prostitution, and help protect prostitutes against abuse by pimps and clients (by enabling prostitutes to report abuse without fear of being arrested). Furthermore, if prostitution were legal, public health regulations could require prostitutes to use condoms and have regular gynecological exams to ensure they are not infected with a sexually transmitted infection and to treat any diseases they may acquire. Just as restaurants must pass a health inspection and display a rating certificate, prostitutes could be required to obtain a similar certificate of health.

Prostitution has been legalized in some districts of rural Nevada and in some countries, including Germany where prostitutes work in large dormitories and are checked regularly by a physician for sexually transmitted infections. Clients make their selection by observing the available women on closed-circuit television monitors. These bordellos are sometimes safer and healthier environments for both prostitutes and clients than street prostitution.

Surprisingly, even some prostitutes oppose legalizing their trade. In Nevada, where prostitution is legalized, some prostitutes resent the legal conditions of their employment. Legal prostitutes cannot discriminate against certain customers by refusing to service them: They must service whoever comes in the door. They also feel that the law interferes with their private lives. For example, legal prostitutes can go to town only during certain hours and cannot appear in the company of a client in a restaurant. The stigmatization of the profession through fingerprinting and registration makes it difficult for prostitutes to leave the profession and enter another.

In Australia, approximately 20,000 sex workers spend an average of 2.5 years in the industry. In Victoria, Australia, sex work is legal in licensed brothels, while street-based sex work and sex work in unlicensed brothels remain illegal. Begum and colleagues (2013) interviewed 14 women in three focus groups who currently or recently were sex workers in a legal brothel and over age 18.

The women reported that while legalization has brought increased safety (condom use, less violence) there is still the stigma. They also commented that being a legal sex worker is both economically rewarding and entrapping (e.g., women stay in the profession since they can't earn high incomes outside of prostitution). In addition, the women felt empowered (they were earning good incomes), but they also felt demeaned by the male clients. One woman said:

> But I think my worst experience … is … men … just disrespecting you—they can pound you because they've paid that money, they can do what they want. They can put their fingers inside, they can do those extra things …

17.6g Prostitution and STIs/AIDS

Prostitutes are at high risk for infecting (and being infected by) their clients with sexually transmitted infections, including HIV. Such a risk occurs worldwide in reference to prostitution.

The consequences of AIDS among prostitutes are devastating. They not only infect clients, but their children may also be born with HIV; and as the prostitute becomes progressively weaker, her children may be forced into prostitution to earn money. When the mother dies, the child may be left to survive alone in the streets or grow up in an orphanage.

BVT *Lab*

Visit **www.BVTLab.com** to explore the student resources available for this chapter.

The U.S. is a major sex traffic destination with 50,000 women and children victims of sex traffic criminals annually.
Source: E. Fred Johnson Jr.

17.6h Sex Trafficking

According to the Victims of Trafficking and Violence Protection Act of 2000, **sex trafficking** is the "recruitment, harboring, transportation, provision, or obtaining of a person for the purpose of a commercial sex act."

National DATA

The United States is one of the largest trafficking destination countries where approximately 50,000 women and children are trafficked into the country each year. The average age for recruitment is between 11 and 14 (Hom & Woods, 2013).

Sex trafficking
Related to prostitution, using force and deception to transfer persons into situations of extreme exploitation

Hom and Woods (2013) reemphasized the commercial sexual exploitation of women and girls through forced prostitution and sex-trafficking as a human rights and public health issue. They noted that these survivors face complex mental health problems from the trauma and violence and provided examples given to service workers. Several themes emerged.

1. *Pimp Enculturation* These are life events leading up to the induction into sex trafficking and include a difficult home life with early abuse, rape by parent/stepparent, running away from home, and being vulnerable (needing love/someone to care for them) to a pimp. Prostitutes are kept in the sex trade (13 to 15 sex tricks a day) by being told by the pimp that he is the only one who cares about them and will take care of them, and that they have no place to go. The girls are also controlled by violent means—beatings, starvation, coercive drug use, and rape. One service provider reported knowing women who had suffered "ruptured spleens, broken bones that never healed, stabbings, and gunshot wounds. … Sexually transmitted infections, pregnancy, HIV, and complications from abortions" were common.

2. *Aftermath* The effects of the trafficking and exploitation include posttraumatic stress disorder (PTSD), dissociation, anxiety, sleep disorders/nightmares, low self-esteem, and depression. These women often are unable to return to their families upon rescue or escape because of the shame associated with being a prostitute or having been trafficked.

3. *Healing the Wound* Talking with an outreach person who establishes trust and encourages the girls to consider an alternative life offers the possibility of escape. The prostitutes are given trafficking hotline numbers and told there are people, other than their pimp or trafficker, who care about them. The recovery path is slow and long and holistic—meeting the "spiritual, mental, psychological, physical and vocational education needs" of the trafficked woman. The needs are also basic—safe shelter, food, and acquiring identification—as well as future needs basic to a new life, including education and job readiness skills.

> *The only way to stop this trafficking in and profiting from the use of women's bodies is for prostitution to be legalized. Legalization will open it up to regulation; and regulation means safety.*
>
> Jeannette Angell, *Callgirl*

In January 2013 the Safe Harbor Act no longer treats prostitutes as criminals to be prosecuted and put in jail, but as victims who are exploited. Hence, prostitutes are put into treatment systems which include safety from their pimps, education to learn alternative skills for becoming independent, and help in healing from prior abuse.

Chapter **Summary**

Sex is used to generate income. This chapter examines the various ways.

Sex in Advertising

Sex in advertising continues to increase. The advertiser uses sex to get the attention of the viewer and punches in the product.

Sexuality and the Internet

Sexual content of the Internet is extensive. The Internet features erotic photos and web cams whereby some females strip/dance (via SKYPE) for their long distance partners. Other webcam strippers generate income from nude dancing.

Benefits of sexuality on the Internet include getting sex information, anonymous STI testing, finding a mate, finding a sex partner, maintaining a long-distance relationship, experiencing sexual fantasies/cybersex, connecting disenfranchised/marginal groups, and enabling individuals to try out a new identity. Disadvantages include the spread of STIs/HIV, cybersex crime, deception, supporting Internet addiction, and providing a playground for pedophiles.

Sex and the Law

An unending debate in U.S. society exists around the issue of private rights versus social morality: Should consenting adults be permitted to engage in any sexual behaviors they choose, or should the law define morally acceptable parameters? The Supreme Court has taken the position that free speech (including pornography) on the Internet should be protected. One of the ways that society has achieved compromise and balance between the radically opposing views of private versus public morality has been to view certain sexual behaviors on a continuum of offensiveness and to assign relative penalties for engaging in them. For example, child sexual abuse and rape are regarded as severely offensive and are subject to strong social sanctions, whereas frottage is viewed less severely.

Sexuality Businesses

Three businesses that emphasize the sale of sex are phone sex, strip clubs, and erotic massage parlors. Phone sex (sometimes referred to as "guided masturbation") is a telephone conversation between a caller and a sex worker (also referred to as "phone-actress," "fantasy artist," or "adult phone entertainer") who verbally arouses, stimulates, and moves the caller toward orgasm in exchange for money. Erotic massage parlors provide sexual manual manipulation, oral sex, and sometimes sexual intercourse in exchange for money. Erotic massage is to be differentiated from therapeutic massage where sex is "never appropriate in massage—it's illegal."

Strip clubs exist primarily for the heterosexual male. A stripper (also known as an "erotic dancer," "lap dancer," "private dancer," "table dancer," "nude entertainer") may feel increased pressure from the management to offer manual manipulation, oral sex, and sexual intercourse. The O'Farrell Theater in San Francisco built "private cabanas" with sofas and invited customers to take advantage of the club's private spaces saying, "What you do on your side of the curtain is your little secret." Girls stay in the business because of the money and the amount of free time.

Pornography

Literally translated, pornography means "stories of prostitutes." Something is "obscene" if it appeals to a prurient (sick) interest in sex, is offensive to the community, and has no redeeming social value. Pornography has become more brazen and extreme. The acronym CURBFHP—Children, Urination, Rape, Bestiality, Fisting, Homicide, and Pain—reflects the type of contemporary pornography that is, increasingly, becoming the target of federal prosecution.

The effects of pornography have been studied extensively. There is no evidence that explicit sexual material plays a significant role in causing individual or social harm. However, prolonged exposure to pornography results in people believing that less common sexual practices are more common than they are. Also pornography depicting sexual aggression as pleasurable to the victim increases the acceptance of the use of coercion in sexual relations, and exposure to violent pornography increases punitive behavior toward women. Children who participate in the production of pornography experience adverse and enduring effects; the possession of child pornography carries a 5-year prison term.

Wright (2013) examined national data on pornography exposure of U.S. males over a 27-year period and found that exposure to pornography (for males) was associated with having more positive attitudes toward teenage sex, adult premarital sex, and extramarital sex. Pornography consumption was also positively related to actually engaging in extramarital sex. Other associations included having more sexual partners and engaging in paid sex behavior. As was true with males, Wright and colleagues (2013) found that U.S. women exposed to pornography had more positive attitudes toward extramarital sex, adult premarital sex, and teenage sex. Women who consumed pornography also had more sexual partners in the prior year and prior 5 years, and were more likely to have engaged in extramarital sex and paid sex.

Prostitution

Prostitution is defined as providing sexual behavior through the use of one's body (typically manual stimulation, oral sex, sexual intercourse, and anal sex) in exchange for money, drugs, or other goods. Prostitution is one type of sex work, which is earning one's living by providing sexual services. Other types of sex work include posing/acting for pornographic photographs/DVDs, being a phone sex actress, stripping, lap dancing, providing an erotic massage, and being a professional dominant. Although prostitutes are typically thought of as adult women, men are also prostitutes (gigolos) as are children.

Sex trafficking is the "recruitment, harboring, transportation, provision, or obtaining of a person for the purpose of a commercial sex act." The United States is one of the largest trafficking destination countries where approximately 50,000 women and children are trafficked into the country each year. It is estimated that between 100,000 to 300,000 American minors are at risk of commercial sexual exploitation with the average age for recruitment being between 11 and 14 years of age. The consequences are devastating for those who are sex trafficked.

These survivors face complex mental health problems from the trauma and violence they are exposed to.

Web Links

Prostitution
Child Prostitution
ECPAT

www.ecpat.org.uk

COYOTE (Call Off Your Old Tired Ethics)

http://www.walnet.org/csis/groups/coyote.html

Pornography
Internet and Cybersex Addition

http://www.helpguide.org/mental/internet_cybersex_addiction.htm

Internet Protection for Children
CyberPatrol

http://www.cyberpatrol.com/

Cybersitter

http://www.cybersitter.com/

Regulation of Pornography on the Internet

http://www.missingkids.com

Victims of Pornography

http://www.victimsofpornography.org/

Sex Industry
Exotic Dancers Alliance

http://www.bayswan.org/eda-sf/

Key Terms

Brothel   507

Call girl   507

Camming   498

Chicken porn   503

Child pornography   503

Courtesan   508

Cybersex   488

Degrading pornography   501

Erotica   501

Erotic massage parlors   500

Escort   508

Kiddie porn   503

Lap dance   499

Madam   507

Mama san   507

Obscenity   501

Phone sex   497

Pornography   501

Prostitution   505

Sex trafficking   514

Sex work   505

Table dance   499

Therapeutic massage   500

Violent pornography   501

Additional study resources are available at www.BVTLab.com

Glossary

A

Abortion 335
Deliberate termination of a pregnancy through chemical or surgical means

Absolutism 7
A belief system that is based on the unconditional power and authority of religion, law, or tradition

Abstinence 199
Condition of having refrained from having sexual intercourse

Acquaintance rape 456
Nonconsensual sex between people who are dating or on a date (also called Date rape.)

Acquired dysfunction 359
Sexual dysfunction that a person is currently experiencing but has not always experienced

Acquired immunodeficiency syndrome (AIDS) 438
Last stage of HIV infection in which the immune system of a person's body is so weakened that it becomes vulnerable to infection and disease (opportunistic infections)

Adolescence 234
Developmental period in which youths move from childhood to adulthood

Agnosia 297
Loss of auditory, sensory, or visual comprehension

Alzheimer's disease 297
Progressive and degenerative brain disease progressing from mild memory loss, through significant cognitive impairment, to very serious confusion and the loss of ability to manage activities of daily living, such as dressing, eating, and bathing

Ambivalence 11
Conflicting feelings that coexist, producing uncertainty or indecisiveness about a person, object, idea, or course of action

Amenorrhea 78
Absence of menstruation for 3 or more months during which a woman is not pregnant, menopausal, or breastfeeding

Amniocentesis 123 , 350
Prenatal test in which a needle is inserted (usually in the 16th or 17th week of pregnancy) into the pregnant woman's uterus to withdraw fluid, which is analyzed to see if the cells carry XX (female) or XY (male) chromosomes, and to identify chromosomal defects

Analingus 214
Licking of and/or insertion of the tongue into the partner's anus (also known as rimming.)

Androgyny 136
Having traits stereotypically associated with both masculinity and femininity

Aphasia 297
Impaired communicative ability

Aphrodisiac 89
Any food, drink, drug, scent, or device that arouses and increases sexual desire

Apraxia 297
Inability to perform coordinated movements

Areola 68
Darkened ring around the nipple that keeps the nipples lubricated by secretions of oil during breastfeeding

Asceticism 198
Belief that rising above carnal lust and the pursuit of sensual pleasure into a life of self-discipline and self-denial is desirable

Asymptomatic 423
Producing no symptoms or signs, or as in some STIs, yielding symptoms so mild that medical care is not sought

Autoerotic asphyxiation 204
Cutting off one's air supply to enhance one's orgasm but misjudging the extent of doing so such that accidental death occurs

Aversive conditioning 414
Type of behavior therapy that involves pairing an aversive or unpleasant stimulus with a previously reinforcing stimulus; used in sex offender treatment to decrease deviant sexual arousal and reduce the probability of engaging in paraphilic behavior

B

Bartholin's glands 63
Glands located at the base of the minor lips of the female genitalia that secrete a small amount of mucous to the inner surfaces of the labia minora

Benign Prostatic Hyperplasia (BPH) 106
Normal enlargement of the man's prostate, as he ages, which may eventually require treatment

Biosexology 28
Study of the biological aspects of sexuality

Biosocial framework 29
Theoretical framework that emphasizes the interaction of one's biological/genetic inheritance with one's social environment to explain and predict human behavior

Biphobia 283
Fearful, negative, discriminatory reactions toward bisexuals

Bisexuality 260
Emotional and sexual attraction to members of both sexes

Blended orgasm 84
Orgasm whereby the woman experiences both vulval contractions and deep uterine enjoyment

Brainstorming 188
Problem-solving strategy of suggesting as many alternatives as possible without evaluating them

Breast-conserving therapy 304
Removal of the cancerous lump rather than the whole breast (also called Lumpectomy.)

Brothel 507
Place, typically a house or rented space, where prostitutes service their customers

Bulbourethral glands 105
Pea-sized structures attached to the urethra in the penis that secrete droplets of clear, sticky fluid prior to ejaculation (also known as Cowper's glands)

C

Call girl 507
Sex worker who is called on the phone and asked to come to the customer's room to provide sexual service

Camming 498
The use of a webcam to facilitate the customer seeing/directing/interacting with the female performer

Candidiasis 435
Vaginal yeast infection that tends to occur in women during pregnancy, when they are on oral contraceptives, or when they have poor resistance to infection

Case study 50
Research method that involves conducting an in-depth, detailed analysis of an individual, group, relationship, or event

Celibacy 198
Condition of refraining from sexual intercourse, especially by reason of religious vows; also used to refer to being unmarried

Cerebral palsy 296
Condition often caused by brain damage that occurs before or during birth or in infancy, resulting in muscular impairment and sometimes speech and learning disabilities

Cervical cap 327
Thimble-shaped contraceptive device made of rubber or polyethylene that fits tightly over the cervix and is held in place by suction

Cervix 73
Narrower portion of the uterus, which projects into the vagina

Chastity 198
State of not having had sexual intercourse; also implies moral purity or virtuousness in both thought and conduct

Chicken porn 503
See Child pornography

Childhood 230
Developmental time frame that extends from age 2 to age 12 and involves physical, cognitive, social, and sexual development

Child pornography 503
Image that depicts a clearly prepubescent human being in a sexually explicit manner (also called Kiddie porn and Chicken porn)

Chlamydia 434
Common sexually transmitted infection caused by the microorganism chlamydia trachomatis, often asymptomatic, and therefore known as "the silent disease"

Chorionic villus sampling (CVS) 351
Prenatal diagnostic test of cells from the chorion (membrane surrounding the fetus) (performed at 10 to 12 weeks gestation) to identify chromosomal abnormalities and some other diseases

Chromosomes 122
Threadlike structures of DNA within the cell nucleus that carry genes and transmit hereditary information

Chronic obstructive pulmonary disease (COPD) 303
Collective term for diseases that affect the flow of air into the body, such as asthma, bronchitis, and emphysema (Individuals with COPD often experience fatigue due to decreased oxygen intake and the effort involved in breathing.)

Circumcision 99
Surgical procedure in which the foreskin of the penis is pulled forward and cut off (also known as male genital mutilation)

Classical conditioning 31
Behavior modification technique whereby an unconditioned stimulus and a neutral stimulus are linked to elicit a desired response

Classic rape 457
Rape by a stranger which may involve a weapon (also called Predatory rape.)

Climacteric 252
Term often used synonymously with menopause, refers to changes that both men and women experience at midlife

Clitoris 63
Sensory organ located at the top of the labia minora of the female genitalia

Closed-ended question 178
Type of question that yields little information and can be answered in one word

Cognitive/affective theories 32
As related to sexuality, theories that emphasize the role of thought processes and emotions in sexual behavior

Cognitive behavioral sex therapy 383
Treatment method emphasizing that negative thoughts and attitudes about sex interfere with sexual interest, pleasure, and performance

Cohabitation 244
Living situation in which two heterosexual adults involved in an emotional and sexual relationship share a common residence for 4 nights a week for 3 months

Coitus 214
Sexual union of a man's penis and a woman's vagina (also known as Sexual intercourse)

Coitus interruptus 329
Practice whereby the man withdraws his penis from the vagina before he ejaculates (Coitus interruptus is also known as withdrawal)

Coming out 268
(Shortened form of "coming out of the closet") Sequence of defining one's self as homosexual in sexual orientation and disclosing one's self-identification to others

Communication 170
Exchange of messages between two or more people

Compersion 153
The opposite of jealousy, whereby a person feels positive about a lover's emotional and sexual enjoyment with another person

Complimentary-needs theory 163
Theory of mate selection that states that one tends to select mates whose needs are opposite and complementary to one's own needs

Comprehensive sex education programs 18
Programs that discuss abstinence as well as the use of contraception

Conflict theory 36
Sociological theory that views society as consisting of different parts competing for power and resources

Conversion therapy 267
Therapy designed to change the sexual orientation of a person, usually homosexual to heterosexual

Coolidge effect 249
The effect of novelty and variety on sexual arousal—such as when a novel partner is available, a sexually satiated male regains capacity for arousal

Corona 97
Raised rim on the glans of the penis that is especially sensitive to touch

Correlation 53
Statistical index that represents the degree of relationship between two variables

Courtesan 508
Woman in Renaissance Europe who provided social and sexual companionship for money or support by upper-middle/upper class men

Courtship disorder 412
Distortion of the standard sequence of interpersonal events in courtship that lead to the development of an intimate relationship; used as a theory to explain rape, the rapist short-circuits the courtship stages and progresses immediately to intercourse

Covert sensitization 414
Therapeutic technique that involves instructing the client to use negative thoughts as a way of developing negative feelings associated with a deviant sexual stimulus

Critical sexuality studies 25
Generic term for current core content of sexuality, theory and research that is multifaceted and multidisciplinary (crossing several social science and humanities disciplines)

Cross-dressing 407
Dressing in the clothes of the other gender, typically a man dressing in a woman's clothes

Cryptorchidism 103
Undescended testes

Cunnilingus 213
Stimulation of the clitoris, labia, and vaginal opening of the woman by her partner's tongue and lips

Curvilinear correlation 53
Relationship that exists when two variables vary in both the same and opposite directions

Cybersex 488
Engaging in self-stimulation while online to include "looking at pictures, engaging in sexual chat, exchanging explicit sexual emails, and sharing mutual sexual fantasies while masturbating"

Cystitis 65, 220
Bladder inflammation/infection

D

Date rape 456
Nonconsensual sex between people who are dating or on a date (also called Acquaintance rape.)

Deductive research 27
Sequence of research starting with a specific theory, generating a specific expectation or hypothesis based on that theory, and then gathering data that will either support or refute the theory

Defense of Marriage Act 280
Legislative act that denied federal recognition of homosexual marriage and allowed states to ignore same-sex marriages licensed elsewhere

Degrading pornography 501
Sexually explicit material that degrades, debases, and dehumanizes people, typically women

Delayed ejaculation 377
Absence or delay of ejaculation

Dementia 297
Brain disorder involving multiple cognitive deficits, including memory impairment and at least one of the following: aphasia, agnosia, apraxia, or loss of ability to think abstractly and to plan, initiate, sequence, monitor, and stop complex behavior

Dental dam 213
Thin piece of latex that covers the vulva during cunnilingus, or the anus during analingus

Dependent variable 40
Variable that is measured to assess what, if any, effect the independent variable has on it

Depo-Provera 321
A synthetic compound similar to progesterone injected into the woman's arm or buttock that protects her against pregnancy for 3 months by preventing ovulation

Descriptive research 52
Qualitative or quantitative research that describes sexual processes, behaviors, and attitudes, as well as the people who experience them

Determinism 21
Belief that one's choices are largely determined by heredity and environment

Diabetes mellitus 296
Chronic disease in which the pancreas fails to produce sufficient insulin, which is necessary for metabolizing carbohydrates and fats

Diaphragm 326
Shallow rubber dome attached to a flexible, circular steel spring, 2–4 inches in diameter, that can be inserted vaginally to cover the cervix and prevent sperm from entering the uterus

Dichotomous model 261
(Also referred to as the "either-or" model of sexuality) Way of conceptualizing sexual orientation that prevails not only in views on sexual orientation but also in cultural understandings of biological sex (male vs. female) and gender (masculine vs. feminine)

Dilation and curettage (D & C) 336
Abortion procedure whereby a metal surgical instrument is used to scrape any remaining fetal tissue and placenta from the uterine walls after suctioning the contents of the uterus

Dilation and evacuation (D & E) 336
Abortion procedure during the second trimester (13–24 weeks' gestation) whereby the cervix is dilated and the fetal parts inside are dismembered so they can be suctioned out

Dilation and suction (D & S) 336
Abortion procedure during the first 12 weeks whereby the cervix is dilated before the suction procedure occurs

Direct laboratory observation 49
In human sexuality research, the actual observation of individuals engaging in sexual behavior, which Masters and Johnson and Alfred C. Kinsey utilized

Disability 291
Health condition that involves functional deficits in performing activities of daily living

Discrimination 282
Behavior that involves treating categories of individuals unequally

Double mastectomy 304
Removal of both breasts

Down low 250
Behavior of keeping one's activity private; term used to describe men who have sex with men but do not label themselves as gay or bisexual

Dysmenorrhea 80
Painful menstruation

Dyspareunia 380
The recurrent or persistent genital pain associated with intercourse or attempts at sexual intercourse

E

Eclectic view 37
View that recognizes the contribution of multiple perspectives to the understanding of sexuality

Ecstasy 310
Drug which has both stimulant and psychedelic effects that can result in increased energy; enhanced sense of pleasure and self-confidence; and feelings of peacefulness, acceptance, and closeness with others; also known as MDMA, X or E (Use of the drug is also associated with dangerous risks such as heart failure.)

Ectopic pregnancy   74, 346
Condition in which a fertilized egg becomes implanted in a site other than the uterus

Ego   30
Freud's term for that part of an individual's psyche that deals with objective reality

Ejaculatory inevitability   108
The feeling a male has when he becomes aware that he is going to ejaculate and cannot stop the process

Electra complex   128
In psychoanalysis, term that refers to a daughter's (unconscious) sexual desire for her father; refers to the Greek myth in which Electra assists her brother in killing their mother and her lover to avenge their father's death.

Embryo   344
Developing organism from conception to the 8th week of pregnancy

Emergency contraception   330
Contraceptive administered within 72 hours following unprotected intercourse; referred to as the "morning-after pill"

Emission   108
First phase of a male orgasm in which semen pools in the urethral bulb and ejaculatory pressure builds

Empirical evidence   26
Data that can be observed, measured, and quantified

Endogamy   162
Cultural expectation that one will select a marriage partner within one's own social group, such as race, religion, and social class

Endometriosis   80, 304
Growth of endometrial tissue outside the uterus, in the Fallopian tubes or abdominal cavity, which may cause pain

Epididymis   103
Part of the spermatic duct system connecting the testicles with the vas deferens

Erectile disorder   372
Persistent or recurrent inability to attain, or to maintain until completion of sexual activity, an adequate erection

Erotica   501
Sexually explicit material that is neither a degrading nor violent portrayal of consensual sexual activity

Erotic massage parlors   500
Places that provide sexual services (manual manipulation, oral sex, and sometimes sexual intercourse) in exchange for money

Erotophilia   197
Propensity to have very positive views of and emotional responses to sexuality

Erotophobia   197
Propensity to have very negative views of and emotional responses to sexuality

Escort   508
Another term for call girl which implies a wider range of behavior, such as being a social companion for an evening that typically ends in sexual intimacy

Essure   333
Permanent sterilization procedure that requires no cutting and only a local anesthetic in a 0.5 hour procedure that blocks the Fallopian tubes

Evolutionary theories   29
Theories that explain human sexual behavior and sexual anatomy on the basis of human evolution (See also Sociobiological theories.)

Exchange theory   163
Theory of mate selection that holds that partners select each other on the basis of who offers the greatest rewards at the lowest cost

Excitement phase   83
Phase of sexual response cycle whereby increasing arousal is manifested by increases in heart rate, blood pressure, respiration, overall muscle tension, and vasocongestion, or increased blood flow to the genital region

Exhibitionistic disorder   400
Paraphilia that involves an intense, recurrent (over a period of at least 6 months) sexual urge, often accompanied by sexually arousing fantasies, to expose one's genitals to a stranger

Exogamy   162
Cultural expectation to marry outside one's own family group

Experimental research   44
Research methodology that involves manipulating the independent variable to determine how it affects the dependent variable

Expulsion   109
Second phase of a male orgasm in which semen is expelled by vigorous contractions of the muscles surrounding the root of the penis, pelvic region, and genital ducts

External locus of control   20
The perspective that successes and failures are determined by fate, chance, or some powerful external source

Extradyadic sexual involvement   248
Sexual relationship that occurs outside the couple, as when an individual of a dyad (couple) becomes sexually involved with someone other than the partner or mate

Extrafamilial child sexual abuse   470
Attempted or completed forced sex, before a child reaches the age of 14, by a person who is unrelated to the child by blood or marriage

Extramarital affair 246
Sexual intercourse between a spouse and someone other than the person he or she is married to

F

Fallopian tubes 74
Oviducts, or tubes, that extend about 4 inches laterally from either side of the uterus to the ovaries that transport the ovum from an ovary to the uterus

Family balancing 123
Act of selecting the sex of a child before it is conceived for a "balanced" one boy, one girl family and involves separating sperm carrying the X and Y chromosomes

Family of origin 143
Family into which an individual is born

Family of procreation 143
Family one begins by finding a mate, and having and rearing children

Fellatio 212
Oral stimulation of a man's genitals

Female condom 324
Lubricated, polyurethane adaptation of the male condom that is about 6.5 inches long and has flexible rings at both ends—one inserted vaginally, which covers the cervix, and one external, which partially covers the labia

Female genital alteration 65
Cutting or amputating some or all of the female external genitalia: the prepuce (or hood) of the clitoris and shaft of the clitoris, the labia minora, and the labia majora (also called Female genital mutilation)

Female genital cutting, female genital mutilation 65
See Female genital alteration

Female orgasmic disorder (FOD) 375
A persistent or recurrent difficulty, delay in, or absence of experiencing orgasm following sufficient stimulation and arousal

Female sexual interest/arousal disorder 365
The persistent or recurrent inability to attain or maintain sufficient sexual excitement or a lack of genital lubrication/swelling or other somatic responses

Feminist theories 36
Perspectives that analyze discrepancies in equality between men and women, and how these imbalances affect sexuality, research studies in sexuality, and sexual healthcare delivery

Fetal alcohol syndrome (FAS) 348
Possible negative consequences (e.g., facial malformation, low birth weight) for the fetus and infant of the mother who drinks alcohol during pregnancy

Fetishism 405
Paraphilia that involves a pattern, of at least 6 months' duration, of deriving sexual arousal or sexual gratification from actual or fantasized inanimate objects or nongenital body parts

Fetus 344
Developing organism from the 8th week of pregnancy forward

Field research 49
Method of data collection that involves observing and studying social behaviors in settings in which they occur naturally

Fisting 214
Insertion of several fingers or an entire closed fist and forearm (typically lubricated with a non-petroleum-based lubricant) into a partner's rectum and sometimes the lower colon; term also used to describe insertion of hand into vagina

Focus group 47
Interviews conducted in a small group and typically focused on one subject

Follicle-stimulating hormone 75
Hormone responsible for the release of an egg from the ovary

Forced sex 454
Acts of sex (or attempted sex) in which one party is nonconsenting, regardless of the age and sex of the offender and victim—whether or not the act meets criteria for what legally constitutes rape (also called Rape.)

Forcible rape 454
Sexual force involving three elements: vaginal, oral, or anal penetration; the use of force or threat of force; and non-consent of the victim

Foreplay 210
Also referred to as sexual touching, the broad category of activities which are usually undertaken with the goal of increasing one's own and/or one's partner's sexual arousal and pleasure

Free will 21
Belief that individuals are ultimately in charge of their own destinies

Frenulum 97
Thin strip of skin on the underside of the head of the penis that connects the glans with the shaft

Friends with benefits 152
Nonromantic friends who also have a sexual relationship

Frotteuristic disorder 401
Paraphilia that involves recurring, intense, sexual urges (for at least 6 months), accompanied by fantasies, of touching or rubbing—often with the genitals—against a nonconsenting person

Fundus 73
Broad, rounded part of the uterus

G

Gender 116
Social and psychological characteristics associated with being female or male

Gender dysphoria 117
Condition in which one's gender identity does not match one's biological sex

Gender identity 117
Psychological state of viewing one's self as a girl or a boy, and later as a woman or man

Gender postmodernism 137
State in which there is a dissolution of male and female categories as currently conceptualized in Western capitalist society

Gender role ideology 120
Socially prescribed role relationships between women and men in any given society

Gender roles 120
Social norms that dictate appropriate female and male behavior

Gender role transcendence 136
Abandonment of gender schema, or becoming "gender aschematic," so that personality traits, social and occupational roles, and other aspects of an individual's life become divorced from gender categories

Generalized dysfunction 359
Sexual dysfunction that occurs with all partners, in all contexts and settings

Genital herpes 435
Viral infection that may cause blistering, typically of the genitals, and may also infect the lips, mouth, and eyes

Genital warts 436
See Human papillomavirus

GHB (Gamma hydroxybutyrate) 456
also known as "liquid ecstasy" because like X, it inspires a tendency to be touchy-feely and relaxed. It is a more powerful drug that may cause deep sedation.

Glans 97
Small rounded body of tissue on the head of the penis that can swell and harden

Gonorrhea 432
Bacterial infection that is sexually transmitted; also known as "the clap," "the drip," "the whites," and "morning drop"

G-spot 72
Alleged highly sensitive area on the front wall of the vagina 1 to 2 inches into the vaginal canal (also called the Grafenberg spot)

H

Hate crimes 283
Bringing harm to an individual because he or she is viewed as belonging to a group of which one does not approve

Hedonism 8
Sexual value that reflects a philosophy that the pursuit of pleasure and the avoidance of pain are the ultimate values and motivation for sexual behavior

Hepatitis B 437
Inflammatory disease of the liver caused by a virus

Herpes simplex virus type 1 (HSV-1) 435
Viral infection that may cause blistering, typically of the lips and mouth, and may also infect the genitals

Herpes simplex virus type 2 (HSV-2) 435
See Genital herpes

Heterosexism 275
Belief, stated or implied, that heterosexuality is superior (e.g., morally, socially, emotionally, and behaviorally) to homosexuality

Heterosexuality 260
Sexual orientation whereby the predominance of emotional and sexual attraction is to persons of the other sex

Highly active antiretroviral therapy (HAART) 440
Combination of drugs an HIV-infected person takes to treat the virus; also known as "cocktail therapy"

High risk group 426
Certain behaviors help to identify who will become infected with an STI

Homogamy theory 163
Theory of mate selection that holds that individuals are attracted to and become involved with those who are similar in such characteristics as age, race, religion, and social class

Homonegativity 278
Construct that refers to antigay responses including negative feelings (fear, disgust, anger), thoughts, and behavior

Homophobia 278
Negative emotional responses toward, and aversion to, homosexuals

Homosexuality 260
Sexual orientation that involves the predominance of emotional and sexual attractions to persons of the same sex

Honor killing 463
Killing of a woman in the Arab world (e.g., Jordan) who is raped or who has intercourse before marriage, which brings great shame to her parents/family (She may be killed to absolve the family of the shame.)

Honor killing   64
The killing of an unmarried female who has had sex (which brings dishonor to her parents) done by the parents or another family member in order to restore the family's honor (they occur in middle eastern countries such as Jordan)

Hooking up   151
Meeting someone and becoming sexually involved that same evening with no commitment or expectation beyond the encounter

Hormones   87
Chemical messengers that travel from cell to cell via the bloodstream

Hostile environment sexual harassment   478
Environment whereby deliberate or repeated unwanted sexual comments or behaviors affect one's performance at work or school

Human immunodeficiency virus (HIV)   438
Virus that attacks the immune system and may lead to AIDS

Human papillomavirus (HPV)   436
Sexually transmitted viral infection that may produce genital warts

Hymen   64
Thin mucous membrane that may partially cover the vaginal opening

Hyperactive sexual desire disorder   370
Very high (hyperactive) sexual interest, which influences persons to behave as though they are driven to sexual expression and the pursuit of sex, which may have negative effects on the health, relationships, or career of the individual

Hyperventilation   83
Abnormally heavy breathing, resulting in loss of carbon dioxide from the blood, sometimes resulting in lowered blood pressure and fainting

Hypothesis   40
A tentative and testable proposal or an educated guess about the outcome of a research study

Hysterectomy   304, 332
Surgical removal of the uterus

I

"I" statements   179
Statements that focus on the feelings and thoughts of the communicator without making a judgment on what the other person says or does

Id   30
Freud's term that refers to instinctive biological drives, such as the need for sex, food, and water

Independent variable   40
Variable that is presumed to cause or influence the dependent variable

Induced abortion   335
The deliberate termination of a pregnancy through chemical or surgical means.

Inductive research   27
Sequence of research that begins with specific empirical data, which are then used to formulate a theory to explain the data

Infancy   230
First year of life following birth

Inhibited male orgasm   378
Persistent or recurrent delay in or absence of orgasm following a normal sexual excitement phase

Intact dilation and extraction (D & X)   337
Abortion procedure involving breech delivery of fetus (except for the head) and partial evacuation of the brain, resulting in the vaginal delivery of a dead fetus

Intellectual disability   299
Condition that involves subaverage intellectual functioning and deficits in adaptive behavior (also referred to as *mental retardation*)

Internal locus of control   20
The belief that successes and failures in life are attributable to one's own abilities and efforts

Intersex development   126
Congenital variations in the reproductive system, sometimes resulting in ambiguous genitals

Interstitial cells   102
Cells that are housed in the testes and produce testosterone (also known as Leydig's cells)

Interview survey research   46
Type of research in which trained interviewers ask respondents a series of questions, and either take written notes or tape-record the respondents' answers either over the telephone or face-to-face

Intrafamilial child sexual abuse   467
Exploitative sexual contact or attempted or forced sex that occurs between related individuals when the victim is under the age 18 (Also known as incestuous child abuse.)

Intrauterine device   326
(IUD) Object inserted into the uterus by a physician to prevent the fertilized egg from implanting on the uterine wall

Introitus   64
Vaginal opening

Involuntary abstinence   199
Condition of not having sexual relations due to environmental factors, such as not having a partner or being confined to an institution that does not encourage sexual expression

J

Jealousy   156
Emotional response to a perceived or real threat to an important or valued relationship

Jessica Lunsford Act   475
Florida law that establishes a mandatory sentence of 25 years in prison for a person convicted of a sex crime against a child, and on release, the person must wear a global positioning device

K

Kegel exercises   72
Voluntary contractions of the PC muscle, as though stopping the flow of urine after beginning to urinate, performed several times at several sessions per day

Kiddie porn   503
See Child pornography

Klinefelter's syndrome   124
Condition that occurs in males and results from the presence of an extra X sex chromosome (XXY), resulting in abnormal testicular development, infertility, low interest in sex (low libido), and, in some cases, mental retardation

L

Labia majora   63
("major lips") Two elongated folds of fatty tissue that extend from the mons veneris to the perineum

Labia minora   63
("little lips") Two smaller elongated folds of fatty tissue that enfold the urethral and vaginal openings

Laparoscopy   332
Surgery using a laparoscope; sometimes used for tubal ligation

Lap dance   499
Type of dance also known as "friction dance" or "straddle dance" that involves varying amounts of physical contact and can result in sexual release on the part of the customer

Lesbian death bed   366
Sustained drop-off in sexual frequency of lesbian couples in long-term relationships

LGBT   260
Lesbian, gay, bisexual, transgender

Libido   31
The sex drive

Lifelong dysfunction   359
Sexual dysfunction that a person has always experienced; for example, a person may have always lacked sexual desire

Locus of control   20
An individual's beliefs about the source or cause (internal or external) of his or her successes and failures

Looking glass self   182
Idea that the image people have of themselves is a reflection of what other people tell them about themselves

Lovemap   411
Mental representation or template of one's idealized lover that develops early in the individual's life

M

Madam   507
Woman who runs a house of prostitution

Male G-spot   104
The prostate gland, which can be stimulated by a partner who inserts an index finger, up to the second knuckle, (facing the partner) into the anus and bends the finger in a "come hither" motion

Male hypoactive sexual desire disorder   370
Persistent or recurrent deficiency (or absence) of sexual fantasies, thoughts, and/or desire for (or receptivity to) sexual activity, which causes personal distress

Mama san   507
Asian woman who runs a house of prostitution

Mammogram   69
Low-dose X-ray technique used by radiologists to detect small tumors inside the breast

Manscaping   223
Removal of body hair by men (mostly single) as a grooming behavior to present one's best sexual self to one's partner

Marital rape   454
Forcible rape by one's spouse; now illegal in all states

Mastectomy   304
Surgical removal of one breast

Masturbation   200
Natural, common, and nonharmful means of sexual self-pleasuring that is engaged in by individuals of all ages, sexual orientations, and levels of functioning (also called Autoerotic behavior)

Meatus   97
Opening to the urethra at the tip of the penis

Medical abortion   337
Intentional termination of pregnancy through the use of pharmaceutical drugs

Medicalization of sexual dysfunctions 358
Emphasizes that sexual dysfunctions have a medical or biological basis rather than an emotional or relationship cause

Medical model view of intellectual disability 299
View that the individual is coping with a personal tragedy—which implies adjusting to limited functioning—and that his/her sexual needs are nonexistent

Megan's Law 475
Federal law that requires that convicted sex offenders register with local police when they move into a community

Menarche 77
First menstruation

Menopause 252
Permanent cessation of menstruation that occurs in middle age

Menorrhagia 78
Excessive or prolonged menstruation

Menstrual suppression 77
Use of hormones or drugs to inhibit menstruation

Menstrual synchrony 77
Increased tendency for women living in close proximity to have their menstrual cycles occur at relatively the same time

Menstruation or menses 77
Sloughing off of blood, mucus, and lining of the uterus

Mental disorders 301
Mental states characterized by mild to severe disturbances in thinking, mood, and/or behavior associated with distress and/or impaired functioning (sometimes called mental illness)

Middle age 252
Time in a person's life that begins when the last child leaves home and continues until retirement or the death of either spouse.

Mifepristone 337
Synthetic steroid that effectively inhibits implantation of a fertilized egg by making the endometrium unsuitable for implantation which, in effect, aborts the fetus; may be used within the first 7 weeks of pregnancy (See also RU-486.)

Miscarriage 351
Unintended termination of a pregnancy.

Mittelschmerz 329
Ovulatory pain

Mons veneris 63
Soft cushion of fatty tissue that lies over the pubic symphysis (joint between the left and right pubic bones)

Multidimensional model 262
Way of conceptualizing sexual orientation which suggests that a person's orientation consists of various independent components (including emotions, lifestyle, self-identification, sexual attraction, fantasy, and behavior) and that these components may change over time

Multiple sclerosis 295
Progressive disease that attacks the central nervous system

Mutual monogamy 441
A relationship in which both partners agree to be sexually faithful to each other

Myotonia 83
Muscle contractions

Natural selection 29
Theory that individuals who have genetic traits that are adaptive for survival are more likely to survive and pass on their genetic traits to their offspring

N

NEA-TDS 322
(Norethindrone acetate transdermal system) a contraceptive patch worn continuously for 7 days and then replaced with a new patch (rotating sites on the abdomen, buttocks or hips)

Negative correlation 53
Relationship between two variables that change in opposite directions

Nexplanon/Implanon NXT or Implanon 320
Nexplanon/Implanon NXT is a single flexible plastic rod implant the size of a matchstick that releases a progestin hormone called etonogestrel

Nongonococcal urethritis 434
Infection of the urethra—the tube that carries urine from the bladder

Nonparticipant observation 49
Type of research in which investigators observe the phenomenon being studied, but do not actively participate in the group or the activity

Nonverbal messages 174
Type of communication in which facial expressions, gestures, bodily contact, and tone of voice predominate

NuvaRing 321
Soft, flexible, and transparent ring approximately 2 inches in diameter that is worn inside the vagina and provides month-long pregnancy protection

O

Obscenity 501
Label for sexual material that meets three criteria: (a) The dominant theme of the material must appeal to a prurient interest in sex; (b) the material must be patently offensive to the community; and (c) the sexual material must have no redeeming social value

Obsessive relational intrusion 159
Behavior of a stranger or an acquaintance who repeatedly invades one's physical or symbolic privacy in his or her attempts to have an intimate relationship

Occupational sex segregation 121
Tendency for women and men to pursue different occupations

Oedipal complex 128
Freud's term based on the legend of the Greek youth Oedipus, who unknowingly killed his father and married his mother; involves the young boy's awakening sexual feelings for his mother as he becomes aware he has a penis and his mother does not.

Oligomenorrhea 78
Irregular monthly periods

Oophorectomy 304, 332
Surgical removal of the ovaries

Open-ended question 178
Broad question designed to elicit a great deal of information

Open relationships 155
Each partner agrees that the other can have sexual (and sometimes emotional) relationships with someone outside the couple relationship

Operant conditioning 411
Learning theory which states that behavior is learned in reference to its consequences. A behavior that is punished will decrease in frequency a behavior that is reinforced will increase in frequency

Operant learning theory 31
Explanation of human behavior that emphasizes that the consequences of a behavior influence whether or not that behavior will occur in the future

Operational definition 41
Working definition, how a variable is defined in a particular study

Operationalize 41
Define how a variable will be measured

Oral herpes 435
Sores of the lip and mouth, often caused by herpes simplex virus type I, but can also be caused by herpes simplex virus type II

Orchiectomy 305
Surgical removal of the testicles

Orgasm 83
Climax of sexual excitement, experienced as a release of tension involving intense pleasure

Orgasmic headache 109
A sudden and severe headache that occurs at the time of, or shortly, after orgasm

Ortho Evra 322
Contraceptive transdermal patch, worn for 3 weeks (anywhere on the body except the breasts) and changed on a weekly basis, that delivers hormones to a woman's body through skin absorption

Os 73
Opening of the cervix (opening to the uterus)

Ostomy surgery 306
Surgery whereby a portion of the large or small intestine or urinary system is rerouted and brought to the skin surface of the abdomen where the contents are collected in a bag (Cancers of the colon, rectum, bladder, cervix, or ovaries are typical causes of ostomy surgery.)

Outercourse 441
Sexual activities that do not involve exposing a partner to blood, semen, or vaginal secretions

Ovaries 74
Female gonads, attached by ligaments on both sides of the uterus, that have the following two functions: producing ova and producing the female hormones estrogen and progesterone

P

Pap test 73
Procedure in which surface cells are scraped from the vaginal walls and cervix, and examined under a microscope to detect the presence of cancer

Paraphilia 396
Overdependence on a culturally unacceptable or unusual stimulus for sexual arousal and satisfaction

Paraplegia 294
Paralysis of the lower half of the body

Parental investment 127
Any investment by a parent that increases the offspring's chance of surviving and thus increases reproductive success

Partial-birth abortions 337
Nonmedical term used by abortion opponents to describe abortions performed very late in pregnancy in which the terminated fetus is delivered (See Intact dilation and extraction.)

Participant observation   49
Type of observation in which the researcher participates in the phenomenon being studied to obtain an insider's perspective of the people and/or behavior being observed

Partner notification laws   173
Set of laws that require healthcare providers to advise all persons with serious sexually transmitted infections about the importance of informing their sex or needle-sharing partner (or partners)

Patriarchy   37
System of social organization in which the father is the head of the family and family descent is traced through the male line

Pedophilic disorder   404
Sexual arousal in reference to a child

Pelvic inflammatory disease (PID)   429
Inflammation of the pelvic organs often requiring hospitalization and surgery (PID is associated with complications such as infertility, ectopic pregnancy, and chronic abdominal pain.)

Penectomy   306
Surgical removal of part or all of the penis

Penile strain gauge   107
Flexible band that fits around the base of the penis and expands as the penis enlarges, measuring circumference—a way of measuring male arousal via penis size

Penis   96
Primary male external sex organ which, in the unaroused state, is soft and hangs between the legs

Performance anxiety   361
Excessive concern over adequate sexual performance, which may result in sexual dysfunction

Perineum   63
Area of skin between the opening of the vagina and anus

Periodic abstinence   327
Refraining from sexual intercourse during the 1 to 2 weeks each month when the woman is thought to be fertile; also known as *rhythm method, fertility awareness*, and *natural family planning*

Persistent genito-pelvic pain/penetration disorder   379
Involves recurrent difficulties accomplishing vaginal penetration during intercourse, pain during vaginal intercourse/penetration attempts and fear/anxiety surrounding such attempts

Peyronie's disease (PD)   98, 381
Disease that causes a painful curving or bending in the penis during erection

Pharmaceutical abortion   337
See Medical abortion

Pheromones   88
Chemicals that activate the behavior of same-species organisms

Phone sex   497
Telephone conversation between a caller and a sex worker who verbally arouses, stimulates, and moves the caller toward orgasm in exchange for money

Physiological theories   29
Theories that describe and explain how physiological processes affect and are affected by sexual behavior

Plan B   239
A high dose progestin pill that acts to prevent ovulation or fertilization of an egg

Plateau phase   83
Second phase of Masters and Johnson's model of the sexual response cycle, which involves the continuation of sexual arousal, including myotonia (muscle contractions), hyperventilation (heavy breathing), tachycardia (heart rate increase), and blood pressure elevation

PLISSIT model   386
Method of sex therapy that involves four treatment levels: permission, limited information, specific suggestions, and intensive therapy

Polyamory   153
Involvement of more than three individuals in a pair-bonded relationship (some of the individuals may be married to each other) who have an emotional, sexual, and sometimes parenting relationship

Polyfidelity   155
Partners in the group remain faithful (sexually exclusive) to everyone else in the group

Pornography   501
Sexually explicit pictures, writing, or other images, usually pairing sex with power and violence

Positive correlation   53
Relationship between two variables that exists when both variables change in the same direction

Post abortion syndrome   354
Purportedly, the range of adverse psychological effects women who have had an abortion experience

Postcoital contraception   330
See Emergency contraception

Post-traumatic stress disorder   464
Mental health diagnostic category that characterizes a particular set of symptoms following traumatic events (including military combat, natural disasters, or other events that invoke terror, helplessness, and fear of loss of life), experienced by many rape victims

Preconceptual sex selection   123
Selection of the sex of a child before it is conceived (See also Family balancing.)

Predatory rape 457
Rape by a stranger which may involve a weapon (also called Classic rape.)

Premature ejaculation 371
See Rapid ejaculation

Premenstrual dysphoric disorder 82
(PMDD) A proposed diagnostic category, indicating a more severe form of PMS, which interferes with the work, social activities, and the relationships of a woman

Premenstrual syndrome 81
(PMS) Physical and psychological symptoms caused by hormonal changes from the time of ovulation to the beginning of, and sometimes during, menstruation

Prenatal sex selection 123
Selection of whether to continue the pregnancy based on the sex of the fetus.

Primacy/recency effect 177
Tendency of individuals to remember best what occurs first and last in a sequence

Primary dysfunction 359
See Lifelong dysfunction

Primary sex characteristics 116
Characteristics that differentiate women and men, such as external genitalia (vulva and penis), gonads (ovaries and testes), sex chromosomes (XX and XY), and hormones (estrogen, progesterone, and testosterone)

Principle of least interest 164
Theory that holds that the person who has the least interest in a relationship controls the relationship

Prostate gland 104
Chestnut-sized structure in the male, located below the bladder and in front of the rectum, that produces much of the seminal fluid

Prostitution 505
Act of providing sexual behavior (typically manual stimulation, oral sex, sexual intercourse, anal sex) through the use of one's body in exchange for money, drugs, or other goods

Pseudohermaphroditism 126
Condition in which an individual is born with gonads matching the sex chromosomes, but genitals resembling those of the other sex

Psychoanalytic theory 30
Freud's theory that emphasizes the role of unconscious processes in one's life

Psychosexology 28
Area of sexology focused on how psychological processes influence and are influenced by sexual development and behavior

Puberty 234
Developmental stage in which a youth achieves reproductive capacity

Pubic lice 431
Parasitic insects found in coarse body hair of humans, causing itching; also known as "crabs"

Pubococcygeus 72
Muscle surrounding the opening to the vagina that can influence sexual functioning, in that if it is too tense, vaginal entry may be difficult or impossible

Punishment 32
Consequence that decreases or terminates a behavior

Purging 119
Cross-dresser's act of destroying the clothes of the other sex as an expression of trying to become free of the drive to cross-dress (rarely has any long-term effect, and the person returns to cross-dressing)

Purging 407
Act of throwing away or burning one's clothes as a desperate means of ending one's cross-dressing

Q

Quadriplegia 294
Paralysis from the neck down

Quid pro quo sexual harassment 478
Type of sexual harassment whereby the individual is provided benefits (promotions, salary raises) in exchange for sexual favors

R

Radical prostatectomy 305
Surgical removal of the prostate

Rape 454
Act of sex (or attempted sex) in which one party is nonconsenting, regardless of the age and sex of the offender and victim—whether or not the act meets criteria for what legally constitutes rape (also called Forced sex.)

Rape myths 455
Generally false but widely held attitudes and beliefs that serve to justify male sexual aggression against women (also called Rape-supportive beliefs.)

Rape-supportive beliefs 455
See Rape myths

Rape trauma syndrome 464
Acute and long-term reorganization process that occurs as a result of forcible rape or attempted rape

Rapid ejaculation 371
Ejaculation which always or nearly always occurs prior to or within about 1 minute of vaginal penetration, the inability to delay ejaculation on all or nearly all vaginal penetrations, and the presence of negative personal consequences, such as distress, bother, frustration and/or the avoidance of sexual intimacy

Real-life experience 118
Living in the social role of the other sex for a year, prior to beginning hormonal or surgical therapy

Reflective listening 179
Communication technique in which one person restates the meaning of what his or her partner has said in a conversation

Reinforcement 32
Consequence that maintains or increases a behavior

Relativism 7
A sexual value that emphasizes that sexual decisions should be made in the context of a particular situation

Representative sample 45
Sample the researcher studies that is representative of the population from which it is taken

Resolution phase 84
Final phase of Masters and Johnson's model of the sexual response cycle that describes the body's return to its pre-excitement condition

Retarded ejaculation 378
See Inhibited male orgasm

Retrograde ejaculation 109
Ejaculation during which a man experiences an orgasm where the ejaculate does not come out of the penis but is emptied, instead, into the bladder

Rohypnol 456
Drug used in date rape scenarios which causes profound and prolonged sedation, a feeling of well- being, and short-term memory loss; also known as dulcitas, the "forget me drug"

RU-486 337
Known as the "abortion pill" and approved for use up to 49 days since the onset of the last menstrual period.

S

Salpingectomy 332
Tubal ligation or "tying of the tubes"; sterilization procedure whereby the woman's Fallopian tubes are cut out and the ends are tied, clamped, or cauterized so that eggs cannot pass down the Fallopian tubes to be fertilized

Sample 45
Portion of the population that the researcher studies to attempt to make inferences about the whole population

Satiation 245
A stimulus loses its value with repeated exposure

Satiation 370
Result of a stimulus losing its value with repeated exposure

Scabies 431
Infestation of the skin by microscopic mites that causes intense itching

Schizophrenia 302
Mental disorder characterized by social withdrawal and disturbances in thought, motor behavior, and interpersonal functioning

Scopophilia 399
Also called Voyeuristic disorder.

Scrotum 100
Sac, located below the penis, that contains the testicles

Secondary dysfunction 359
See Acquired dysfunction

Secondary sex characteristics 66
Characteristics that differentiate males and females that are not linked to reproduction (e.g., beard in men, high voice in women)

Secondary victimization 463
Experience in which a person has been raped and seeks help, but despite being the victim is blamed for the rape by those from whom she or he seeks help

Self-fulfilling prophecy 176
Behaving in such a way to make expectations come true, e.g., caustically accusing a partner of infidelity may lead that partner to be unfaithful

Semenarche 235
A boy's first seminal ejaculation

Semen-conservation doctrine 202
From early Ayurvedic teachings in India, the belief that general good health in both sexes depends on conserving the life-giving power of "vital fluids" (semen and vaginal fluids)

Seminal vesicles 104
Two small glands about 2 inches in length, located behind the bladder in the male, which secrete fluids that mix with sperm to become semen

Seminiferous tubules 103
Part of the spermatic duct system, located within the testicles

Sensate focus 367
Treatment used in sex therapy developed by Masters and Johnson whereby the partners focus on pleasuring each other in nongenital ways

Sex 116
Term that refers to the biological distinction between being female and being male, usually categorized on the basis of the reproductive organs and genetic makeup

Sex roles 120
Roles filled by women or men that are defined by biological constraints and can be enacted only by members of one biological sex only such as (wet nurse, sperm donor, child bearer)

Sex trafficking 514
Related to prostitution, using force and deception to transfer persons into situations of extreme exploitation

Sex work 505
Way in which one earns a living by providing sexual services, such as acting in a pornographic video, being a stripper, or being a phone sex worker

Sexology 28
Unique discipline that identifies important questions related to sexuality issues and finds and integrates answers from biology, psychology, and sociology based on scientific methods of investigation

Sexting 235
Sending sexually explicit text or photos via cell phone

Sexual addiction 409
Sometimes described as an intimacy disorder manifested by a compulsive cycle of preoccupation and ritualization of sexual behavior and despair

Sexual anatomy 61
Term referring to internal and external genitals, also called sex organs

Sexual aversion disorder 368
Persistent or recurrent phobic aversion to and avoidance of sexual contact with a sexual partner

Sexual celibacy 200
State of not having sexual intercourse or activity

Sexual coercion 454
Use of force (actual or threatened) to engage a person in sexual acts against that person's will

Sexual debut 233
One's first sexual intercourse

Sexual disorder 388
Diagnosis that a disturbance in sexual desire or the psycho-physiological components of one's sexual response cycle cause significant distress and interpersonal difficulty

Sexual double standard 8
One standard for women and another for men regarding sexual behavior (i.e., in U.S. society it is normative for men to have more sexual partners and women to have fewer partners)

Sexual dysfunctions 358
A heterogeneous group of disorders that are typically characterized by a clinically significant disturbance in a person's ability to respond sexually or to experience sexual pleasure

Sexual fantasies 209
Cognitions, or thoughts and/or images, that are sexual in nature

Sexual fluidity 262
Capacity for variation in one's erotic responses depending on the situation

Sexual guilt 159
Personal emotional reaction to engaging in sexual behavior that violates personal sexual values

Sexual harassment 477
Unwelcome sexual advances, requests for sexual favors, and other verbal or physical conduct of a sexual nature when submission to or rejection of this conduct explicitly or implicitly affects an individual's employment; unreasonably interferes with an individual's work performance; or creates an intimidating, hostile, or offensive work environment

Sexual identity 120
Composite term that refers to factors including one's biological sex, gender identity, gender role, and sexual orientation

Sexual intercourse 214
Sexual union of a man's penis and a woman's vagina (also known as coitus)

Sexual masochism disorder 402
Paraphilia characterized by recurrent, intense, sexual urges and sexually arousing fantasies of at least 6 months' duration, in which sexual arousal or gratification is obtained through enacting scripts that involve suffering and pain

Sexual orientation 260
Classification of individuals as heterosexual, bisexual, or homosexual based on their emotional, cognitive, and sexual attractions as well as their self-identity and lifestyle

Sexual physiology 62
Vascular, hormonal, and central nervous system processes involved in genital functioning

Sexual sadism disorder 404
Paraphilia characterized by recurrent, intense, sexual urges and sexually arousing fantasies, of at least 6 months' duration, involving acts that hurt or humiliate the sexual partner

Sexual self-concept 5
The way an individual thinks and feels about his or her body, self-evaluation of one's interest in sex, and evaluation of oneself as a sexual partner

Sexual touching 210
See Foreplay

Sexual values 5
Moral guidelines for making sexual choices

Sexually transmitted infections (STIs) 422
Infections transmitted primarily through sexual activity; a more recent term sometimes used to avoid the negative connotations sometimes associated with STD

She-male 118
Person who looks like a woman and has the breasts of a woman (from hormonal or surgical enlargement), yet has the genitalia and reproductive system of a man

Situational dysfunction 359
Sexual dysfunction that occurs with one partner or in one situation only

Social learning theory 32
Framework that emphasizes the process of learning through observation and imitation

Social model view of intellectual disability 299
Views the intellectually disabled person as the product of specific social definitions which involve oppression and discrimination of disabled persons

Social scripts 35
Shared interpretations that have three functions: to define situations, name actors, and plot behaviors

Sociobiological theories 29
Framework that explains human sexual behavior and sexual anatomy as functional for human evolution (See also Evolutionary theories.)

Sociobiology 126
Framework in which social behavior is viewed as having a biological basis in terms of being functional in human evolution

Sociosexology 28
Aspect of sexology that is concerned with the way social and cultural forces influence and are influenced by sexual attitudes, beliefs, and behaviors

Spectatoring 373
Self-monitoring one's own sexual responses to the point that a sexual dysfunction may occur

Spermicide 322
Chemical that kills sperm

Spinbarkeit 329
The slippery, elastic, raw egg white consistency of the cervical mucus that becomes evident at the time of ovulation and signals that it is likely the woman has ovulated

Sponge 325
Disk-shaped polyurethane device containing the spermicide nonoxynol-9 that protects for repeated acts of intercourse over 24 hours, without the need for supplying additional spermicide

Spontaneous abortion 335
the unintended termination of a pregnancy

Spurious correlation 54
Pattern that exists when two variables appear to be related but only because they are both related to a third variable

Stalking 161
Extreme form of obsessive relational intrusion that may involve following a victim, property damage, home invasion, or threats of physical harm

Sterilization 332
Permanent surgical procedure that prevents reproduction

Stoma 306
Protruding portion of the large or small intestine (bowel) or urinary system that is rerouted and brought to the skin surface of the abdomen during ostomy surgery (also called ostomy.)

Structural-functional theory 36
Framework that views society as a system of interrelated parts that influence each other and work together to achieve social stability

Substance abuse 307
Overuse or overdependence on drugs or chemicals that results in a failure to fulfill role obligations at work, school, or home, the effects of which include danger (e.g., driving while impaired), recurrent substance-related legal problems, and continued substance use despite its negative effect on social or interpersonal relationships. (also called substance dependence.)

Suction curettage 335
Abortion procedure performed the first 6 to 8 weeks of pregnancy whereby a hollow plastic rod is inserted into the woman's uterus where the fetal tissue is evacuated

Superego 30
Freud's term for the conscience, which functions by guiding the individual to do what is morally right and good

Surgical menopause 304
Sudden decrease in estrogen resulting from removal of the ovaries that can lead to decreased desire, vaginal dryness, and dyspareunia

Survey research 45
Research that involves eliciting information from respondents using questions

Symbolic interaction theory 32
Sociological theory that focuses on how meanings, labels, and definitions learned through interaction affect one's attitudes, self-concept, and behavior

Syphilis 433
Sexually transmitted (or congenital) infection caused by a spirochete (Treponema pallidum) that if untreated, can progress to a systemic infection through three stages and be fatal

Systems theory 37
Theoretical framework that emphasizes the interpersonal and relationship aspects of sexuality

T

Table dance   499
Type of dance in which the woman dances or disrobes on the customer's table or in front of the seated customer

Tachycardia   83
Increased heart rate

Testes   101
Male glands that develop from the same embryonic tissue as the female gonads (the ovaries) and produce spermatozoa and male hormones (also called testicles)

Theory   28
Set of ideas designed to answer a question or explain a particular phenomenon

Therapeutic massage   500
Non-erotic massage by a person who has received academic training at one of the more than 400 accredited programs, completed a supervised internship, and has a therapeutic massage license

Thermascan   70
Digital infrared imaging or infrared mammography is an alternative method for identifying breast disease that might ultimately lead to breast cancer

Touch-and-ask-rule   179
Sexual technique whereby each touch and caress is accompanied by the question "How does that feel?" and is followed by feedback from the partner

Toucheurism   402
Related to frotteurism, paraphilia, that involves actively using one's hands on the victim

Transgender   260
Term that refers to individuals who express some characteristics other than their assigned gender, which is usually based on their biological sex (male or female)

Transgendered   117
Term that refers to individuals of one biological sex (female or male) who express behavior not typically assigned to their gender

Transgendered individuals   260
Persons who do not fit neatly into either the male or female category, or their behavior is not congruent with the norms and expectations of their sex

Transgenderist   118
Individual who lives in a gender role that does not match his or her biological sex but who does not surgically alter his or her genitalia (as does a transsexual)

Transsexuals   117
Persons with the biological/anatomical sex of one gender (e.g., male) but the self-concept of the other sex (e.g., female)

Transvestic disorder   406
Sexual arousal by dressing in the gender of the other sex

Transvestic fetishism   406
Paraphilia that involves recurrent, intense, sexual urges and sexually arousing fantasies, of at least 6 months' duration, that involve cross-dressing (e.g., a man dressing in a woman's clothes)

Transvestite   407
Broad term for an individual who may dress or present himself or herself in the gender of the other sex; a more pejorative term than *cross-dresser*

Transvestites   118
Broad term for individuals who may dress or present themselves in the gender of the other sex; a more pejorative term than cross-dresser

Traumatic brain injury   298
Closed head injury that results from an exterior force and creates a temporary or enduring impairment in brain functioning

True hermaphroditism   126
Rare condition in which individuals are born with both ovarian and testicular tissue (These individuals, called hermaphrodites, may have one ovary and one testicle, feminine breasts, and a vaginal opening beneath the penis.)

Turner's syndrome   124
Condition that occurs in females resulting from the absence of an X chromosome (XO)

U

Ultrasound scan   350
Procedure whereby sound waves are used to project an image of the developing fetus on a video screen; used in prenatal testing

Umbilical cord   344
Flexible cord that connects the developing fetus and the placenta; this cord contains two arteries and a vein that facilitate this exchange

Unidimensional continuum model   261
Identification of one's sexual orientation on a scale from 0 (exclusively heterosexual) to 6 (exclusively homosexual) suggesting that most people are not on the extremes but somewhere in between

Urethra   65
Short tube that connects the bladder with the urethral opening

Urethritis   381
Inflammation of the urethra

Uterine orgasm   84
In contrast to "clitoral" orgasm, an orgasm caused by deep intravaginal stimulation and involving contractions in the uterus as well as vagina

Uterus   73
Womb; a hollow, muscular organ in which a fertilized egg may implant and develop

V

Vacuum aspiration   335
See Suction curettage

Vagina   71
Muscular tube 3- to 5-inches long that extends from the vulva to the cervix of the uterus

Vaginismus   380
Recurrent or persistent involuntary spasm of the musculature of the outer third of the vagina that interferes with vaginal penetration

Vaginitis   435
Infection of the vagina

Variable   40
Any measurable event or characteristic that varies or is subject to change

Vas deferens   104
Tube from the ejaculatory ducts to the testes that transports sperm

Vasectomy   333
Minor surgical procedure whereby the vas deferens are cut so as to prevent sperm from entering the penis

Vasocongestion   83
Increased blood flow to the genital region

Vees   155
Three-person relationships in which one member is sexually connected to each of the two others

Verbal messages   174
Words individuals say to each other

Vestibule   64
Smooth tissue surrounding a woman's urethral opening

Violent pornography   501
Sexually explicit visual images of sexual violence usually directed by men toward women

Virginity   197
State of not having experienced sexual intercourse

Voluntary abstinence   199
Forgoing sexual intercourse for a period of time by choice

Voyeuristic disorder   399
Paraphilia that involves recurrent, intense urges to look at unsuspecting people who are naked, undressing, or engaging in sexual behavior (See also Scopophilia.)

Vulva   62
External female genitalia

Vulval orgasm   84
An orgasm that results primarily from manual stimulation of the clitoris and is characterized by contractions of the outer third of the vagina (also called Clitoral orgasms)

Vulvodynia   381
Burning, stinging, irritation, or knife-like pain of the vulva for more than 3 months without obvious visible lesions

W

Win-win solution   188
Outcome of an interpersonal conflict whereby both people feel satisfied with the agreement or resolution

Y

Yang   202
In Chinese thought, the male force that is viewed as active

Yin   202
In Chinese thought, the female force that is seen as passive

"You" statements   180
In communication theory, those statements that blame or criticize the listener and often result in increasing negative feelings and behavior in the relationship

References

A

Adolfsen, A., Iedema, J., & Keuzenkamp, S. (2010). Multiple dimensions of attitudes about homosexuality: Development of a multifaceted scale measuring attitudes toward homosexuality. *Journal of Homosexuality, 57,* 1237–1257.

Affonso, D. D., & Mayberry, L. J. (1989). Common stressors reported by a group of childbearing American women. In P. N. Stern (Ed.), *Pregnancy and parenting* (pp. 41–55). New York: Hemisphere.

Aguilar, J. (2013). Situational sexual behaviors: The ideological work of moving toward polyamory in communal living groups. *Journal of Contemporary Ethnography, 42,* 1–4, 129.

Alanko, K., Salo, B., Mokros, A., & Santtila, P. (2013). Evidence for heritability of adults men's sexual interest in youth under age 16 from a population-based extended twin design. *Journal of Sexual Medicine, 10,* 1090–1099.

Albersen, M., Linsen, L., Tinel, H., Sandner, P., & Van Renterghem, K. (2013). Synergistic effects of BAY 60-4522 and vardenafil on relaxation of corpus cavernosum tissue of patients with erectile dysfunction and clinical phosphodiesterase type 5 inhibitor failure. *Journal of Sexual Medicine, 10,* 1268–1277.

Allen, E. S., & Atkins, D. C. (2012). The association of divorce and extramarital sex in a representative U.S. sample. *Journal of Family Issues, 33,* 1477–1493.

Allen, P. L. (2000). *The wages of sin: Sex and disease, past and present.* Chicago: University of Chicago Press.

Almendarez, R., & Wilson, A. D. (2013). The effect of gender and ethnicity on the sexual behaviors of adolescents. *Family Journal, 21,* 104–111.

Almond, D., Edlund, L., & Milligan, K. (2013). Son preference and the persistence of culture: Evidence from South and East Asian Immigrants to Canada. *Population & Development, 39,* 75–95.

Althof, S. E., Rosen, R. C., Perelman, M. A., & Rubio-Aurioles, E. (2013). Standard operating procedures for taking a sexual history. *Journal of Sexual Medicine, 10,* 26–35.

Alz.org. (2013). Retrieved from http://www.alz.org/alzheimers_disease_facts_and_figures.asp#prevalence

Amato, P. R. (2004). Tension between institutional and individual views of marriage. *Journal of Marriage and Family, 66,* 959–965.

American Cancer Society. (2013a). *Testicular cancer.* Retrieved July 24, 2013, from http://www.cancer.org/cancer/testicularcancer/index

American Cancer Society. (2013a). *New breast cancer cases for 2013.* Retrieved from http://www.cancer.org/acs/groups/content/@epidemiologysurveilance/documents/document/acspc-037114.pdf

American Cancer Society. (2013b). *Deaths from breast cancer to 2013.* Retrieved from http://www.cancer.org/acs/groups/content/@epidemiologysurveilance/documents/document/acspc-037115.pdf

American Cancer Society. (2013b). *Prostate cancer.* Retrieved from http://www.cancer.org/cancer/prostatecancer/index

American College of Obstetricians and Gynecologists. (2012). Retrieved January 8, 2012, from http://www.acog.org/~/media/For%20Patients/faq014.pdf?dmc=1&ts=20130804T1749212078

American Psychiatric Association. (2013). *Diagnostic and statistical manual of mental disorders, Fifth edition, DSM-5 (TM).* Arlington, VA: American Psychiatric Association.

Amezcua-Prieto, C., Olmedo-Requeno, R., Jimenez-Mejias, E., Hurtado-Sabchez, F., Mozas-Moreno, J., Lardelli-Claret, P., & Jimemez-Moleon, J. J. (2013). Changes in leisure time physical activity during pregnancy compared to the prior year. *Maternal and Child Health Journal, 17,* 623–638.

Andrews, T., & Knaak, S. (2013). Medicalized mothering: Experiences in breastfeeding in Canada and Norway. *The Sociological Review, 61,* 88–110.

Angier, N. (1999). *Woman: An intimate geography.* New York, NY: Anchor.

Annon, J. (1976). The PLISSIT model. *Journal of Sex Education and Therapy, 2,* 1–15.

APA. (2010). *Ethical Principles of Psychologists and Code of Conduct.* Retrieved from American Psychological Association: http://www.apa.org/ethics/code/index.aspx

APA. (2012). *About APA.* Retrieved from American Psychological Association: http://www.apa.org/about/index.aspx

Apostolou, M. (2013, July 6). The evolution of rape: The fitness benefits and costs of a forced-sex mating strategy in an evolutionary context. *Aggression and Violent Behavior.*

Arakawa, D. R., Flanders, C. E., & Heck, R. (2013). Positive psychology: What impact has it had on sex research publication trends? *Sexuality and Culture, 17,* 305–320.

Aramburu, A. C. (2013). Relational and sexual fluidity in females partnered with male-to-female transsexual persons. *Journal of Psychiatric & Mental Health Nursing, 20,* 142–149.

Atwood, J. D., & Klucinec, E. (2011). Current state of sexuality and therapy. In J. L. Wetchler (Ed.), *Handbook of clinical issues in couple therapy* (pp. 95–114). New York: Routledge-Taylor & Francis Group.

Aubrey, J. S., & Smith, S. E. (2013). Development and validation of the endorsement of the Hookup Culture Index. *Journal of Sex Research, 50,* 435–448.

Averett, S. H., Corman, H., & Reichman, N. E. (2013). Effects of being overweight on risky sexual behavior of adolescent girls. *Economic Inquiry, 51,* 605–619.

B

Babin, E. A. (2013). An examination of predictors of nonverbal and verbal communication of pleasure during sex and sexual satisfaction. *Journal of Social and Personal Relationships, 30,* 270–292.

Bahouq, H., Fadoua, A., Hanan, R., Ihsane, H., & Najia, H. (2013). Profile of sexuality in Moroccan chronic low back pain patients. *BMC Musculoskelatal Disorders, 14,* 1472.

Bailey, J. M. (2003). *The man who would be queen: The science of gender-bending and transsexualism.* Washington, DC: Joseph Henry Press.

Bancroft, J. H. (1989). *Human sexuality and its problems* (2nd ed.). New York, NY: Churchill Livingston.

Bandini, E., Fisher, A. D., Castellini, G., Lo Sauro, C., Lelli, Z. L., Meriggiola, M. C., ... Ricca, V. (2013). Gender identity and disorder and eating disorders: Similarities and differences in terms of body uneasiness. *Journal of Sexual Medicine, 10,* 1012–1023.

Barelds-Dijkstra, D. P., & Barelds, P. (2007). Relations between different types of jealousy and self and partner perceptions of relationship quality. *Clinical Psychology & Psychotherapy, 14,* 176–188.

Barrett, E. S., Tran, V., Thurston, S., Jasienska, G., Furberg, A. S., Ellison, P. T., & Thune, I. (2013). Marriage and motherhood are associated with lower testosterone concentrations in women. *Hormones & Behavior, 63,* 72–79.

Barriger, M., & Velez-Blasini, C. J. (2013). Descriptive and injunctive social norm overestimation in hooking up and their role as predictors of hook up activity in a college student sample. *Journal of Sex Research, 50,* 84–94.

Bartosch, J., Berry, W., Maodush-Pitzer, D., Hunter-Geboy, C., Thompson, P. M., & Woodard, L. (1989). *God's gift of sexuality: A study for young people in the reformed tradition in the Presbyterian church (USA) and Reformed Church in America.* Louisville, KY: Presbyterian Publishing House.

Bartz, D., & Greenberg, J. (2008). Sterilization in the United States. *Rev Obstet Gynecol, Winter, 1(1),* 23–32.

Basler-Francis, E. (2013). Personal communication. The Be Frank Educational Collaborative, Chicopee, MA.

Basson, R. (2001a). Are the complexities of women's sexual function reflected in the new consensus definitions of dysfunction? *Journal of Sex and Marital Therapy, 27,* 105–112.

Basson, R. (2001b). Human sex-response cycles. *Journal of Sex and Marital Therapy, 27,* 33–43.

Bauerlein, M. (2010). Literary learning in the hyperdigital age. *Futurist, 44,* 24–25.

Beaudoin, G., Hebert, M., & Bernier, A. (2013). Contribution of attachment security to the prediction of internalizing and externalizing behavior problems in preschooler victims of sexual abuse. *European Review of Applied Psychology, 63,* 147–157.

Beaver, T., Knox, D., & Kiskute, V. (2010). "I Kissed a Girl": Heterosexual women who report same sex kissing. Southern Sociological Society Annual Meeting. Atlanta, April.

Becerra, R. M. (2012). The Mexican American family. In R. Wright, Jr., C. H. Mindel, T. V. Tran, & R. W. Habenstein (Eds.), *Ethnic families in America* (5th ed., pp. 100–111). Upper Saddle River, NJ: Pearson.

Bedi, R., Muller, R. T., & Thornback, K. (2013). Object relations and psychopathology among adult survivors of childhood abuse. *Psychological Trauma: Theory, Research, Practice, and Policy, 5,* 233–240.

Begum, S., Hocking, J. S., Groves, J., Fairley, C. K., & Keogh, L. A. (2013). Sex workers talk about sex work: Sex contradictory characteristics of legalized sex work in Melbourne, Australia. *Culture, Health & Sexuality, 15,* 85–100.

Bem, D. J. (1996). Exotic becomes erotic: A developmental theory of sexual orientation. *Psychological Review, 103,* 320–335.

Benotsch, E. G., Snipes, D. J., Martin, A. M., & Bull, S. S. (2013). Sexting, substance use and sexual risk behavior in young adults. *Journal of Adolescent Health, 52,* 307–313.

Bergdall, A. R., Kraft, J. M., Andes, K., Carter, M., Hatfield-Timajchy, K., & Hock-long, L. (2012). Love hooking up in the new millennium: Communication technology and relationships among urban African American and Puerto Rican young adults. *Journal of Sex Research, 49,* 570–582.

Berman, S. M., London, E. D., Morgan, M., & Rapkin, A. J. (2013). Elevated gray matter volume of the emotional cerebellum in women with premenstrual dysphoric disorder. *Journal of Affective Disorders, 146,* 266–271.

Bermant, G. (1976). Sexual behavior: Hard times with the Coolidge effect. In M. H. Siegel, & H. P. Zeigler (Eds.), *Psychological research: The inside story* (pp. 76–103). New York: Harper and Row.

Bernal, A. T., d'Aniello, C., & Vasquez, W. F. (2013). Gender distribution in COAMFTE-accredited programs. *Journal of Feminist Family Therapy: An International Forum, 25,* 93–111.

Bernert, D. J., & Ogeltree, R. J. (2013). Women with intellectual disabilities talk about their perceptions of sex. *Journal of Intellectual Disability Research, 57,* 240–249.

Bernstein, D. I., Bellamy, A. R., Hook, E. W., Levin, M. L., Wald, A., Ewell, M. G., & Belshe, R. B. (2012). Epidemiology, clinical presentation, and antibody response to primary infection with herpes simplex virus type 1 and type 2 in young women. *Clinical Infection Diseases, 56(3),* 344–351.

Berry, M. D. (2013). Historical revolutions in sex therapy: A critical examination of men's sexual dysfunctions and their treatment. *Journal of Sex & Marital Therapy, 39,* 21–39.

Berry, M. D. (2013b). The history and evolutions of sex therapy and its relationship to psychoanalysis. *International Journal of Applied Psychoanalytic Studies, 10,* 53–74.

Bersamin, M., Zamboanga, B. L., Schwartz, S. J., Donnellan, M. B., Hudson, M., Weisskirch, R. S., ... Caraway, S. J. (2013). Risky business: Is there an association between casual sex and mental health among emerging adults? *Journal of Sex Research.* doi:10.1080/00224499.2013.772088

Berthet, N., Bertolus, C., Gessain, A., & Goudot, P. (2012). Clinical relevance of systematic human papillomavirus (HPV) diagnosis in oral squamous cell carcinoma. *Infections Agents and Cancer, 7(13),* 1–2.

Bertolus, C., Goudot, P., Gessain, A., & Berthet, N. (2012). Clinical relevance of systematic human papillomavirous (HPV) diagnosis in oral squamous cell carcinoma. *Infectious Agents and Cancer, 7(13),* 1–2.

Blackstrom, L., Armstrong, E. A., & Puentes, J. (2012). Women's negotiation of cunnilingus in college hookups and relationships. *Journal of Sex Research, 49,* 1–12.

Blackwell, C. W., & Dziegielewski, S. F. (2012). Using the Internet to meet sexual partners: Research and practice implications. *Journal of Social Service Research, 38,* 46–55.

Blumer, M. L., Papaj, A. K., & Erolin, K. S. (2013). Feminist family therapy for treating female survivors of childhood sexual abuse. *Journal of Feminist Family Therapy: An International Forum, 25,* 65–79.

Bockting, W. O., Miner, M. H., Romine, R. E., Hamilton, A., & Coleman, E. (2013). Stigma, mental health, and resilience in an online sample of U.S. transgender population. *American Journal of Public Health, 103*, 1–9.

Bolen, R. M. (2001). *Child sexual abuse: Its scope and our failure.* New York: Kluwer Academic/Plenum Publishers.

Boncinelli, V., Scaletti, D. G., Nanini, C., Daino, D., & Genazzani, A. R. (2013). Sexual fantasies and female hypoactive desire. *Sexologies: European Journal of Sexology and Sexual Health, 22*, 16–19.

Bonet, M. L., Marchand, M., Kaminski, A., Fohran, A., Betoko, A., Charles, M. A., & Blondel, B. (2013). Breastfeeding duration, social and occupational characteristics of mothers in the French 'EDEN mother-child' cohort. *Maternal and Child Health Journal, 17*, 714–722.

Boylan, S. M., Greenwood, D. C., Alwan, N., Cooke, M. S., Dolby, V. A., Hay, W. M., … Cade, J. E. (2013). Does nausea and vomiting of pregnancy play a role in the association found between maternal caffeine intake and fetal growth restriction? *Maternal and Child Health Journal, 17*, 601–608.

Bradshaw, C., Kahn, A. S., & Saville, B. K. (2010). To hook up or date: Which gender benefits? *Journal Sex Roles, 49*, 661–669.

Brainline.org. (2013). Retrieved from http://www.brainline.org/landing_pages/categories/abouttbi.html?gclid=CIE28XG87gCFQto7AodW2sAdg

Brannock, J. C., & Chapman, B. F. (1990). Negative sexual experiences with men among heterosexual women and lesbians. *Journal of Homosexuality, 19*, 105–110.

Braun, V. (2009). 'The women are doing it for themselves': The rhetoric of choice and agency around female genital 'cosmetic surgery.' *Australian Feminist Studies, 24*, 233–249.

Breed, R., Knox, D., & Zusman, M. (2004). Gender differences in coping with jealousy. Poster, Annual Research Symposium, East Carolina University.

Brison, D., Seftel, A., & Sadeghi-Nejad, H. (2013). The resurgence of the vacuum erection device (VED) for treatment of erectile dysfunction. *Journal of Sexual Medicine, 10*, 1124–1135.

Brooks, G. R. (1995). *The centered syndrome.* San Francisco: Jossey-Bass.

Brooks-Gunn, J., & Ruble, D. N. (1980). Menstrual attitude questionnaire (MAQ). *Psychosomatic, 42*, 505–507.

Brown, S. (2013). Is counseling necessary? Making the decision to have an abortion. A qualitative interview study. *The European Journal of Contraception and Reproductive Health Care, 18*, 44–48.

Brown, S. M., & Porter, J. (2013). The effects of religion on remarriage among American women: Evidence from the National Survey of Growth. *Journal of Divorce and Remarriage, 54*, 142–162.

Bullough, V. L. (1990). History in adult human sexual behavior with children and adolescents in Western societies. In J. R. Frierman (Ed.), *Pedophilia* (pp. 69–90). New York: Springer-Verlag.

Bullough, V. L. (1998). History, the historian, and sex. In G. G. Brannigan, E. R. Allgeier, & A. R. Allgeier, *The sex scientists* (pp. 1–14). New York, NY: Longman.

Bullough, V. L. (2003). Masturbation: An historical overview. In W. O. Bockting, & E. Coleman (Eds.), *Masturbation as a means of achieving sexual health* (pp. 17–33). New York: Haworth.

Bulmer, S. M., Irfan, S., Mugno, R., Barton, B., & Ackerman, L. (2010). Trends in alcohol consumption among undergraduate students at a northeastern public university, 2002–2008. *Journal of American College Health, 58*, 383–390.

Bunger, R. (2013). Professor of Anthropology, East Carolina University. Personal communication.

Burgess, A. W., & Holstrom, I. L. (1974). Rape trauma syndrome. *American Journal of Psychiatry, 131*, 981–986.

Burgess, A. W., Hartman, C. R., Kelley, S. J., Grant, C. A., & Gray, E. B. (1990). Parental response to child sexual abuse trials involving day care settings. *Journal of Traumatic Stress, 3*, 395–405.

Burri, A. (2013). Bringing sex research into the 21st century: Genetic and epigenetic approaches on female sexual function. *Journal of Sex Research, 50*, 318–328.

Burton, L. M., Bonilla-Silva, E., Bucklew, R., & Freeman, E. H. (2010). Critical race theories, colorism, and the decade's research on families of color. *Journal of Marriage and Family, 72*, 440–459.

Buss, D. M. (1989). Sex differences in human mate preferences: Evolutionary hypotheses tested in 37 cultures. *Behavioral and Brain Sciences, 12*, 1–13.

Buss, D. M. (1990). International preferences in selecting mates: A study of 37 cultures. *Journal of Cross-Cultural Psychology, 21*(4), 5–47.

Buunk, A. P., Goor, J., & Solano, A. C. (2010). Intrasexual competition at work: Sex differences in the jealousy-evoking effect of rival characteristics in work settings. *Journal of Social and Personal Relationships, 27*, 671–684.

Buxton, A. P. (2001). Writing our own script: How bisexual men and their heterosexual wives maintained their marriages after disclosure. *Journal of Bisexuality, 1*, 155–189.

C

Cambridge, P., Beadle-Brown, J., Milne, A., Mansell, J., & Whelton, B. (2011). Patterns of risk in adult protection referrals for sexual abuse and people with intellectual disability. *Journal of Applied Research In Intellectual Disabilities, 24*, 118–132.

Campo-Englestein, L. (2013). Raging hormones, domestic incompetence, and contraceptive indifference: Narratives contributing to the perception that women do not trust men to use contraception. *Culture, Health and Sexuality,* 283–295.

Cantor, J. M., Blanchard, A. D., Paterson, A. D., & Bogaert, A. F. (2002). How many gay men owe their sexual orientation to fraternal birth order? *Archives of Sexual Behavior, 31*, 63–71.

Carey, A. R., & Trap, P. (2013, May 30). Frequent users of social network sites/services. *USA Today*, p. A1.

Carnes, P. J. (2001). Cybersex, courtship, and escalating arousal: Factors in addictive sexual desire. *Sexual Addiction & Compulsivity, 8*, 45–78.

Caron, S. L., & Hinman, S. P. (2012). "I took his V-card": An exploratory analysis of College student stories involving male virginity loss. *Sexuality and Culture,* Online September.

Carpenter, L. M. (2010). Like a virgin… again?: Secondary virginity as an ongoing gendered social Construction. *Sexuality and Culture, 14*, 253–270.

Cartaxo, Peixoto, J., Rolim, M. L., Neto, & deAbreu, L. C. (2013). Adolescence and sexuality. *HealthMed, 7*, 1094–1097.

Carter, J., Stabile, C., Guinn, A., & Sonoda, Y. (2013). The physical consequences of gynecologic cancer surgery and their impact on sexual, emotional, and quality of life issues. *Journal of Sexual Medicine, 10,* 21–34.

Carvalheira, A., & Leal, I. (2013). Masturbation among women: Associated factors and sexual response in a Portuguese community sample. *Journal of Sex Marital Therapy, 39,* 347–367.

Carvalho, J., Gomes, A. Q., Laja, P., Oliveira, C., Vilarinho, S., Janssen, E., & Nobre, P. (2013, March 22). Gender differences in sexual arousal and affective responses to erotica: The effects of type of film and fantasy instructions. *Archives of Sexual Behavior.*

Cavaglion, G., & Rashty, E. (2010). Narratives of suffering among Italian female partners of cybersex and cyber-porn. *Sexual Addiction & Compulsivity, 17,* 270–287.

Cavazos-Rehg, P., Krauss, M., Spitznagel, E., Schootman, M., Cottler, L., & Bierut, L. (2013). Characteristics of sexually active teenage girls who would be pleased with becoming pregnant. *Maternal & Child Health Journal, 17,* 470–476.

Cecen-Frogul, A. R., & Kaf Hasirci, O. (2013). The effectiveness of psycho-educational school-based child sexual abuse prevention training program on Turkish elementary students. *Kuram ve Uygulamada Egitiim Bilimleri, 13,* 725–729.

Center for Disease Control and Prevention. (2011a). CDC Grand Rounds: Chlamydia prevention: challenges and strategies for reducing disease burden and sequelae. *MMWR, 60,* 370–373.

Centers for Disease Control and Prevention. (2010e). *Trends in the prevalence of sexual behaviors national YRBS: 1991–2009.* Retrieved from http://www.cdc.gov/HealthyYouth/yrbs/pdf/us_sexual_trend_yrbs.pdf

Centers for Disease Control and Prevention. (2010a). *HIV testing basics for consumers.* Retrieved from http://www.cdc.gov/hiv/basics/testing.html

Centers for Disease Control and Prevention. (2010b). *Parasites—Scabies.* Retrieved from http://www.cdc.gov/parasites/scabies/

Centers for Disease Control and Prevention. (2010c). Sexually transmitted disease treatment guidelines. *MMWR, (59)RR-12,* 1–109.

Centers for Disease Control and Prevention. (2010d). "HIV and Other STD Prevention and United States Students" Atlanta, GA: CDC.

Centers for Disease Control and Prevention. (2011b). *10 ways STDs impact women differently from men.* Retrieved from http://www.cdc.gov/nchhstp/newsroom/docs/STDs-Women-042011.pdf

Centers for Disease Control and Prevention. (2011c). Recommendations on the use of quadrivalent human papillomavirus vaccine in males-Advisory committee on immunization practices. *MMWR, 60*(50), 1705–1708.

Centers for Disease Control and Prevention. (2012, March 21). *HIV Incidence.* Retrieved from http://www.cdc.gov/hiv/topics/surveillance/incidence.htm

Centers for Disease Control and Prevention. (2012a). *2010 HIV Surveillance Report, 17 (3).* Retrieved from http://www.cdc.gov/hiv/pdf/statistics_2010_HIV_Surveillance_Report_vol_17_no_3.pdf

Centers for Disease Control and Prevention. (2012b). *HIV Surveillance by Race/Ethnicity (through 2011).* Retrieved from http://www.cdc.gov/hiv/pdf/statistics_surveillance_raceEthnicity.pdf

Centers for Disease Control and Prevention. (2012c). *HIV Surveillance in men who have sex with men (MSM).* Retrieved from http://www.cdc.gov/hiv/pdf/statistics_surveillance_MSM.pdf

Centers for Disease Control and Prevention. (2012e). *Sexually Transmitted Disease Surveillance 2011.* Retrieved from U.S. Department of Health and Human Services: http://www.cdc.gov/std/stats11/surv2011.pdf

Centers for Disease Control and Prevention. (2012f). *Trends in HIV-related risk behaviors among high school students—United States, 1991-2011.* Retrieved July 24, 2012, from MMWR: http://www.cdc.gov/mmwr/preview/mmwrhtml/mm6129a4.htm?s_cid=mm6129a4_w

Centers for Disease Control and Prevention. (2013a). *Condoms and STDs: Fact sheet for public health personnel.* Retrieved from http://www.cdc.gov/condomeffectiveness/latex.htm

Centers for Disease Control and Prevention. (2013b). *Recent press coverage about drug-resistant gonorrhea.* Retrieved May 8, 2013, from http://www.cdc.gov/std/gonorrhea/Resistant-Gonorrhea-Press.htm

Cerebralpalsy.org. (2013). Retrieved from http://cerebralpalsy.org/about-cerebral-palsy/prevalence-of-cerebral-palsy/

Chang, J., Ward, R., Padgett, D., & Smith, M. F. (2012, November 1). Do feminists hook up more? Examining pro-feminism attitude in the context of hooking-up. Phoenix, AZ: Paper, National Council on Family Relations.

Chao, J. K., Lin, Y., Ma, M., Lai, C., Ku, Y., Kuo, W., & Chao, I. (2011). Relationship among sexual desire satisfaction and quality of life in middle-aged and older adults. *Journal of Sex & Marital Therapy, 37,* 386–403.

Chen, A. S., Leung, M., Chen, C. H., & Yang, S. C. (2013). Exposure to Internet pornography among Taiwanese adolescents. *Social Behavior and Personality, 41,* 157–164.

Chen, C., Yamada, T., & Walker, E. M. (2011). Estimating the cost-effectiveness of a classroom-based abstinence and pregnancy avoidance program targeting preadolescent sexual risk behaviors. *Journal of Children & Poverty, 17,* 87–109.

Chen, S. F., Yn, F. S., Chang, Y. C., Fu, E., Nieh, S., & Lin, Y. S. (2012). Role of human papillomavirus infection in carcinogenesis of oral squamous cell carcinoma with evidence of prognostic association. *Journal of Oral Pathological Medicine,* 9–15.

Chen, Y. J., Chen, C. C., Lin, M. W., Chen, T. J., Li, C. Y., Hwang, C. Y., ... Liu, H. N. (2013). Increased risk of sexual dysfunction in male patients with psoriasis: A nationwide population-based follow up study. *Journal of Sexual Medicine, 10,* 1212–1218.

Cherner, R. A., & Reissing, E. D. (2013). A psychological investigation of sexual arousal in women with lifelong vaginismus. *Journal of Sexual Medicine, 10,* 1291–1303.

Cheuang, I. (2010). *10 Ancient methods of birth control.* Retrieved July 26, 2013, from http://listverse.com/2010/11/14/10-ancient-methods-of-birth-control/

Cheung, M. C., Chan, A. S., Han, Y. M., Sze, S. L., & Fan, N. H. (2013). Self-schema on responses to sex appeal in advertising. *Journal of Promotion Management, 19,* 373–391.

Chiesa, A., Leucci, V., Serretti, A., & De Ronchi, D. (2013). Antipsychotics and sexual dysfunction: Epidemiology, mechanisms and management.

Clinical Neuropsychiatry: Journal of Treatment Evaluation, 10, 31–36.

Chonody, J. M. (2013). Measuring sexual prejudice against gay men and lesbian women: Development of the Sexual Prejudice Scale (SPS). *Journal of Homosexuality, 60,* 895–926.

Chonody, J. M., Smith, K. S., & Litle, M. A. (2012). Legislating unequal treatment: An exploration of public policy on same-sex marriage. *Journal of GLBT Family Studies, 8,* 270–286.

Chung, E., & Brock, G. (2013). Sexual rehabilitation and cancer survivorship: A state of the art review of current literature and management strategies in male sexual dysfunction among prostate cancer survivors. *Journal of Sexual Medicine, 10,* 102–11.

Clarke, K. (2013). Pedagogical moments: affective sexual literacies in film. *Sex Education: Sexuality, Society, and Learning, 13,* 263–275.

Cohen, J. (2010). Painful failure of promising genital herpes vaccine. *Science, 15*(330), 304.

Cohen, M. S., Chen, Y. Q., McCauley, M., Gamble, T., Hosseinipour, M. C., Kumarasamy, N., & Fleming, T. R. (2011). Prevention of HIV-1 infection with early antiretroviral therapy. *New England Journal of Medicine, 365,* 493–505.

Cohn, A. M., Zinzow, H. M., & Resnick, H. S. (2013). Correlates of reasons for not reporting rape to the police: Results from a national telephone probability sample of women with forcible or drug-or-alcohol facilitated/incapacitated rape. *Journal of Interpersonal Violence, 28,* 455–473.

Colapinto, J. (2000). *As nature made him: The boy who was raised as a girl.* New York, NY: Harper Collins.

Coleman, J. L., & Shukla, D. (2013). Recent advances in vaccine development for herpes simplex virus types I and II. *Human Vaccines and Immunotherapy, 9*(4).

Coll, J. E., Draves, P. R., & Major, M. E. (2008). An examination of underage drinking in a sample of private university students. *College Student Journal, 42,* 982–985.

Collier, K. L., van Beusekom, G., Bos, H. W., & Sandfort, T. G. (2013). Sexual orientation and gender identity/expression related peer victimization in adolescence. *Journal of Sex Research, 50,* 299–317.

Cooley, C. H. (1964). *Human nature and the social order.* New York: Schocken.

Cooper, L. M. (1994). Motivations for Alcohol Use Among Adolescents: Development and Validation of a four-factor model. *Psychological Assessment, 6,* 117–128.

Corbett, S. L., & Morgan, K. D. (1983). The process of lesbian identification. *Free Inquiry in Creative Sociology, 11,* 81–83.

Coren, E., Thomae, M., Hutchfield, W. I., & Iredale, W. (2013). Report on the implementation and results of an outcomes-focused evaluation of child sexual abuse interventions in the UK. *Child Abuse Review, 22,* 44–59.

Costa, R. M., Miller, G. F., & Brody, S. (2012). Women who prefer longer penises are more likely to have vaginal orgasms (but not clitoral orgasms): Implications for an evolutionary theory of vaginal orgasm. *Journal of Sexual Medicine,* 3079–3088.

Craissati, J., & Blundell, R. (2013). A community service for high-risk mentally disordered sex offenders: A follow up study. *Journal of Interpersonal Violence, 28,* 1178–1200.

Cramer, R. E., Lipinski, R. E., Meteer, J. D., & Houska, J. A. (2008). Sex differences in subjective distress to unfaithfulness: Testing competing evolutionary and violation of fidelity expectations hypotheses. *The Journal of Social Psychology, 148,* 389–406.

Creek, S. J. (2013). "Not getting any because of Jesus": The centrality of desire management the identity of Gay, celibate Christians. *Symbolic Interaction, 36,* 119–136.

Cubbins, L. A., & Tanfer, K. (2000). The influence of gender on sex: A study of men's and women's self-reported high-risk sex behavior. *Archives of Sexual Behavior, 29,* 229–256.

Cutler, W. B., Friedmann, E., & McCoy, N. L. (1998). Pheromonal influences on sociosexual behavior in men. *Archives of Sexual Behavior, 27,* 1–13.

D

da Silva, C. H., Hernandez, A. R., & Agranonik, M. (2013). Maternal age and low birth weight: A reinterpretation of their association under a demographic transition in southern Brazil. *Maternal and Child Health Journal, 17,* 539–544.

Dalbudak, E., Evren, C., Aldemir, S., Coskun, K. S., Ugurlu, H., & Yildirim, F. G. (2013). Relationship of internet addiction severity with depression, anxiety, and alexthymia, temperament and character in university students. *Cyberpsychology, Behavior, and Social Networking, 16,* 272–278.

D'Amico, E., & Julien, D. (2012). Disclosure of sexual orientation and gay, lesbian, and bisexual youth's adjustment: Associations with past and current parental acceptance and rejection. *Journal of GLBT Family Studies, 8,* 215–242.

Darnton, K. (2012, February 12). Deception at Duke. 60 Minutes/CBS Television.

Dauda, C. (2013). Providential understandings of childhood and public policy: The politics of generation, future adulthood and moral regulation of sexuality in liberal democracies. *Sexuality and Culture, 17,* 275–304.

Davies, E., Mangongi, N. P., & Carter, C. L. (2013). Is timing everything? A meeting report of The Society for Women's Health research round table on menopausal hormone therapy. *Journal of Women's Health, 22,* 303–311.

Dawson, S. J., Suschinsky, K. D., & Lalumiere, M. L. (2012). Habitation of sexual responses in men and women: A test of the preparation hypothesis of women's genital responses. *Journal of Sexual Medicine, 10,* 990–1000.

DeBlock, A., & Adriaens, P. R. (2013). Pathologizing sexual deviance. *Journal of Sex Research, 50,* 276–298.

DeHaan, S., Kuper, L. E., Magee, J. C., Bigelow, L., & Mustanski, B. S. (2013). The interplay between online and offline explorations of identity, relationships, and sex: A mixed-methods study with LGBT youth. *Journal of Sex Research, 50,* 421–434.

DeHart, D. D., & Birkimer, J. C. (1997). The Student Sexual Risks Scale. Columbia, SC, & Louisville, KY: University of South Carolina, College of Social Work; & University of Louisville.

Dekker, A., & Schmidt, G. (2003). Patterns of masturbatory behavior: Changes between the sixties and the nineties. In W. O. Bockting, & E. Coleman (Eds.), *Masturbation as a means of achieving sexual health* (pp. 35–48). New York: Haworth.

Deming, M. E., Covan, E. K., Swan, S. C., & Billings, D. L. (2013). Exploring rape myths, gendered norms, group processing, and the social context of rape among college women: A qualitative analysis. *Violence Against Women, 19*, 465–485.

Demirgoz Bal, M., Dereli Yilmaz, S., & Kizilkaya Beji, N. (2013). Sexual health in patients with gynecological cancer: A qualitative study. *Sexuality and Disability, 31*, 83–92.

Dempsey, A. F., Abraham, L. M., Dalton, V., & Ruffin, M. (2009). Understanding the reasons why mothers do or do not have their adolescent daughters vaccinated against human papillomavirus. *Annals of Epidemiology, 19*(8), 531–538.

DePaulo, B. M., Ansfield, M. E., Kirkendol, S. E., & Boden, J. M. (2004). Serious Lies. *Basic & Applied Social Psychology, 26*, 147–167.

DePaulo, B. M., Kiekendol, S. E., Kashy, D. A., Wyer, M. M., & Epstein, J. A. (1996). Lying in everyday life. *Journal of Personality and Social Psychology, 70*, 979–997.

Derlega, V. J., Metts, S., Petronio, S., & Marulis, S. T. (1993). *Self-disclosure.* Newbury Park, CA: Sage.

Diamond, L. M., & Savin-Williams, R. C. (2000). Explaining diversity in the development of same-sex sexuality among young women. *Journal of Social Issues, 56*, 297–313.

Diamond, M. (1995). Biological aspects of sexual orientation and identity. In L. Diamont, & R. D. McAnulty (Eds.), *The psychology of sexual orientation, behavior, and identity: A handbook* (pp. 45–80). Westport, CT: Greenwood Press.

Diamond, M., & Sigmundson, H. K. (1997). Sex reassignment at birth. *Archives of Pediatric Adolescent Medicine, 151*, 298–304.

DiDonato, L., & Strough, J. (2013). Do college students' gender-typed attitudes about occupations predict their real world decisions? *Sex Roles, 68*, 536–549.

Diokno, A. C., Brown, M. B., & Herzog, A. R. (1990). Sexual functioning in the elderly. *Archives of Internal Medicine, 150*, 197–200.

Donnelly, J. (1997). Sexual satisfaction for a woman with severe cerebral palsy. *Sexuality and Disability, 15*, 16–26.

Douglas, M. (2013). Throat cancer caused by cunnilingus. Retrieved June 2, 2013, from http://metro.co.uk/2013/06/02/michael-douglas-suggests-sti-from-oral-sex-caused-his-throat-cancer-3825496/

Dourado, M., Finamore, C., Barroso, M. F., Santos, R., & Laks, J. (2010). Sexual satisfaction in dementia: Perspectives of patients and

spouses. *Sexuality and Disability, 28*, 195–203.

Drake, B. (2013, June 13). *LGBT Americans in changing times: Tell us your story.* Retrieved from Pew Research Center: http://www.pewresearch.org/fact-tank/2013/06/13/lbgt-americans-in-changing-times-tell-us-your-story/

Drouin, M., Vogel, K. N., Surbey, A., & Stills, J. R. (2013). Let's talk about sexting, baby: Computer-mediated sexual behaviors among young adults. *Computer in Human Behavior, 29*, A25–A30.

Druckerman, P. (2007). *Lust in Translation.* New York: Penguin Group.

Ducharme, J. K., & Kollar, M. M. (2012). Does the "marriage benefit" extend to same-sex union?: Evidence from a sample of married lesbian couples in Massachusetts. *Journal of Homosexuality, 59*, 580–591.

Dugard, J. (2011). *A Stolen Life: A memoir by Jaycee Dugard.* New York: Simon and Schuster.

Duncan, B. L., & Rock, J. W. (1993). Saving relationships: The power of the unpredictable. *Psychology Today, 26*, 46–51, 86, 95.

Dunsieth, N. W., Nelson, E. B., Bursman-Lovins, L. A., Holcomb, J. L., Beckman, D., Welge, J. A., … McElroy, S. L. (2004). Psychiatric and legal features of 113 men convicted of sexual offenses. *Journal of Clinical Psychiatry, 65*, 293–300.

Dupree, M. G., Mustanski, B. S., Bocklandt, S., Nievergelt, C., & Hamer, D. H. (2004). A candidate gene study of CYP19 (Aromatase) and male sexual orientation. *Behavior Genetics, 34*, 243–250.

Dysart-Gale, D. (2010). Social justice and social determinants of health: Lesbian, gay, bisexual, transgendered, intersexed, and queer youth in Canada. *Journal of Child & Adolescent Psychiatric Nursing, 23*, 23–28.

E

Easterling, B. D., Knox, D., & Brackett, A. (2012). Secrets in romantic relationships: Does sexual orientation matter? *Journal of GLBT Family Studies, 8*, 198–210.

Easterling, B., Nelms, B. J., & Knox, D. (2012). The Relationship Talk: Assessing partner commitment. *College Student Journal, 46*, 178–182.

Easton, S. D., Renner, L. M., & O'Leary, P. (2013, Jan 10). Suicide attempts among men with histories of child sex abuse: Examining abuse severity, mental health, and masculine norms. *Child Abuse and Neglect.*

Einsenberg, M., Madsen, N., Oliphant, J. A., & Sieving, R. E. (2013). Barriers to providing the sexuality education that teachers believe students need. *Journal of School Health, 83*, 335–342.

Elder, W. B., Brooks, G. R., & Morrow, S. L. (2012). Sexual self-schemas of heterosexual men. *Psychology of Men and Masculinity, 13*, 166–179.

Eliason, M. (2001). Bi-negativity: The stigma facing bisexual men. *Journal of Bisexuality, 1*, 137–154.

Ellis, L. (1989). *Theories of rape: Inquiries into the causes of sexual aggression.* New York: Hemisphere.

Ellis, L. (1996). Theories of homosexuality. In R. C. Savin-Williams, & K. M. Cohen (Eds.), *The lives of lesbians, gays, and bisexuals: Children to adults* (pp. 11–34). Fort Worth, TX: Harcourt Brace.

Ellis, L., & Ames, M. A. (1987). Neurohormonal functioning and sexual orientation: A theory of homosexuality-heterosexuality. *Psychological Bulletin, 101*, 233–258.

Elnashar, A., & Abdelhady, R. (2007). The impact of female genital cutting on health of newly married women. *International Journal of Gynecology & Obstetrics, 97*, 238–244.

Engsheden, N., Fabian, H., & Sarkadi, A. (2013). Offering relationship education (PREP) for couples during pregnancy: Self-selection patterns. *Family Relations, 62*, 676–685.

Equal Employment Opportunity Commission (EEOC). (2013). Retrieved 8 2013, August, from http://www.eeoc.gov/laws/types/sexual_harassment.cfm

Erbil, N. (2013). The relationships between sexual function, body image and body mass index among women. *Sexuality and Disability, 31*, 63–70.

Erenel, A. S., & Kilinc, F. N. (2013). Does obesity increase sexual dysfunction in women? *Sexuality and Disability, 31*, 53–62.

Erkut, S., Grossman, S. J., Frye, A. A., Ceder, I., Charmaraman, L., & Tracy, A. J. (2013). Can sex education delay early sexual debut? *Journal of Adolescence, 33*, 482–497.

Erlandsson, K., Jinghede Nordvall, C., Ohman, A., & Haggstrom-Nordin, E. (2013). Qualitative interviews with adolescents about "friends-with-benefits" relationships. *Public Health Nursing, 30,* 47–57.

Esterberg, K. (1997). *Lesbian and bisexual identities. Constructing communities, constructing selves.* Philadelphia: Temple University Press.

Everaerd, W., Laan, E. M., Both, S., & van der Velde, J. (2000). Female sexuality. In L. T. Szuchman, & F. Muscarella (Eds.), *Psychological perspectives on human sexuality* (pp. 101–146). New York, NY: Wiley.

F

Faccini, L., & Saide, M. A. (2013). "Can you breathe?" Autoerotic asphyxiation and asphyxiophilia in a person with an intellectual disability and sex offending. *Sexuality and Disability, 30,* 97–101.

Fader Wilkenfeld, B., & Ballan, M. (2011). Educators attitudes and beliefs towards the sexuality of individuals with developmental disabilities. *Sexuality and Disability, 29,* 351–361.

Fazio, A., Joe-Laidler, K., Moloney, M., & Hunt, G. (2010). Gender, sexuality, and ethnicity as factors of club-drug use among Asian Americans. *Journal of Drug Issues, 40,* 405–432.

Feng, G. C., & Guo, S. Z. (2013). Tracing the route of China's Internet censorship: An empirical study. *Telematics and Informatics, 30,* 335–345.

Fennell, J. (2013). Personal communication. Department of Sociology, Gallaudet University.

Fergusson, D. M., McLeod, G. F., & Horwood, L. J. (2013, April 24). Childhood sexual abuse and adult developmental outcomes: Findings from a 30-year-old longitudinal study in New Zealand. *Child Abuse & Neglect.*

Ferraro, M. M., & Casey, E. (2005). *Investigating child exploitation and pornography.* Boston: Elsevier Academic Press.

Fielder, R. L., Carey, K. B., & Carey, M. P. (2013). Are hookups replacing romantic relationships? A longitudinal study of first year female college students. *Journal of Adolescent Health, 52,* 657–659.

Fieldera, R. L., & Careya, M. P. (2010). Prevalence and characteristics of sexual hookups among first-semester female college students. *Journal of Sex & Marital Therapy, 36,* 346–359.

Finer, L. B., & Philbin, J. M. (2013). Sexual initiation, contraceptive use, and pregnancy among young adolescents. *Pediatrics, 131,* 886–891.

Finger, W. W., Lund, M., & Slagle, M. A. (1997). A guide to assessment and treatment in family practice. *Journal of Family Practice, 44,* 33–43.

Fisher, A. D., Bandini, E., Rastrelli, G., Corana, G., Monami, M., Mannucci, E., & Maggi, M. (2012a). Sexual and cardiovascular correlates of male unfaithfulness. *Journal of Sexual Medicine, 9,* 1508–1518.

Fisher, N. L., & Pina, A. (2013). An overview of the literature on female-perpetrated adult male sexual victimization. *Aggression and Violent Behavior, 18,* 54–61.

Fisher, W. A., & Grenier, G. (1994). Violent pornography, anti-woman thoughts, and anti-woman acts: In search of reliable effects. *The Journal of Sex Research, 31,* 23–28.

Fitzgerald, C., & Withers, P. (2013). "I don't know what a proper woman means": What women with intellectual disabilities think about sex, sexuality and themselves. *British Journal of Learning Disabilities, 41,* 5–12.

Fjelstrom, J. (2013). Sexual orientation change efforts and the search for authenticity. *Journal of Homosexuality, 60,* 801–827.

Flacy, M. (2013, July 12). *Nearly 1 in 10 Americans use smartphones during sex.* Retrieved from Fox News: http://www.foxnews.com/tech/2013/07/12/nearly-1-out-10-americans-use-smartphones-during-sex/?intcmp=features

Fletcher, G., Dowsett, G. W., Duncan, D., Slavin, S., & Corboz, J. (2013). Advancing sexuality studies: A short course on sexuality theory and research methodologies. *Sex Education, 13,* 319–335.

Flood, M. (2013). Male and female sluts. *Australian Feminist Studies, 75,* 95–107.

Flowers, A. (1998). *The fantasy factory: An insider's view of the phone sex industry.* Philadelphia, PA: University of Pennsylvania Press.

Foster, D. G., Kimport, K., Gould, H., Roberts, S. C., & Weitz, T. A. (2013). Effect of abortion Protestors on women's emotional response to abortion. *Contraception, 87,* 81–87.

Foulds, K. (2013). The continua of identities in post colonial curricula: Kenyan students' perceptions

of gender in school textbooks. *International Journal of Educational Development, 33,* 165–174.

Fox, S., & Rainie, L. (2002). *Vital decisions: How Internet users decide what information to trust when they or their loved ones are sick.* Retrieved September 10, 2013, from Pew Internet & American Life Project: www.pewinternet.org/

Frank, K. (2002). *G-strings and sympathy: Strip club regulars and male desire.* Durham, NC: Duke University Press.

Frank, K. (2003). "Just trying to relax": Masculinity, masculinizing practices and strip club regulars. *The Journal of Sex Research, 40,* 61–76.

Freysteinsdóttir, F. J. (2013). Department of Social Work. University of Iceland. Personal communication.

Friedrich, W. N., Fisher, J., Broughton, D., Houston, M., & Shafran, C. R. (1998). Normative sexual behavior in children: a contemporary sample. *Pediatrics, 101*(4). Retrieved from Pediatrics: http://www.pediatrics.org/cgi/content/full/101/4/e9

Frith, H. (2013). Labouring on orgasms: embodiment, efficiency, entitlement and obligations in heterosex. *Culture, Health & Sexuality: An International Journal for Research, Intervention and Care, 15,* 494–510.

Frye-Cox, N. E., & Hesse, C. R. (2013). Alexithymia and marital quality: The mediating roles of loneliness and intimate communication. *Journal of Family Psychology, 27,* 203–211.

Fugl-Meyer, K. S., Bohm-Starke, N., Damsted Petersen, C., Fugl-Meyer, A., Parish, S., & Giraldi, A. (2013). Standard operating procedures for female sexual pain. *Journal of Sexual Medicine, 10,* 83–93.

G

Gagnon, J. H. (1977). *Human sexualities.* Glenview, IL: Scott Foresman.

Gagnon, J. H., & Simon, W. (1973). *Sexual conduct: The social sources of human sexuality.* Chicago: Aldine.

Galinsky, A. M. (2012). Sexual touching and difficulties with sexual arousal and orgasm among U.S. older adults. *Archives of Sexual Behavior, 41,* 875–890.

Galinsky, A. M., & Sorenstein, F. L. (2013). Relationship commitment, perceived equity, and sexual enjoyment among young adults in the United States. *Archives of Sexual Behavior, 42,* 93–104.

Gallop, C. (2013). *Make love, not porn*. Retrieved from YouTube: http://www.youtube.com/watch?v=HJ3kP-0Mu3k

Galperin, A., Haselton, M. G., Frederick, D. A., Poore, J., Hippel, W. V., Buss, D. M., & Gonzaga, D. C. (2013). Sexual regret: Evidence for evolved sex differences. *Archives of Sexual Behavior, 42,* 1145–1161.

Gao, J., Zhang, X., Su, P., Liu, J., Xia, L., Yang, J., … Liang, C. (2013). Prevalence and factors associated with the complaint of premature ejaculation and the four premature ejaculation syndromes: A large observational study in China. *Journal of Sexual Medicine, 10,* 1874–1881.

Gardner, M., Martin, A., & Grooks-Gunn, J. (2012). Exploring the link between caregiver affect and adolescent sexual behavior: Does neighbor disadvantage matter? *Journal of Research on Adolescence, 22,* 135–149.

Gates, G. J. (2011). *How many people are lesbian, gay, bisexual and transgender? The Williams I Institute. UCLA School of Law.* Retrieved from http://williamsinstitute.law.ucla.edu/wp-content/uploads/Gates-How-Many-People-LGBT-Apr-2011.pdf

Gatzeva, M., & Paik, A. (2011). Emotional and physical satisfaction in noncohabitating, cohabitating and marital relationships: The importance of jealous conflict. *Journal of Sex Research, 48,* 29–42.

Gault-Sherman, M., & Draper, S. (2012). What will the neighbors think? The effects of moral communities on cohabitation. *Review of Religious Research, 54,* 45–67.

Geller, P., Psaros, C., & Kornfield, S. L. (2010). Satisfaction with pregnancy with loss aftercare: are women getting what they want? *Archives of Women's Mental Health, 13,* 111–124.

Geonet, M., De Sutter, P., & Zech, E. (2013). Cognitive factors in female hypoactive sexual desire disorder. *Sexologies: European Journal of Sexology and Sexual Health, 22,* 9–15.

Ghanem, H., Glina, S., Assalian, P., & Buvat, J. (2013). Position paper: Management of men complaining of a small penis despite an actual normal size. *Journal of Sexual Medicine, 10,* 294–303.

Giami, A. (2013). Social epidemiology of premature ejaculation. *European Journal of Sexology and Sexual Health, 22,* 27–32.

Gibbs, N. (2012, August 27). Your life is fully mobile: Time Mobility Survey. *Time Magazine,* p. 32 and following.

Gill, R., & Febbraro, A. R. (2013). Experiences and perceptions of sexual harassment in the Canadian forces combat arms. *Violence Against Women, 19,* 269–287.

Gilla, D. L., Morrow, R. G., Collinsc, K. E., Lucey, A. B., & Schultze, A. M. (2010). Perceived climate in physical activity settings. *Journal of Homosexuality, 57,* 895–913.

Giraldi, A., Rellini, A. H., Pfaus, J., & Laan, E. (2013). Female sexual arousal disorders. *Journal of Sexual Medicine, 10,* 58–73.

Glina, S., Sharlip, I. D., & Hellstrom, W. J. (2013). Modifying risk factors to prevent and treat erectile dysfunction. *Journal of Sexual Medicine, 10,* 115–119.

Gogno, M., Jones, D., & Ibarlucia, I. (2013). The challenges of sexology in Argentina. *International Journal of Sexual Health (25),* 13–26.

Goldstein, R. L., Upadhyay, U. D., & Raine, T. R. (2013). With pills, patches, rings and shots: Who still uses condoms? A longitudinal cohort study. *Journal of Adolescent Health, 52,* 77–82.

Gonzalez-Oretega, E., & Orgaz-Baz, B. (2013). Minors' exposure to online pornography. Prevalence, motivations, contents and effects. *Anales de Psicologia, 29,* 319–327.

Gotta, G. R., Green, J., Rothblum, E., Solomon, S., Balsam, K., & Schwartz, P. (2011). Heterosexual, lesbian, and gay male relationships: A comparison of couples in 1975 and 2000. *Family Process, 50,* 353–376.

Gottfried, J. A., Vaala, S. E., Bleakley, A., Hennessy, M., & Jordan, A. (2013). Does the effect of exposure to TV sex on adolescent sexual behavior vary by genre? *Communication Research, 40,* 73–95.

Gottman, J. (1994). *Why marriages succeed or fail … And how you can make yours last.* New York, NY: Simon & Schuster.

Gottman, J. M., Coan, J., Carrere, S., & Swanson, C. (1998). Predicting marital happiness and stability from newlywed interactions. *Journal of Marriage and the Family, 60,* 5–22.

Graham, S. (1848). *Lecture to young men on chastity, intended also for the serious consideration of parents and guardians* (10th ed.). Boston: C.H. Price.

Greeff, A. P., & De Bruyne, T. (2000). Conflict management style and marital satisfaction. *Journal of Sex and Marital Satisfaction, 26,* 321–334.

Green, R. J., Bettinger, M., & Zacks, F. (1996). Are lesbian couples fused and gay male couples disengaged? In J. Laird, & R. J. Green (Eds.), *Lesbians and gays in couples and families* (pp. 185–230). San Francisco: Jossey Bass.

Grey, R., & Shepherd, L. J. (2013). 'Stop rape now?': Masculinity, responsibility, and conflict-related sexual violence. *Men and Masculinities, 16,* 115–135.

Griffiths, M. D. (2012). Internet sex addiction: A review of empirical research. *Addiction Research & Theory, 20,* 111–124.

Grov, C., Wells, B. E., & Parsons, J. T. (2013). Self-reported penis size and experiences with condoms among gay and bisexual men. *Archives of Sexual Behavior, 42,* 313–322.

Groy, C., Hirshfield, S., Remien, H., Humberstone, M., & Chiasson, M. A. (2013). Exploring the venue's role in risky sexual behavior among gay and bisexual men: An event-level analysis from a national online survey in the U.S. *Archives of Sexual Behavior, 42,* 291–302.

Guendelman, S., Pearl, M., Kosa, J. L., Graham, S., Abrams, B., & Kharrazi, M. (2013). Association between preterm delivery and pre-pregnancy body mass (BMI), exercise and sleep during pregnancy among working women in Southern California. *Maternal and Child Health Journal, 17,* 723–731.

Guler, T., Yavuz, U., Ozkum, D., & Demirdamar, R. (2013). Effects of perimenstrual complaints on sexuality and disability and coping strategies oF university students. *Sexuality and Disability, 31,* 93–101.

Guttmacher Institute. (2012). Abortion facts. Retrieved Jan 13, 2012, from http://www.guttmacher.org/media/presskits/abortion-US/statsandfacts.html

Guttmacher Institute. (2012). *State policies in brief: Sex and HIV education.* Retrieved from http://www.guttmacher.org/statecenter/spibs/spib_SE.pdf.

Guttmacher Institute. (2013). *State Policies in Brief: An overview of abortion laws.* Retrieved July 27, 2013, from http://www.guttmacher.org/statecenter/spibs/spib_OAL.pdf

H

Haapsamo, H., Kuusikko-Gauffin, S., Ebeling, H., Larinen, K., Penninkilampi-Kerola, V., Soini, H., & Moilanen, I. (2013). Communication development and characteristics of influencing factors: a follow up study from 8 to 36 months. *Early Child Development, 183,* 321–334.

Hall, K. S., Moreau, C., & Trussell, J. (2012). Young women's perceived health and lifetime sexual experience: Results from the National Survey of Family Growth. *Journal of Sexual Medicine, 9,* 1382–1391.

Hall, K. S., Moreau, C., Trussell, J., & Barber, J. (2013). Role of young women's depression and stress symptoms in their weekly use and nonuse of contraceptive methods. *Journal of Adolescent Health, April 9.*

Hall, S., & Knox, D. (2013). Relationship and sexual behaviors of a sample of 4,567 university students. Unpublished data collected for this text. Department of Family and Consumer Sciences, Ball State University and Department of Sociology, East Carolina University.

Handlovsky, I., Bungay, V., & Kolar, K. (2012). Condom use as situated in a risk context: Women's experiences in the massage parlour industry in Vancouver, Canada. *Culture, Health & Sexuality, 14,* 1007–1020.

Hannaford, P. C. (2013). Mortality among oral contraceptive users: An evolving story. *The European Journal of Contraception and Reproductive Health Care, 18,* 1–4.

Harris, A. L., & Vitzthum, V. J. (2013). Darwin's legacy: An evolutionary view of women's reproductive and sexual functioning. *Journal of Sex Research, 50,* 207–246.

Harris, A. L., Sutherland, M. A., & Hutchinson, M. K. (2013). Parental influences of sexual risk among urban American adolescent males. *Journal of Nursing Scholarship, 45,* 141–150.

Harry, J. (1990). A probability sample of gay males. *Journal of Homosexuality, 19,* 89–104.

Harvard Health Letter. (2013). Considering testosterone therapy? *38,* 5.

Hauge, L. J., Aaro, L. E., Torgersen, L., & Vollrath, M. E. (2013). Smoking during consecutive pregnancies among primiparous women in the population-based Norwegian Mother and Child Study. *Nicotine & Tobacco Research, 15,* 428–434.

Healthy People 2020. (2012). *Topics and Objectives. Sexually transmitted diseases.* Retrieved from http://www.healthypeople.gov/2020/topicsobjectives2020/overview.aspx?topicid=37

Helweg-Larsen, M., & Collins, B. E. (1994). The UCLA multidimensional condom attitudes scale: Documenting the complex determinants of condom use in college students. *Health Psychology, 13*(3), 224–237.

Hendrick, S. S., & Hendrick, C. (1992). *Romantic love.* Newbury Park, CA: Sage.

Hennessy, M., Romer, D., Valois, R. F., Vanable, P., Carey, M. P., Stanton, B., … Salazar, L. F. (2013). Safer sex media messages and adolescent sexual behavior: 3 year follow up results from Project IMPPACS. *American Journal of Public Health, 103,* 34–140.

Hequembourg, A. L., & Dearing, R. L. (2013). Exploring shame, guilt, and risky substance use among sexual minority men and women. *Journal of Homosexuality, 60*(4), 615–638.

Herbenick, D., Hensel, D., Smith, N. K., Reece, M., Sanders, S. A., & Fortenberry, J. D. (2013). Pubic hair removal and sexual behavior Findings from a prospective daily diary study of sexually active women in the United States. *Journal of Sexual Medicine, 10,* 678–685.

Herman-Kinney, N. J., & Kinney, D. A. (2013). Sober as deviant: The stigma of sobriety and how some college students "stay dry" on a "wet" campus. *Journal of Contemporary Ethnography, 42,* 64–103.

Heron, K. E., & Smyth, J. M. (2013). Discrepancy and negative affect in women's everyday lives: An ecological momentary assessment evaluation of self-discrepancy theory. *Journal of Social and Clinical Psychology, 32,* 276–295.

Hertlein, K. M., & Piercy, F. P. (2012). Essential elements of Internet infidelity treatment. *Journal of Marital & Family Therapy, 38,* 257–570.

Hicks, T. V., & Leitenberg, H. (2001). Sexual fantasies about one's partner versus someone else: Gender differences in incidence and frequency. *The Journal of Sex Research, 38,* 43–50.

Higgins, J. A., Trussell, J., Moore, N. B., & Davison, J. K. (2010). Virginity lost, satisfaction gained? Physiological and psychological sexual satisfaction at heterosexual debut. *Journal of Sex Research, 47,* 384–394.

Hillis, S. D.; Marchbanks, P. A.; Ratlif Taylor, L.; Peterson, H. B.; and the U.S. Collaborative Review of Sterilization Working Group. (2000). Poststerilization regret: Findings from the United States collaborative review of sterilization. *Obstetrics and Gynecology, 93,* 889–895.

Hines, T. M. (2001). The G spot: A modern gynecologic myth. *American Journal of Obstetrics & Gynecology, 185,* 359–362.

Hintistan, S., & Cilingir, D. (2013). Sexual dysfunction in Turkish men and women with type 2 diabetes mellitus. *Sexuality and Disability, 31,* 31–41.

Holland, L., Matthews, T. L., & Schott, M. R. (2012). "That's so Gay!" Exploring college students' attitudes toward the LGBT population. *Journal of Homosexuality, 60,* 575–595.

Hollomotz, A. (2013). Exploiting the Fifty Shades of Grey craze for the disability and sexual rights agenda. *Disability & Society, 28,* 418–422.

Hom, K. A., & Woods, S. J. (2013). Trauma and its aftermath for commercially sexually exploited women as told by frontline providers. *Issues in Mental Health Nursing, 34,* 75–81.

Horowitz, A. D., & Spicer, L. (2013). "Having sex" as a graded and hierarchical construct: A comparison of sexual definitions among heterosexual and lesbian emerging adults in the U.K. *Journal of Sex Research, 50,* 139–150.

Hosain, G. M., Latini, D. M., Kauth, M., Goltz, H. H., & Helmer, D. A. (2013). Sexual dysfunction among male veterans returning from Iraq and Afghanistan: Prevalence and correlates. *Journal of Sexual Medicine, 10,* 516–523.

Hostetler, A. J. (2009). Single by choice? Assessing and understanding voluntary singlehood among mature gay men. *Journal of Homosexuality, 56,* 499–531.

Hughes, M., & Umberson, D. (2004, April). Sexual behavior and mental health: Is sex really good for people? Atlanta: Paper, Southern Sociological Association.

Humphreys, L. (1975). *Tearoom trade: Impersonal sex in public places. (Enlarged edition with a retrospect on ethical issues.).* New York, NY: Aldine.

Humphreys, T. P. (2013). Cognitive frameworks of virginity and first intercourse. *Journal of Sex Research, 50*, 664–675.

I

Iasenza, S. (2001). Lesbian sexuality post-Stonewall to postmodernism: Putting the 'Lesbian Death Bed' concept to bed. *Journal of Sex Education and Therapy, 25*, 59–69.

Internet Pornography Statistics. (2013). Retrieved from http://internet-filter-review.toptenreviews.com/internet-pornography-statistics.html

J

Jaishankar, J. (2009). Sexting: A new form of victimless crime? *International Journal of Cyber Criminology, 3*, 21–25.

Jayson, S. (2011, March 30). Is dating dead? *USA Today*, p. A1.

Jayson, S. (2012, October 18). Couples of all kinds are cohabitating. *USA Today*, p. A1.

Jenkins, D. D., & Vazsonyi, A. T. (2013). Psychosocial adjustment during the transition from adolescence to young adulthood: Developmental evidence from sexual minority and heterosexual youth. *Journal of Positive Psychology, 8*, 181–195.

Jensen, H. M., Gron, R., Lidegaard, O., Dedersen, L. H., Andersen, P. K., & Kessing, L. V. (2013). The effects of maternal depression and use of antidepressants during pregnancy on risk of a child small for gestational age. *Psychopharmacology*(228), 199–205.

Jesser, C. J. (1978). Republished with permission of The Society for the Scientific Study of Sex, from "The Sexual Signaling Behaviors Inventory". *The Journal of Sex Research, 14(2)*, 118–128.

Jesser, C. J. (1998). The sexual signaling behaviors inventory. In C. M. Davis, W. L. Yarber, R. Bauserman, G. Schreer, & S. L. Davis, *Sexuality Related Measures* (pp. 423–424). Thousand Oaks, CA: Sage.

Ji, K., Finkelhor, D., & Dunne, M. (2013, April 30). Child sexual abuse in China: A meta-analysis of 27 studies. *Child Abuse and Neglect.*

Jiann, B. P., Su, C. C., & Tsai, J. Y. (2013). Is female sexual function related to the male partner's erectile function? *Journal of Sexual Medicine, 10*, 420–429.

Johnson, K. (2001, August 9). 100 arrested in Net child porn ring. *USA Today*, p. 1A.

Joller, P., Gupta, N., Seitz, D., Frank, C., Gibson, M., & Gill, S. (2013). Approach to inappropriate sexual behavior in people with dementia. *Canadian Family Physician, 59*, 255–260.

Jones, J. H. (1993). *Bad blood: The Tuskegee Syphilis Experiment (new and expanded edition)*. New York, NY: The Free Press.

Jones, M. T. (2013). Mediated exhibitionism: The naked body in performance and virtual space. *Sexuality and Culture, 14*, 253–269.

Jones, R. K., Moore, A. M., & Frohwirth, L. F. (2011). Perceptions of male knowledge and support among U.S. women obtaining abortions. *Women's Health Issues, 21*, 117–123.

Jose Acuna, M., Carlos Martin, J., Graciani, M., Cruces, A., & Gotor, F. (2010). A comparative study of the sexual function of institutionalized patients with schizophrenia. *Journal of Sexual Medicine, 7*, 3414–3423.

K

Kai-Ching Yu, C. (2012). Pornography consumption and sexual behaviors as correlates of erotic dreams and nocturnal emissions. *Dreaming, 22*, 230–239.

Kaiser, A., Reid, D., & Boschen, K. A. (2013). Experiences of parents with spinal cord injury. *Sexuality and Disability, 30*, 123–137.

Kalfoglou, A., Kammersell, M., Philpott, S., & Dahl, E. (2013). Ethical arguments for and against sperm sorting for mon-medical sex selection: A review. *Reproductive BioMedicine Online, 26*, 231–239.

Kalish, R., & Kimmel, M. (2011). Hooking up. *Australian Feminist Studies, 26*, 137–151.

Kamen, C., Burns, M., & Beach, S. R. (2011). Minority stress in same-sex male relationships: When does it impact relationship satisfaction. *Journal of Homosexuality, 58*, 1372–1390.

Kane, M. D. (2013). Finding "safe" campuses: Predicting the presence of LGBT student groups at North Carolina colleges and universities. *Journal of Homosexuality, 60*, 828–852.

Kaplan, D. L., Jones, E. L., Olson, E. C., & Yunzal-Butler, C. B. (2013). Early age of first sex and health risk in an urban adolescent population. *Journal of School Health, 83*, 350–356.

Kaplan, H. (1979). *Disorders of sexual desire*. New York, NY: Brunner/Mazel.

Kaplan, H. S. (1974). The classification of the female sexual dysfunctions. *Journal of Sex and Marital Therapy, 2*, 124–138.

Karlsen, M., & Traeen, B. (2013). Identifying 'friends with benefits' scripts among young adults in the Norwegian cultural context. *Sexuality & Culture, 2013*, 83–99.

Karraker, A., & DeLamater, J. (2013). Past year inactivity among older married persons and their partners. *Journal of Marriage and Family, 75*, 142–163.

Karten, E. Y., & Wade, J. C. (2010). Sexual orientation change efforts in men: A client perspective. *Journal of Men's Studies, 18*, 84–102.

Kasearu, K. (2010). Intending to marry...students' behavioral intention towards family forming. *TRAMES: A Journal of the Humanities & Social Sciences, 14*, 3–20.

Kedde, H., Van de Wiel, H. B., Schultz, W. C., & Wijsen, C. (2013). Sexual dysfunction in young women with breast cancer. *Supportive Care in Cancer, 21*, 271–280.

Keels, M., Lee, Z., Knox, D., & Wilson, K. (2013). Lecture versus DVD and attitude change toward female masturbation. *Education (in press)*.

Keenan, M. (2012). *Child sexual abuse and the Catholic Church: Gender, power, and organizational culture*. Oxford: Oxford University Press.

Kelly, A., Kupul, M., Aeno, H., Shih, P., Naketrumb, R., Neo, J., ... Vallely, A. (2013). Why women object to male circumcision to prevent HIV in a moderate-prevalence setting. *Qualitative Health Research, 23*, 180–193.

Kempeneers, P., Andrianne, R., Bauwens, S., Georis, I., Pairous, J. F., & Blairy, S. (2013). Functional and psychological characteristics of Belgian men with premature ejaculation. *Archives of Sexual Behavior, 42*, 51–66.

Kendler, K. S., Thomton, L. M., Gilman, S. E., & Kessler, R. C. (2000). Sexual orientation in a U.S. national sample of twin and nontwin sibling pairs. *The American Journal of Psychiatry, 157*, 1843–1846.

Kerr, D. L., Santurri, L., & Peters, P. (2013). A comparison of lesbian, bisexual, and heterosexual college undergraduate women on selected mental health issues. *Journals of American College Health, 61,* 185–194.

Khajehpour, M., Simbar, M., Jannesari, S., Ramezani-Tehrani, F., & Majd, H. A. (2013). Health status of women with intended and unintended pregnancies. *Public Health, 127,* 58–64.

Kiernan, K. (2000). European perspectives on union formation. In J. L. Waite (Ed.), *The ties that bind* (pp. 40–58). New York: Aldine de Gruyter.

Kijak, R. (2013). The sexuality of adults with intellectual disability in Poland. *Sexuality and Disability, 31,* 109–123.

Kimbrough, A. M., Guadagno, R. E., Muscanell, N. L., & Dill, J. (2013). Gender differences in mediated communication: Women connect more than men do. *Computers in Human Behavior, 29,* 896–900.

Kingston, D. A., & Bradford, J. M. (2013). Hypersexuality and recidivism among sexual offenders. *Sexual Addiction & Compulsivity, 20,* 91–105.

Kinsey, A. C., Pomeroy, W. B., & Martin, C. E. (1948). *Sexual behavior in the human male.* Philadelphia: Saunders.

Kinsey, A. C., Pomeroy, W. B., Martin, C. E., & Gebhard, P. H. (1953). *Sexual behavior in the human female.* Philadelphia, PA: Saunders.

Kirk, K. M., Bailey, J. M., Dunne, M. P., & Martin, N. G. (2000). Measurement models for sexual orientation in a community twin sample. *Behavior Genetics, 30,* 345–356.

Kirk, M., & Boyer, P. J. (2002). *American porn (a PBS Frontline Home Video).* Boston, MA: WGBH Educational Foundation.

Knox, D. (2000). *Divorced dad's survival book.* Reading, MA: Perseus Publishing Co.

Knox, D., Hatfield, S., & Zusman, M. E. (1998). College student discussion of relationship problems. *College Student Journal, 32,* 19–21.

Knox, D., Schacht, C., & Turner, J. (1993). Sexual lies among university students. *College Student Journal, 27,* 269–272.

Kohlberg, L. (1966). A cognitive-developmental analysis of children's sex-role concepts and attitudes. In E. E. Maccoby (Ed.), *The development of sex differences* (pp. 82–172). Standford, CA: Standford University Press.

Kohlberg, L. (1969). State and sequence: The cognitive-developmental approach to socialization. In D. A. Goslin (Ed.), *Handbook of socialization theory and research* (pp. 347–480). Chicago, IL: Rand McNally.

Kohlberg, L. (1976). Moral stages and moralization: The cognitive-developmental approach. In T. Lickona (Ed.), *Moral development and behavior* (pp. 31–53). New York, NY: Holt, Rinehart, & Winston.

Koop, C. E. (1987). Report of the General's workshop on Pornography and Public Health. *American Psychologist, 42,* 944–945.

Korchmaros, J. D., Powell, C., & Stevens, S. (2013). Chasing sexual orientation: A comparison of commonly used single-indicator measures of sexual orientation. *Journal of Homosexuality, 60,* 596–614.

Krieger, J. L., & Sarge, M. A. (2013). A serial mediation model of message framing on intentions to receive the human papillomavirus (HPV) vaccine: Revisiting the role of threat and efficacy perception. *Health Communication, 28*(1), 5–19.

Kucuk, L., Kaya, H., Kucuk, M., Yogun, O., & Buzlu, S. (2013). The relationship between depression and perception of sexuality in patients with type II diabetes: In Turkey. *Sexuality and Disability, 31,* 43–52.

Kuper, L. E., Nussbaum, R., & Mustanski, B. (2012). Exploring the diversity of gender and sexual orientation identities in an online sample of transgender individuals. *Journal of Sex Research, 49,* 244–254.

Kurdek, L. A. (1994). Conflict resolution styles in gay, lesbian, heterosexual nonparent, and heterosexual parent couples. *Journal of Marriage and the Family, 56,* 705–722.

Kurdek, L. A. (1995). Lesbian and gay couples. In A. R. D'Augelli, & C. J. Patterson (Eds.), *Lesbian, gay, and bisexual identities over the lifespan: Psychological perspectives* (pp. 243–261). New York: Oxford University Press.

Kurdek, L. A. (2008). Change in relationship quality for partners from lesbian, gay male, and heterosexual couples. *Journal of family psychology, 22,* 701–711.

Kwon, K. A., Han, S., Jeon, H. J., & Bingham, G. E. (2013). Mothers' and fathers' parenting challenges, strategies, and resources in toddlerhood. *Early Child Development & Care, 183,* 415–429.

L

Laan, E., Rellini, A. H., & Barnes, T. (2013). Standard operating procedures for female orgasmic disorder: Consensus of the International Society for Sexual Medicine. *Journal of Sexual Medicine, 10,* 74–82.

Lakeman, R., McAndrew, S., MacGabhann, L., & Warne, T. (2013). 'That was helpful ... no one has talked to me about that before': Research participation as a therapeutic activity. *International Journal of Mental Health Nursing, 22,* 76–84.

Lambert, L. K. (2013). Internet sex addiction. *Journal of Addiction Medicine, 72,* 145–146.

Lancet. (2013, Jan 5). A global awakening, from India. *The Lancet, 381,* 2.

Langan, P. A., & Dawson, J. M. (1988). Felony sentences in State Courts 1988. Washington, DC: Bureau of Justice Statistics of the U.S. Department of Justice.

Langevin, R., & Lang, R. A. (1987). The courtship disorders. In G. D. Wilson (Ed.), *Variant sexuality: Research and theory* (pp. 202–228). Baltimore, MD: Johns Hopkins University Press.

Lawrence, Q., & Penaloza, M. (2013, March 21). Sexual violence victims say military justice system is broken. *NPR.*

Lee, J. T., Lin, C. L., Wan, G. H., & Liang, C. C. (2010). Sexual positions and sexual satisfaction of pregnant women. *Journal of Sex & Marital Therapy, 36,* 408–420.

Lee, J. W., Ha, Y. S., Park, S. C., Seo, Y., & Lee, H. S. (2013). Orgasmic headache treated with nimodipine. *Journal of Sexual Medicine, 10,* 1893–1896.

Lee, T., & Hicks, G. R. (2011). An analysis of factors affecting attitudes toward same-sex marriage: Do the media matter? *Journal of Homosexuality, 58,* 1391–1408.

Leeming, D., Williamson, I., Lyttle, S., & Johnson, S. (2013). Socially sensitive lactation: Exploring the social context of breastfeeding. *Psychology and Health, 28,* 350–368.

Leeners, B., Kruger, T. H., Brody, S., Schmidlin, S., Naegli, E., & Egli, M. (2013). The quality of sexual experience in women correlates with post-orgasmic prolactin surges: Results from an experimental prototype study. *Journal of Sexual Medicine, 10,* 1313–1319.

Lermann, J., Haeberle, L., Merk, S., Henglein, K., Beckmann, M., Mueller, A., & Mehlhorn,

G. (2013). *European Journal of Obstetrics & Gynecology and Reproductive Biology, 167,* 210–213.

Levchenko, P., & Solheim, C. (2013). International marriages between Eastern European-born women and U.S.-born men. *Family Relations, 62,* 30–41.

Lever, J. (1994, August 23). The 1994 Advocate survey of sexuality and relationships: The men. *The Advocate,* 16–24.

Levitt, M. J., Silver, M., & Franco, N. (1996). Troublesome relationships: A part of human experience. *Journal of Social and Personal Relationships, 13,* 523–536.

Lew-Starowicz, M., & Rola, R. (2013). Prevalence of sexual dysfunctions among women with multiple sclerosis. *Sexuality and Disability, 31,* 141–153.

Lick, D. J., Patterson, C. J., & Schmidt, K. M. (2013). Recalled social experiences and current psychological adjustment among adults reared by gay and lesbian parents. *Journal of GLBT Family Studies, 9,* 230–253.

LifeWay Student Ministry. (2013). *True love waits.* Retrieved May 6, 2013, from LifeWay: http://www.lifeway.com/article/true-love-waits-overview

Lincoln, R., & Coyle, I. R. (2013). No-one knows you're a dog on the Internet: Implications for proactive police investigation of sexual offenders. *Psychiatry, Psychology and Law, 20,* 294–300.

Lindau, S. T., Schumann, L. P., Laumann, E. O., Levinson, W., O'Muircheartaigh, C. A., & Waite, L. J. (2007). A study of sexuality and health among older adults in the United States. *The New England Journal of Medicine, 357,* 762–774.

Linz, D., Donnerstein, E., & Penrod, S. (1987). The findings and recommendations of the Attorney General's Commission on Pornography: Do the psychological 'facts' fit the political fury? *American Psychologist, 42,* 946–953.

Linz, D., Paul, B., Land, K. C., Williams, J. R., & Ezell, M. E. (2004). An examination of the assumption that adult businesses are associated with crime in surrounding areas: A secondary effects study in Charlotte, North Carolina. *Law & Society Review, 38,* 69–104.

Livingston, J. A., Bay-Cheng, L. Y., Hequembourg, A. L., Testa, M., & Downs, J. S. (2013). Mixed drinks and mixed messages: Adolescent girls on alcohol and sexuality.

Psychology of Women Quarterly, 37, 38–50.

Lo, S. S., & Kok, W. M. (2013). Sexuality of Chinese women around menopause. *Maturitas, 74,* 190–195.

Lofstrom, E. (2012). Students' ethical awareness and conceptions of research ethics. *Ethics and Behavior, 22,* 349–361.

Loftus, E. F. (1993). The reality of repressed memories. *American Psychologist, 48,* 518–537.

Looi, C., Seow, P., Zhang, B., So, H., Chen, W., & Wong, L. (2010). Leveraging mobile technology for sustainable seamless learning: a research agenda. *British Journal of Educational Technology, 41,* 154–169.

LoPiccolo, J. (1992). Postmodern sex therapy for erectile failure. In R. C. Rosen, & S. R. Leiblum (Eds.), *Erectile disorders: Assessment and treatment* (pp. 171–197). New York: Guiliford Press.

LoPiccolo, J., & Lobitz, C. (1972). The role of masturbation in the treatment of orgasmic dysfunction. *Archives of Sexual Behavior, 2,* 163–171.

Lottes, I. L. (1991). Belief systems: Sexuality and rape. *Journal of Psychology and Human Sexuality, 4,* 37–59.

Lottes, I. L. (1998). Rape Supportive Attitudes Scale. In C. M. Davis, W. L. Yarber, R. Bauserman, G. Schreer, & S. L. Davis (Eds.), *Handbook of sexuality-related measures* (p. 504). Thousand Oaks, CA: Sage.

Lottes, I. L., & Weinberg, M. S. (1996). Sexual coercion among university students: A comparison of the United States and Sweden. *The Journal of Sex Research, 34,* 67–76.

Lowenstein, L., Mustafa, S., & Burke, Y. (2013). Pregnancy and normal sexual function. Are they compatible? *Journal of Sexual Medicine, 10,* 621–622.

Lu, S., Huang, H., Xu, G., Cai, Y., Huang, F., & Ye, X. (2013). Substance use, risky sexual behaviors, and their associations in a Chinese sample of senior high school students. *BMC Public Health, 13,* 1–10.

Lundrigan, S., & Mueller-Johnson, K. (2013). Male stranger rape: A behavioral model of victim-offender interaction. *Criminal Justice and Behavior, 40,* 763–783.

Luo, T. Y. (2013). After sexual harassment: Secondary harm from women coping with sexual harassment incident. *Chinese Journal*

of Guidance and Counseling, 33, 155–191.

Lyons, A., Pitts, M., & Grierson, J. (2013). Growing old as a gay man: Psychological well-being of a sexual minority. *Research on Aging, 35,* 275–295.

Lyons, H., Manning, W., Giordano, P., & Longmore, M. (2013). Predictors of heterosexual casual sex among young adults. *Archives of Sexual Behavior, 42,* 585–593.

M

Ma, L., Lv, Z., Su, J., Wang, J., Yan, D., Wei, J., & Pei, S. (2013). *Consistent condom use increases the colonization of lactobacillus crispatus in the vagina.* Retrieved from http://www.plosone.org/article/info:doi/10.1371/journal.pone.0070716

MacKell, J. (2004). *Brothels, bordellos, & bad girls: Prostitution in Colorado, 1860–1930.* Albuquerque, NM: University of New Mexico Press.

MacMillan, H. L., Tanaka, M., Duku, E., Vaillancourt, T., & Boyle, M. H. (2013). Child physical and sexual abuse in community sample of young adults: Results from the Ontario Child Health Study. *Child Abuse & Neglect, 37,* 14-21.

Maggi, M., Buvat, J., Corona, G., Guay, A., & Torres, L. O. (2013). Hormonal causes of male sexual dysfunctions and their management. *Journal of Sexual Medicine, 10,* 661–677.

Magoun, H. W. (1981). John B. Watson and the study of human sexual behavior. *The Journal of Sex Research, 17,* 368–378.

Major, B., Appelbaum, M., & West, C. (2008, August 13). Report of the APA task force on mental health and abortion.

Marelich, W. D., & Lundquist, J. (2008). Motivations for sexual intimacy: Development of a needs-based sexual intimacy scale. *International Journal of Sexual Health, 20,* 177–186.

Marelich, W. D., Shelton, E., & Grandfield, E. (2013). Correlates and factor replication of the need for sexual intimacy scale(NSIS). *Electronic Journal of Human Sexuality, 16.* Retrieved January 6, 2013, from www.ejhs.org

Marini, I., Wang, X., Etzbach, C. A., & Del Castillo, A. (2013). Ethnic, gender, contact differences in intimacy attitudes toward wheelchair users. *Rehabilitation Counseling Bulletin, 56,* 135–145.

Mark, K. P., & Herbenick, D. (2013). The influence of attraction to partner on heterosexual women's sexual and relationship satisfaction in long-term relationships. *Archives of Sexual Behavior,* September.

Markman, H., Stanley, S., & Blumberg, S. L. (1994). *Fighting for your marriage: Positive steps for preventing divorce and preserving a lasting love.* San Francisco: Jossey-Bass.

Markowitz, L. E., Dunne, E. F., Saraiva, M., Lawson, H. W., Chesson, H., & Unger, E. (2007). Quadrivalent human papillomavirus vaccine recommendations of the Advisory Committee on Immunization Practices (ACIP). *Morbidity and Mortality Weekly, 56,* 1–24.

Marques, M., & Ressa, N. (2013). The sexuality education initiative: a programme involving teenagers, schools, parents, and sexual health services in Los Angeles, Ca. *Reproductive Health Matters, 41,* 124–135.

Martin, B. A., & Dula, C. (2010). More than skin deep: Perception of, and stigma against, tattoos. *College Student Journal, 44,* 200–206.

Martin, C. L., Kornienko, O., Schaefer, D. R., Hanish, L. D., Fabes, R. A., & Goble, P. (2013). The role of sex of peers and gender-typed activities in your children's peer affiliative networks. *Child Development, 84,* 921–937.

Masters, N. T., Casey, E., Wells, E. A., & Morrison, D. M. (2013). Sexual scripts among young active men and women: Continuity and change. *Journal of Sex Research, 50,* 409–420.

Masters, W. H., & Johnson, V. E. (1966). *Human sexual response.* Boston: Little, Brown.

Masters, W. H., & Johnson, V. E. (1970). *Human sexual inadequacy.* Boston : Little, Brown.

Mauras, C. P., Grolnick, W. S., & Friendly, R. W. (2013). Time for "The Talk"... Now What? Autonomy support and structure in mother-daughter conversations about sex. *Journal of Early Adolescence, 33,* 458–481.

Maurelli, K., & Ronan, G. (2013). A time-series analysis of the effectiveness of sex offender notification laws in the USA. *Journal of Forensic Psychiatry & Psychology, 24,* 128–143.

Mauro, T. (1997, March 18). Taming the Internet. *USA Today,* p. 1A.

Mayo Foundation for Medical Education and Research. (1998–2013). Retrieved from https:// www.mayoclinic.com/health/ depo-provera/MY00995

Mays, V. M. (2012). Research challenges and bioethics responsibilities in the aftermath of the presidential apology to the survivors of the U.S. Public Health Services Syphilis Study at Tuskegee. *Ethics and Behavior, 22,* 419–430.

Mbotho, M., Cilliers, M., & Akintola, O. (2013). Sailing against the tide? Sustaining sexual abstinence among Christian youth in a university setting in South Africa. *Journal of Religion and Health, 52,* 208–222.

McCarthy, B., & McCarthy, E. (1984). How much do you know about sexuality? In *Sexual Awareness: Enhancing Sexual Pleasure* (pp. 13–14). New York: Carroll & Graf.

McCarthy, O., Carswell, K., Murray, E., Free, C., Stevenson, F., & Bailey, J. V. (2012). What young people want from a sexual health website: Design and development of Sexunzipped. *Journal of Medical Internet Research, 14,* online.

McCauley, J. L., Kilpatrick, D. G., Walsh, K., & Resnick, H. S. (2013). Substance use among women receiving post-rape medical care, associated post-assault concerns and current substance abuse: Results from a national telephone household probability sample. *Addictive Behaviors, 38,* 1952–1957.

McClintock, M. (1971). Menstrual synchrony and suppression. *Nature, 229,* 244–245.

McGinty, K., Knox, D., & Zusman, M. E. (2003). Nonverbal and verbal communication in "involved" and "casual" relationships among college students. *College Student Journal, 37,* 68–71.

McKee, R. W., Green, E. R., & Hamarman, A. M. (2012). Foundation best practices for online sexuality education. *American Journal of Sexuality Education, 7,* 378–403.

McLaren, S., Gibbs, P. M., & Watts, E. (2013). The interrelations between age, sense of belonging, and depressive symptoms among Australian gay men and lesbians. *Journal of Homosexuality, 60,* 1–15.

McLean, K. (2004). Negotiating (non) monogamy: Bisexuality and intimate relationships. In R. C. Fox (Ed.), *Current research on bisexuality* (pp. 82–97). New York: Harrington Park Press.

McMahon, C. G., Jannini, E., Waldinger, M., & Rowland, D. (2013). Standard operating procedures in the disorders of orgasm and ejaculation. *Journal of Sexual Medicine, 10,* 204–229.

McWilliams, K., Newton, G. S., & Avila-Mora, E. (2013, June 9). Memory for child sexual abuse information: Stimulated memory error and individual differences. *Memory and Cognition.*

Meese, G. (2013). Successful bonding is important. *Deutsches Arzteblatt International, 110,* 13.

Mena, J. A., & Vaccaro, A. (2013). Tell me you love me no matter what: Relationships and self-esteem among GLBQ young adults. *Journal of GLBT Family Studies, 9,* 3–23.

Merrill, J., & Knox, D. (2010). *Finding Love from 9 to 5: Trade Secrets of an Office Love.* Santa Barbara, CA: Praeger.

Merrill, J., & Knox, D. (2010). *When I fall in love again: A new study on finding and keeping the love of your life.* Santa Barbara, California: Praeger.

Merta, C. (2010, June 10). *Kinsey Institute fights for funding for sexuality research.* Retrieved from Indiana Daily Student: http://www. idsnews.com/news/orienter/story. aspx?story_id=75967&section=iu

Messman-Moore, T. L., Ward, R. M., & DeNardi, K. A. (2013). The impact of sexual enhancement alcohol expectancies and risky behavior on alcohol-involved rape among college women. *Violence Against Women, 19,* 449–464.

Metzl, J. M. (2004). Voyeur nation? Changing definitions of voyeurism. *Harvard Review of Psychiatry, 12,* 127–131.

Michael, R. T., Gagnon, J. H., Laumann, E. O., & Kolata, G. (1994). *Sex in America: A definitive survey.* Boston, MA: Little, Brown.

Michielson and Merck FDA-Approved Patient Labeling. (2012). Taken from http://www.merck.com/prod-uct/usa/pi_circulars/n/nexplanon/ nexplanon_ppi.pdf, Copyright © 2011 MSD Oss B.V., a subsidiary of Merck & Co., Inc., Revised: 05/2012.

Mill, J. S. (1859/1985). *On liberty.* New York: Penguin. (Original work published in 1859).

Miller, S. A., & Byers, E. S. (2004). Actual and desired duration of foreplay and intercourse: Discordant and misperceptions within heterosexual couples. *The Journal of Sex Research, 41,* 301–309.

Mock, S. E., & Eibach, R. P. (2012). Stability and change in sexual orientation identity over a ten year period in adulthood. *Archives of Sexual Behavior, 41,* 641–648.

Money, J. (1986). *Lovemaps: Clinical concepts of sexual/erotic health and pathology, paraphilia, and gender transportation in childhood, adolescence, and maturity.* New York: Irvington.

Money, J. (1987). Sin, sickness or status? Homosexual gender identity and psychoneuroendocrinology. *American Psychologist, 42,* 384–399.

Money, J. (1988). *Gay, straight, and in-between.* New York: Oxford University Press. doi: 10.1176/appi.pn. 2013.5a19

Mongeau, P. A., Knight, K., Williams, J., Eden, J., & Shaw, C. (2013). Identifying and explicating variation among friends with benefits relationships. *Journal of Sex Research, 50,* 37–47.

Monro, S. (2000). Theorizing transgender diversity: Towards a social model of health. *Sexual and Relationship Therapy, 15,* 33–42.

Montgomery, M. J., & Sorell, G. T. (1997). Differences in love attitudes across family life stages. *Family Relations, 46,* 55–61.

Moore, M. J., Barr, E. M., & Johnson, T. M. (2013). Sexual behaviors of middle school students: 2009 Youth Risk Behavior Survey results from 16 locations. *Journal of School Health, 83,* 61–68.

Moran, M. (2013). *DSM V* to distinguish paraphilias from paraphilic disorders. *Professional News,* May 3. doi: 10.1176/appi.pn. 2013.5a19.

Moreau, C., Trussell, J., & Bajos, N. (2013). Religiosity, religious affiliation, and patterns of sexual activity and contraceptive use in France. *The European Journal of Contraception and Reproductive Health Care, 18,* 168–180.

Morell, V. (1998). A new look at monogamy. *Science, 281,* 1982.

Moreno, J. A., Arango-Lasprilla, J. C., Gan, C., & McKerral, M. (2013). Sexuality after traumatic brain injury: A critical review. *NeuroRehabilitation, 32,* 69–85.

Morotti, E., Battaglia, B., Paradisi, R., Persico, N., Zampieri, M., Venturoli, S., & Battaglia, C. (2013). Body mass index, Stunkard Figure Rating Scale, and sexuality in young Italian women. *Journal of Sexual Medicine, 10,* 1034–1043.

Morrow, L. C. (2012). Cyclical role-playing and stigma. Exploring the challenges of stereotype performance among exotic dancers. *Deviant Behavior, 33,* 357–374.

Moser, C. (1992). Lust, lack of desire, and paraphilias: Some thoughts and possible connections. *Journal of Sex and Marital Therapy, 18,* 65–69.

Mouilso, E. R., & Calhoun, K. S. (2013). The role of rape myth acceptance and psychopathy in sexual assault perpetration. *Journal of Aggression, Maltreatment & Trauma, 22,* 159–174.

Muccigrasso, L. (1991). Sexual abuse prevention strategies and programs for persons with developmental disabilities. *Sexuality and Disability, 9,* 261–271.

Murray, D. R., Jones, D. N., & Schaller, M. (2013). Perceived threat of infections disease and its implications for sexual attitudes. *Personality and Individual Differences, 54,* 103–108.

N

National Coalition of Anti-Violence Programs. (2012). *2011 National hatecrimes report: Anti-lesbian, gay, bisexual and transgender violence in 2011.* New York: National Coalition of Anti-Violence Programs.

National Multiple Sclerosis Society. (2013). Retrieved from http://www.nationalmssociety.org/about-multiple-sclerosis/what-we-know-about-ms/faqs-about-ms/index.aspx

Nelms, B. J., Knox, D., & Easterling, B. (2012). THE RELATIONSHIP TALK: Assessing Partner Commitment. *College Student Journal, 46,* 178–182.

Nelson, C. J., & Kenowitz, J. (2013). Communication and intimacy-enhancing interventions for men diagnosed with prostate cancer and their partners. *Journal of Sexual Medicine, 10,* 127–132.

Nelson, C. J., & Mulhall, J. P. (2013). Psychological impact of Peyronie's disease: A review. *Journal of Sexual Medicine, 10,* 653–660.

Neuman, H. B., Park, J., Fuzesi, S., & Temple, L. K. (2012). Rectal cancer patients' quality of life with a temporary stoma: Shifting perspectives. *Diseases of the Colon and Rectum, 55,* 1117–1124.

Neuman, M. G. (2008). *The truth about cheating: Why men stray and what you can do to prevent it.* New York: Wiley & Sons.

Nichcy.org. (2013). Retrieved from http://nichcy.org/disability/specific/intellectual

Nicoletti, A. (2007). Female genital cutting. *Journal of Pediatric & Adolescent Gynecology, 20,* 261–262.

Niehuis, O., Buellesbach, J., Gibson, J. D., Pothmann, D., Hanner, C., Mutti, N. S., … Schmitt, T. (2013). Behavioural and genetic analysis of Nasonia shed light on the evolution of sex pheromones. *Nature, 494,* 345–348.

Notarius, C., & Markman, H. (1994). *We can work it out. Making sense of marital conflict.* New York: Putnam.

NPR. (2002, July 25). *Remembering Tuskegee.* Retrieved July 20, 2013, from National Public Radio: http://www.npr.org/programs/morning/features/2002/jul/tuskegee/

Nunes, K. L., & Jung, S. (2013). Are cognitive distortions associated with denial and minimization among sex offenders. *Sex Abuse: Journal of Research and Treatment, 25,* 166–188.

O

Ocobock, A. (2013). The power and limits of marriage: Married gay men's family relationships. *Journal of Marriage and Family, 75,* 191–205.

Office of Population Research & Association of Reproductive Health Professionals. (2013). Retrieved from http://ec.princeton.edu/questions/qa-otc-access.html

O'Hare, F., & O'Donohue, W. (1998). Sexual harassment: Identifying risk factors. *Archives of Sexual Behavior, 27,* 561–579.

Olmstead, S. B., Roberson, P. N., Fincham, F. D., & Pasley, K. (2012). *Hooking up and risky sex behaviors among first semester college men: What is the role of pre-college experience?* Phoenix, AZ: Presentation, National Council on Family Relations.

Omarzu, J., Miller, A. N., Shultz, C., & Timmerman, A. (2012). Motivations and emotional consequences related to engaging in extramarital relationships. *International Journal of Sexual Health, 24,* online June.

Oselin, S. S., & Blasyak, A. (2013). Contending with Violence: Female prostitutes' strategic responses on the streets. *Deviant Behavior, 34,* 274–290.

Oswalt, S. B., & Wyatt, T. J. (2011). Sexual orientation and differences in mental health, stress, and academic performance in a national sample of U.S. college students. *Journal of Homosexuality,* 1255–1280.

Owen, J., & Fincham, F. D. (2011). Effects of gender and psychosocial factors on 'Friends with Benefits' relationships among young adults. *Archives of Sexual Behavior, 40,* 311–320.

Ozay, B., Knox, D., & Easterling, B. (2012, March). YOU'RE DATING WHO? Parental attitudes toward interracial dating. New Orleans: Poster, Southern Sociology annual meeting.

P

Padilla, Y. C., Crisp, C., & Rew, D. L. (2010). Parental acceptance and illegal drug use among, gay, lesbian, and bisexual adolescents: results from a national survey. *Social Work, 55,* 265–276.

Pakula, B., & Shoveller, J. A. (2013). Sexual orientation and self-reported mood disorder diagnosis among Canadian adults. *BMC Public Health, 13,* 1–7.

Papp, L. M., Goeke-Morey, M. C., & Cummings, E. M. (2013). Let's talk about sex: A diary investigation of couples' intimacy conflicts in the home. *Couple and Family Psychology: Research and Practice, 2,* 60–72.

Parackal, S. M., Parackal, M. K., & Harraway, J. A. (2013). Prevalence and correlates of drinking in early pregnancy among women who stopped drinking on pregnancy recognition. *Maternal and Child Health Journal, 17,* 520–529.

Parchomiuk, M. (2013). Model of intellectual disability and the relationship of attitudes towards the sexuality of persons with an intellectual disability. *Sexuality and Disability, 31,* 125–139.

Parker, M. G., & Yau, M. K. (2012). Sexuality, identity, and women with spinal cord injury. *Sexuality and Disability, 30,* 15–27.

Parker, M., Knox, D., & Easterling, B. (2011, February 24–26). SEXTING: Sexual content/Images in romantic relationships. Philadelphia, PA: Poster, Eastern Sociological Society.

Parsons, J., Starks, T., DuBois, S., Grov, C., & Golub, S. (2013). Alternatives to monogamy among gay male couples in community survey: Implications for mental health and sexual risk. *Archives of Sexual Behavior, 42,* 303–312.

Patrick, K., Heywood, W., Smith, A. M., Simpson, J. M., Shelley, J. M., Richters, J., & Pitts, M. K. (2013). A population-based study investigating the association between sexual and relationship satisfaction and psychological distress among heterosexuals. *Journal of Sex and Marital Therapy, 39,* 56–70.

Paul, K. (2013). Refusing to be a man? Men's responsibility for war rape and the problem of social structures in feminists and gender theory. *Men and Masculinities, 16,* 93–114.

Paul, L. A., Walsh, K., & McCauley, J. L. (2013). College women's experiences with rape disclosure: A national study. *Violence Against Women, 19,* 486–502.

Pazmany, E., Bergeron, S., Oudenhove, L., Verhaeghe, J., & Enzlin, P. (2013). Body image and genital self-image in pre-menopausal women with dyspareunia. *Archives of Sexual Behavior, 42,* 999–1010.

Pedrelli, P., Bentley, K., Vitali, M., Clain, A. J., Nyer, M., Fava, M., & Farabaugh, A. H. (2013). Compulsive use of alcohol among college students. *Psychiatry Research, 205,* 95–102.

Perelman, M. A. (2013). Delayed ejaculation. *Journal of Sexual Medicine, 10,* 1189–1190.

Peters, A. W. (2013). "Things that involve sex are just different." US Anti-trafficking Law and Policy on the books in their minds and in action. *Anthropological Quarterly, 86,* 221–255.

Peters, J. M., Dinsmore, J., & Toth, P. (1989). Why prosecute child abuse? *South Dakota Law Review, 34,* 649–659.

Pew Research Center. (2012a, May 14). *Half say view of Obama not affected by gay marriage decision: Independents mostly unmoved.* Retrieved from Pew Research Center: http://www.people-press. org/2012/05/14/half-say-view-of-obama-not-affected-by-gay-marriage-decision/

Pew Research Center. (2013, June 6). *In gay marriage debate, both supporters and opponents see legal recognition as "inevitable."* Retrieved from Pew Research Center: http://www.people-press.org/2013/06/06/in-gay-marriage-debate-both-supporters-and-opponents-see-legal-recognition-as-inevitable

Pew Research Center. (2013). *Public opinion on abortion and Roe v. Wade.* Retrieved from http://www.pewforum.org/Abortion/Public-Opinion-on-Abortion-and-Roe-v-Wade.aspx

Pfeifer, L. R., Miller, R., Li, T., & Hsiao, Y. (2013). Perceived marital problems in Taiwan. *Contemporary Family Therapy: An International Journal, 35,* 91–104.

Pflieger, J., Cook, E. C., Niccolai, L. M., & Connell, C. M. (2013). Racial/ethnic differences in patterns of sexual risk behavior and rates of sexually transmitted infections among female young adults. *American Journal of Public Health, 103,* 1–7.

Phillips, G., & Over, R. (1995). Differences between heterosexual, bisexual and lesbian women in childhood experiences. *Archives of Sexual Behavior, 24,* 1–20.

Pierce, L., Dahl, M. S., & Nielsen, J. (2013). In sickness and in wealth: Psychological and sexual costs of income comparison in marriage. *Personality and Social Psychology Bulletin, 39,* 359–374.

Pilver, C. E., Libby, D. J., & Hoff, R. A. (2013). Premenstrual dysphoric disorder as a correlate of suicidal ideation, plans, and attempts among a nationally representative sample. *Social Psychiatry and Psychiatric Epidemiology, 48,* 437–446.

Pinello, D. R. (2008). Gay marriage: For better or for worse? What we've learned from the evidence. *Law & Society Review, 42,* 227–230.

Ping, M., Brewer-Asling, M., & Mangus, J. H. (2013). A case study on the economic impact of optimal breastfeeding. *Maternal and Child Health Journal, 17,* 9–13.

Pinon, Jr., R. (2002). *Biology of human reproduction.* Sausalito, CA: University Science Books.

Pittman, J. C. (2013). *Center for Integrative Medicine.* Retrieved from http://www.carolinacenter.com/ (Personal communication with Dr. Pittman)

Pivetti, M., & Melotti, G. (2013). Prenatal genetic testing: An investigation of determining factors affecting the decision-making process. *Journal of Genetic Counseling, 22,* 76–89.

Pizer, J. C., Sears, B., Mallory, C., & Hunter, N. D. (2012). Evidence of persistent and pervasive workplace discrimination against GLBT people: The need for Federal legislation prohibiting discrimination and providing for equal employment benefits. *Loyola of Los Angeles Review, 45,* 715–779.

Planned Parenthood Federation of America Inc., 2013. Retrieved August 5, 2013, from https://www.plannedparenthood.org/

health-topics/birth-control/cervi-cal-cap-20487.htm

Policy Statement. (2010). Ritual Genital Cutting of Female Minors. *Pediatrics, 125,* 1088–1093.

Pollard, M. (2011). *Evidence-based care for breastfeeding mothers: A resource for midwives and allied health-care professionals.* New York, NY: Routledge.

Potok, M. (2010). Anti-gay hate crimes: Doing the math. *Intelligence Report, 140* (Winter), p. 29.

Price-Glynn, K. (2010). *Strip club: Gender, power and sex work.* New York, New York: University Press.

Prior, J., Hubbard, P., & Birch, P. (2013). Sex worker victimization, modes of working and location in New South Wales. *Journal of Sex Research, 50,* 574-586.

Procon.org. (2013). Retrieved from http://prostitution.procon.org/view.source.php?sourceID=000599

Prost, H., Burnett, A., Brock, G., Ghanem, H., Guiliano, F., Glina, S., ... Sharlip, I. (2013). SOP conservative (medical and mechanical) treatment of erectile dysfunction. *Journal of Sexual Medicine, 10,* 130–171.

Pryor, J. H., Eagan, K., Hurtado, S., Blake, L. P., Berdan, J., & Case, M. H. (2012). *The American freshman: National norms fall 2012.* Los Angeles, CA: Higher Education Research.

Purkett, T. (2013). Sexually transmitted infections. A presentation to "Courtship and Marriage" class at East Carolina University. Greenville, NC.

Q

Quinn, C., Happell, B., & Browne, G. (2012). Opportunity lost? Psychiatric medications and problems with sexual function: a role for nurses in mental health. *Journal of Clinical Nursing, 21,* 415–432.

Quinn, C., Happell, B., & Welch, A. (2013). Talking about sex as part of our role: Making and sustaining practice change. *International Journal of Mental Health Nursing, 22,* 231–240.

R

Rako, S., & Friebely, J. (2004). The pheromonal influences on sociosexual behavior in postmenopausal women. *Journal of Sex Research, 41,* 372–381.

Raso, R. (2008). How to handle workplace romance, foster interpersonal skills. *Nursing Management, 39,* 56–57.

Ravanipour, M., Tayebeh, M. G., & Tahereh, G. (2013). Elderly women's views about sexual desire during old age: A qualitative study. *Sexuality and Disability, 31,* 179–188.

Raymond, E. G., & Grimes, D. A. (2012). The comparative safety of legal induced abortion and childbirth in the United States. *Obstetrics and Gynecology, 119,* 215–219.

Reay, B., Attwood, N., & Gooder, C. (2013). Inventing sex: The short history of sex addiction. *Sexuality and Culture, 17,* 1–19.

Reece, M., Herbenick, D., & Fortenberry, J. D. (2012, May 8). *The National Survey of Sexual Health and Behavior.* Retrieved 2012, from http://www.nationalsexstudy.indiana.edu/graph.html

Reece, M., Herbenick, D., Fortenberry, J. D., & et al. (2012). *The National Survey of Sexual Health and Behavior.* Retrieved May 8, 2013, from http://www.nationalsexstudy.indiana.edu/graph.html

Reich, S. M., Subrahmanyam, K., & Espionoza, G. (2012). Friending, IMing, and hanging out face-to-face: Overlap in adolescents' online and offline social networks. *Development Psychology, 48,* 356–368.

Reis, M., Ramiro, L., de Matos, M. G., & Diniz, J. A. (2013). Determinants influencing male condom use among university students in Portugal. *International Journal of Sexual Health, 25,* 115–127.

Resource Guide to Coming Out for African Americans. (2011). Available from Human Rights Campaign.

Reverby, S. M. (2012). Reflections on apologies and the studies in Tuskegee and Guatemala. *Ethics and Behavior, 22,* 493–495.

Reyes, H. L., & Foshee, V. A. (2013). Sexual dating aggression across grades 8 through 12: Timing and predictors of onset. *Journal of Youth and Adolescence, 42,* 581–595.

Rham, G., Renck, B., & Ringsberg, K. C. (2013). Psychological distress among women who were sexually abused as children. *International Journal of Social Welfare, 22,* 269–278.

Risman, B., & Schwartz, P. (2004). After the sexual revolution: Gender politics in teen dating. In M. Strombler, D. M. Baunach,

E. O. Burgess, D. Donnelly, & W. Simonds (Eds.), *Sex matters: The Sexuality and society reader* (pp. 272–279). Boston: Pearson, Allyn & Bacon.

Robinson, M. (2013). Polyamory and monogamy as strategic identities. *Journal of Bisexuality, 13,* 21–38.

Rodoo, P., & Hellberg, D. (2013). Girls who masturbate in early infancy: diagnostics, natural course and long-term follow-up. *Acta Paediatrica, 102,* 762–766.

Rogow, D., Haberland, N., DelValle, A., Lee, N., Osakue, G., Sa, Z., & Skaer, M. (2013). Integrating gender and rights into sexuality education: field reports on using It's All One. *Reproductive Health Matters, 21,* 154–166.

Rosenbaum, M. S., Daunt, K. L., & Jiang, A. (2013). Craigslist exposed: The Internet-mediated hookup. *Journal of Homosexuality, 60,* 505–531.

Rosser, B. R., Dwyer, M., Coleman, E., Miner, M., Metz, M., Robinson, B. E., & Bockting, W. O. (1995). Using sexually explicit material in adult sex education: An eighteen-year comparative analysis. *Journal of Sex Education and Therapy, 21,* 117–128.

Rossi, N. E. (2010). "Coming out": Stories of gay and lesbian young adults. *Journal of Homosexuality, 57,* 1174–1191.

Roth, S., & Friedman, M. J. (1997). *Childhood trauma remembered: A report on the current scientific knowledge base and its applications.* Available from ISTSS, 60 Revere Drive, Suite 500, Northbrook, IL 60062: International Society for Traumatic Stress Studies.

Rothman, E. F., Sullivan, M., Keyes, S., & Boehmer, U. (2012). Parents supportive reactions to sexual orientation disclosure associated with better health: Results from a population-based survey of LGB adults in Massachusetts. *Journal of Homosexuality, 59,* 186–200.

Rubin, E. (1987). *Abortion, politics, and the courts: Roe v. Wade and its aftermath* (2nd ed.). Westport, CT: Greenwood Press.

Runfola, C. D., Von Holle, A., Trace, S. E., Brownley, K. A., Hofmeier, S. M., Gagne, D. A., & Bulik, C. M. (2013). Body dissatisfaction in women across the lifespan: Results of the UNC-SELF and Gender and Body Image (GABI) studies. *European Eating Disorders Review, 21,* 52–59.

Russell, S. T., Ryan, C., Toomey, R. B., Diaz, R. M., & Sanchez, J.

(2011). Lesbian, gay, bisexual and transgender adolescent school victimization: Implications for young adult health and adjustment. *Journal of School Health, 81,* 223–230.

Russell, V. M., Baker, L. R., & Mcnulty, J. K. (2013). Attachment insecurity and infidelity in marriage: Do studies of dating relationships really inform us about marriage? *Journal of Family Psychology, 27,* 241–251.

Rutledge, S. E., Siebert, D. C., & Chonody, J. (2012). Attitudes toward gays and lesbians: A latent class analysis of university students. *Journal of Social Service Research, 38,* 18–28.

Rye, B. J., Meaney, G. J., Yessis, J., & McKay, A. (2012). Uses of the "Comfort with Sexual Matters for Young Adolescents" scale: A measure of erotophobia-erotophilia for youth. *The Canadian Journal of Human Sexuality, 21,* 91–100.

Rye, B. J., Serafini, T., & Bramberger, T. (2013). Unpublished data. St. Jerome's University.

S

Sabbah, K. (2013). "Sex and the married John: Profiling male sexual behaviors with street prostitutes." Department of Sociology, California State University, Northridge, Northridge, CA.

Sahay, R. D., Haynes, E. N., Rao, M. B., & Pirko, I. (2012). Assessment of sexual satisfaction in relation to potential sexual problems in women with multiple sclerosis: A pilot study. *Sexuality and Disability, 30,* 227–236.

Saleem, H. T., & Surkan, P. J. (2013, June 22). Parental pregnancy wantedness and child social-emotional development. *Maternal and Child Health Journal.*

Salter, A. (1988). *Treating child sex offenders and victims: A practical guide.* Newbury Park, CA: Sage.

Sanday, P. R. (1981). The socio-cultural context of rape: A cross-cultural study. *Journal of Social Issues, 37,* 5–27.

Sanday, P. R. (1995). Pulling train. In P. S. Rothenberg (Ed.), *Race, class and gender in the United States* (3rd ed., pp. 396–402). New York: St. Martin's Press.

Sandberg, S. (2013). *Lean in: Women, work, and the will to lead.* New York, NY: Alfred A. Knopf.

Sanders, T. L. (2008). *Paying for pleasure: Men who buy sex.* Cullompton, Devon: Willan.

Santo-Iglesias, P., Calvillo, G., & Sierra, C. J. (2013). A further examination of Levine's model of sexual desire. *Psychology and Sexual Desire, 4,* 34–45.

Satterwhite, C. L., Torrone, E., Meites, E., Dunne, E. F., Mahajan, R., Ocfemia, C. B., & Weinstock, H. (2013). Sexually transmitted infections among U.S. women and men: Prevalence and incidence estimates, 2008. *Sexually Transmitted Diseases, 40*(3), 187–193.

Sbraga, T. P., & O'Donohue, W. (2000). Sexual harassment. *Annual Review of Sex Research, 11,* 258–285.

Schoentjes, E., & Deboutte, D. (1999). Child Sexual Behavior Inventory: A Dutch-speaking normative sample. *Pediatrics, 104,* 885–893.

Scribano, P. V., Stevens, J., & Kaizar, E. (2013). The effects of intimate partner violence before, during, and after pregnancy in nurse visited first time mothers. *Maternal and Child Health Journal, 17,* 307–318.

Seeman, M. V. (2013). Clinical interventions for women with schizophrenia: pregnancy. *Acta Psychiatrica Scandinavica, 127,* 12–22.

Senn, C. Y. (2013). Education on resistance to acquaintance sexual assault: Preliminary promise of a new program for young women in high school and university. *Canadian Journal of Behavioral Science/Revue, 45,* 24–33.

Serughetti, G. (2013). Prostitution and client's responsibility. *Men and Masculinities, 16,* 35–48.

Shaley, O., Baum , N., & Itzhaki, H. (2013). "There's a man in my bed." The first experience of sex among modern-orthodox newlyweds in Israel. *Journal of Sex & Marital Therapy, 39,* 40–55.

Sharpe, A. (2012). Transgender marriage and the legal obligation to disclose gender history. *Modern Law Review, 75,* 33–53.

Shdaimah, C. S., & Wiechelt, S. A. (2013). Crime and compassion: Women in prostitution at the intersection of criminality and victimization. *International Review of Victimology, 19,* 23–35.

Shikai, X. (1990). Treatment of impotence in traditional Chinese medicine. *Journal of Sex Education and Therapy, 16,* 198–200.

Shin, K., Shin, H., Yang, J. A., & Edwards, C. (2010). Gender role identity among Korean and American college students: Links to gender and academic achievement. *Social Behavior & Personality: An International Journal, 38,* 267–272.

Shin, S. H., Hong, H. G., & Jeon, S. M. (2012). Personality and alcohol use: The role of impulsivity. *Addictive Behaviors, 37,* 102–107.

Short, M. B., Catallazzi, M., & Beitkopf, C. R. (2013). Adolescent intimate heterosexual relationships: Measurement issues. *Journal of Pediatric and Adolescent Gynecology, 26,* 3–6.

SIECUS. (2013). *Position statement on masturbation.* Retrieved June 6, 2013, from SIECUS: http://www.siecus.org/index.cfm?fuseaction=page.viewPage&pageId=494&parentID=472

Simister, J. G. (2010). Domestic violence and female genital mutilation in Kenya: Effects of ethnicity and education. *Journal of Family Violence, 25,* 247–257.

Simms, D., & Byers, E. (2013). Heterosexual daters' sexual initiation behaviors: Use of the theory of planned behavior. *Archives of Sexual Behavior, 42,* 105–116.

Simon, J., Caramelli, K., Thomas, H., & Reape, K. (2013). Efficacy and safety of a weekly progestin-only transdermal system for prevention of pregnancy. *Contraception, 88,* 316.

Simon, S., & Hoyt, C. L. (2013). Exploring the effect of media images on women's leadership self-perceptions and aspirations. *Group Processes & Intergroup Relations, 16,* 232–245.

Simopoulos, E. F., & Trinidad, A. C. (2013). Male erectile dysfunction: Integrating psychopharmacology and psychotherapy. *General Hospital Psychiatry, 35,* 33–38.

Singer, I. (1973). *The goals of human sexuality.* New York, NY: Norton.

Smith, D., & Stewart, S. (2003). Sexual aggression and sports participation. *Journal of Sport Behavior, 26,* 384–394.

Smith, M. (2013). Youth viewing sexually explicit material online: Addressing the elephant on the screen. *Sexuality Research & Social Policy: A Journal of the NRSC, 10,* 62–75.

Snipes, D. J., & Benotsch, E. G. (2013). High-risk cocktails and high-risk sex: Examining the relation between alcohol mixed with energy drink consumption, sexual behavior, and drug use in college students. *Addictive Behaviors, 38,* 1418–1423.

Sophie, J. (1985/1986). A critical examination of stage theories of lesbian identity development. *Journal of Homosexuality, 21,* 39–51.

Sprecher, S., Barbee, A., & Schwartz, P. (1995). 'Was it good for you, too?' Gender differences in first sexual intercourse experiences. *The Journal of Sex Research, 32,* 3–15.

Staley, C., & Prause, N. (2013). Erotica viewing effects on intimate relationships and self/partner. *Archives of Sexual Behavior, 42,* 613–624.

Stanberry, L. R., & Rosenthal, S. L. (2013). *Sexually transmitted diseases: Vaccines, prevention and control.* London: Elsevier.

Starcevic, V. (2013). Is Internet addiction a useful concept? *Australian and New Zealand Journal of Psychiatry, 47,* 16–19.

Stayton, W. R. (1992). A theology of sexual pleasure. *SIECUS Report, 20*(4), 9–15.

Stephenson, K. R., Rellini, A. H., & Meston, C. M. (2013). Relationship satisfaction as a predictor of treatment response during cognitive behavioral sex therapy. *Archives of Sexual Behavior, 42,* 143–152.

Sternberg, R. J. (1986). A triangular theory of love. *Psychological Review, 93,* 119–135.

Stetson, D. M. (2004). The invisible issue: Trafficking of women and girls in the United States. In J. Outshoorn (Ed.), *The politics of prostitution: Women's movements, democratic states and the globalization of sex commerce* (pp. 245–264). New York: Cambridge University Press.

Stock, M. L., Peterson, L. M., Houlihan, A. E., & Walsh, L. A. (2013). Influence of oral sex and oral cancer information on young adults' oral sexual-risk cognitions and likelihood of HPV vaccination. *Journal of Sex Research, 50,* 95–102.

Stockman, J. K., & Lucea, M. B. (2013). Forced sexual initiation, sexual intimate partner violence and HIV risk in women: A global review of the literature. *AIDS and Behavior, 17,* 832–847.

Stone, N., Inghamand, R., & Gibbins, K. (2013). 'Where do babies come from?' Barriers to early sexuality communication between parents and young children. *Sex Education, 13,* 228–240.

Strassberg, D., McKinnon, R., Sustaita, M., & Rullo, J. (2013). Sexting by high school students: An exploratory and descriptive study. *Archives of Sexual Behavior, 42,* 15–21.

Stroebel, S. S., O'Keefe, S. L., Beard, K. W., Kuo, S. Y., Swindell, S., & Stroupe, W. (2013). Brother-sister incest: Data from anonymous computer assisted self-interviews. *Journal of Child Sexual Abuse: Research, Treatment, & Program Innovations for Victims, Survivors, & Sex Offenders, 22,* 255–276.

Strommen, E. E. (1989). You're a what? Family member reactions to the disclosure of homosexuality. *Journal of Homosexuality, 18,* 37–58.

Strong, S. M., Devendra, S., & Randall, P. K. (2000). Childhood gender nonconformity and body dissatisfaction in gay and heterosexual men. *Sex Roles, 43,* 427–439.

Suarez, Z. E., & Perez, R. M. (2012). The Cuban American family. In R. Wright, C. H. Mindel, T. V. Tran, & R. W. Habenstein (Eds.), *Ethnic families in America* (5th ed., pp. 100–128). Upper Saddle River, NJ: Pearson.

Sugiura-Ogasawara, M., Suzuki, S., Ozaki, Y., Katano, K., Suzumori, N., & Kitaori, T. (2013). Frequency of recurrent spontaneous abortion and its influence on further marital relationship and illness: The Okazaki Cohort study in Japan. *The Journal of Obstetrics and Gynecology Research, 39,* 126–131.

Sullivan, A. (1997). The conservative case. In A. Sullivan (Ed.), *In same-sex marriage: Pro and con* (pp. 146–154). New York: Vintage Books.

Sullivan, A. K., Savage, E. J., Lowndes, C. M., Paul, G., Murphy, G., Carne, S., … Gill, O. N. (2013). Non-disclosure of HIV status in UK sexual health clinics—a pilot study to identify non-disclosure within a national unlinked anonymous seroprevalence survey. *Sexually Transmitted Infections, 89,* 120–121.

Sullivan, J. F., Stember, D. S., Deveci, S., Akin-Olugbade, Y., & Mulhall, J. P. (2013). Ejaculation profiles of men following radiation therapy for prostate cancer. *Journal of Sexual Medicine, 10,* 1410–1416.

Swindell, S., Stroebel, S. S., O'Keefe, S. L., Beard, K. W., Robinett, S. R., & Kommor, M. J. (2011). Correlates of exhibition-like experiences in childhood and adolescence: A model for development of exhibitionism in heterosexual males. *Sexual Addiction and Compulsivity, 18,* 135–156.

Syme, M. L., Klonoff, E. A., Macera, C. A., & Brodine, S. K. (2013). Predicting sexual decline and dissatisfaction among older adults: The role of partnered and individual physical and mental health factors. *Journal of Gerontology Series B: Psychological Sciences & Social Sciences, 68,* 323–332.

Syvertsen, J. L., Robertson, A. M., Rolon, M. L., Palinkas, A., Rangel, M. G., & Strathdee, S. A. (2013). "Eyes that don't see, heart that doesn't feel": Coping with sex work in intimate relationships and its implications for HIV/STI prevention. *Social Science and Medicine, 87,* 1–8.

T

Tang, C. S., Lai, E. D., Phil, M., & Chung, T. K. (1997). Assessment of sexual functioning for Chinese college students. *Archives of Sexual Behavior, 26,* 79–90.

Tang, C. S., Siu, B. N., Lai, E. D., & Chung, T. H. (1996). Heterosexual Chinese women's sexual adjustment after gynecologic cancer. *The Journal of Sex Research, 33,* 189–195.

Tannahill, E. (1982). *Sex in history.* New York: Scarborough.

Tannen, D. (1990). *You just don't understand: Women and men in conversation.* London: Virago.

Temple, J. R., Paul, J. A., vanden Berg, P., McElhany, J. A., & Temple, B. W. (2012). Teen sexting and its association with sexual behaviors. *Archives of Pediatric Adolescent Medicine, 166,* 828–833.

ter Bogt, T. F., Engles, R. C., Bogers, S., & Kloosterman, M. (2010). "Shake It Baby, Shake It": Media preferences, sexual attitudes and gender stereotypes among adolescents. *Sex Roles, 63,* 844–859.

The National Data Book. (2012). *Statistical Abstract of the United States, 2012–2013* (131st ed.). Washington, DC: Bureau of the Census.

Theobold, D., & Farrington, D. P. (2013). The effects of marital breakdown on offending: results for a prospective longitudinal survey of males. *Psychology, Crime & Law, 19,* 391–408.

Thomsen, D., & Chang, I. J. (2000). *Predictors of satisfaction with first intercourse: A new perspective for sexuality education.* Minneapolis, MN: Poster presentation at the 62nd Annual Conference for the National Council on Family Relations.

Thomson, E., & Bernhardt, E. (2010). Education, values, and cohabitation in Sweden. *Marriage & Family Review, 46,* 1–21.

Tissot, S. A. (1758/1766). *Onania, or a treatise upon the disorders produced by masturbation (A. Hume Trans.).* London: J. Pridden (Original work published 1758).

Tobias, S., & Cahill, S. (2003). *School lunches, the Wright brothers, and gay families.* Retrieved from National Gay and Lesbian Task Force: http://www.thetaskforce.org

Toffol, E., Koponen, P., & Partonen, T. (2013). Miscarriage and mental health: Results of two population-based studies. *Psychiatry Research, 205,* 151–158.

Traeen, B., & Thuen, F. (2013). Relationship problems and extradyadic romantic and sexual activity in a web-sample of Norwegian men and women. *Scandinavian Journal of Psychology, 54,* 137–145.

Traupmann, J., Petersen, R., Utne, M., & Hatfield, E. (1981). Measuring equity in intimate relations. *Applied Psychological Measurement, 5,* 467–480.

Tripodi, S. J., & Pettus-Davis, C. (2013). Histories of childhood victimization and subsequent mental health problems, substance use, and sexual victimization for a sample of incarcerated women in the U.S. *International Journal of Law and Psychiatry, 36,* 30–40.

Troiden, R. R. (1989). The formation of homosexual identities. *Journal of Homosexuality, 17,* 43–73.

Truong, K. D., Reifsnider, O. S., Mayorga, M. E., & Spitler, H. (2013). Estimated number of preterm births and low birth weight children born in the United States due to maternal binge drinking. *Maternal and Child Health Journal, 17,* 677–688.

Turner, D., Basdekis-Jozsa, R., & Briken, P. (2013). Prescription of testosterone-lowering medication for sex offender treatment in German forensic-psychiatric institutions. *Journal of Sexual Medicine, 10,* 570–578.

Twamley, K. (2013). Love and desire amongst middle-class Gujarati Indians in the UK and India. *Cultural, Health & Sexuality: An International Journal for Research, Invention and Care, 15,* 327–340.

Tyiska, C. (1998). Working with victims of crime with disabilities. *Office for Victims of Crime Bulletin.* Washington, DC: U.S. Department of Justice, Office for Victims of Crime.

U

U.S. Bureau of the Census. (2012–2013). *Statistical Abstract of the United States* (131st ed.). Washington, DC: U.S. Department of Commerce.

U.S. Department of Health and Human Services Releases Report on LGBT Health. (2012).

Udry, J. R. (1998). Doing sex research on adolescents. In G. G. Brannigan, E. R. Allgeier, & A. R. Allgeier, *The Sex Scientists* (pp. 49–60). New York, NY: Longman.

Uecker, J., & Regnerus, M. (2011). *Premarital sex in America: How young Americans meet, mate, and think about marrying.* United Kingdom: Oxford University Press.

Ullrich, H. E. (1977). Caste differences between Brahmin and non-Brahmin women in a South Indian village. In A. Schlegel (Ed.), *Sexual stratification: A cross-cultural view* (pp. 94–108). New York, NY: Columbia University Press.

United Family Services. (2004). North Carolina Coalition Against Sexual Assault, Prevent Child Abuse, NC. *Dangers Online: Preventing Child Pornography.*

United States Department of Agriculture. (2013, August 1). Parents projected to spend $241,080 to raise a child born in 2012. USDA report.

U.S. Department of Health & Human Services Food and Drug Administration. Medical Devices Essure™ System—P020014. (2012). Retrieved November 29, 2012, from http://www.fda.gov/MedicalDevices/ProductsandMedicalProcedures/DeviceApprovalsandClearances/Recently-ApprovedDevices/ucm083087.htm

U.S. Department of Health & Human Services Health Resources and Services Administration, Women's Preventative Services Guidelines. (2013). Retrieved August 2013, from http://www.hrsa.gov/womensguidelines/

Ussher, J. M., & Perz, J. (2013). PMS as a gendered illness linked to the construction and relational experience of hetero-femininity. *Sex Roles, 68,* 132–150.

V

Vail-Smith, K., Whetstone, L., & Knox, D. (2010). The illusion of safety in monogamous undergraduate relationships. *American Journal of Health Behavior, 34*(1), 12–20.

van Bergen, D. D., Bos, H. M., Lisdonk, J. V., Keuzenkamp, S., & Sandfort, T. G. (2013). Victimization and suicidality among Dutch lesbian, gay, and bisexual youths. *American Journal of Public Health, 103,* 70–72.

Van Overveld, M., de Jong, P. J., Peters, M. L., van Lankveld, J., Melles, R., & ter Kuile, M. M. (2013). The Sexual Disgust Questionnaire; A psychometric study and a first exploration in patients with sexual dysfunctions. *Journal of Sexual Medicine, 10,* 396–407.

Van San, M., & Bovenkerk, F. (2013). Secret seducers: True tales of pimps in the red light district of Amsterdam. *Crime Law and Social Change, 60,* 67–80.

Vandenbosch, L., Vervloessem, D., & Eggermont, S. (2013). "I Might Get Your Heart Racing in My Skin-Tight Jeans" Sexualization on Music Entertainment Television. *Communication Studies, 64,* 178–194.

Vault.com. (2013, February 14). *The Results Are In: Vault's 2013 Office Romance Survey.* Retrieved from Vault.com: http://www.vault.com/blog/workplace-issues/the-results-are-in-2013-office-romance-survey/

Vazonyi, A. I., & Jenkins, D. D. (2010). Religiosity, self control, and virginity status in college students from the "Bible belt": A research note. *Journal for the Scientific Study of Sex, 49,* 561–568.

Vickers, R. (2010). Sexuality of the elderly. Presentation. Sociology of Human Sexuality. East Carolina, April.

Vivancos, R., Abubakar, I., Phillips-Howard, P., & Hunter, P. R. (2013). School-based sex education is associated with reduced risky sexual behavior and sexually transmitted infections in young adults. *Public Health, 127,* 53–57.

Vokey, M., Tefft, B., & Tysiaczny, C. (2013). An analysis of hyper-masculinity in magazine advertisements. *Sex Roles, 68,* 562–576.

von Krafft-Ebing, R. F. (1965). *Psychopathia Sexualis.* New York, NY: Arcade.

W

Wakeling, H., Beech, A. R., & Freemantle, N. (2013). Investigating treatment change and its relationship to recidivism in a sample of 3773 sex offenders in the UK. *Psychology, Crime & Law, 19,* 233–252.

Walker, J., Golub, S. A., Bimbi, D. S., & Parsons, J. T. (2012). Butch bottom-femme top? An exploration of lesbian stereotypes. *Journal of Lesbian Studies, 16,* 90–107.

Walker, S., Sanci, L., & Temple-Smith, M. (2013). Sexting: Young women's and men's views on its nature and origins. *Journal of Adolescent Health, 52,* 697–701.

Waller, W., & Hill, R. (1951). *The family: A dynamic interpretation.* New York: Hold, Rinehart and Winston.

Wallis, C. (2011). Performing gender: A content analysis of gender display in music videos. *Sex Roles, 64,* 160–172.

Walsh, S. (2013, February 7). *Match's 2012 Singles in America Survey.* Retrieved from Hooking Up Smart: http://www.hookingupsmart.com/2013/02/07/hookinguprealities/matchs-2012-singles-in-america-survey/

Walters, A., & Burger, B. (2013). 'I Love You, and I Cheated': Investigating disclosures of infidelity to primary romantic partners. *Sexuality and Culture, 17,* 20–49.

Wang, C., & Swerdloff, R. S. (2010). *Hormonal approaches to male contraception.* Retrieved from Curr Opin Urol. 2010 Nov;20(6):520-4. doi: 10.1097/MOU.0b013e32833f1b4a.

Wang, R. H., Jian, S. Y., & Yang, Y. M. (2013). Psychometric testing of the Chinese version of the Contraceptive Behavior Scale: A preliminary study. *Journal of Clinical Nursing, 22,* 1066–1072.

Ward, K. M., Atkinson, J. P., Smith, C. A., & Windsor, R. (2013). A friendships and dating program for adults with intellectual and developmental disabilities: A formative evaluation. *Intellectual and Developmental Disabilities, 51,* 22–32.

Web MD. (2013). *Video on testicular exam.* Retrieved July 24, 2013, from http://www.webmd.com/sex/video/marks-testicular-self-exam

Weiderman, M. W. (1999). Volunteer bias in sexuality research using college student participants. *The Journal of Sex Research, 36,* 59–66.

Weinberg, M. S., & Lottes, I. L. (1995). Swedish or American heterosexual college youth: Who is more permissive? *Archives of Sexual Behavior, 24,* 409–437.

Weinberg, M. S., Williams, C. J., & Calhan, C. (1995). "If the shoe fits ...": Exploring the male homosexual foot fetishism. *The Journal of Sex Research, 32,* 17–27.

Whipple, B. (1999). Beyond the G spot: Recent research findings in women's sexuality. *Contemporary Sexuality, 33,* (11–12), 1, 2, 4.

Whitton, S. W., Weitbrecht, E. M., Kuryluk, A. D., & Bruner, M. R. (2013). Committed dating relationships and mental health among college students. *Journal of American College Health, 61,* 176–183.

Wiederman, M. W. (2000). Women's body image self-consciousness during physical intimacy with a partner. *The Journal of Sex Research, 37,* 60–68.

Williams, D. J., Prior, E., & Wegner, J. (2013). Commentary: Resolving social problems associated with sexuality: Can a "Sex Positive" approach help? *Social Work Advance Access, 58.*

Williams, L. R., Wray-Lake, L., Loken, E., & Maggs, J. L. (2012). The effects of adolescent heavy drinking on the timing and stability of cohabitation and marriage. *Families in Society, 93,* 181–188.

Williams, L., & Russell, S. (2013). Shared social and emotional activities within adolescent romantic and non-romantic sexual relationships. *Archives of Sexual Behavior, 42,* 649–658.

Williams, S., & Thompson, M. P. (2013). Examining the prospective effects of making a virginity pledge among males across their 4 years of college. *Journal of American College Health, 61,* 114–120.

Willoughby, B. J., & Carroll, J. S. (2012). Correlates of attitudes toward cohabitation: Looking at the associations with demographics, relational attitudes, and dating behavior. *Journal of Family Issues, 33,* 1450–1476.

Willoughby, B. J., Farero, A. M., & Busby, D. M. (2013). Exploring the effects of sexual desire discrepancy among married couples. *Archives of Sexual Behavior,* September.

Wilson, A. M. (2013). How the methods used to eliminate foot binding in China can be employed to eradicate female genital mutilation. *Journal of Gender Studies, 22,* 17–37.

Wlodarski, R., & Dunbar, R. I. (2013). Examining the possible functions of kissing in romantic relationships. *Archives of Sexual Behavior,* October.

Wolak, J., & Finkelhor, D. (2013, July 25). Are crimes by online predators different from crimes by sex offenders who know youth in person? *Journal of Adolescent Health.*

Wolf, R., & Heath, B. (2013, June 24). Rainbow rulings: In two 5-4 rulings, Supreme Court backs recognition of same-sex marriage. *USA Today,* pp. A-1.

Wood, H., Sasaki, S., Bradley, S. J., Singh, D., Fantus, S., Owen-Anderson, A., ... Zucker, K. J. (2013). Patterns of referral to a gender identity service for children and adolescents (1976-2011): Age, sex, ratio and sexual orientation. *Journal of Sex & Marital Therapy, 13,* 1–6.

Woodford, M., Levy, D., & Walls, N. (2013). Sexual prejudice among Christian college students, denominational teachings and personal religious beliefs. *Review of Religious Research, 55,* 105–130.

Woodhams, J., & Cooke, C. (2013, June 6). Suspect aggression and victim resistance in multiple perpetrator rapes. *Archives of sexual behavior.*

World Health Organization. (2013). *Global summary of the AIDS epidemic: 2011.* Retrieved from http://www.who.int/hiv/data/2012_epi_core_en.png

Wright, P. J. (2013). U.S. males and pornography, 1973–2010: Consumption, predictors, correlates. *Journal of Sex Research, 50,* 60–71.

Wright, P. J. (2013). U.S. males and pornography, 1973-2010: Consumption, predictors, correlates. *Journal of Sex Research, 50,* 60–71.

Wright, P. J., Bae, S., & Funk, M. (2013, June 4). United States women and pornography through four decades: Exposure, attitudes, behaviors, individual differences. *Archives of Sexual Behavior.*

Wright, P. J., Randall, A. K., & Arroyo, A. (2013). Father-daughter communication about sex moderates the association between exposure to MTV's 16 and Pregnant/Teen Mom and female's pregnancy-risk behavior. *Sexuality and Culture, 17,* 50–66.

Wright, R. G., LeBlanc, A. J., & Badgett, L. (2013). Same-sex legal marriage and psychological well-being. Findings from the California health interview survey. *American Journal of Public Health, 103,* 339–346.

X

Xishan, H., Xiso-Lu, Z., Juan, Z., Lin, Z., & Kunio, S. (2012). Relationships among androgyny, self-esteem, and trait coping style of Chinese university students. *Social Behavior & Personality: An International Journal, 40,* 1005–1014.

Y

Yiou, R., Ebrahiminia, V., Mouracade, P., Lingombet, O., & Abbou, C. (2013). Sexual quality of life in women partnered with men using intracavernous alprostadil after radical prostatectomy. *Journal of Sexual Medicine, 10,* 1355–1362.

Youssouf, S. (2013). Female genital mutilations–A testimony. *The European Journal of Contraception and Reproductive Health Care, 18,* 5–9.

Z

Zamboni, B. D., & Crawford, I. (2003). Using masturbation in sex therapy: Relationships between masturbation, sexual desire, and sexual fantasy. In W. O. Bockting, & E. Coleman (Eds.), *Masturbation as a means of achieving sexual health* (pp. 123–141). New York: Haworth.

Zengel, B., Edlund, J. E., & Sagarin, B. J. (2013). Sex differences in jealousy in response to infidelity: Evaluation of demographic moderators in a national random sample. *Personality and Individual Differences, 54,* 47–51.

Zhang, C. E. (2013). Anecdotal writing on illicit sex in Song China 960–1279. *Journal of the History of Sexuality, 22,* 253–280.

Zhang, X. (2010). Charging children with child pornography-Using the legal system to handle the problem of "sexting." *Computer Law & Security Review, 26,* 251–259.

Zollman, G., Rellini, A., & Desrocher, D. (2013). The mediating effect of daily stress on the sexual arousal function of women with a history of childhood sexual abuse. *Journal of Sex and Marital Therapy, 39,* 176–192.

Zweig, J. M., Barber, B. L., & Eccles, J. S. (1997). Sexual coercion and well-being in young adulthood. *Journal of Interpersonal Violence, 12,* 291–308.

Name Index

Subject Index